MW00386595

Aruba Certified Mobility Professional
OFFICIAL CERTIFICATION STUDY GUIDE
(EXAM HPE6-A44)

HPE Press
660 4th Street, #802
San Francisco, CA 94107

Aruba Certified Mobility Professional (ACMP) V8
Official Certification Study Guide
(Exam HPE6-A44)

Published by:

Hewlett Packard Enterprise Press
660 4th Street, #802
San Francisco, CA 94107

ISBN: **978-1-942741-76-3**

Printed in Mexico

WARNING AND DISCLAIMER

This book provides information about the topics covered in the Title (HPE0-) certification exam. Every effort has been made to make this book as complete and as accurate as possible, but no warranty or fitness is implied.

The information is provided on an "as is" basis. The author, and Hewlett Packard Enterprise Press, shall have neither liability nor responsibility to any person or entity with respect to any loss or damages arising from the information contained in this book or from the use of the discs or programs that may accompany it.

The opinions expressed in this book belong to the author and are not necessarily those of Hewlett Packard Enterprise Press.

TRADEMARK ACKNOWLEDGEMENTS

GOVERNMENT AND EDUCATION SALES

This publisher offers discounts on this book when ordered in quantity for bulk purchases, which may include electronic versions. For more information, please contact U.S. Government and Education Sales 1-855-447-2665 or email sales@hpepressbooks.com.

Feedback Information

At HPE Press, our goal is to create in-depth reference books of the best quality and value. Each book is crafted with care and precision, undergoing rigorous development that involves the expertise of members from the professional technical community.

Readers' feedback is a continuation of the process. If you have any comments regarding how we could improve the quality of this book, or otherwise alter it to better suit your needs, you can contact us through email at hpepress@epac.com. Please make sure to include the book title and ISBN in your message.

We appreciate your feedback.

Publisher: Hewlett Packard Enterprise Press

HPE Aruba Contributors: Fardin Rahim Raoufi, Kevin Zhu, Kimberly Graves, Leo Banville, Venu Dhanraj Puduchery

HPE Press Program Manager: Michael Bishop

About the Authors

The material in this Study Guide was developed by the Aruba Education Development team of Leo Banville, Venu Dhanraj Puduchery, Kevin Zhu, Fardin Rahim Raoufi, and Kimberly Graves.

About the Technical Editor

Steve Sowell has been an IT professional and entrepreneur since 1984, with a focus on WLAN technologies for the past 16 years. He has sold, designed, and deployed WLANs covering millions of square feet, for sporting arenas, hospitals, offices, and outdoor areas. He has been a courseware developer, editor, and author for fifteen years, and an industry-certified instructor and engineer since 1994.

Introduction

This study guide is based on the Aruba courseware title Scalable WLAN Design and Implementation. It will help you to prepare to take the Aruba Certified Mobility Professional (ACMP) exam. The material in this book will also help you to understand advanced features of an HPE Aruba WLAN solution, and to understand, deploy, and configure scalable HPE Aruba-based WLAN systems.

Certification and Learning

Hewlett Packard Enterprise Partner Ready Certification and Learning provides end-to-end continuous learning programs and professional certifications that can help you open doors and succeed in the idea economy. We provide continuous learning activities and job-role based learning plans to help you keep pace with the demands of the dynamic, fast paced IT industry; professional sales and technical training and certifications to give you the critical skills needed to design, manage and implement the most sought-after IT disciplines; and training to help you navigate and seize opportunities within the top IT transformation areas that enable business advantage today.

As a Partner Ready Certification and Learning certified member, your skills, knowledge, and real-world experience are recognized and valued in the marketplace. To continue your professional and career growth, you have access to our large HPE community of world-class IT professionals, trend-makers and decision-makers. Share ideas, best practices, business insights, and challenges as you gain professional connections globally.

To learn more about HPE Partner Ready Certification and Learning certifications and continuous learning programs, please visit http://certification-learning.hpe.com.

Audience

This book is designed for presales solution architects involved in supporting the sale of scalable, enterprise-class HPE Aruba WLAN solutions. It is also designed for engineers that need to learn how to deploy and configure these solutions.

Assumed Knowledge

Typical candidates for this certification are networking IT professionals with a minimum of one to two years' experience in deploying mobility solutions for the enterprise. It is assumed that you have a good understanding of working with WLAN technologies and have an interest in learning about how to deploy the HPE Aruba product portfolio in larger, more complex, and more scalable solutions.

Since this book covers more advanced level topics and information, it is assumed that you have already completed the Implementing Aruba WLAN course or have studied the material within the related Aruba Certified Mobility Associate Study Guide.

Minimum Qualifications

The pre-requisite qualifications for the Aruba Certified Mobility Professional (ACMP) V8 certification are the Aruba Certified Mobility Associate (ACMA) V8 or Aruba Certified Mobility Associate (ACMA) V6.4 certifications.

Relevant Certifications

After you pass these exams, your achievement may be applicable toward more than one certification. To determine which certifications can be credited with this achievement, log in to The Learning Center and view the certifications listed on the exam's More Details tab. You might be on your way to achieving additional certifications.

Preparing for Exam HPE6-A44

This self-study guide does not guarantee that you will have all the knowledge you need to pass the exam. It is expected that you will also draw on real-world experience and would benefit from completing the hands-on lab activities provided in the instructor-led training.

Recommended HPE Training

Recommended training to prepare for each exam is accessible from the exam's page in The Learning Center. See the exam attachment, "Supporting courses," to view and register for the courses.

Obtain Hands-on Experience

You are not required to take the recommended, supported courses, and completion of training does not guarantee that you will pass the exams. Hewlett Packard Enterprise strongly recommends a combination of training, thorough review of courseware and additional study references, and sufficient on-the-job experience prior to taking an exam.

Exam Registration

To register for an exam, go to http://certification-learning.hpe.com/tr/certification/learn_more_about_exams.html

CONTENTS

1 Introduction and Aruba Architecture

LEARNING OBJECTIVES

- ✓ This module provides a review of the Aruba architecture. You will learn about controller roles, redundancy, and licensing before exploring hierarchy and configuration.
- ✓ Then you will review Mobility Controller (MC) use as an L2 switch or L3 router, along with packet flow, remote access, tunnel node, and IAP.
- ✓ Next, you will learn about Aruba features, roles, policies, and rules. Finally, you will review clustering, redundancy, and the MultiZone feature.

Aruba Architecture review

OS 8.X architecture

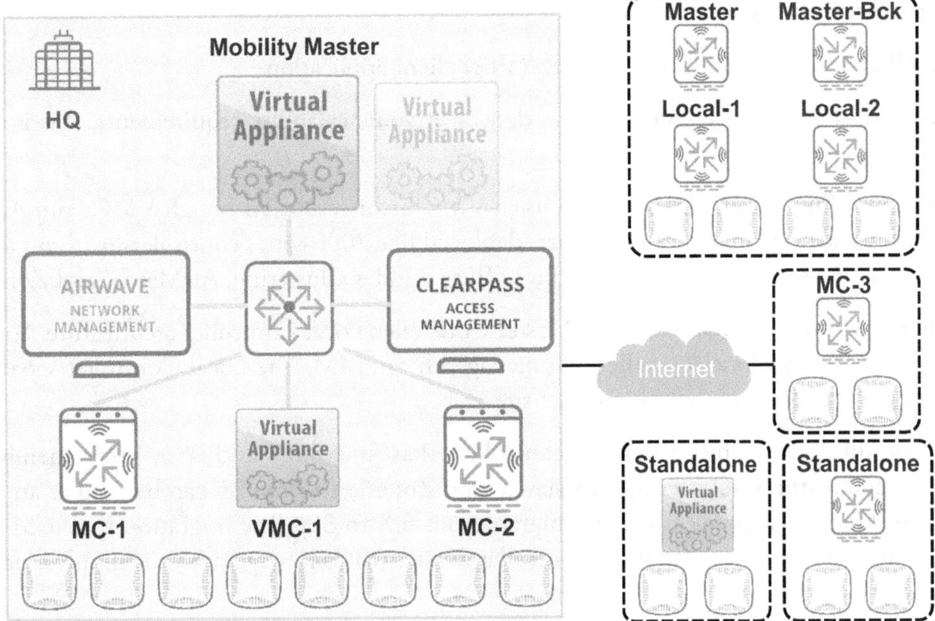

Figure 1-1 OS 8.X architecture

Figure 1-1 shows several possibilities for HPE Aruba architectural design. You choose the design that suits you best, based on scalability needs and perhaps on the pre-existing equipment.

A Mobility Master (MM) architecture can be used for medium and large networks. Figure 1-1 shows a Virtual Machine (VM)-based Virtual Mobility Master (VMM), which can run on VMware or KVM systems. You could also opt for a Hardware Mobility Master (HMM, also known as MM-HW). This is a hardened x86-based appliance, dedicated specifically to act as an ArubaOS 8 MM. For resiliency, a standby MM can be deployed on another hardware or a virtual appliance.

This design supports from 500 to 10,000 devices and up to 100,000 clients. To achieve this scalability, the MM centralizes system management and configuration but does not terminate Access Points (APs). MM is the next generation controller, with significantly more functionality and flexibility. The MM manages Mobility Controllers (MCs) and VM-based MCs (VMCs), which terminate APs. This architecture became available as of ArubaOS 8. You cannot implement this architecture with earlier ArubaOS versions.

An MC can be a part of an MM solution, as described above. An MC can also act as a so-called "standalone" controller as described below.

The MC architecture can be used for the 7000-series MCs. These "standalone" controllers can support up to 64 APs and 24 Ethernet ports. The MC can also terminate various types of VPN connections, as listed below:

- Site-to-site VPN connections from remote MCs
- Remote Access Points (RAPs)
- Instant Access Points (IAPs)
- The HPE Aruba Virtual Intranet Access (VIA) client application

If you have existing 7000-series controllers that meet your scalability requirements, this is a viable option.

Another option for smaller networks is to use a VMC architecture. Although VMCs run ArubaOS 8.x, you can create a standalone architecture, deployed like 7000-series controllers, without an MM. However, you lose some advanced 8.x features. This includes Clustering, AirMatch, and Zones.

Controllers that run ArubaOS 6.X use a Master Controller/Local Controller architecture. You know that the MC is a standalone controller, not managed by an MM. The Local Controller serves under an MC, perhaps deployed locally at another site.

You can use this same architecture with controllers that run v8.0.1 and later. Just remember, you lose higher-end features (Clustering, AirMatch, and Zones). This option can be used as an interim solution—a kind of "stepping-stone" to migrate from 6.X to 8.X. The migration tool used for this purpose makes reference to a Mobility Controller Master (MCM)—again, this is simply a non-MM Mobility Controller Master.

Finally, the Figure 1-1 shows two options that can add compelling value to your deployment, as described below:

- AirWave is an SNMP-based network operations system that can manage wired and wireless infrastructure from Aruba and many third-party systems. You get granular visibility into devices, users, and applications. This increases your situational awareness toward a more proactive approach to network management.
- ClearPass is a policy manager for mobility solutions. It improves upon legacy, AAA-based authorization with context-aware policies. ClearPass can intelligently profile devices, validate endpoint health, enable Bring Your Own Device (BYOD) and Internet of Things (IoT) onboarding, all while facilitating guest access and third-party integration.

Master-Local versus MM-MC

Master-Local

An MC can only be deployed as a physical controller, and it can terminate APs. For Master-Local deployments, the Master pushes only partial configuration to all the locals. This includes AP-Groups, Local DB, Whitelist DB, and similar items. The master will not validate the configuration before pushing to the locals. In other words, issues related to syntax and the range of parameter values will not be detected.

In this model, the master cannot push L2 and L3 configuration. This means that things such as VLAN, interface, and IP routing parameters must be configured separately on each local controller.

Also, features such as the Zero-Touch Provisioning (ZTP) and Disaster Recovery mode are not supported for local controllers.

MM-MC

The MM can be deployed on both physical and virtual (VM) appliances, but they cannot terminate APs. The MM can push full configuration to all of its managed MCs, using ZTP. The MM also validates configurations before pushing them to these MCs.

ZTP automates deployment of managed devices, enabling a more “plug-n-play” type of solution. With ZTP, managed devices acquire information from the network and provision themselves automatically.

During disruptions in MM-to-MC connectivity, you can enable Disaster Recovery mode on the managed MCs. This can help you to restore connectivity.

MC as L2 switch or L3 router

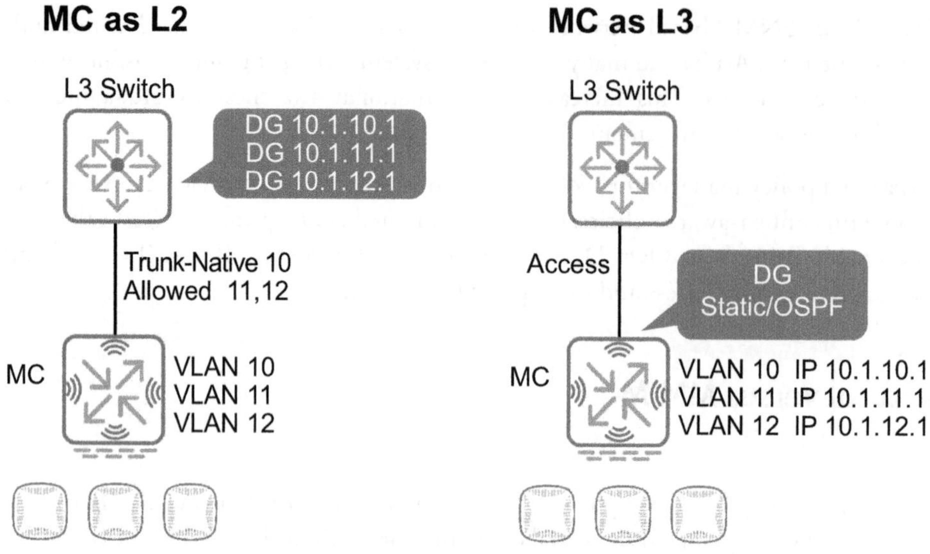

Figure 1-2 MC as L2 switch or L3 router

The MC can be configured as a switch with simple VLANs, or as a router with IP addresses and routes.

In the left portion of Figure 1-2, the Default Gateways (DG) for VLANs 10–12 are on an upstream, external L3 router. In this case, the MC uses L2 *switching* to move user traffic to this router.

In the right portion of Figure 1-2, the VLANs are defined on the MC with IP addresses. These IP addresses act as the DGs for VLANs. Therefore, all user traffic is *routed* from the MC to the uplink L3 router. Of course, in this scenario you must configure some type of routing on the MC—either static routes or the Open Shortest Path First (OSPF) routing protocol.

HPE Aruba typically recommends that you deploy your MC as an L2 switch.

AP terminology

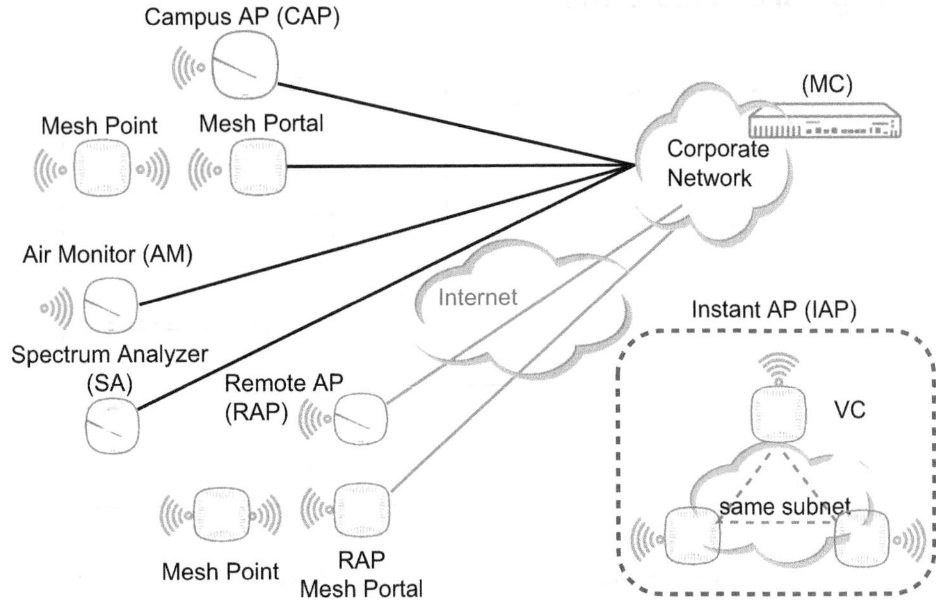

Figure 1-3 AP terminology

APs can be configured in many ways to assume specific roles in the WLAN architecture. Figure 1-3 shows these AP roles, which are described as follows:

- **Campus AP (CAP)**—Often simply referred to as an AP or regular AP. CAPs operate as a typical AP. They connect to a controller, acquire their configuration, and then service WLAN users.
- **Mesh AP**—These are campus APs that use the radio interface as an uplink. The Mesh *Portal* has a physical connection to the corporate network. The Mesh *Point* uses its radio to get an uplink to the corporate network.
- **Air Monitor (AM)**—APs in this mode do not provide service to WLAN clients. AMs constantly scan the radio environment to gather IDS and RF information.
- **Spectrum AP (SA)**—SAs can be setup (temporarily or permanently) to capture radio signals for analysis. APs that gather spectrum data across all operating channels, but do not service clients, are called Spectrum Monitors (SM). APs that DO service clients and also gather spectrum data on the channel of operation are said to be operating in hybrid mode.
- **Remote AP (RAP)**—These operate very much like CAPs. However, a RAP must go through the Internet to reach a controller. To do so, RAPs setup a VPN tunnel to the controller. A RAP can also be setup as a remote mesh portal. This is basically a RAP with mesh portal capabilities.
- **Instant AP (IAP)**—IAPs operate more autonomously, without need for a controller. All IAPs in the same subnet form a cluster. They elect one IAP to serve as a Virtual Controller (VC), and thus operate independent of a hardware controller.

Configuration hierarchy

Partial configuration model (Master-Local)

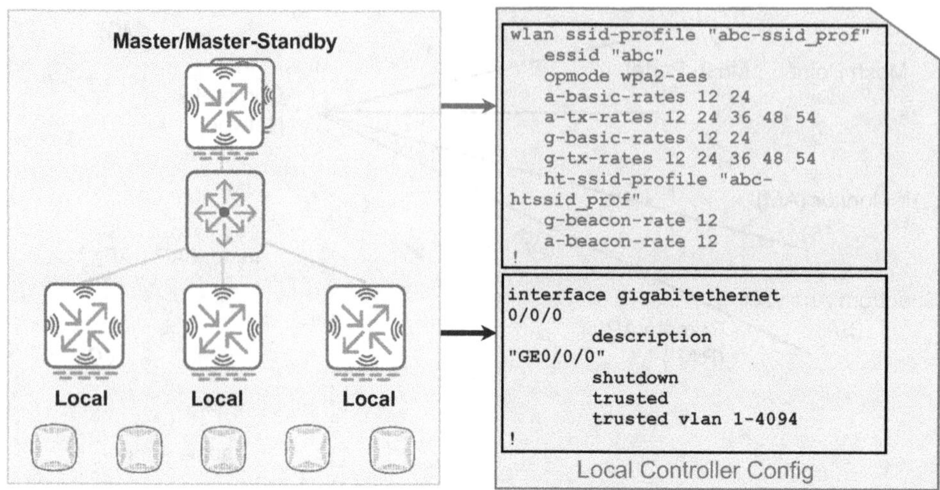

Figure 1-4 Partial configuration model (Master-Local)

Prior to ArubaOS 8, the solution used a partial configuration model. The master pushes only WLAN configuration and database information, as shown in the top text box of Figure 1-4.

It cannot push L2 and L3 configuration. This includes VLAN, Interface, and IP routing configuration. This type of configuration, shown in the bottom text box in Figure 1-4, must be configured separately on each local controller.

Full configuration model (Mobility Master)

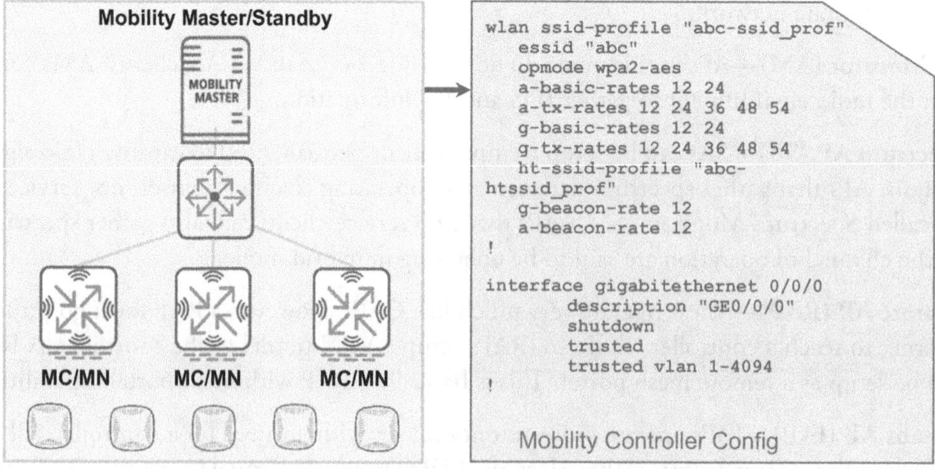

Figure 1-5 Full configuration model (Mobility Master)

The MM architecture is supported as of ArubaOS 8. The MM can push full configuration down to managed devices. As shown in Figure 1-5, this includes L2 and L3 settings, such as VLAN, interface, and IP routing configuration.

Hierarchical configuration/monitoring model

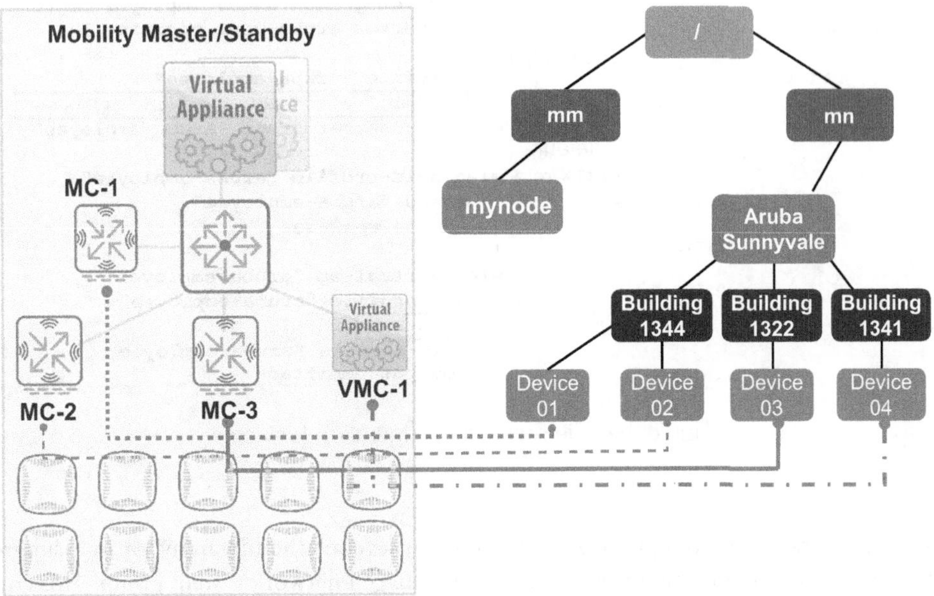

Figure 1-6 Hierarchical configuration/monitoring model

Recall that Aruba's GUI layout is hierarchical in nature for both configuration and monitoring functions. For configuration, groups and subgroups are created. Devices can be added to a subgroup, directly to a group, or even to the system group. The creation of groups and subgroups increases configuration efficiency and options.

In the example, a global configuration created at the top of the hierarchy is pushed down to the Sunnyvale group (and to any other groups that may be created). You might then make modifications to the Sunnyvale group, which are pushed down to its subgroups—Building 1344, 1322, and 1341.

If needed, you can make more modifications in a specific subgroup, say, Building 1322. These modifications would flow down to the devices in that group. Finally, you can modify the settings for specific devices. All of the appropriate configuration is pushed down to the MCs and VMCs.

Hierarchical configuration (device)

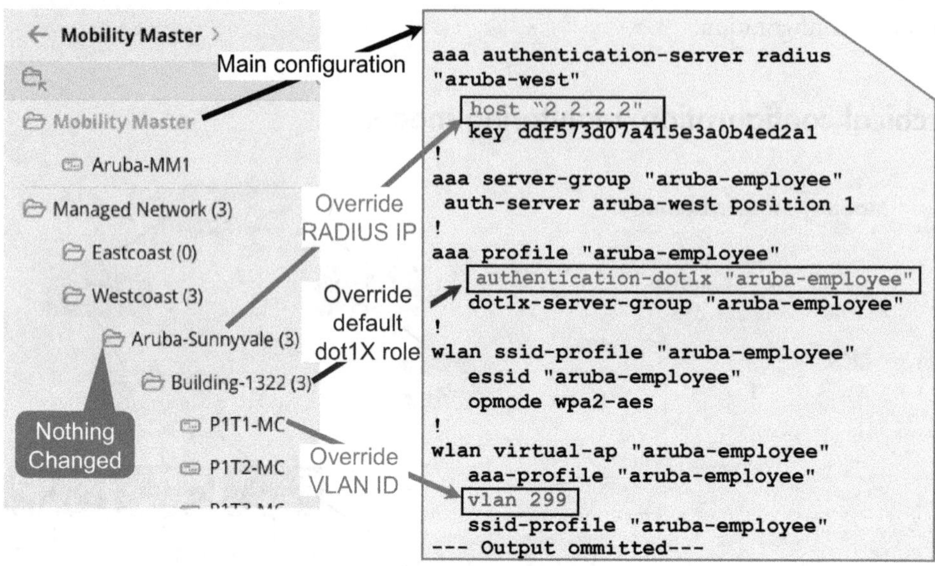

Figure 1-7 Hierarchical configuration (device)

You can perform the main configuration at the highest level of the hierarchy, or in a subgroup. In Figure 1-7, the main configuration was done on the managed network system group. This configuration is pushed down to the groups and subgroups. No change was made at the group level in Westcoast.

Westcoast may have been created just to separate equipment for monitoring purposes. However, a change was made in the subgroup named Aruba-Sunnyvale, overriding the RADIUS IP address. This change will affect Aruba-Sunnyvale subgroups. However, this will not affect the LA and Portland subgroups, as they are not subgroups of Aruba-Sunnyvale.

Another change was made for all devices in Building 1322, overriding the default dot1X role. This change only affects devices in that building and will not affect devices in the other buildings.

Finally, a VLAN change was made to device P1T1-MC. Of course, this change only occurs for that specific device and will not affect other devices in the Building 1322 subgroup. This is the final configuration that P1T1-MC will receive.

Forwarding WLAN user traffic

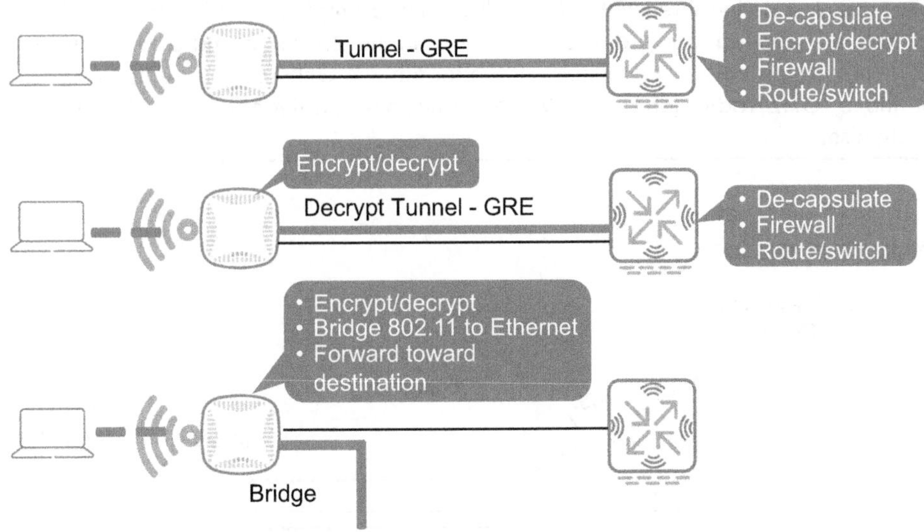

Figure 1-8 Forwarding WLAN user traffic

Figure 1-8 shows three ways that end-user traffic can be forwarded. You also see how responsibilities are shared between the AP and controller.

In tunnel mode, APs create GRE tunnels to the controller. Specifically, each AP creates one tunnel per WLAN, per radio, plus one more for a keepalive mechanism.[1] All user traffic to the AP normally arrives encrypted. The AP sends this encrypted traffic, via the GRE tunnel, directly to the controller.

The controller de-capsulates packets from GRE tunnel headers, then decrypts and firewalls them. If permitted by the firewall, the controller then switches or routes these packets onto the network.

In decrypt tunnel node, APs create GRE tunnels to the controller. All user traffic received by the AP normally arrives encrypted. The AP decrypts this traffic, then sends it via GRE tunnel to the controller. The controller de-capsulates packets from the GRE headers and firewalls them. If permitted by the firewall, the controller then switches or routes packets onto the network.

For a bridged WLAN, the AP receives packets and decrypts them. The AP then performs a translational bridging function, which converts the 802.11 WLAN frames into standard Ethernet frames, and then forwards them toward their destination. This is not recommended for deployment. The risk here is that in bridged mode, the stateful firewall is not enforced.

Note

[1]Suppose you define three WLANs—SSIDs named Employees, Guests, and VoIP. These WLANs are applied to a group of APs, for both the 2.4 GHz and 5 GHz radios. Each AP in the group forms seven tunnels—three for the 2.4 GHz radio (one per WLAN), three for the 5 GHz radio (one per WLAN), and one additional tunnel for a keepalive mechanism.

Remote access options

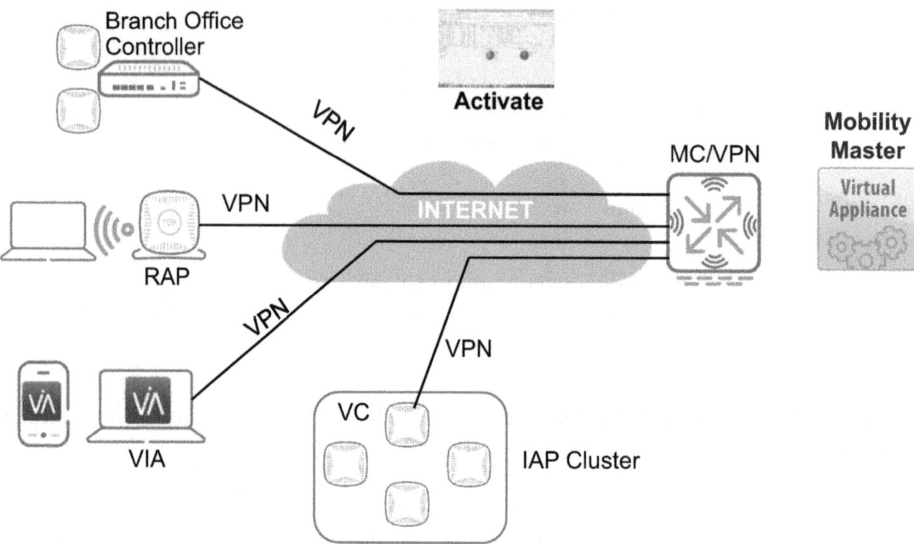

Figure 1-9 Remote access options

In a campus environment, APs can access MCs via the corporate network. Not all branch and home offices have direct access to the corporate network. For connectivity between branch office controllers and the corporate MM, you can create a site-to-site connection. To accommodate this, configure an MC at the corporate office with VPN settings. The branch office MC forms a VPN connection to this corporate MC/VPN. If the VPN fails, the branch office MC continues to provide local service.

For small or home office locations, you can use a Remote AP (RAP). Each RAP forms a VPN connection to the MC/VPN for corporate access. If access to the controller is lost, then only bridged SSIDs can remain up.

When at home or on the road, you can use HPE Aruba's Virtual Intranet Access client (VIA). VIA is a VPN client application that can be installed on Windows or MAC OS devices. This ensures that remote users can gain secure remote access to the corporate network.

IAP clusters can also setup a VPN back to a controller to provide end-user access to the corporate network. If the VPN is lost, the cluster is not affected.

Tunneled node

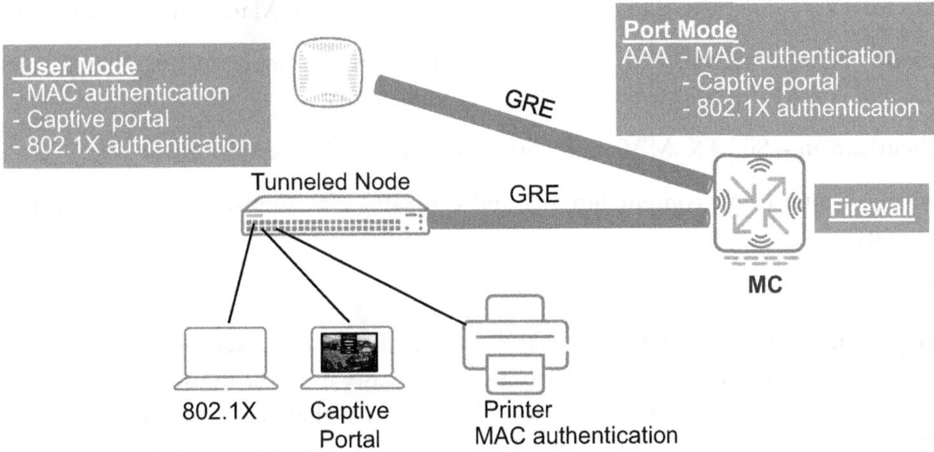

Figure 1-10 Tunneled node

With the Tunneled Node feature, wired network clients can have the same security as WLAN clients. There are two forms of tunneled node—Port mode and User mode.

In Port mode, you configure Aruba Switch VLANs to form a GRE tunnel to an MC. You can use any port on the Aruba switch for 802.1X, captive portal, or MAC authentication.

In User mode, the switch forwards all authentication sessions to ClearPass. ClearPass returns values that tell the switch to tunnel the traffic to an MC, where it is firewalled.

This will be discussed in length in Chapter 16, which is dedicated to the tunneled node feature.

IAP clusters

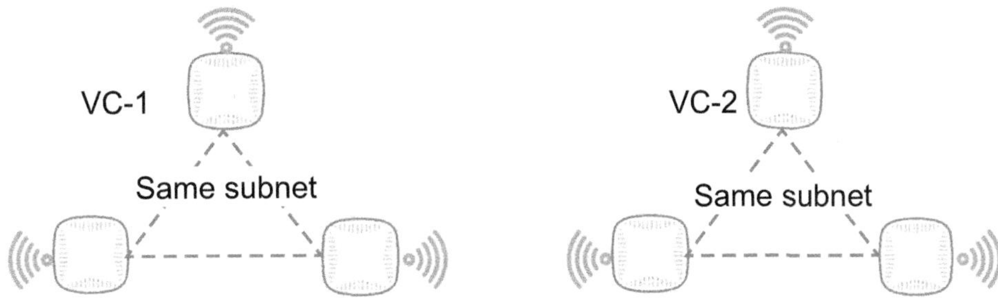

Figure 1-11 IAP clusters

IAPs are a set of APs that do not need a controller. All IAPs on the same subnet form a cluster. One IAP is elected to be the Virtual Controller (Figure 1-11).

IAPs have many of the same capabilities as a controller, which are as follows:

- **Radio features**—Adaptive Radio management (ARM), Client Match, and spectrum analysis.
- **Firewall**—Stateful firewall with roles and policies. You can define WLAN-based rules, Voice ACLs, and AppRF, for improved application layer visibility.
- **Authentication**—802.1X, MAC authentication, and captive portals.
- **Services**—Cloud-based content filtering and can categorize user devices, and display applications in use.
- **IDS/IPS**—Improves network security posture.
- **Management**—Intuitive GUI to manage each IAP cluster. However, managing several clusters via separate GUIs can be more cumbersome. In this case, it is best to use a management system like AirWave or Central. Activate is a cloud-based system that can automatically direct IAPs to AirWave or Central. A new IAP cluster is directed to AirWave or Central to receive all of its configuration.

Learning check

1. When planning a hierarchy what should be taken into consideration?
   a. The number of MMs
   b. The naming convention
   c. The configuration needs
   d. The monitoring needs
   e. The number of MC and APs

Aruba OS Features

Aruba firewall

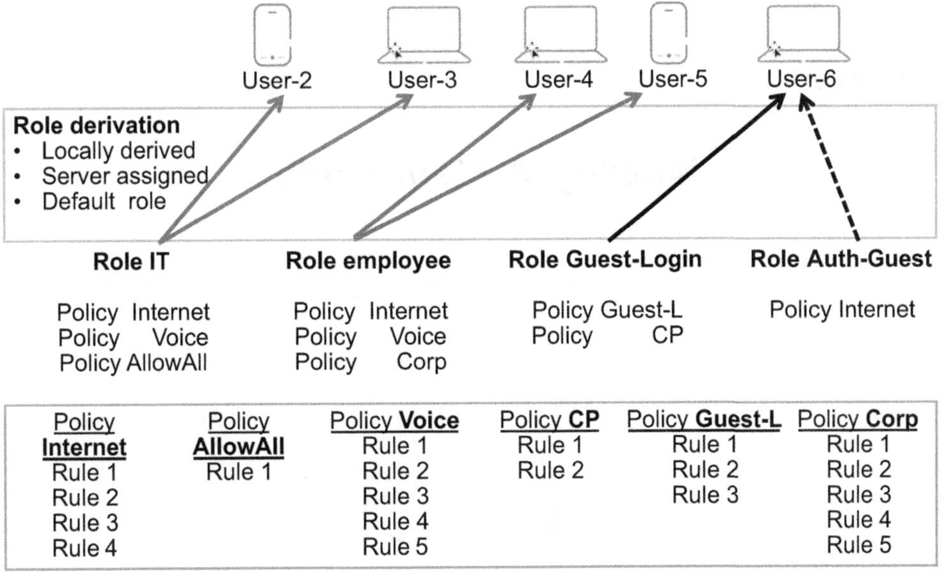

Figure 1-12 Aruba firewall

Figure 1-12 shows the relationship between rules, policies, roles, and role derivation. The example shows six policies. These firewall policies are stateful, bi-directional, and dynamic. Each policy consists of a set of ordered rules. Traffic is compared against these rules using typical "top-down" processing, like an access list. When traffic matches a rule, an action is taken, and no other policy rules are processed. The typical actions are "permit" and "deny," but you can also log or apply QOS to the traffic.

 **Note**

The first few frames in a traffic flow are inspected and rule-matched, and the action is applied as described. Since this information is cached, the same action is applied to subsequent frames in this traffic flow, without need for rule processing. This enhances system efficiency.

So we know that policies are composed of rules. In turn, recall that roles are composed of policies. As users connect, a role is derived for them. This role derivation can be handled on the local controller or indicated by a server. Another option is to apply a default authentication role.

In Figure 1-12, User-2 and User-3 are assigned to the IT role, which has three policies applied—Internet, Voice, and AllowAll. When one of these users send traffic, their packets are inspected. The rules in the first policy (Internet, in this example) are inspected first, in the described "top-down" fashion. Upon a match, that rule's action is invoked. If there is no match in the top (Internet) policy, then the next policy (Voice) is processed. If there is no match in any of a role's policy rules, then an implicit Deny ALL is applied.

Roles, policies, and rules were discussed in the previous IAW course. This advanced course is focused on role derivation, soon to be discussed.

Clustering overview

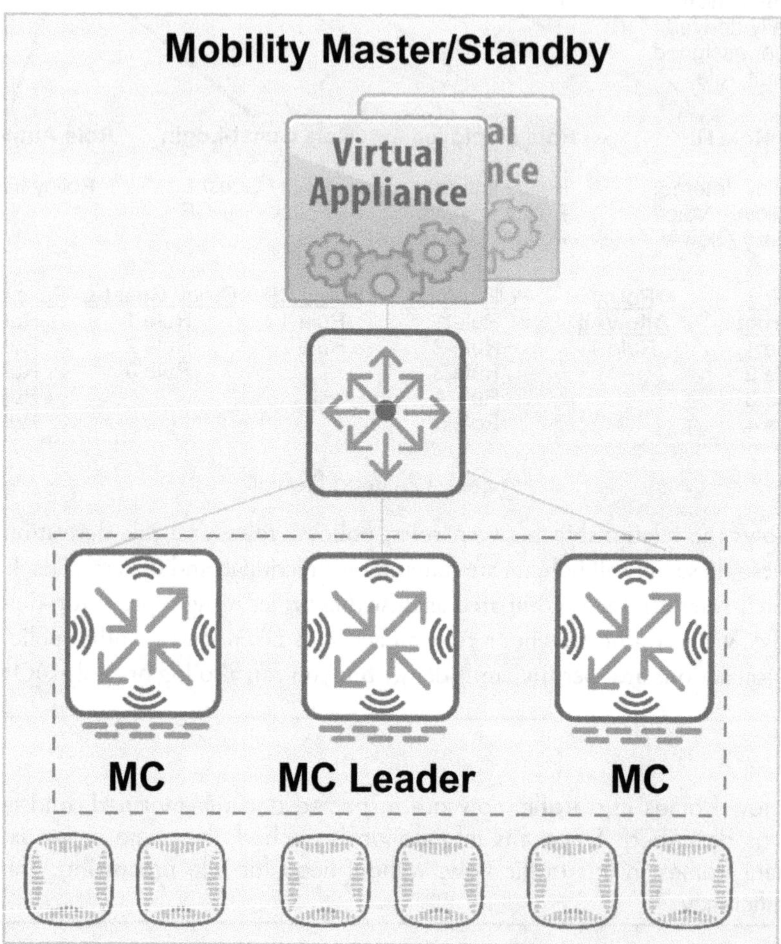

Figure 1-13 Clustering overview

HPE Aruba's MC clustering feature offers redundancy, hitless client and AP failover, seamless client mobility, and user and AP load balancing across clustered MCs. These MCs need not be the same model and can either be L2 or L3 connected.

Figure 1-13 shows three MCs, organized into a cluster, all managed by the same MM. One MC acts as the cluster leader. Only the MM architecture supports clustering. Since the MM itself has no APs, it does not participate in a cluster. To support the features described, AOS 8.0 introduces the concept of AP Anchor Controllers (AAC) and User Anchor Controllers (UAC), as described below.

Seamless client roaming

With clustering, each connected client terminates on a dedicated MC, called the UAC, regardless of which AP they connect to. When a client connects to AP1, AP1 builds a tunnel back to the UAC. When the client roams to AP2, AP1 deletes the tunnel, and AP2 creates one. Thus, the client always connects to the same MC, which reduces latency and dropped frames.

Client load balancing and hitless failover

Users that join the cluster are always initially terminated on the UAC, regardless of connected AP. However, users are evenly load-balanced among cluster members. To move a client to another controller, the AP builds a new GRE tunnel to the designated MC. Also, the user information is duplicated on another MC. If this MC with user information fails, the user and AP continue on the backup MC, and a new backup is selected. This gives hitless failover for clients. Moving from one AP to another is simple because the new APs build a GRE to the user's MC.

Hitless AP failover

As APs boot, they connect to their Active AAC (A-AAC). The AP also builds a standby tunnel to a Standby AAC (S-AAC), which is selected by the cluster leader. Should the A-AAC fail, the AP seamlessly fails over to the S-AAC

Also, seamless upgrade of APs and MCs can be done in a cluster.

MM AirMatch

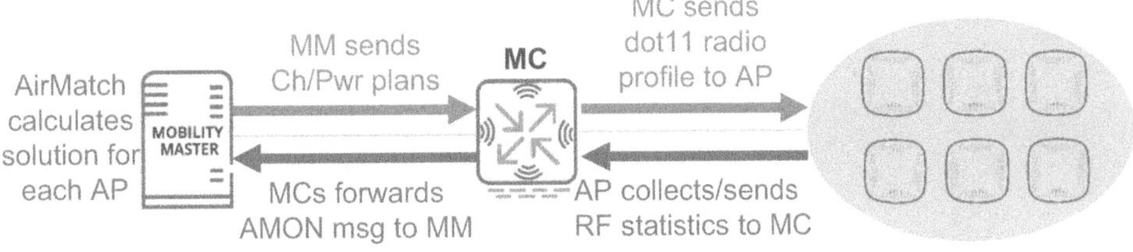

Figure 1-14 MM AirMatch

As of AOS 8.0, AirMatch replaces ARM—a legacy, decentralized RF planning mechanism. AirMatch runs on the MM as a centralized RF planning and optimization service. It models the network as a whole and improves the user experience by optimizing RF performance. It is a Loadable Service Module (LSM) in the MM and so can be upgraded independently of the core AOS.

AirMatch uses the past 24 hours of RF information for calculation and deploys channel and power information once a day. AirMatch will also react to detrimental RF events such as radar and high noise. Standalone or Master/Local architectures will use the legacy ARM.

Below is a review of AirMatch operation:

1. APs periodically collect information about their RF neighborhood. They send this information via Application Monitoring (AMON) messages to the MC/managed device.
2. The MC forwards these AMON messages to the MM.
3. AirMatch consumes the RF information and generates an RF solution. This specifies new channel, bandwidth, power, and mode of operation—per radio.
4. The MM sends the solution down to the MC in the form of CLI commands.
5. The MC receives this message, converts it to a "dot11 radio profile override" message, and sends it to the AP. Thus, the AP receives new parameters from its MC and applies the change to its radio configuration.
6. AirMatch calculates the RF channel and power-level solutions based on the past 24 hours of RF information, collected for each AP. Channel and power deployments occur once a day at 5 a.m., in the MM's time zone.
7. AirMatch also minimizes channel coupling, where adjacent radios are assigned to the same channel.

ClientMatch

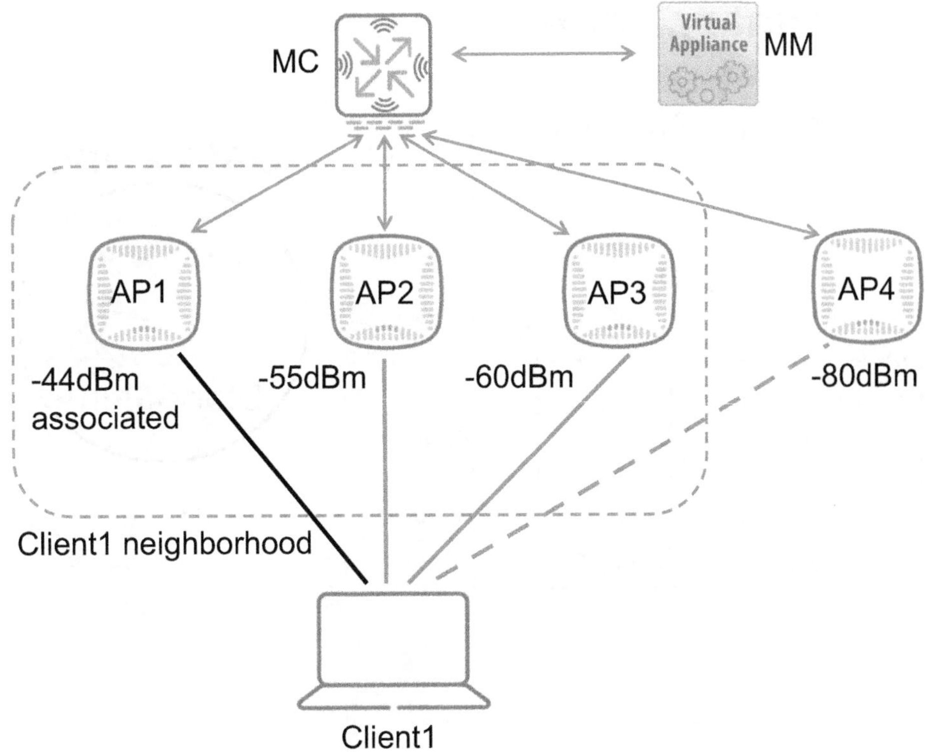

Figure 1-15 ClientMatch

When a client associates with an AP, the network automatically builds a neighborhood table. This is a list of all APs that have heard this client with sufficient radio strength. In Figure 1-15, note that AP4 is not part of Client1's neighborhood. This is because it has received signal strength from Client1 that is too weak.

AP1 decides to steer the client to a different AP radio in the RF neighborhood. Reasons for steering the client to another AP include the following:

- The client is a sticky client—one that does not roam effectively.
- The client is 5 GHz-capable (an attempt to balance the load between 2.4 GHz and 5 GHz usage)
- The AP has too many clients compared with other APs.

The AP sends the client steer request, then identifies and manages the client relocation.

MultiZone AP

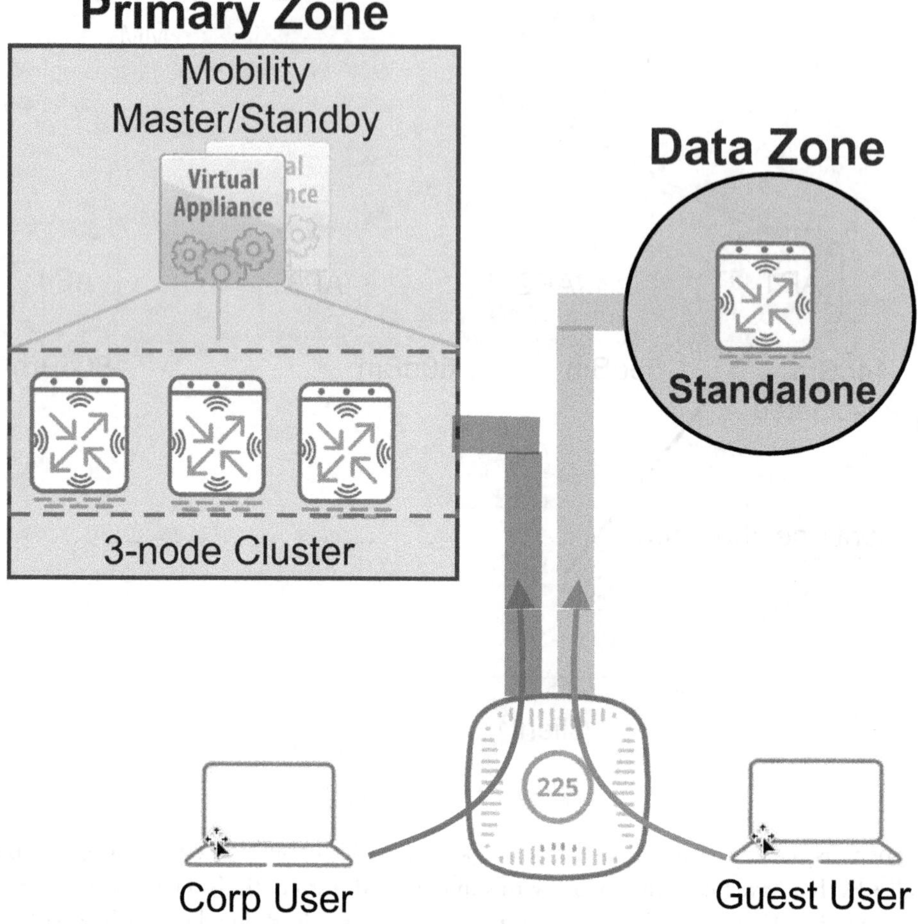

Figure 1-16 MultiZone AP

A zone is a collection of controllers under a single administrative domain. This could be a single controller or a cluster of controllers. The MC controllers in a zone terminate all the tunnels for the APs that they control.

However, the MultiZone feature enhances this situation and gives you more flexibility in your WLAN deployments. A MultiZone deployment allows APs to terminate different WLAN tunnels to different controllers that reside in different zones.

In Figure 1-16, you see a primary zone, which is a collection of controllers under a single administration domain. There is also a data zone—typically a standalone controller with access to the APs in the primary zone. The data zone does not control the APs, but can place WLANs on primary zone APs.

For example, you have a standalone controller in the DMZ. This controller puts the Guest WLAN on the corporate APs. This means that all corporate APs support connectivity for guests. So the APs are all controlled by corporate MCs in the Primary zone, and corporate employee WLANs are tunneled to these same controllers. However, all Guest WLAN traffic is tunneled to the controller in the DMZ.

This gives you a more distinct separation between corporate and guest traffic.

Loadable Service Modules

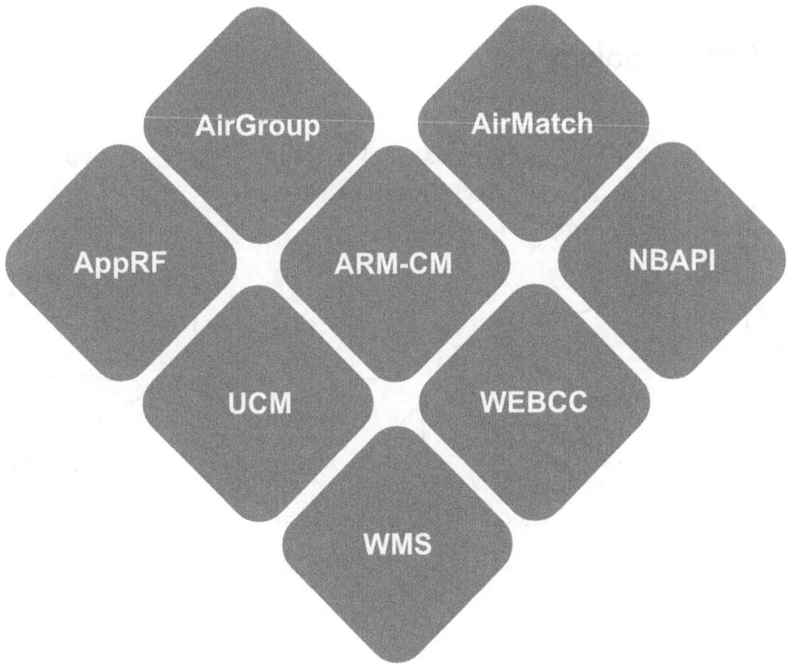

Figure 1-17 Loadable Service Modules

Loadable Service Modules (LSM) enable you to dynamically upgrade or downgrade individual system features without requiring an entire system reboot. Services are delivered as individual packages, which contain the version, as well as instructions for loading and running the service.

Every service module has a corresponding service package, which can be downloaded from the Aruba support site and installed on the MM.

For example, the file for AirMatch is "ArubaOS_MM_8.0.1.0-svcs-ctrl_airmatch_56862." Aruba's Application Visibility and Control feature can be referred to as simply "AppRF." The file for this feature is "ArubaOS_MM_8.0.1.0-svcs-ctrl_appRF_56862."

Learning check

2. What features does clustering give you?
    a. Redundancy
    b. Client load balancing
    c. AP balancing
    d. Mobility
    e. IAP load balancing

Multi-site MM/MC topology

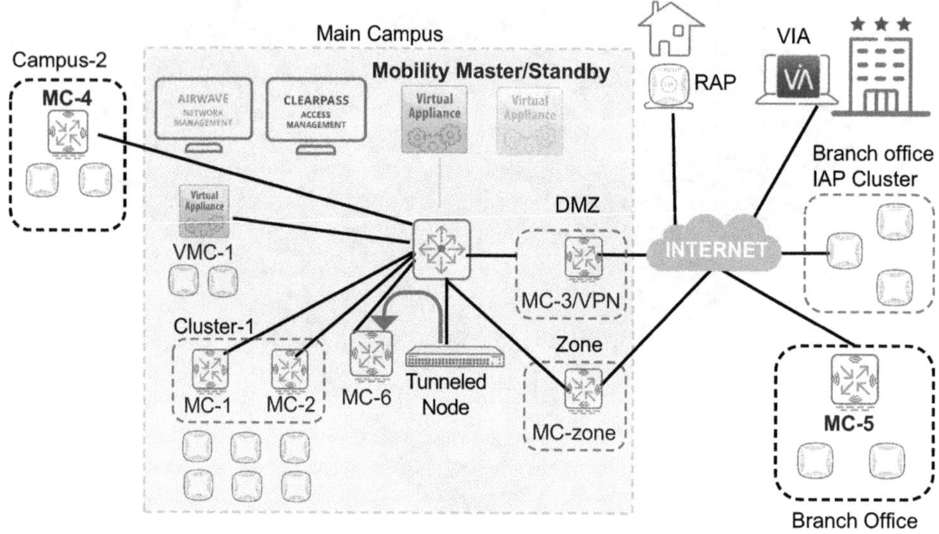

Figure 1-18 Multi-site MM/MC topology

Figure 1-18 shows an example topology. You see the main campus, with a cluster of MCs and a VMC for deployed APs. Campus 2 includes an MC to act as a termination point for Campus 2 APs. However, this MC is controlled by the MM at the Main Campus.

An MC is in the DMZ, to accommodate remote access, since RAPs are deployed in employee homes. The Aruba VIA client is installed on travelling employee laptops.

For small branch offices, IAP clusters or branch office controllers are recommended. Of course, if it is a small office, perhaps a RAP is all you need.

A standalone MC is also placed in the DMZ. Thus, when guests attach to corporate APs, their traffic is tunneled to this controller, and then routed straight out to the internet.

To give the same Wi-Fi experience and security on the wired side, tunnel mode is implemented on the Aruba IP switches.

ClearPass is used for the guest captive portal. It is also used for employee authentication, with profiling and enforcement. AirWave is used to monitor the MM, MCs, and the remote devices. This includes IAP clusters and tunnel node switches.

2 Mobility Master Redundancy

LEARNING OBJECTIVES

✓ Having reviewed HPE Aruba architecture and features in Chapter 1, you will now learn about optimizing deployment redundancy, as relates to the Mobility Master (MM). This chapter begins with an overview of MM redundancy and its components.

✓ Next, you will explore the Virtual Router Redundancy Protocol (VRRP). This includes how it works, how to configure it, and how to validate VRRP packets and status.

✓ Finally, you will learn about MM redundancy DB synchronization. This includes a discussion of IPsec parameter configuration, redundancy status checking, and DB synchronization.

MM redundancy overview

Why MM redundancy?

With HPE Aruba deployments, the MM acts as a single point of configuration for global policies. This includes firewall policies, authentication parameters, and RF configuration. This eases the configuration and maintenance of a wireless network and synchronizes MC configurations.

During MM outages without a backup MM, configurations cannot be modified in the controller network. In addition, the MM manages the WLAN Management Suite (WMS) database for the cluster of controllers. WMS is responsible for aggregating certain IDS and location tracking information, which can be displayed using AirWave. The following functions are also lost during an MM outage:

- Centralized licensing
- Centralized visibility, monitoring and configuring platform
- Wireless Intrusion Detection System (WIDS)
- AirMatch
- Software Defined Network (SDN) functions
- Unified Communication and Collaboration (UCC) function

- Web Content Classification (WebCC) proxy
- AP Whitelist DB and AirGroup classification
- Rule-Based Client Match (RBCM)
- AirGroup classification

Therefore, it is important to deploy a backup MM. This backup MM is a hot standby—during an outage, a backup mobility master will assume the primary MM's responsibilities. Yes, the network continues uninterrupted operation during an MM outage, even without MM redundancy. However, any change in the network topology or configuration requires the MM. Furthermore, there is no charge from HPE Aruba for the backup MM.

MM redundancy overview

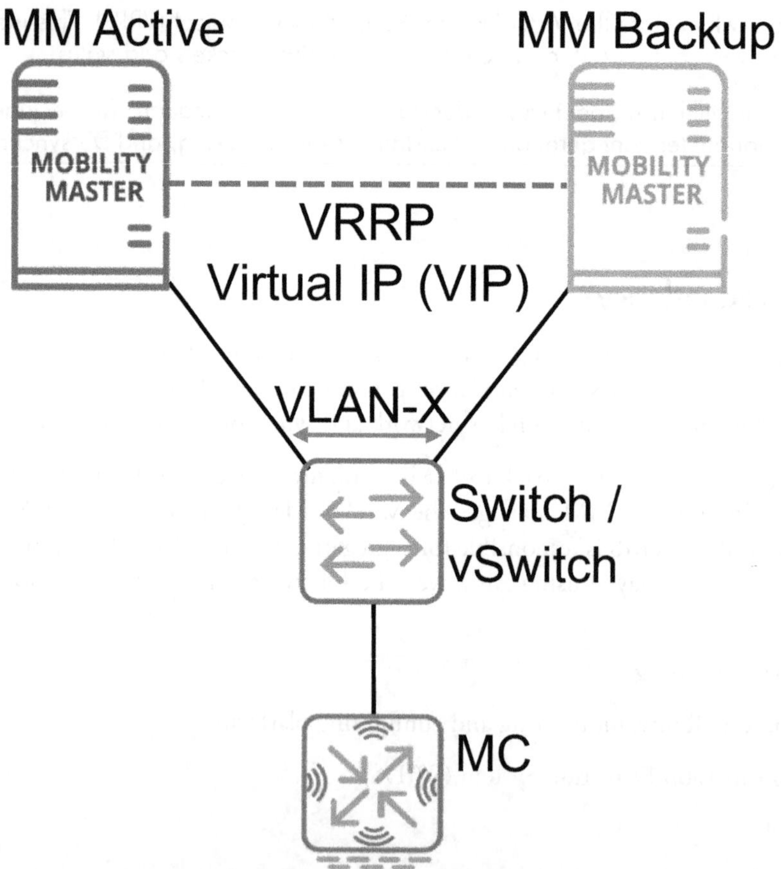

Figure 2-1 MM redundancy overview

For redundancy, deploy the primary and backup MM on the same L2 broadcast domain. Configure them to use the Virtual Router Redundancy Protocol (VRRP), and they can share a single set of licenses (Figure 2-1).

Note

It is a best practice to disable VRRP pre-emption.

Managed devices connect to the MM using the VRRP Virtual IP (VIP) address, which you must configure to support MM redundancy. The primary MM uses this VIP by default. However, if the primary MM becomes unavailable, the secondary MM assumes ownership of the VIP. Thus, managed devices retain seamless connectivity to an MM device. You may define only one backup MM per primary MM.

Note

L3 MM redundancy is on the HPE Aruba roadmap. However, at the time of this writing, you must connect primary and backup MMs on the same L2 broadcast domain.

MM redundancy components

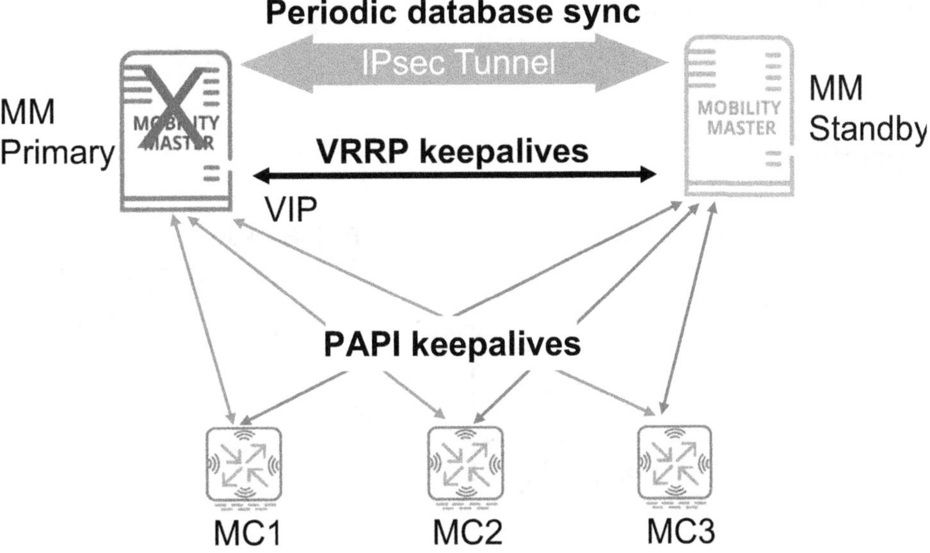

Figure 2-2 MM redundancy components

There are two major components to MM redundancy:

- **VRRP IP**—This IP address is shared between the active (primary) and standby MM. MCs terminating on the active MM should point to this IP address. Thus, in the event of an MM outage, they will failover to the standby MM.
- **Configuration and database synchronization**—An IPsec tunnel forms between the two MMs to synchronize configuration and databases.

As shown in Figure 2-2, VRRP keepalives are periodically transmitted between the MM primary and standby. Should the primary MM fail, the standby MM will cease to receive these keepalives. Thus, the standby MM detects the primary MM as unavailable. The standby MM takes over as the active MM.

Meanwhile, periodic PAPI keepalives will fail between the MC and the previously active MM before they connect to the newly promoted MM.

Note

PAPI is an acronym that stands for Process Application Programming Interface.

Spend some time looking at Figure 2-2 and summarize this in your mind:

- VRRP keepalives are for *MM* failover
- PAPI keepalives are for *MC* failover

VRRP configuration

VRRP operation

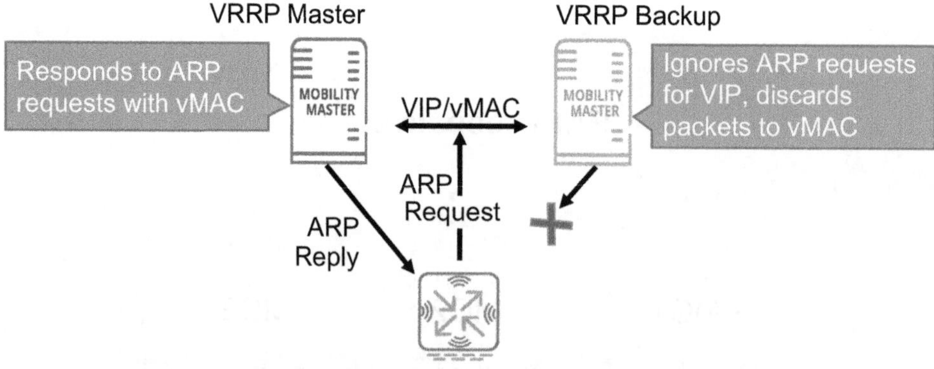

Figure 2-3 VRRP operation

The purpose of VRRP is to provide redundancy. It does this by forming a collection of physical routers into a single Virtual Router. This eliminates single points of failure for Layer 3 routers. This is true whether routers use static or dynamic routing protocols (Figure 2-3).

The VRRP group of routers includes one master and one or more backups. If the current master fails, the backup acts as the new master. When there are several backups in the virtual group, the backup devices elect a new master. The router with the highest priority value wins the election.

To achieve this redundancy, a group of VRRP routers is represented by a single Virtual IP (VIP) address, and an associated Virtual MAC (vMAC) address. Downstream devices communicate with the Virtual Router via this VIP address. When some downstream device broadcasts an ARP request for the VIP, only the VRRP Master responds with its vMAC, in an ARP reply. VRRP backup devices never respond to ARP requests for the VIP, and they discard frames destined for the vMAC.

VRRP configuration

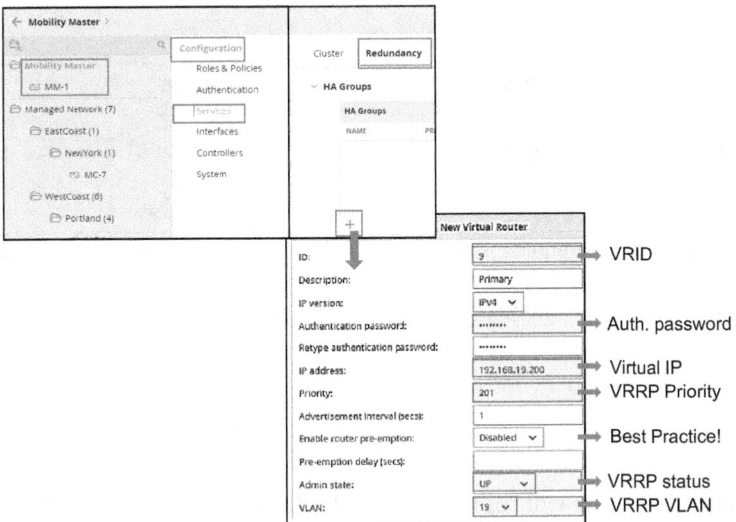

Figure 2-4 VRRP configuration

Figure 2-4 summarizes how to configure MM redundancy.

Navigate to **Mobility Master> select the target MM > Configuration > Services > Redundancy.** (Figure 2-4). Then click "+" to create a new Virtual router.

Now complete the actual VRRP configuration. You assign a Virtual Router ID and configure an authentication password. This mitigates against rogue VRRP routers. You configure the Virtual IP address and a priority. The default priority is 100. Remember, this priority value controls VRRP master election—highest priority wins. Of course, you need to ensure that VRRP is administratively enabled, or "UP," as shown in Figure 2-4. Also, the VLAN must be set. Repeat the above steps on the backup MM.

It is a best practice to leave router pre-emption disabled. This pre-empt feature allows another device to take over as the new master, even though the current master is still functional. Leaving this disabled can prevent flapping, where the primary master appears to go down and up repeatedly.

Since it is not recommended to enable pre-emption for master redundancy, nor should you configure tracking. Tracking may help to prevent flapping, should you decide to enable pre-emption.

Let us look at this pre-emption feature in more detail.

VRRP pre-emption

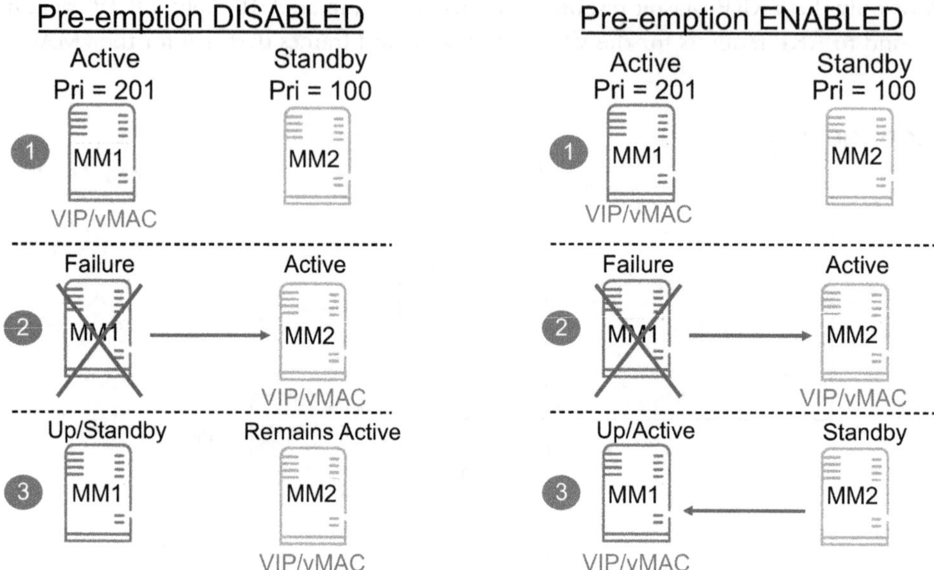

Figure 2-5 VRRP Pre-emption

To understand pre-emption, we will compare how VRRP responds when the feature is enabled versus disabled. In this scenario, MM1 is active, with priority 201. MM2 is standby, with priority 100.

1. In the top-left of Figure 2-5, preemption is disabled on MM1. Since MM1 has a higher priority, it acts as the active device—it “owns” the VIP and vMAC. MM2 is in Standby mode.
2. Next, MM1 fails, and so MM2 takes over as primary. It therefore now “owns” the VIP and vMAC, and so services requests from managed devices.
3. When MM1 comes back up, it is in Standby mode. It receives VRRP messages from MM2, and so remains in Standby mode. Even though MM1 has a higher priority, MM2 is currently a functional, active device. MM1 cannot pre-empt MM2’s status as the master, since pre-empt is disabled. MM2 remains as the active device.

If MM1 had come back on line and did NOT receive VRRP message from MM2, then MM2 must be down. MM1 becomes the Active device, since there is no other device available.

The right side of Figure 2-6 shows a scenario with pre-emption enabled.

1. Just like before, MM1 begins as the active device, since it has the highest priority.
2. Also just like before, when MM1 fails, MM2 takes over as the active device.
3. MM1 comes back in standby mode, as before, and receives VRRP messages from MM2. These messages include MM2's priority. MM1 sees that:
   a. MM1 priority is greater than MM2.
   b. Pre-empt is enabled.
4. MM1 pre-empts MM2's status and resumes its former role as the active device.

VRRP packet capture

```
▷ Frame 15: 60 bytes on wire (480 bits), 60 bytes captured (480 bits) on interface 0
◢ Ethernet II, Src: IETF-VRRP-VRID_09 (00:00:5e:00:01:09), Dst: IPv4mcast_12 (01:00:5e:00:00:12)
  ▷ Destination: IPv4mcast_12 (01:00:5e:00:00:12)
  ▷ Source: IETF-VRRP-VRID_09 (00:00:5e:00:01:09)        ──> vMAC
    Type: IPv4 (0x0800)
    Padding: 000000000000
◢ Internet Protocol Version 4, Src: 192.168.19.11, Dst: 224.0.0.18
    0100 .... = Version: 4
    .... 0101 = Header Length: 20 bytes (5)
  ▷ Differentiated Services Field: 0x00 (DSCP: CS0, ECN: Not-ECT)
    Total Length: 40
    Identification: 0x1301 (4865)
  ▷ Flags: 0x00
    Fragment offset: 0
    Time to live: 255
    Protocol: VRRP (112)
    Header checksum: 0xf49e [validation disabled]
    [Header checksum status: Unverified]
    Source: 192.168.19.11                                 ──> Real IP
    Destination: 224.0.0.18
    [Source GeoIP: Unknown]
    [Destination GeoIP: Unknown]
◢ Virtual Router Redundancy Protocol
  ▷ Version 2, Packet type 1 (Advertisement)
    Virtual Rtr ID: 9                                     ──> VRRP ID
    Priority: 201 (Non-default backup priority)           ──> VRRP Priority
    Addr Count: 1
    Auth Type: Simple Text Authentication [RFC 2338] / Reserved [RFC 3768] (1)
    Adver Int: 1
    Checksum: 0xd649 [correct]
    [Checksum Status: Good]
    IP Address: 192.168.19.200                            ──> VRRP Virtual IP
    Authentication String: aruba123
```

Figure 2-6 VRRP packet capture

Figure 2-6 shows a captured VRRP Packet, with key items highlighted, as described below.

- The vMAC = 00:00:5e:00:01:09. The first five octets will always be the same for any VRRP deployment, and the last octet indicates the VRID. In this case, VRID = 9, so vMAC is 00:00:005e:00:09.
- TTL = 255. Remember, the IPv4 TTL field starts at 255, and decrements for every "hop" through a router. Since the Aruba redundancy feature requires MMs to be on the same subnet, this field should always be 255.
- The source IP address is the actual IP of MC, here it is 192.168.19.11.
- VRRP version = 2.
- VRRP Priority is not equal to 255. In this case, it is 201. A priority level of 255 means that the device has stopped participating in the VRRP group. This can happen when you change the administrative state of the Virtual Router to down.
- The VRRP IP Address reflects your VRRP configuration, as previously described. For this scenario, it is 192.168.19.200.

Checking VRRP status

```
(MM-Primary) [mynode] #show vrrp                                MM-Primary

Virtual Router 9:
   Description Primary
   Admin State UP, VR State MASTER
   IP Address 192.168.19.200, MAC Address 00:00:5e:00:01:09, vlan 1
   Priority 201, Advertisement 1 sec, Preemption Disable Delay 0
   Auth type PASSWORD, Auth data: ********
   tracking is not enabled
```

```
(MM-Backup) [mynode] #show vrrp                                 MM-Backup

Virtual Router 9:
   Description backup
   Admin State UP, VR State BACKUP
   IP Address 192.168.19.200, MAC Address 00:00:5e:00:01:09, vlan 1
   Priority 100, Advertisement 1 sec, Preemption Disable Delay 0
   Auth type PASSWORD, Auth data: ********
   tracking is not enabled
```

Figure 2-7 Checking VRRP status

Figure 2-7 shows output of the command `show vrrp`, for both the primary and backup MMs. Notice that the operational state of the active MM is "'MASTER." In other words, it is active for that VRRP IP address. It will actively respond to the virtual IP and MAC addresses, as shown.

The standby MM's VRRP is "BACKUP" since it is in standby mode. Remember to configure a higher priority level for the active MM—this ensures that it comes up as the active device.

You can also see that features related to pre-emption are disabled. This includes the pre-emption delay and tracking.

Please remember to configure a matching authentication password and VRRP ID on both the MMs. This helps to avoid confusion, in case there is another VRRP instance running on the same VLAN.

Learning check

1. What are some of the MM functions?
   a. Centralized licensing
   b. Centralized visibility, monitoring, and configuration
   c. WIDS
   d. AirMatch
   e. SDN functions
   f. UCC function
   g. WebCC proxy
   h. AP Whitelist DB
   i. Rule-Based Client Match (RBCM)
   j. AirGroup classification

MM redundancy DB synchronization

MM database synchronization

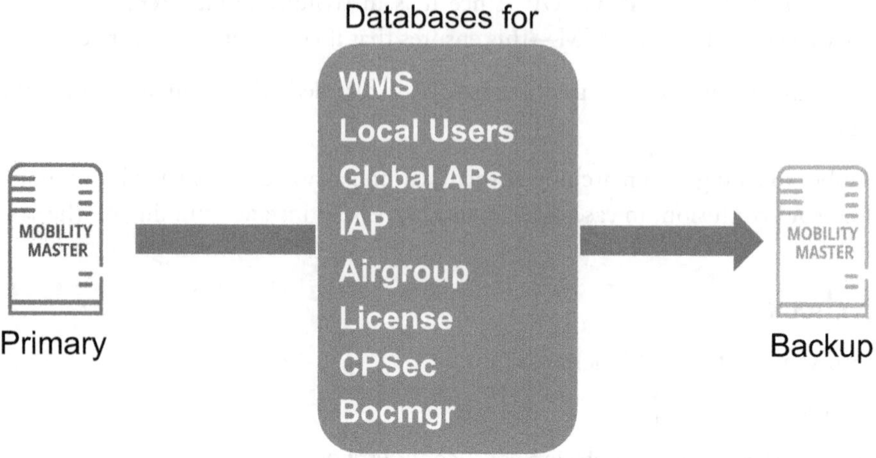

Figure 2-8 MM database synchronization

Once you enable DB synchronization, many important databases are backed up, from Primary to Backup MM. Thus, if the Primary fails, the Backup can assume all MM tasks (Figure 2-8).

For example, say you need to replace a stand-alone MM. The keys installed on the previous MM must be regenerated and added to the new MM.

However, with a redundant solution, there is no need to reinstall keys on the MM. This is because the replacement MM will synchronize its licensing database with the backup. This happens very soon after the new MM comes online.

Other databases that are synchronized include the following:

- **WMS database**—WLAN management database
- **Local User database**—Local users created at the MM level
- **Global AP database**—Information for all APs
- **IAP database**—Tracks of Instant APs (IAP)
- **AirGroup database**—Tracks AirGroup zero configuration networking for Bonjour services
- **License database**—Central licensing repository
- **CPSec database**—Tracks AP-to-Controller CPSec tunnels.
- **Bocmgr database**—Branch Office Controller (BOC) management database

MM synchronization warning

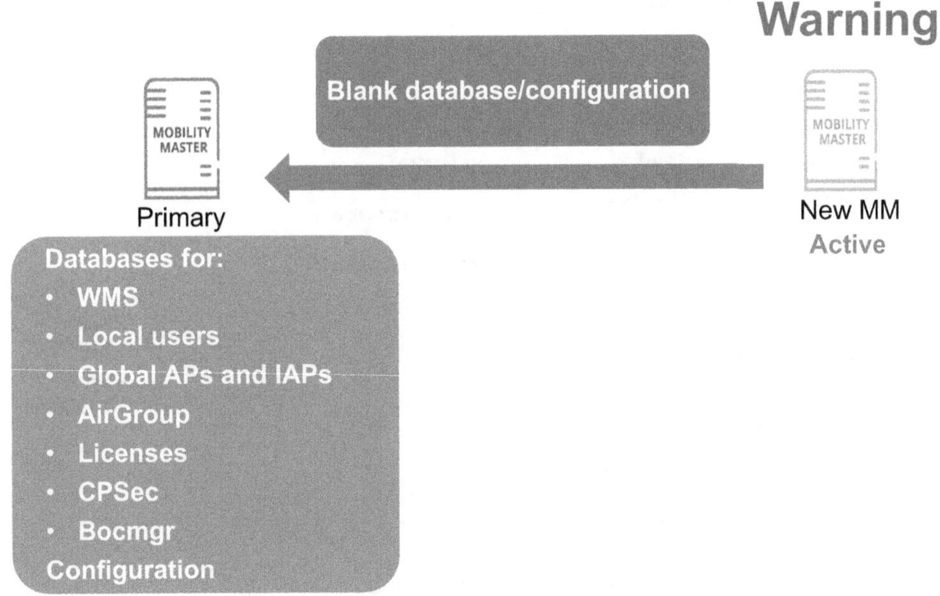

Figure 2-9 MM synchronization warning

The MM redundancy feature adds significant value to your deployment, but you must be careful! Do not mistakenly set an unsynchronized standby MM VRRP to a higher priority than the active MM. If you do, the standby becomes the active MM, and its "blank" configuration and databases are synchronized over to the properly configured MM (Figure 2-9). This will cause the existing configuration and databases to be overwritten. This would be very bad news for you.

Make sure that you set a higher priority on the existing, configured MM!

MM redundancy IPsec parameter

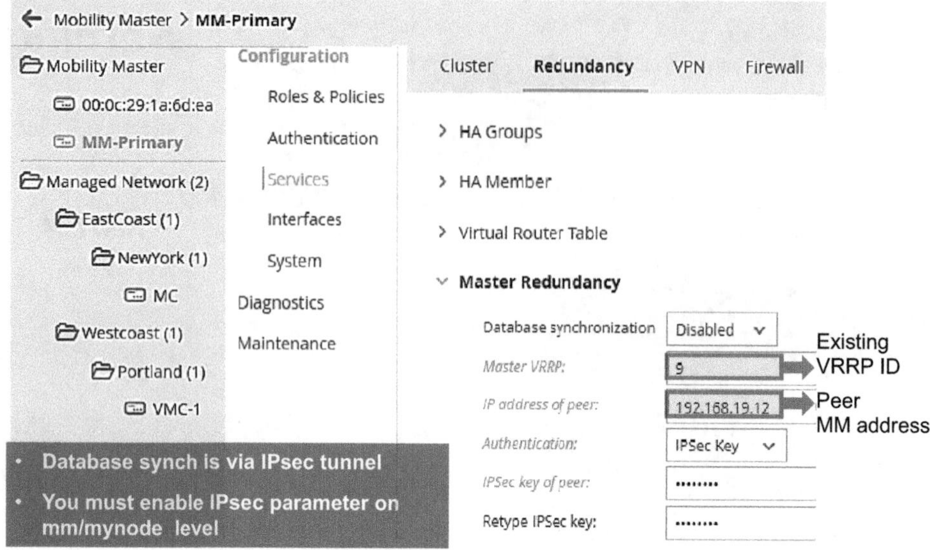

Figure 2-10 MM redundancy IPsec parameter

Database synchronization is accomplished through an IPsec tunnel, established between the two MMs. Figure 2-10 shows how to configure this. The device named MM-Primary is configured with the desired VRRP ID, and with the IP address of its MM peer (the backup MM). This must be configured at the mm/mynode level.

You must do a similar configuration on the MM-Backup device. Configure the same VRRP ID, and use the MM-Primary's IP address in the field labeled "IP address of peer":

The following configuration shows how to accomplish the same thing at the CLI:

```
(MM-Primary) [mynode] (config) #master-redundancy

(MM-Primary) ^[mynode] (config-submode)#master-vrrp 9

((MM-Primary))^[mynode](config-submode)#peer-ip-address  192.168.19.200
IPsec aruba123
```

Enable Master redundancy DB synchronization

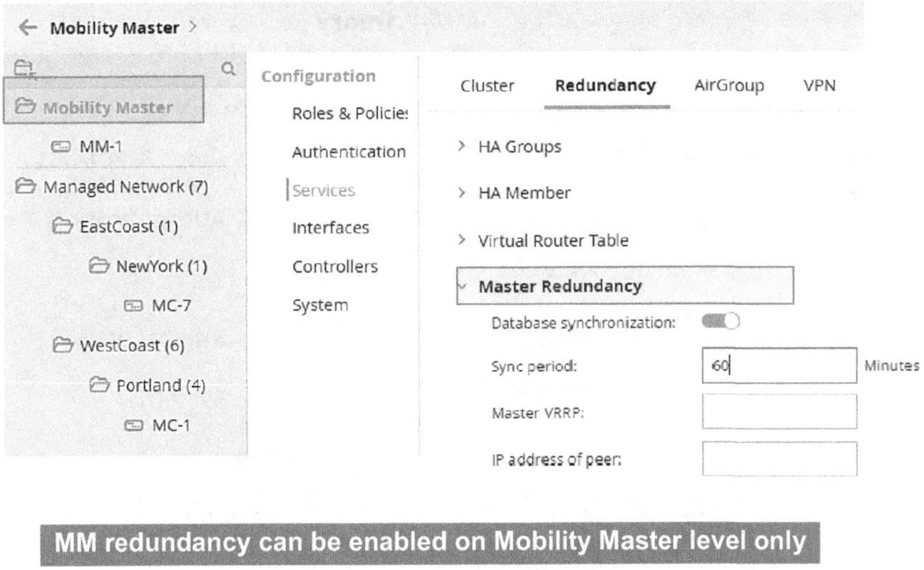

Figure 2-11 Enable Master redundancy DB synchronization

After configuring the VRRP IP address, enable database synchronization (Figure 2-11). Do not forget about the previous warning related to VRRP priority! You may want to go back and double-check that the current MM has a higher priority than the backup MM.

Optionally, you can modify the database synchronization period. In the example, it is set to the default value of 60 minutes. This is the norm. Some engineers have chosen to decrease this value down to 20 minutes, to decrease the likelihood of data loss due to long synchronization times. Be aware that this increases bandwidth and CPU overhead. Again, the default value of 60 minutes is usually fine.

Check MM redundancy status

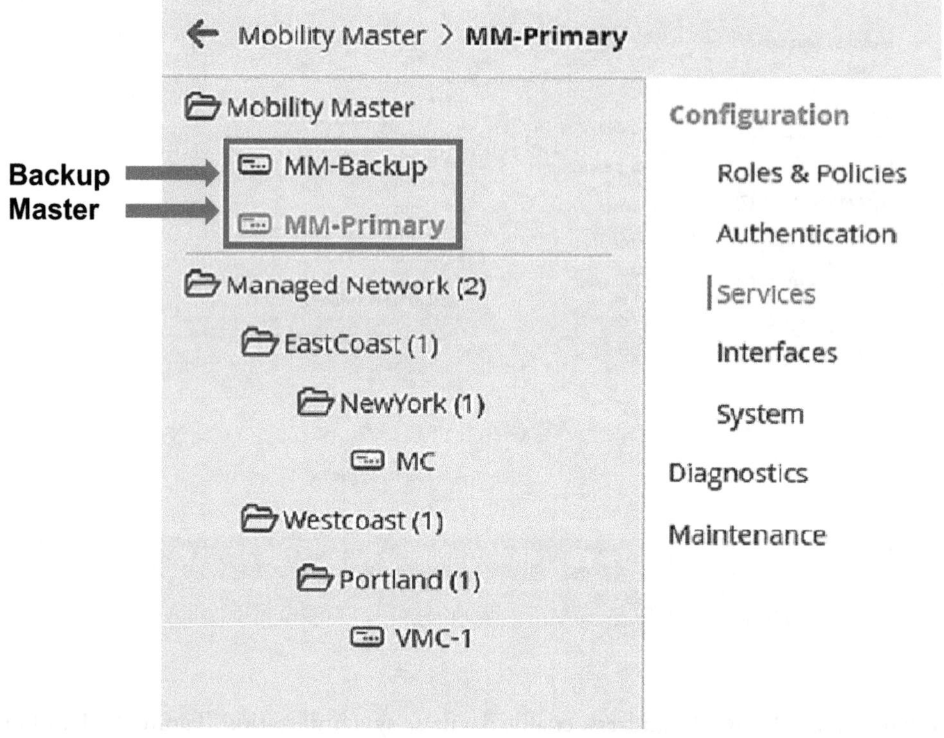

Figure 2-12 Check MM redundancy status

Figure 2-12 shows how to check MM redundancy status, using the GUI. Since two MMs are listed, you can tell that this device is operating as the primary, active MM. If you navigated to this same location on the backup device, you would only see one MM, and no other MCs. This would inform you that indeed the device is operating as the backup MM.

You can see similar information from the CLI, by issuing the command `show switches`, as shown in the following output:

```
(MM-Primary) [mynode] #show switches
All Switches
----------------------------
                IPv6
IP Address      Address  Name       Location Type    Model      Version        status  Configuration State
--------------- -------- ---------  -------- ------- ---------  -------------  ------  -------------------
192.168.19.11   None     MM-Primary Bldg1.   master  ArubaMM    8.0.1.0_27204  up      UPDATE SUCCESSFUL
                                    floor1
192.168.19.12   None     MM-Backup  Bldg1.   standby ArubaMM    8.0.1.0_27204  up      UPDATE SUCCESSFUL
                                    floor1
192.168.19.21   None     VMC-1      Bldg1.   MD      ArubaVMC   8.0.1.0_27204  up      UPDATE SUCCESSFUL
                                    floor1
192.168.19.22   None     MC         Bldg1.   MD      Aruba7005  8.0.1.0_27204  up      UPDATE SUCCESSFUL
                                    floor1
```

You can see the device named MM-Primary is correctly operating as the master, and MM-Backup is operating in standby mode, as it should.

Validating MM DB synchronization

```
(MM-primary) [mynode] # show database synchronize

Last synchronization time: Thu Apr 13 07:42:48 2017
To Master Switch at 10.254.10.101:  succeeded
WMS Database backup file size: 39121 bytes
Local User Database backup file size: 29694 bytes
Global AP Database backup file size: 13375 bytes
IAP Database backup file size: 3750 bytes
Airgroup Database backup file size: 3052 bytes
License Database backup file size: 5358 bytes
CPSec Database backup file size: 3224 bytes
Bocmgr Database backup file size: 6016 bytes
Synchronization took 1 second

1 synchronization attempted
0 synchronization have failed
Periodic synchronization is enabled and runs every 60 minutes
Synchronization doesn't include Captive Portal Custom data
Airmatch database gets synchronized periodically.
Last synchronization time : 2017-04-13 07:22:2019:20:24
```

Figure 2-13 Validating MM DB synchronization

Figure 2-13 shows the use of the command `show database synchronization`. This command shows the MM redundancy status. You can see most recent synchronization time. This helps to verify that synchronization is functioning as expected. You see that the last synchronization was successful, along with the relevant IP address.

Next, you see all the databases that were backed up, and the size of each one.

Near the bottom, you see the number of synchronization attempts, and how many failed. You see the 60-minute synchronization timer, which reflects the configuration shown in the previous Figure 2-11.

 **Note**

DB sync takes place per your configuration, but to force now, use "database synchronize" from the primary.

Learning check

2. The Master Redundancy DB synchronization function can be enabled on mm/mynode level.
   a. True
   b. False

3 Mobility Master and MC Operations

LEARNING OBJECTIVES

- ✓ In this chapter, you will learn more advanced concepts and configurations related to Mobility Masters (MM) and Mobility Controllers (MC). This includes Aruba OS 8.x multicontroller deployments, working with uplink manager, and configuring uplink load balancing.
- ✓ After reviewing configuration hierarchy, you will compare various Master-Local and MM-MC deployment models. Then you will learn about various multicontroller deployments, with an eye toward scalability and high availability.
- ✓ The chapter ends with a discussion of advanced licensing features.

MM redundancy overview

MM architecture

The MM uses a centralized, multitier architecture that provides a clear separation between management, control, and forwarding functions. It also provides high availability and scalability. You configure everything from a single, central interface. This includes both the MM and all of its managed devices. This simplifies and streamlines the configuration process.

The MM consolidates all-master, single master-multiple local, and multiple Master-Local deployments into a single deployment model. The MM can be a hardware appliance or a Virtual Machine (VM).

Architecture at a glance

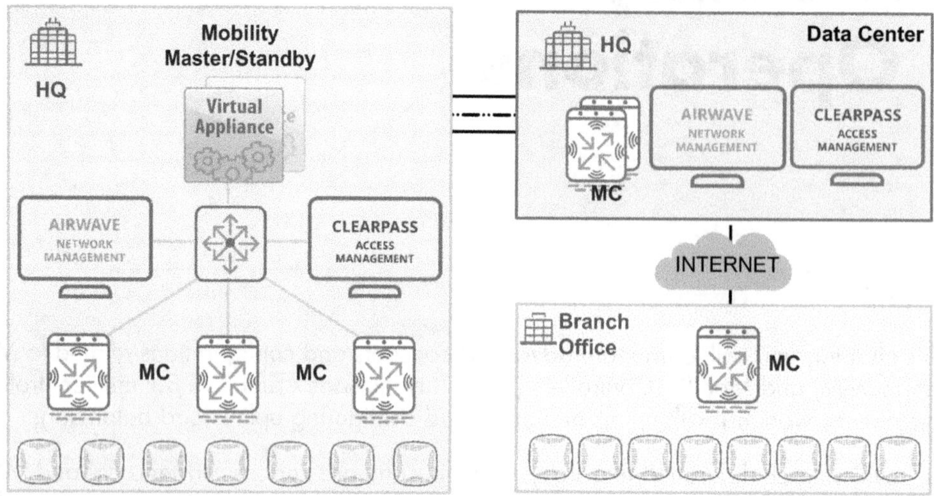

Figure 3-1 Architecture at a glance

The MM is a centralized point from which you perform all configurations—for both the MM itself and for all managed devices (Figure 3-1).

Common configurations across devices are extracted to a shared template. This includes the default configuration. All of this merges with device-specific settings to generate the effective configuration for an individual device.

Traffic from APs and clients are handled by Managed Nodes—the MCs in your deployment. You can deploy Branch Office Controllers (BOC) with minimal effort, using the Zero Touch Provisioning (ZTP) feature.

Multi-Controller configuration

You will learn how to expand your network by adding MCs to an MM controller configuration. Typically, this is the first expansion of a single-controller deployment.

ZTP can be used to automate MC deployment. This means that less skilled, non-IT personnel can deploy MCs to remote sites. Factory-default MCs can autodiscover the MM, join the central configuration application, download configurations from the MM, and become operational. All this occurs with no user intervention.

A cluster is a combination of multiple MCs, working together to provide high availability to all clients. This ensures service continuity during failover events.

Adding MD/MC manually

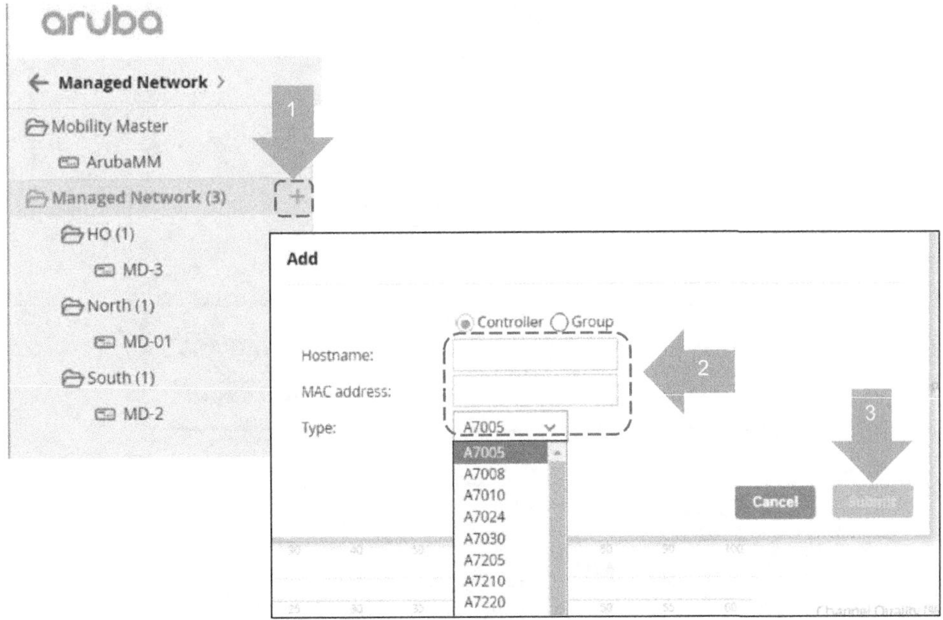

Figure 3-2 Adding MD/MC manually

Prior to MC configuration, you are strongly encouraged to carefully plan and create a group hierarchy. It is very difficult to move an MC from one group or subgroup to another. Remember, the reason for creating group/subgroup hierarchy is to facilitate device configuration and monitoring.

Figure 3-2 shows how to add an MC to a group or subgroup, as described below:

1. Next to Managed Network, click on the groups "+" symbol.
2. Enter the name and MAC address of the MC host. Specify the device type.
3. Click Submit.

The MC is then physically connected to the network, powered up, and directed to the MM—perhaps via ZTP. Then the MC joins the appropriate group and receives its configuration.

MC Zero Touch Provisioning

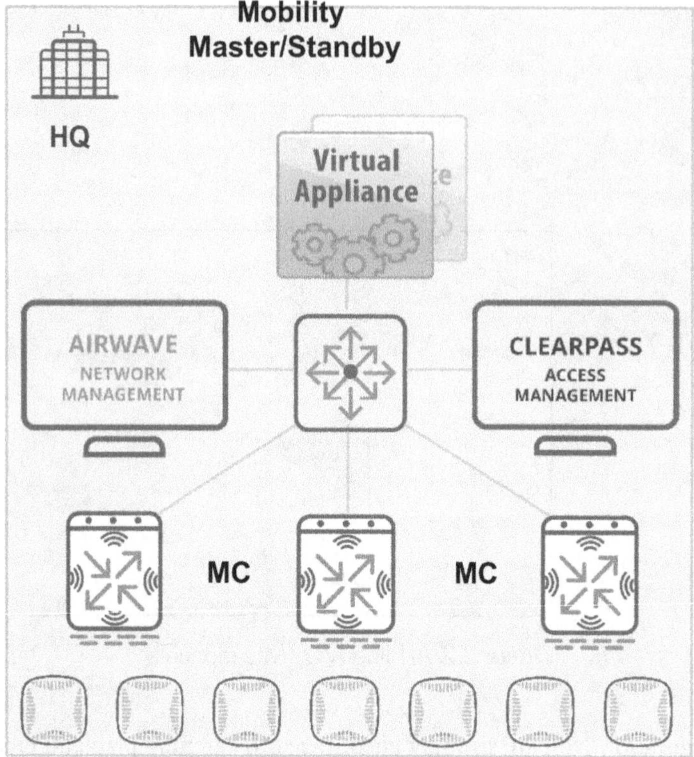

Figure 3-3 MC Zero Touch Provisioning

All controllers can be configured locally (Figure 3-3). Also, if the MC has Internet access, the Activate feature can direct the MC to the MM for configuration, for ZTP.

The MM manages all local and global configuration. Once the MC is in communication with the MM, you can no longer configure the MC directly. This enforces one of the major benefits of the MM architecture—a single point of configuration and management for the entire network.

Learning check

1. Which of the following deployment methods require Aruba activate?
   a. Provisioning/adding local (MD/MC) to the MM manually
   b. Provisioning/adding local (MD/MC) to the MM over ZTP
   c. Deleting a local (MD/MC) from the MM
   d. Renaming a local (MD/MC) in the hierarchy

Licenses

Calculating licensing requirements

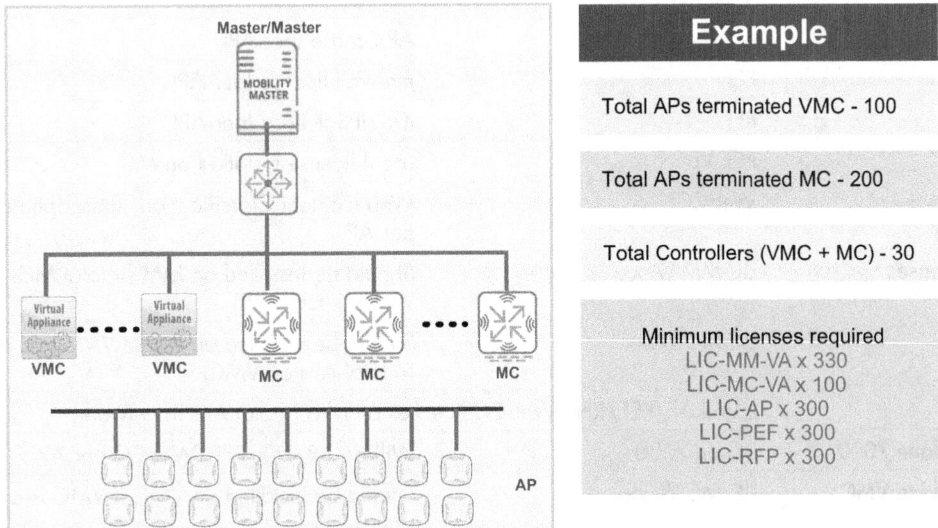

Figure 3-4 Calculating licensing requirements

To deploy APs, you must install the correct number of MM and AP licenses. For example, if you plan to deploy 30 MCs with 300 APs, the minimum licenses required are as follows (Figure 3-4):

- MM licenses: 300 + 30 (AP + MC)
- AP licenses: 300
- VMC licenses: 100
- PEFNG: 300

RFProtect, WebCC, and PEFV licenses are optional.

Licenses

Table 3-1 summarizes HPE Aruba licensing:

Table 3-1 HPE Aruba licensing

Types of licenses	LIC-MM-VA-xx	MM license (500, 1000, 5000, 10000)
	LIC-MC-VA-XX	VMC license (installed on MM if VMC is an MC) per AP on VMC
	AP	AP license (per AP)
	PEF	Firewall license (per AP)
	RFP	IDS/IPS license (per AP)
	PEF VIA	Local license installed on MC
	WebCC	Web Content Classification, subscription based per AP
MM licenses	LIC-MM-VA-xx	Should be installed on MM (= total MCs + VMCs + total APs)
	LIC-MC-VA-xx	Should be installed on MM if VMC is a device (= total APs on VMC)
	Install AP/PEF/RFP/WebCC licenses on MM (=total APs in network)	
Standalone 7000	LIC on 7x00	Will be AP/PEF/RFP/WebCC per AP
Standalone VMC	LIC-MC-VA-xx	Should be installed on VMC if VMC is a standalone
	Install AP/PEF/RFP/WebCC licenses on Standalone VMC	
	APs on VMC standalone	Consume LIC-MC-VA-xx license per AP and AP/PEF/RFP/WebCC licenses per AP
VIA/VPN-Firewall	PEFV to be installed on MC terminating VIA/VPN client connections	
	Mandatory for VIA clients	
	For VPN clients applying firewall policies. This is optional.	

Global pool

The MM uses licensing pools to distribute licenses to many managed devices, across geographic locations. By default, all managed devices are associated with the MM, and share that MM's single global pool of all sharable licenses.

Dedicated pool

AOS allows you to create additional licensing pools at a configuration node. Thus, a group of managed devices at or below that configuration level can share licenses among themselves, but not with other groups.

On the MM, each AP consumes an MM, AP, PEF, and RFP license. Also, each MC (VMC or 7x00) consumes MM licenses. If VMCs report to the MM, the MM also needs the VMC license. Each AP reporting to the VMC consumes 1 MM, 1 MC, 1 AP, 1 PEF, and 1 RFP license.

 **Note**

The SKUs for MM licenses are 500, 1000, 5000, 10000.

 **Note**

The PEF and RFP licenses are not mandatory but highly recommended.

 **Note**

APs that are not licensed may join the MC but will not advertise SSIDs.

There is an ACR license for the advanced cryptography suite B, based on user count. There is also a WebCC-based license for Web classification. This is based on AP count and a yearly subscription.

Below is a simple way to understand the license calculation:

- VMC-VA/AP/PEC/RFP/WEBCC licenses are all AP-based.
- The number of APs terminated to VMC equals the required number of VMC-VA licenses.
- MM-VA licenses equal the number of all MCs plus all APs.

Below is a description of additional licenses:

- **Policy Enforcement Firewall (PEF)**—A per-AP license needed to enable the Aruba Firewall.
- **RF protect (RFP)**—Per-AP license to enable spectrum analysis and wireless intrusion protection.
- **AP**—Required per AP. Unlicensed APs may join the MC, but will not advertise SSIDs.
- **Policy Enforcement Firewall for VPN (PEFV)**—Required for VIA and to apply VPN client policies. You need one license per MC terminating VPN connections.
- **Web Content Classification (WebCC)**—Supports external web-based classification. It is subscription-based, per-AP. The maximum subscription length is ten years.

A Standalone VMC requires one MC, AP, PEF, RFP, and WebCC license, per AP.

So if a VMC has 100 APs, you need a VMC license of 100, AP of 100, PEF-NG of 100, RFP of 100, and WebCC of 100. Remember, WebCC is also subscription-based, as discussed on the previous page.

The 7x00 controller (as a Standalone or in a Master/Local architecture) consumes one AP, PEF, and RFP license per AP. If the 7000 MC series has 100 APs, this MC requires the following: 100 AP licenses, 100 PEF-NG licenses, and 100 RFP licenses.

As stated above, the PEF and RFP licenses are not mandatory but highly recommended. The PEF VIA license allows you to apply firewall policies to VPN clients that connect to the controller. This license is mandatory for the Aruba VIA VPN client. However, it must only be installed on the MC terminating VIA or VPN clients with firewall integration.

Note

There is an Enterprise license that includes all the features and includes an AirWave device license.

Advanced licensing features

The deployment can share licenses from the MM's global pool. You can also dedicate license pools to certain sites across multiple MCs.

Starting with ArubaOS 8.1.0.0, local license pools are shown as separate pools at the same level as the global licensing pool, instead of within the global licensing hierarchy. This provides a clearer indication that those licenses are removed from the global pool.

You can also add device-specific licenses to a physical controller.

The following pages discuss global and dedicated pools in more detail.

Device-specific (physical controller) licenses

Nonsharable licenses are associated with individual managed devices and are managed by the MM. Nonsharable licenses are generated using the serial number of a specific device and can only be assigned to the device for which they were created.

Only PEV and VMC licenses are device- specific (nonsharable) licenses.

License pool

Global pool (MM)

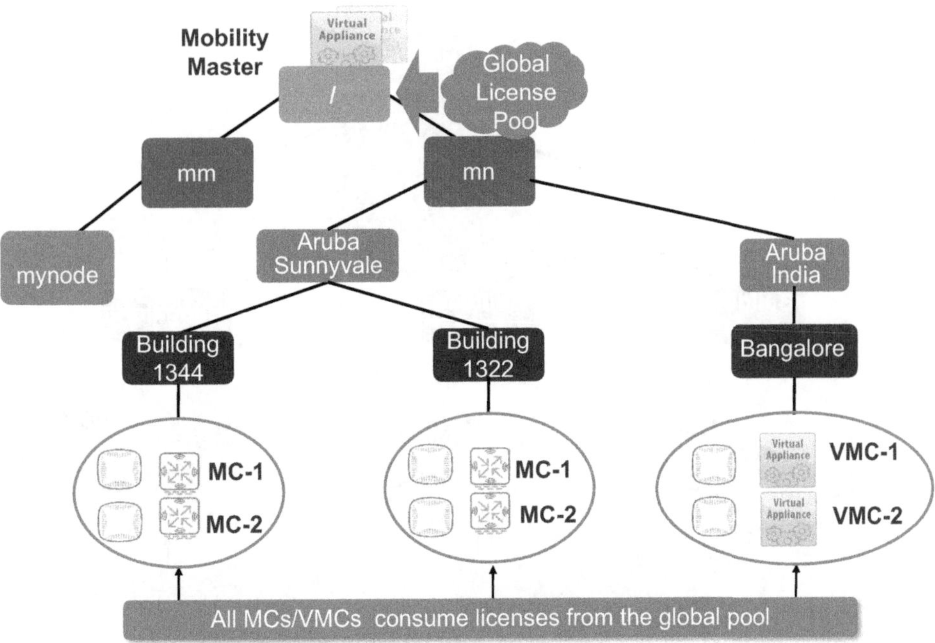

Figure 3-5 Global pool (MM)

By default, all managed devices associated with the same MM share a global pool of licenses (Figure 3-5). This pool is comprised of all sharable licenses added to the MM. In the topology shown, all managed devices are part of the default "/" global license pool, defined at the MM configuration root. The licenses installed on the MM are all sharable between the managed devices within the global license pool.

For example, if there are 100 AP licenses installed on the MM, then all managed devices share that global pool of 100 AP licenses. AP licenses needed by MCs are consumed from the global pool.

Note

If you put something in a license pool below the global pool, it cannot pull from the global pool. Also, in a pool, ALL licenses required must be in the pool, including the MM license.

Dedicated license pools

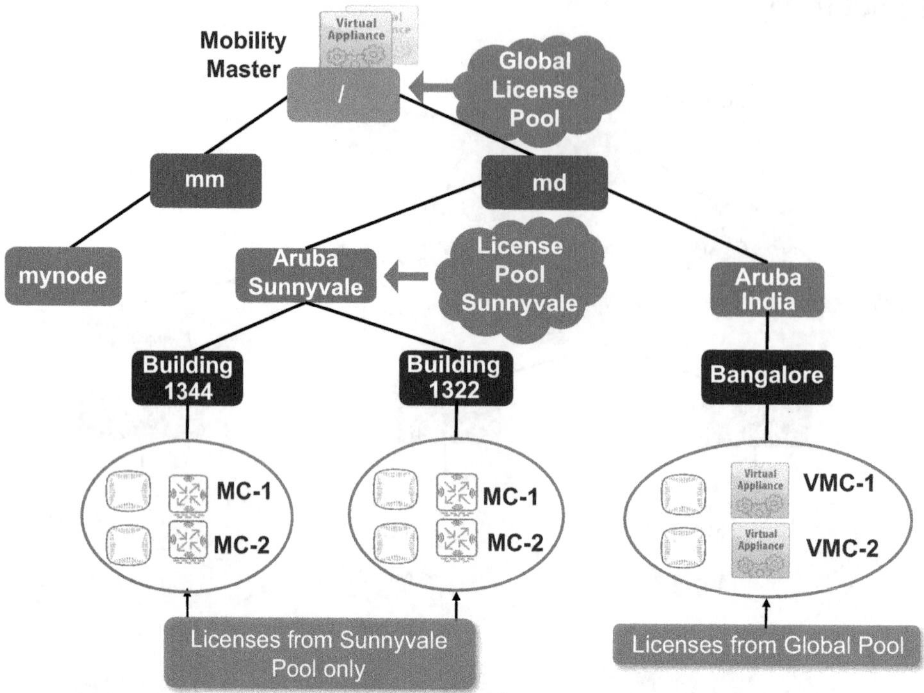

Figure 3-6 Dedicated license pools

ArubaOS 8.x allows you to create individual licensing pools at a configuration node. Thus, managed devices below the node can share licenses among themselves, instead of consuming licenses from the global pool.

Figure 3-6 shows that a license pool has been created for the configuration node /Aruba Sunnyvale. The four managed devices below this node use licenses from the /Sunnyvale pool. Other managed devices, such as Aruba India, continue to use the global pool.

Suppose that the /Sunnyvale license pool is allocated 40 of the 100 AP licenses installed on the MM. The four managed devices of Aruba Sunnyvale can share 40 AP licenses from MM. The global license pool now contains only 60 licenses, which are available for all other managed devices—including Aruba India.

Learning check

2. Which one of the following License types is device (MC) specific?
   a. AP
   b. PEF
   c. PEFV
   d. RFP

Creating a global pool

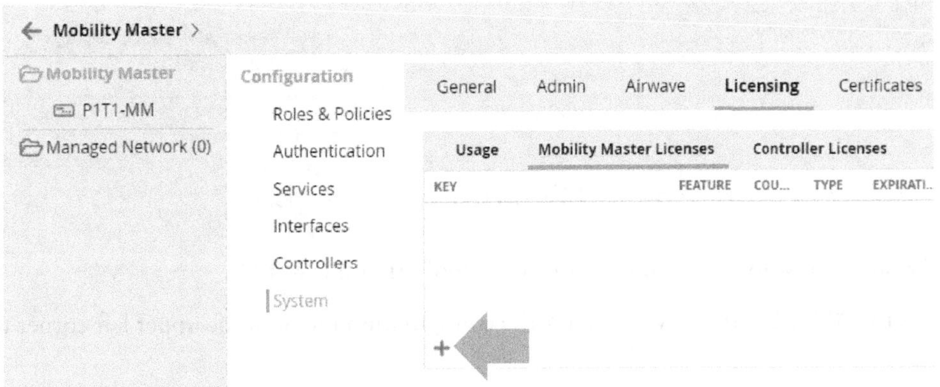

Figure 3-7 Creating a global pool

If you add a controller as a managed device under an MM, all the locally installed licenses become inactive. You must regenerate those keys and reinstall them via the MM.

Figure 3-7 shows how to add licenses to the global pool using the WebUI.

1. Access the MM WebUI. Click the configuration menu in the upper left corner to select MM.
2. Navigate to **Configuration > System > Licensing**.
3. Click the MM Licenses subtab.
4. Click + below the Key table. The Install Licenses window appears.
5. In the Install Licenses window, enter the serial number for one or more licenses. Each license key must be on a separate line.
6. Click OK.

Creating a local license pool

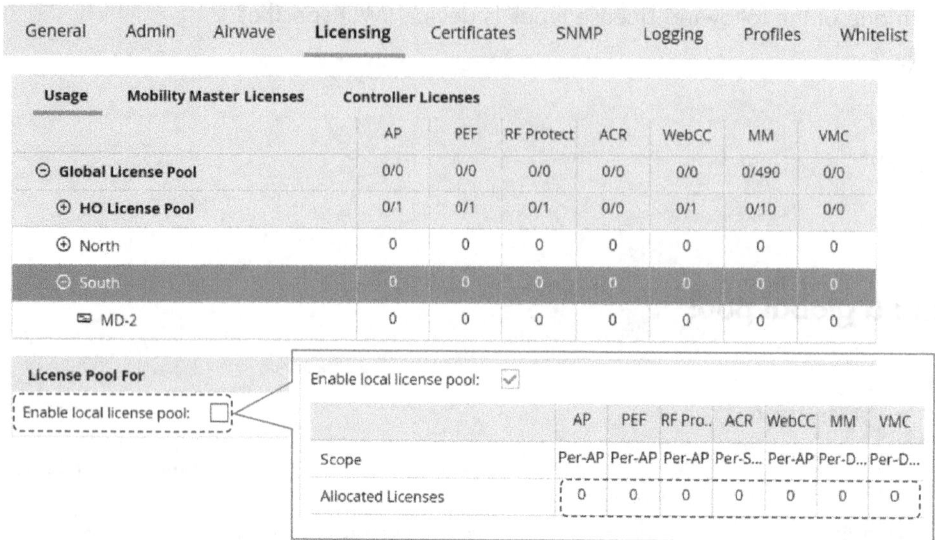

Figure 3-8 Creating a local license pool

Figure 3-8 shows how to add licenses to the local pool using the WebUI.

1. Access the WebUI of the MM and click the configuration menu in the upper left corner to select MM.
2. Navigate to **Configuration > System > Licensing**.
3. Select the Usage sub-tab. The License Usage table shows currently used license counts for each MM configuration node.
4. Select the configuration node for which you want to create a local license pool.
5. Select Enable Local License Pool. Another table appears below the License Usage table, which shows the number of sharable licenses currently allocated to that license pool.
6. Click the allocated licenses value for any license type to change the number of licenses in that license pool. The Allocate Licenses window opens, displaying the number of available licenses that can be allocated to a local pool.
7. Enter the number of permanent and/or evaluation licenses to be added to the selected pool then click Done.

Note

If this is the first time you have enabled a local license pool on this configuration node, this table shows zero allocated licenses for all license types.

Adding a device-specific license

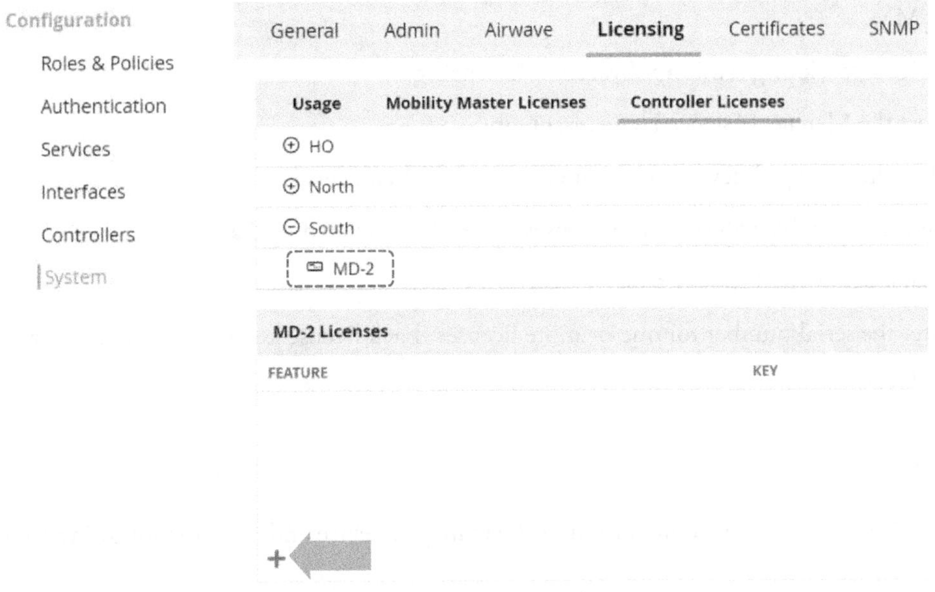

Figure 3-9 Adding a device-specific license

Before you can add a license key to a device, you must first create a nonsharable key, as described below.

Creating a controller-specific nonsharable key

1. Obtain the certificate ID from your Aruba sales representative or reseller. You also need the controller serial number.
2. From the Aruba License Management website, select Activate Certificates on the navigation menu.
3. Click the Product Type drop-down list and select a controller type. Select the MC to create a nonsharable license for a specific managed device.
4. Enter the controller serial number and the certificate ID(s).
5. Review the license agreement and select Yes to accept the agreement.
6. Click Activate Certificates. A copy of the transaction and the software license key is emailed to your licensing user account email address.

Figure 3-9 shows how to create a device-specific license, as described below.

Adding a license key using the WebUI

1. Access the WebUI of the MM and click the configuration menu in the upper left corner to select the MM.
2. Navigate to **Configuration > System > Licensing**.
3. Select the Managed Device Licenses subtab.
4. Select the managed device to which you want to add a license.
5. The Licenses table will show the licenses currently associated to that device.
6. Click + below the Licenses table.
7. Enter the serial number for one or more licenses. Each license key must be on a separate line.
8. Click OK.

Using the CLI

To add a license, go to the configuration of the managed device and issue the following command:

```
License add <key>
```

Learning check

3. Which one of the following license types are consumed per AP?
   a. AP
   b. PEF
   c. PEFV
   d. RFP

4 MultiZone

LEARNING OBJECTIVES

✓ You will learn about the MultiZone feature in this chapter, starting with an overview of concepts and terminology. Then you will learn about MultiZone configuration and troubleshooting, before diving into some common use cases for the MultiZone feature.

MultiZone overview

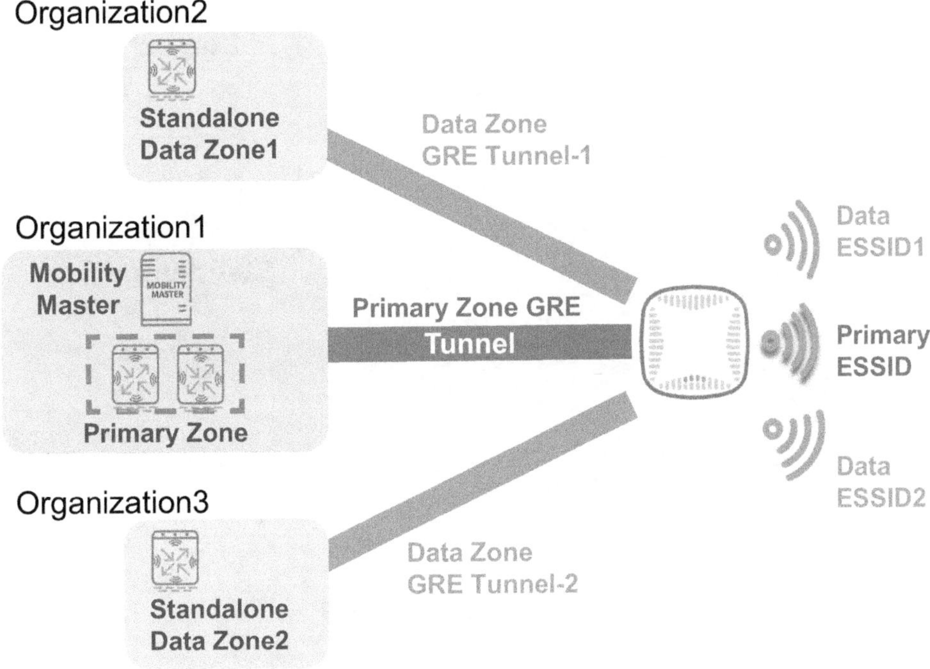

Figure 4-1 MultiZone overview

The MultiZone feature enables you to manage separate WLANs on the same APs, but under separate management and traffic zones, managed by separate controllers. A zone is a collection of managed devices under a single administration domain. Zones can have a single managed device or a cluster setup.

The objectives and benefits of the MultiZone feature include:

- Ability to leverage existing APs to support SSIDs from different controller domains or zones.
- Create secure "containers," such that APs can maintain a separation of WLANs belonging to different organizations.
- A so-called "air wall" is erected between zones, where each administrative domain can only view and manage its own set of SSIDs.

In Figure 4-1, a single AP supports three WLANs, for three separate organizations. The AP terminates each WLAN tunnel to a different controller. This provides separate data and management planes for each organization.

MultiZone terminology

What is a zone?

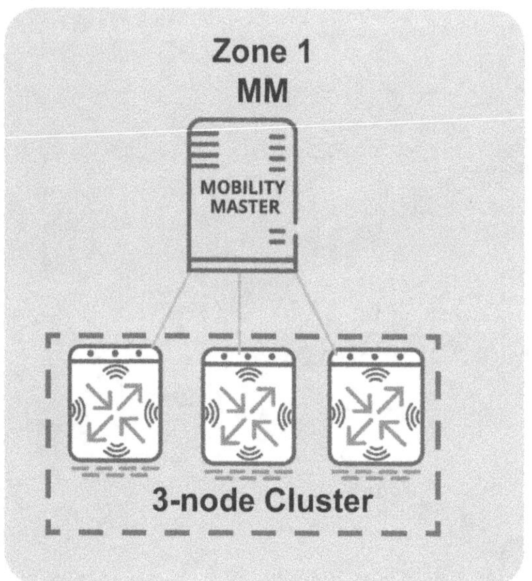

Figure 4-2 What is a zone?

Zones are an important concept of the MultiZone feature (Figure 4-2).

A zone is merely a collection of mobility controllers (MCs) under a single administrative domain. A zone can consist of a standalone 8.x MC, or a Mobility Master and its associated managed devices.

Aruba MultiZone APs can terminate their tunnels to MCs in different zones. ArubaOS 6.x did not support this feature. You can think of an AOS 6.x solution as a single zone deployment, since the AP terminates all WLAN tunnels to a single controller.

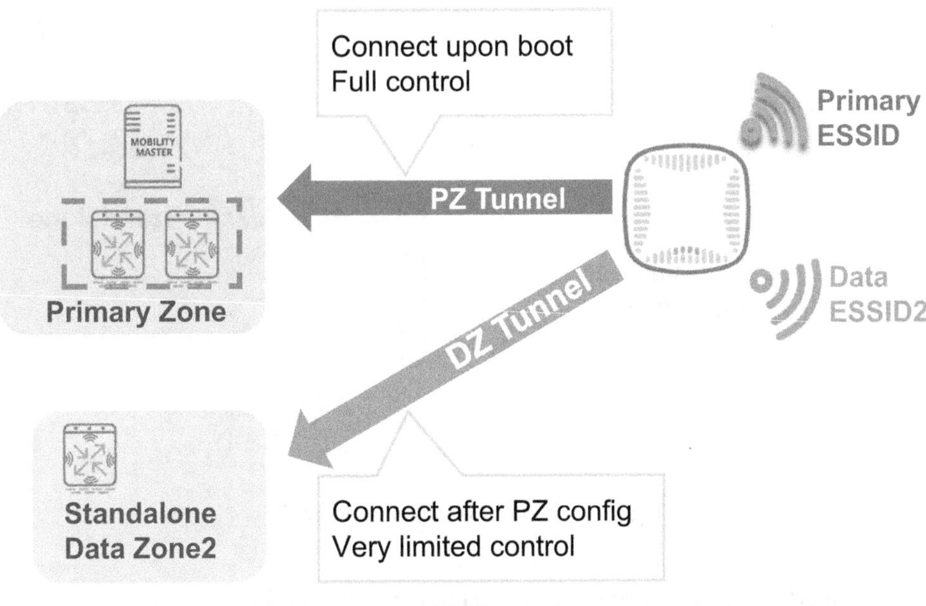

Figure 4-3 Zone roles

Zone roles

In a MultiZone environment (Figure 4-3), there are two zone roles:

- **Primary Zone (PZ)**—APs connect to the Primary Zone (PZ) upon initial boot up. The PZ retains full control of AP management and configuration, including AP, WLAN, and RF profiles. This is where you create a MultiZone profile, to enable the feature.
- **Data Zone (DZ)**—APs connect to these secondary zones after receiving configuration from the PZ. You cannot reboot, upgrade, or provision MultiZone APs from the DZ. This must be done on the PZ. The only configuration allowed is a Virtual AP (VAP) configuration in tunnel mode.

The PZ and DZ need not be on the same Layer 2 subnet. However, they should be able to communicate via your Layer 3 network.

What is a MultiZone AP?

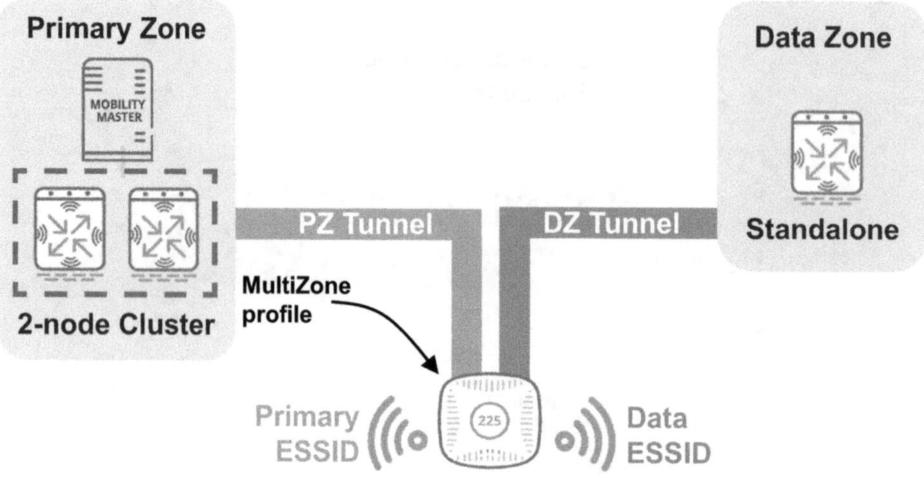

Figure 4-4 What is a MultiZone AP?

In Figure 4-4, an AP boots and forms its initial connection to the PZ's two-node MM cluster. You have configured a MultiZone profile here, which is downloaded to the AP. Thus, the AP acquires the IP address of the standalone DZ controller, to which it establishes GRE data tunnels.

The AP tunnels user traffic from WLAN "Primary" to the PZ. User traffic from WLAN "Data" is tunneled to the DZ.

MultiZone topology examples

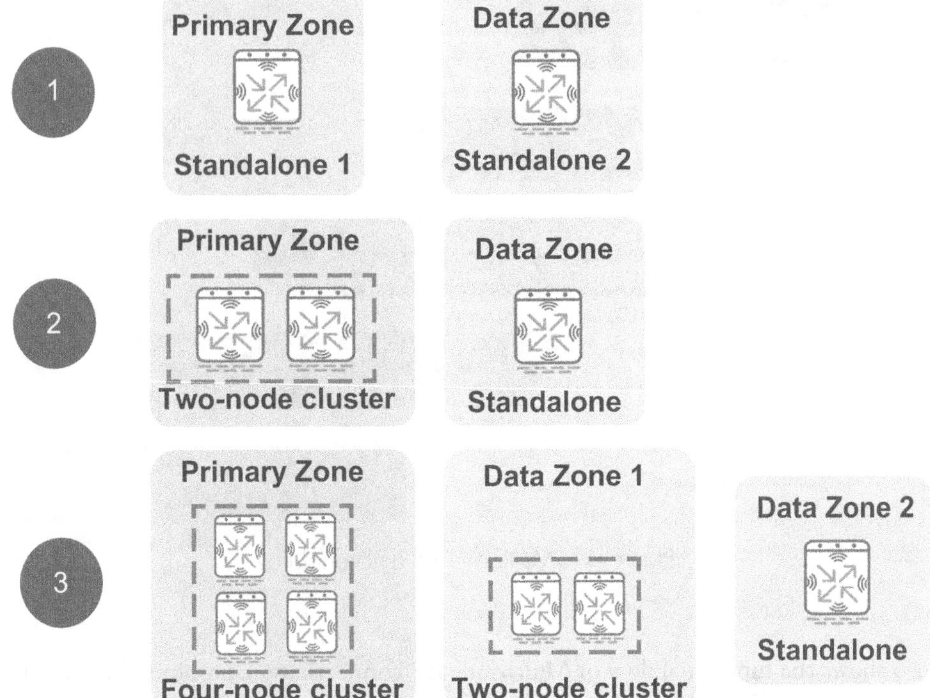

Figure 4-5 MultiZone topology examples

Figure 4-5 shows the flexibility of MultiZone deployments. The first example shows a single, standalone controller in both the PZ and DZ.

The second example still has a single controller in the DZ, but uses a two-node cluster in the PZ, for additional redundancy.

The third example shows a four-node cluster in the PZ, a two-node cluster in DZ1, and a standalone controller in DZ2.

A MultiZone AP can belong to one and only one PZ, and a PZ can support a maximum of four DZs. This is explored later in this chapter.

MultiZone AP functional flow

AP boots, terminates on PZ

AP gets config from PZ

AP connects to each DZ IP, as configured in MultiZone profile

If common PZ config changes, DZ must reboot

AP gets VAP config from DZ

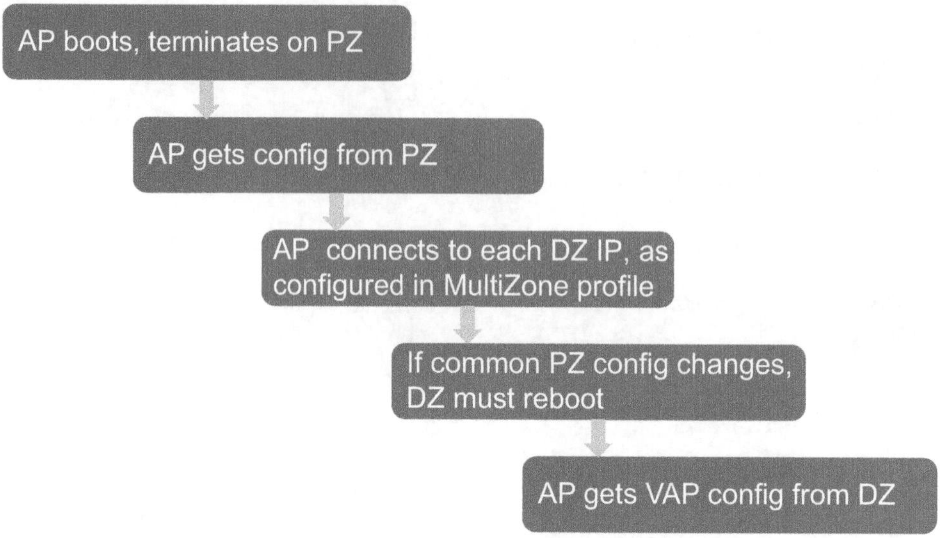

Figure 4-6 MultiZone AP functional flow

Figure 4-6 shows the functional flow of MultiZone AP connectivity. Upon initial boot, APs connect to the PZ controller. The AP gets its typical configuration, including the BSS, radio channel, radio power, and other features.

This can also include a MultiZone profile, which you would configure directly for that AP name, or for the AP group. Thus, the AP enters a MultiZone state and connects to the specified DZs.

You can configure only one MultiZone profile per AP group or AP name. The DZ and PZ must be configured with identical AP group or AP name profiles. When APs connect to a DZ, a flag in the HELLO message indicates that this is a MultiZone AP-to-DZ connection. The DZ can configure additional BSSs.

The AP virtually connects to each DZ independently. Each DZ network change or failure does not affect the management of an AP from other DZs. The DZ can configure the AP separately, and the AP applies each configuration. However, if the PZ fails, all data zones are affected.

MultiZone configuration

MultiZone WebUI configuration

The high-level configuration steps for MultiZone are:

Primary Zone

Step 1: Create a MultiZone profile

Step 2: Configure MultiZone profile parameters

Step 3: Attach the MultiZone profile to an AP group

Data Zone

Step 4: Configure the same AP group name

Step 5: Configure and assign WLANs to the AP group

You will explore each step in the pages that follow.

Step 1: Create MultiZone profile on PZ

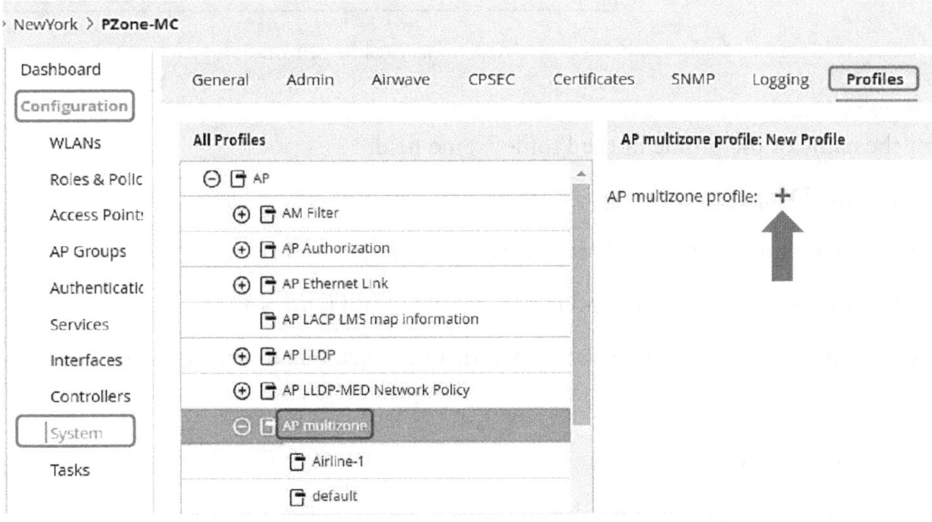

Figure 4-7 Step 1: Create MultiZone profile on PZ

You begin by creating a MultiZone profile (Figure 4-7).

1. In the Managed Network node hierarchy, navigate to **Configuration > System > Profiles > AP**.
2. Click AP MultiZone. AP MultiZone profile: New Profile is displayed.
3. Click + in AP MultiZone profile to add a new profile.

Continue to the next page.

Step 2: MultiZone profile parameters

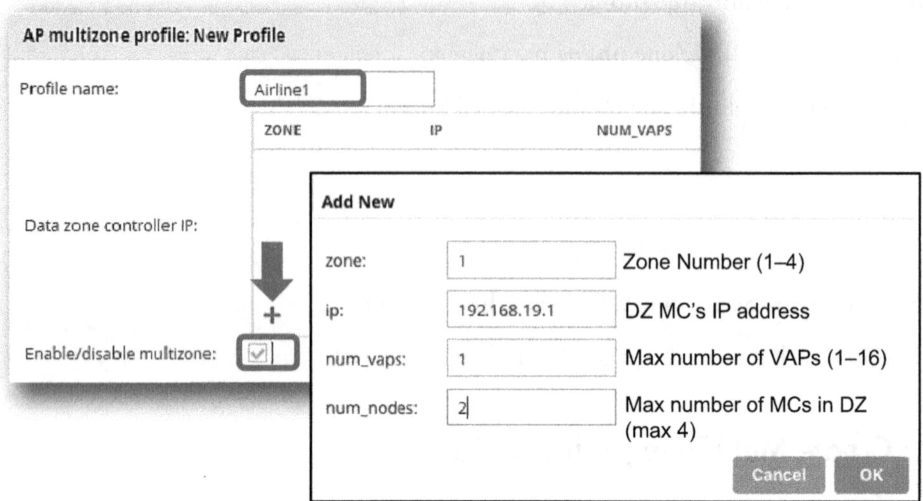

Figure 4-8 Step 2: MultiZone profile parameters

4. Enter the name of the profile in the Profile Name field.
5. Click + in the Data zone controller IP table.
6. Enter the zone number and IP address, as shown in Figure 4-8.
7. Enter the number of virtual APs and nodes, as shown in Figure 4-8.
8. Click OK, then click the Enable/disable MultiZone check box to enable the profile.
9. Click Save.
10. Click Pending Changes.
11. In the Pending Changes window, select the check box and click Deploy changes.

Note

The "num_vaps" and "num_nodes" fields indicate the maximum number of VAPs and nodes, respectively, which the zone can support. In this scenario, you have limited the DZ to a maximum of two VAPs, and two nodes.

Step 3: Attach the MultiZone profile to an AP group

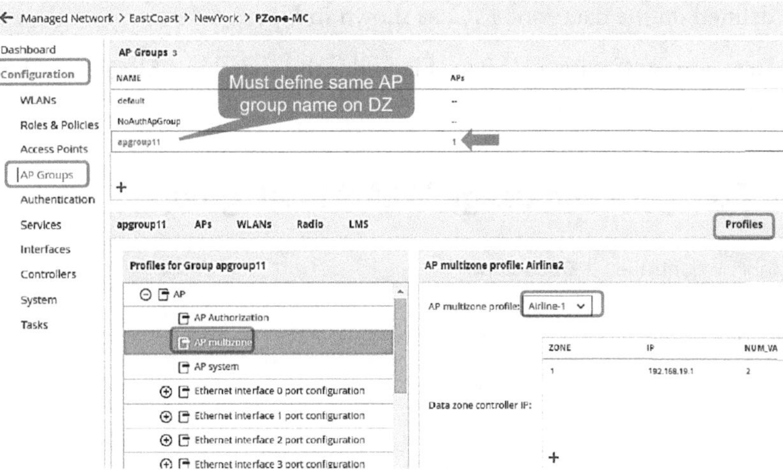

Figure 4-9 Step 3: Attach the MultiZone profile to an AP group

To attach or detach the profile to an AP group:

1. In the Managed Network node hierarchy, navigate to **Configuration > AP Groups**.
2. Add the MultiZone profile to an AP group.

Figure 4-9 shows the Mobility Master WebUI in the primary zone where you have configured a MultiZone profile named Airline1. Also, notice that you are using a group named "apgroup11." You must define this same group name on the DZ.

Step 4: Configure same AP group name in DZ

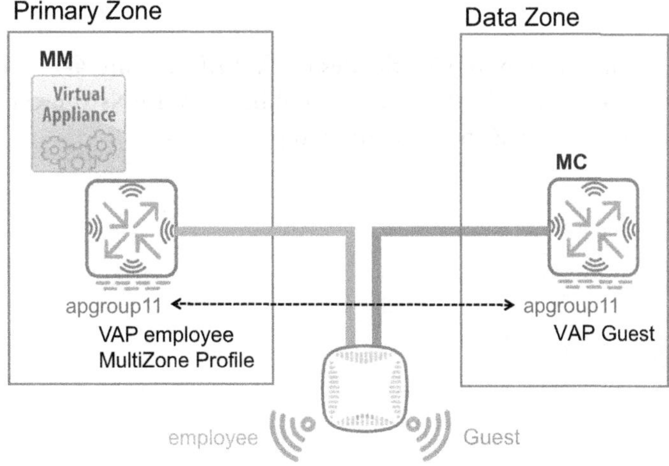

Figure 4-10 Step 4: Configure same AP group name in DZ

You configure the primary zone with a MultiZone profile that is for a specific AP group. This profile is sent to the AP, which then attempts to communicate with the Data Zone MC. The exact AP group name must be defined on the data zone MC, as shown in Figure 4-10.

Configure the Data zone MC with a VAP profile under this matching AP group. The AP will advertise both the PZ and DZ SSIDs.

Step 5: DZ—Configure and assign WLAN to AP group

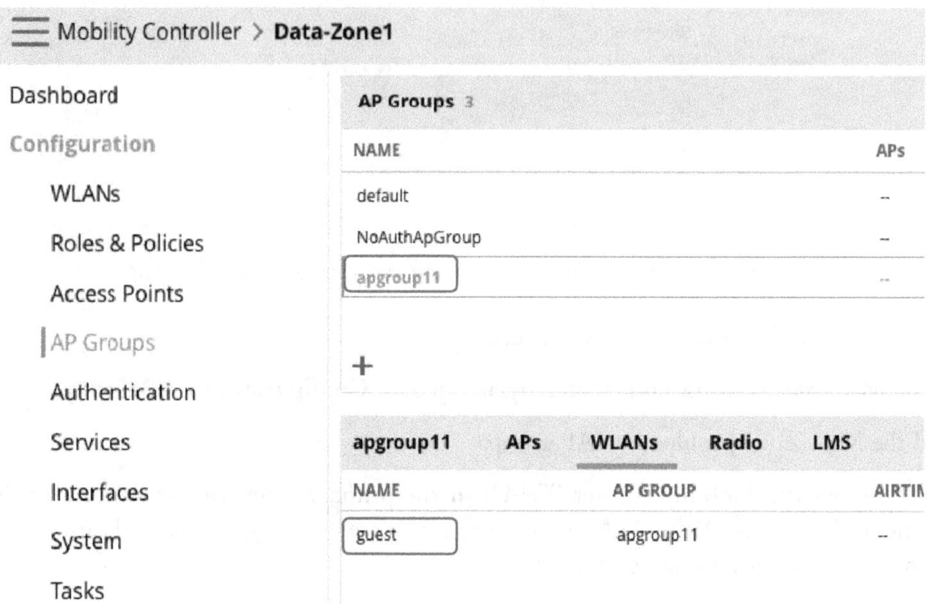

Figure 4-11 Step 5: DZ—Configure and assign WLAN to AP group

Configure the Data Zone's AP group with the desired WLAN (Figure 4-11). Remember, this AP group must match that configured in the PZ. The number of WLANs you can define in the Data Zone is limited, based on Primary Zone configuration parameters.

MultiZone CPsec on DZ

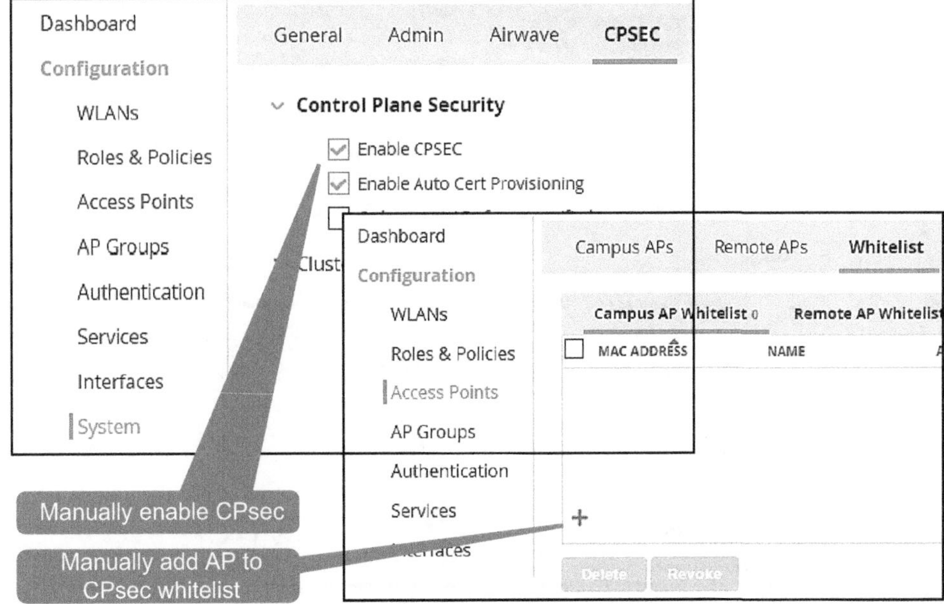

Figure 4-12 MultiZone CPsec on DZ

It is highly recommended that you enable CPSec (Figure 4-12). At the time of this writing, the auto-cert-provision feature is not supported on the DZ. Therefore, you must manually create an AP whitelist on the DZ. Later versions will support auto-cert-provisioning, eliminating the need to manually create an AP whitelist. As of AOS8.1, there is also support for MultiZone without CPsec.

DZ licenses

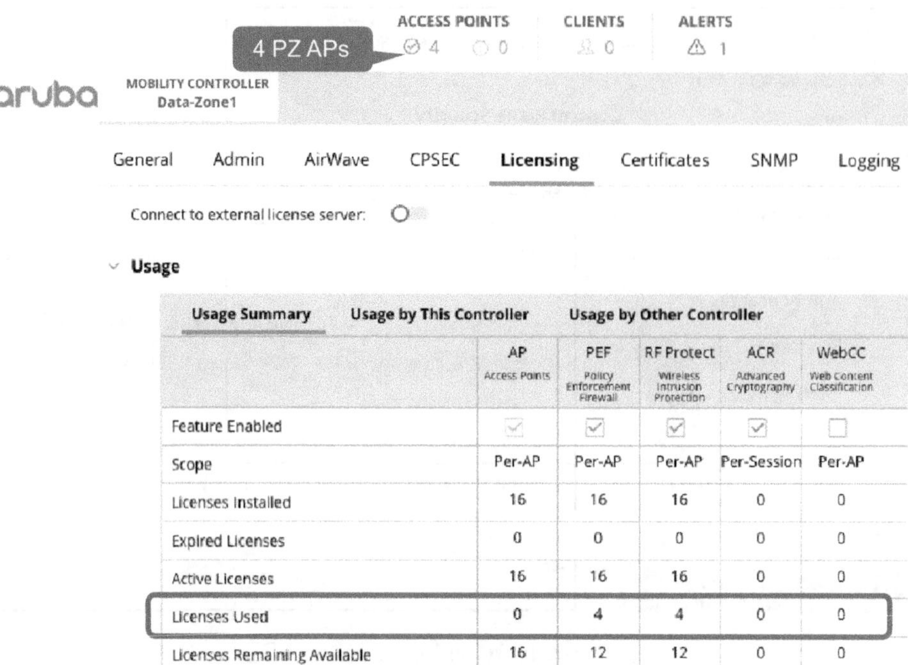

	AP Access Points	PEF Policy Enforcement Firewall	RF Protect Wireless Intrusion Protection	ACR Advanced Cryptography	WebCC Web Content Classification
Feature Enabled	☑	☑	☑	☑	☐
Scope	Per-AP	Per-AP	Per-AP	Per-Session	Per-AP
Licenses Installed	16	16	16	0	0
Expired Licenses	0	0	0	0	0
Active Licenses	16	16	16	0	0
Licenses Used	0	4	4	0	0
Licenses Remaining Available	16	12	12	0	0

Figure 4-13 DZ licenses

The Data Zone does not use an AP license for Primary Zone APs (Figure 4-13). However, if you need firewall services in the DZ, then each Primary Zone AP uses one PEF license and one RFP license.

MultiZone limitations

Mobility Controllers in all zones must run the same ArubaOS version. The DZ and PZ must have the same group names defined. Notice also that you cannot manage PZ and DZ controllers from the same MM. Mesh AP and RAP are not supported, and the following maximums apply:

- Maximum five zones (one PZ and four DZ)
- Maximum 12 controllers for all zones
- Maximum 16 VAPs per radio for all zones

Learning check

1. A DZ can have a different AOS image with a PZ.
    a. True
    b. False

MultiZone common troubleshooting commands

Troubleshooting—show log security

The following shows the output from the command `show log security 10`. The number 10 indicates that you only wish to see the last ten lines of output from the log.

```
(DZone-MC) [mynode] # show log security 10

Mar 14 22:15:04 :103067: <3665> <ERRS> |ike| IKE XAuth failed as the AP 04:bd:88:ca:71:4c is not in whitelist

Mar 14 22:15:06 :133006: <3750> <ERRS> |localdb| User 04:bd:88:ca:71:4c Failed Authentication (Processing USER_QUERY on DBType(3))

Mar 14 22:15:06 :133121: <3750> <WARN> |localdb| make_response: Sending USERDB_REJ-msg to 127.0.0.1:8214 with msgtype:23 id:144 reqtype:6 dbtype:3
```

This example shows that you forgot to add the AP to the whitelist.

Troubleshooting—show ap database

The following shows the use of the command `show ap database`. You can tell that this AP connection is to a DZ controller because the Flags column includes a "z."

```
DZone-MC) [mynode] # show ap database

AP Database
-----------

Name  Group      AP Type  IP Address  Status              Flags  Switch IP     Standby IP
----  -----      -------  ----------  ------              -----  ---------     ---------
ap1   apgroup11  225      10.1.10.51  Up 4d:12h:53m:7s    2z     192.168.19.1  0.0.0.0
```

Troubleshooting—show ap debug multizone

The following shows output from the command `show ap debug multizone`. Zone 0 is the PZ and Zone1 is DZ. The max VAPs is 16, but the PZ has limited the DZ to one WLAN. The PZ can put 15 WLANs on the AP.

```
(DZone-MC) [mynode] #show ap debug MultiZone ap-name ap1

MultiZone Table
---------------
```

```
Zone    Configured IP    Serving IP      Max Vaps Allowed    Nodes    Flags
----    -------------    ----------      ----------------    -----    -----
0       10.1.10.100      10.1.10.100     15 (0~14)           1        2
1       192.168.19.1     192.168.19.1    1 (15~15)           1        2
Flags: C = Cluster; L = Limited nodes; N = Nodes in other zones;
2 = Using IKE version 2;
Number of datazones:1
```

DZ WLAN configuration

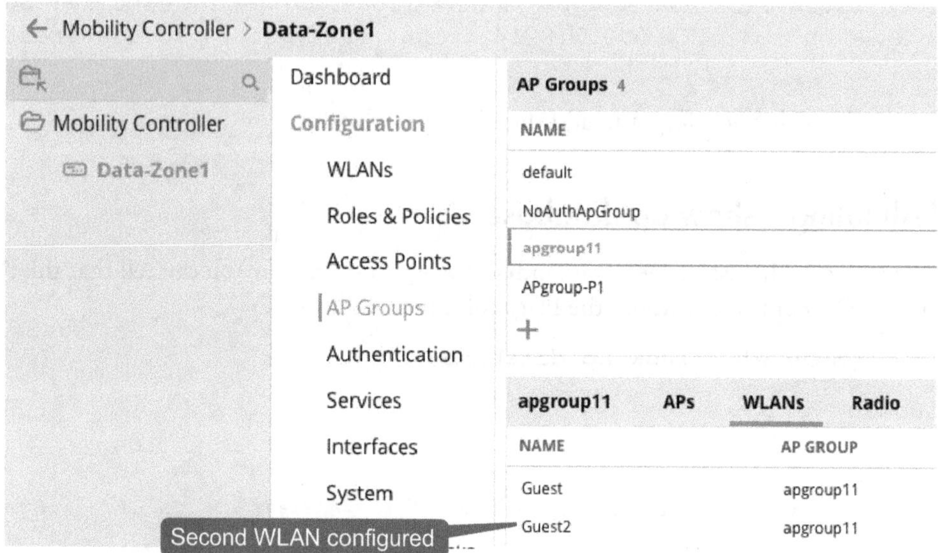

Figure 4-14 DZ WLAN configuration

Figure 4-14 shows the configuration of a WLAN for the DZ. You see a group named "apgroup11." Two WLANs have been defined in this group—one named Guest, and another named Guest2.

Troubleshooting—show ap bss-table

This following shows the output of the command `show ap bss-table`.

```
(DZone-MC) [mynode] # show ap bss-table
fm (forward mode): T-Tunnel, S-Split, D-Decrypt Tunnel, B-Bridge (s-standard,
p-persistent, b-backup, a-always),
n-anyspot cluster (cluster role): U-UAC, A-AAC, sU-Standby UAC,
sA-Standby AAC
```

```
Aruba AP BSS Table
------------------
bss   ess   port   ip   phy   type   ch/EIRP/max-EIRP   cur-cl   ap name
---   ---   ----   --   ---   ----   ----------------   ------   -------
04:bd:88:27:14:cf   guest   N/A   10.1.10.51   g-HT   ap   1/9/0
04:bd:88:27:14:ce   guest   N/A   10.1.10.51   a-HT   ap   36/9/0
in-t(s)  tot-t  mtu  acl-state  acl  fm  cluster  datazone
-------  -----  ---  ---------  ---  --  -------  --------
      0   ap1   0   26s     1500  -   78   T   yes
      0   ap1   0   26s     1500  -   78   T   yes
```

You have used this command in response to user complaints—the WLAN named "Guest2" is not available. Indeed, this WLAN is not listed in the output shown.

Why might this be?

Do you recall the previous output from the command `show ap debug multizone`? That output showed that someone configured MultiZone profile parameters, limiting this DZ to a maximum of one Virtual APs.

To resolve this issue, you must either get by with one VAP, or go back and edit the profile. Raise the num_vaps setting to 2 or more.

Troubleshooting—show log system (n)

The following shows the output of the command `show log system 20`.

```
(Data-Zone1) [mynode] #show log system 20
Jun 13 07:45:56 :305051:  <3706> <WARN> |stm|  Virtual AP "AP1" rejected
for AP "Guest2"; reason: Too many virtual APs configured
```

This command was issued on the DZ MC. The system log shows why the Guest2 WLAN is not being advertised. The second VAP has been rejected by AP1. This is a limitation imposed by the Primary Zone.

Learning check

2. For the DZ, you must add the MultiZone AP whitelist manually, even though auto-cert-provision has been enabled on the DZ.

   a. True

   b. False

MultiZone use cases

MultiZone AP use case—Multi-tenancy

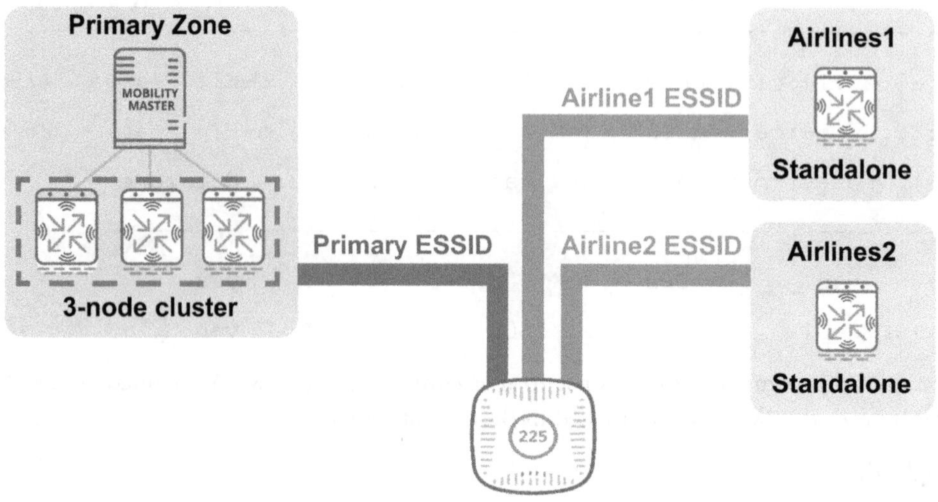

Figure 4-15 MultiZone AP use case—Multi-tenancy

This use case shows a suggested multi-tenant application of the MultiZone feature (Figure 4-15). This could be used in airports or in malls, where each airline or business can leverage MultiZone APs to advertise their own SSIDs.

The PZ comprises a redundant pair of Virtual Mobility Masters and a three-node cluster.

There is a DZ for each airline or business. Each DZ has a single standalone mobility controller.

MultiZone AP use case—guest access

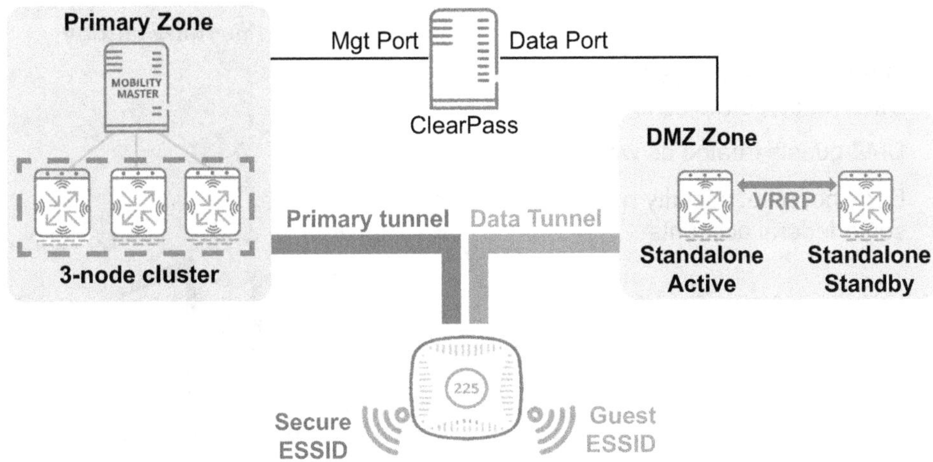

Figure 4-16 MultiZone AP use case—guest access

This use case shows a suggested guest application of the MultiZone feature. This could be used by both federal and security conscious enterprise customers, who desire a conceptual "air wall" between the corporate and guest SSIDs.

The PZ includes a redundant pair of Virtual Mobility Masters and a 3-node cluster.

The DZ is in the corporate DMZ, where a pair of standalone MCs are configured with master-redundancy.

Figure 4-16 also introduces the use of a ClearPass server for centralized access control, with separate interfaces to the Primary and DMZ Data Zone.

Let us explore this use case in more detail, by comparing it to a legacy AOS 6.x solution.

Guest access solution in AOS 6.X

- Guest traffic is always tunneled to DMZ via corporate controller
- DMZ guests treated as wired users
- Does not meet security needs for some federal accounts

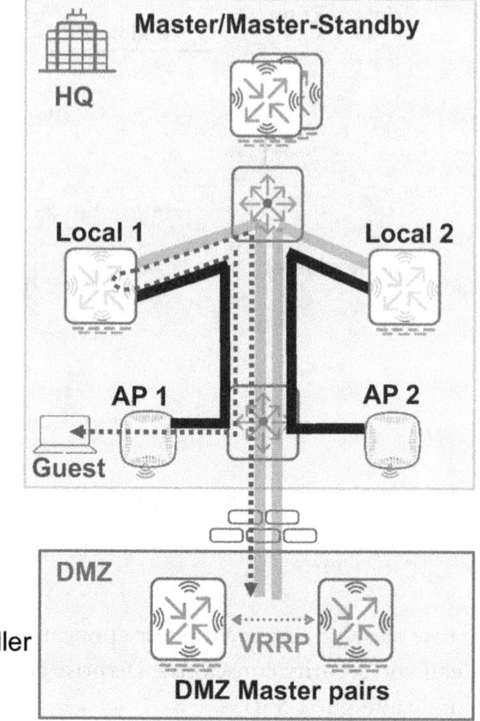

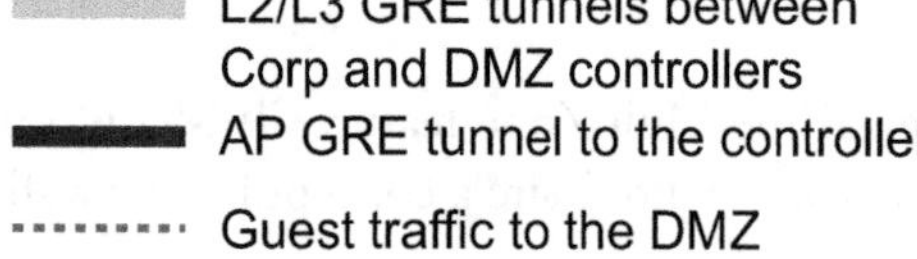

Figure 4-17 Guest access solution in AOS 6.X

Guest access solutions are a popular, often required aspect of most campus networks. This scenario is for a typical AOS 6.x-based campus deployment, before advent of the MultiZone feature.

Figure 4-17 shows the corporate headquarters (HQ), with master and local controllers. APs terminate on the local controllers, as shown. Meanwhile, the DMZ network is firewall-separated from the internal corporate network. This DMZ contains one master controller pair for redundancy.

Remember, AOS 6.x is not MultiZone capable, so all AP WLANs terminate to controllers Local 1 or Local 2. Of course, this includes the guest WLAN.

The corporate local controllers have an L2 GRE tunnel, pointing to the VIP address of the DMZ controller pairs. Layer 3 GRE is also possible, but less common.

A user associates with the Guest SSID on AP1 and sends traffic. This traffic is received by the AP and GRE-tunneled to controller Local 1. Local 1 then GRE-tunnels this traffic to the DMZ controller. You typically configure this tunnel on the DMZ side as "Untrusted," so firewall policy and authentication can be applied to the guest users.

The guest traffic is not sent directly through the AP GRE tunnels, but through the controller-to-controller GRE tunnel. Therefore, the DMZ controller treats guests as wired users.

Do you see the suboptimal path that guest traffic must take? Guest traffic is first tunneled from AP to local controller, and then re-tunneled from local to DMZ controller. There is also a security concern since the corporate controller must also service guest traffic.

Guest access solution in AOS 8.1

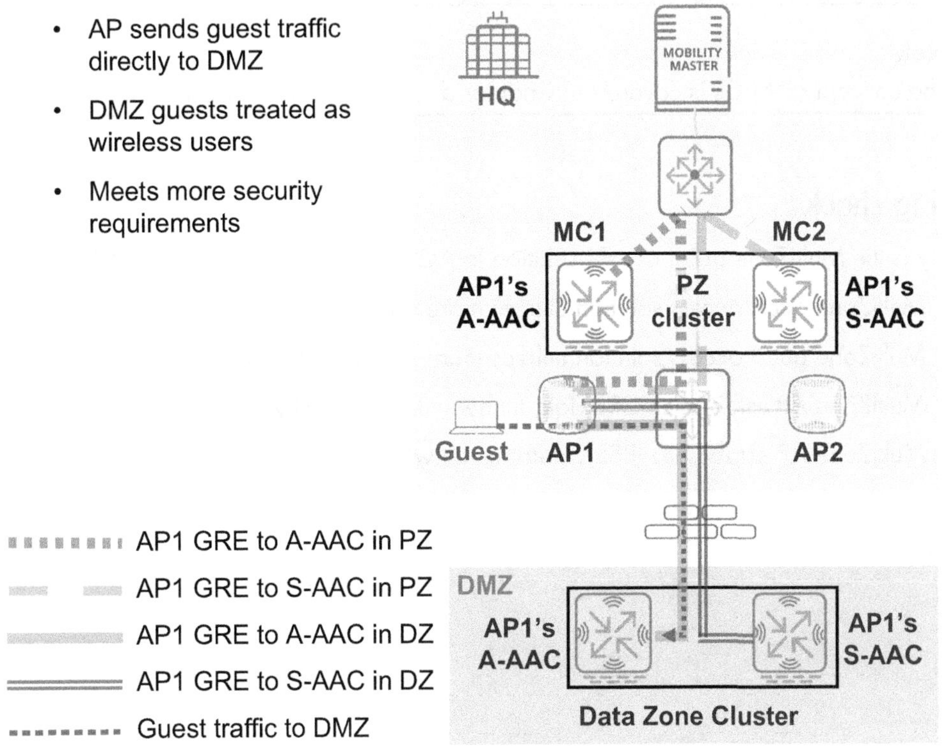

Figure 4-18 Guest access solution in AOS 8.1

Let us see how the AOS 8.x MultiZone feature improves upon the previous scenario (Figure 4-18).

In the corporate network, all MCs are PZ controllers. In this example, two MCs form a PZ cluster for redundancy. AP1 builds a GRE tunnel to its Active AP Anchor Controller (A-AAC) and a GRE tunnel to its Standby AAC (S-AAC).

The two MCs in the DMZ network also form a controller cluster for redundancy. This cluster is configured as a DZ. You did this by configuring a MultiZone profile on the PZ, for AP1's AP group. The AP boots, connects to the PZ, gets its MultiZone configuration, and so builds a GRE tunnel to the DZ's active AAC and another to the standby AAC.

Guests associate with the SSID, which is only configured in the AP group of the DZ controller. This guest traffic is received by the AP, and GRE-tunneled directly to the DZ controller. This traffic is not handled by the corporate local controllers at all, so the solution is considered to be more secure.

Since guest users are tunneled directly from AP to DZ controller, the solution provides a more optimal data flow, as compared to AOS 6.x. Also, the DZ controller treats guests as wireless users. This contrasts with the AOS 6.x solution in which guests are perceived as wired users.

Note

The concept of AACs is covered in Chapter 5—"Clustering Introduction."

Learning check

3. Why is the MultiZone guest access solution in AOS 8.1 more secure than 6.X?
    a. MultiZone guest access solution utilizes more secure encryption.
    b. MultiZone guest access solution utilizes more secure authentication.
    c. MultiZone AP establishes GRE data tunnel with DZ directly.
    d. MultiZone AP establishes IPSEC data tunnel with DZ directly.

5 Introduction to Clusters

LEARNING OBJECTIVES

✓ A cluster combines multiple managed devices to minimize single points of failure. The objective is to provide high-availability WLAN service. This chapter serves as an introduction to this feature.

✓ You will learn what clusters are, why to use them, and how they affect Aruba deployments. Then you will learn how clustering works, with a discussion of cluster leaders, connection types, roles, and failover features.

✓ Finally, you will learn about cluster configuration and monitoring.

Clustering overview

What is clustering?

A cluster combines multiple managed devices to provide high availability for all clients. This ensures service continuity during failover events.

Figure 5-1 shows three Mobility Controllers (MC), named MC1, MC2, and MC3. The dashed-line box around the controllers indicates that they have been configured to work as a cluster. If one cluster member fails, the remaining MCs provide uninterrupted service.

Benefits to this solution include seamless roaming, client and Access Points (AP) load balancing, stateful failover, and seamless cluster upgrades. These features are described in the pages that follow.

ArubaOS 8.x does not support clustering in master controller mode. Clustering is only for MCs/VMCs, in a Mobility Master (MM) deployment.

Why clustering?

The AOS 8 clustering feature was designed primarily for mission-critical networks. The goal is to provide full redundancy to APs and WLAN clients, should one or more cluster members fail. This provides several compelling benefits, as summarized below.

Seamless campus roaming

WLAN clients remain anchored to a single controller (cluster member) regardless of where they roam on campus, or to which AP they connect. Thus, their roaming experience is seamless—their L2/L3 information and sessions remain on the same MC.

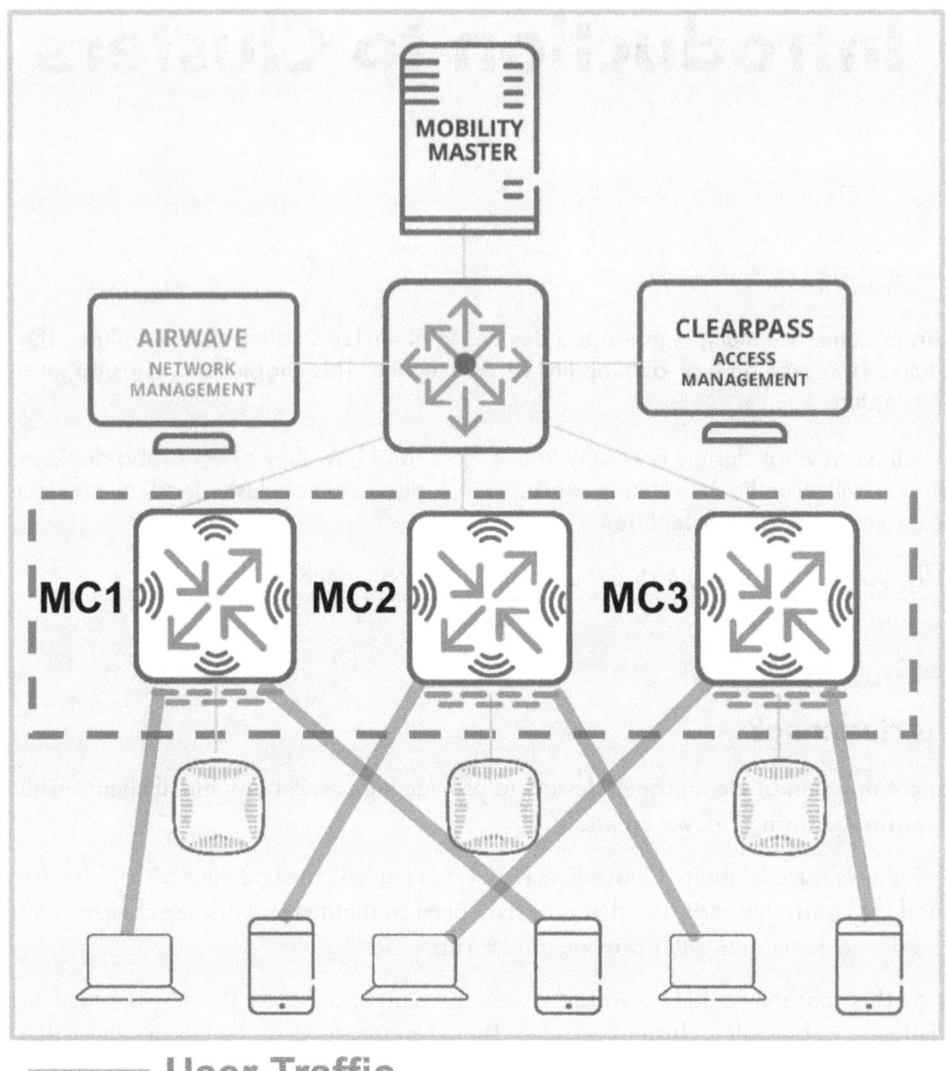

Figure 5-1 What is clustering?

Client stateful failover

There is full redundancy within the cluster. In the event of a cluster member failure, connected clients are failed over to a redundant cluster member. There is no disruption to wireless connectivity, and so high-value sessions are unaffected.

Client load balancing

Clients are automatically load-balanced within the cluster. Clients are moved among cluster members in a stateful manner, which prevents disruption of service.

AP load balancing

As of AOS 8.1, APs are automatically load-balanced across cluster members.

Cluster deployment considerations

The following highlights cluster deployment considerations:

- The cluster feature requires an MM-based deployment.
- Only MCs can be actual cluster members—MMs cannot be cluster members.[1]
- There is no license required to use the clustering feature.
- Cluster members can terminate Campus APs (CAP) and Remote APs (RAP). Mesh APs will be supported in a future version.

Note

[1]Remember, MMs provide centralized management, configuration, and control for your deployment. APs do not terminate to an MM, nor are clients directly serviced by the MM. Therefore, the fact that MMs cannot be cluster members does not reduce the effectiveness of the cluster solution.

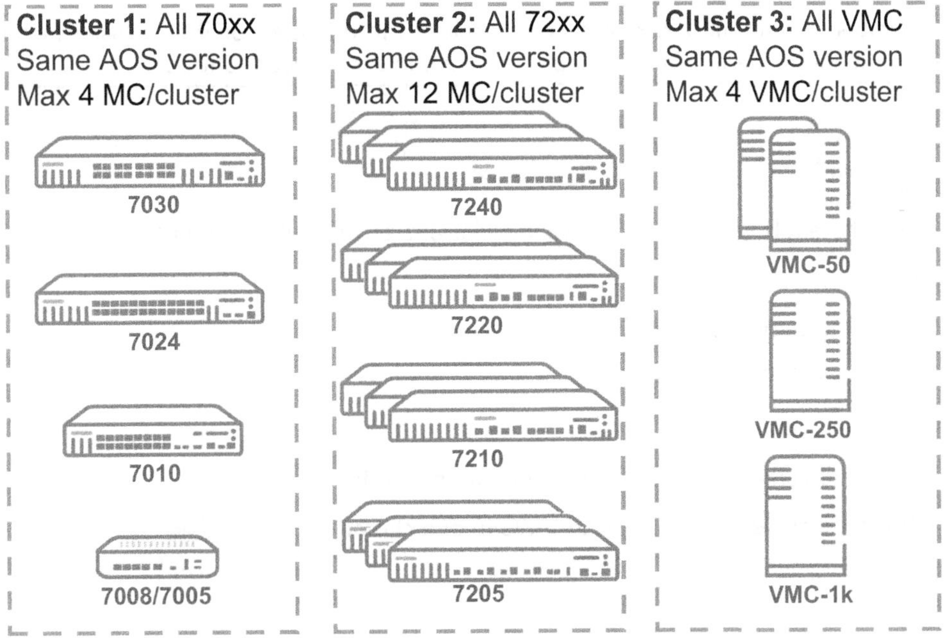

Figure 5-2 Cluster considerations and capacity

Additional cluster deployment considerations are shown in Figure 5-2, as described below.

- Currently, the 72xx, 70xx, and Virtual Mobility Controllers (VMC) support clustering.
- All cluster members must run the same ArubaOS version (8.0 and higher).
- A mix of hardware (7xxx) and VMC in the same cluster is NOT supported
- A mix of 72xx and 70xx MCs in the same cluster is not recommended. Should you do so, the maximum number of cluster members is reduced to four.
- When the cluster terminates RAPs, max cluster members are reduced to four.
- The clustering feature and the HA AP Fast Failover feature are mutually exclusive.

Cluster capacity

Figure 5-2 also indicates cluster capacity, based on platform.

- For 72xx—up to 12 MCs per cluster[1]
- For 70xx—up to 4 MCs per cluster
- For VMCs—up to 4 VMs per cluster

 **Note**

Remember, if you mix 72xx and 70xx platforms in a cluster, or if the cluster members terminate RAPs, the maximum number of controllers is reduced to four.

Learning check

1. In which of the following scenarios will the cluster size be limited to four?
   a. When the cluster terminates RAP
   b. When the cluster uses VMC
   c. When the cluster uses 70XX
   d. When the cluster uses 72XX
   e. When the cluster uses 72XX and 70XX in one cluster
   f. When the cluster uses 70XX and VMC in one cluster

Clustering mechanism

Cluster handshake

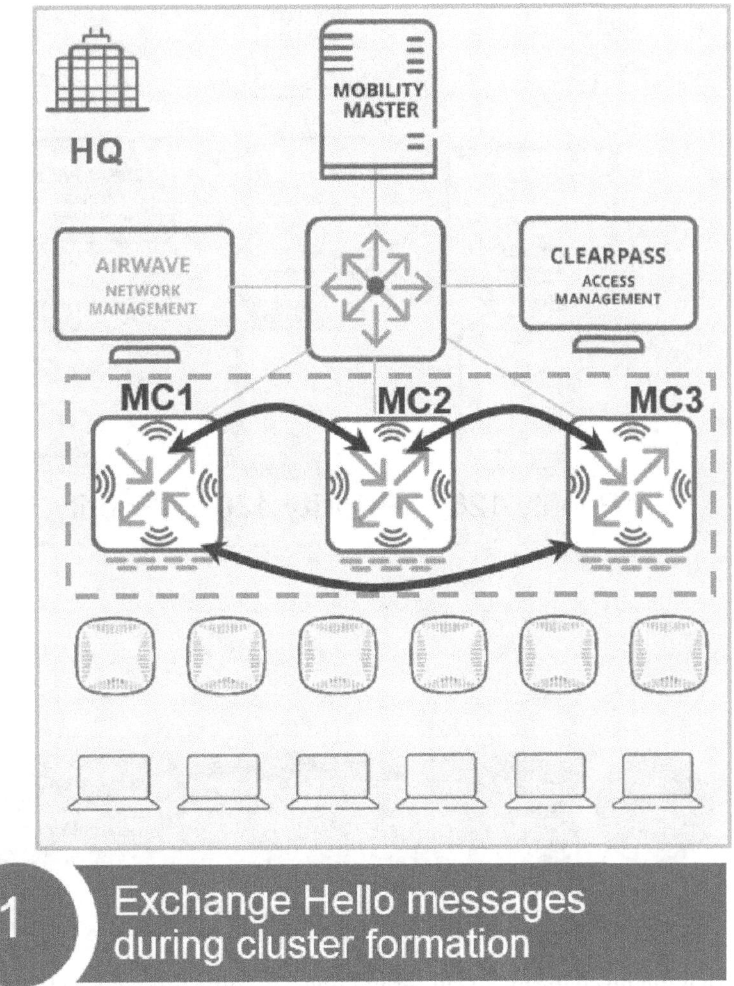

Figure 5-3 Cluster handshake

When you configure MCs as members of the same cluster, they engage a handshaking mechanism (Figure 5-3). Sent among each other, these handshake messages determine cluster reachability and eligibility. This insures that all cluster members see each other and that the cluster is fully meshed.

Cluster leader election

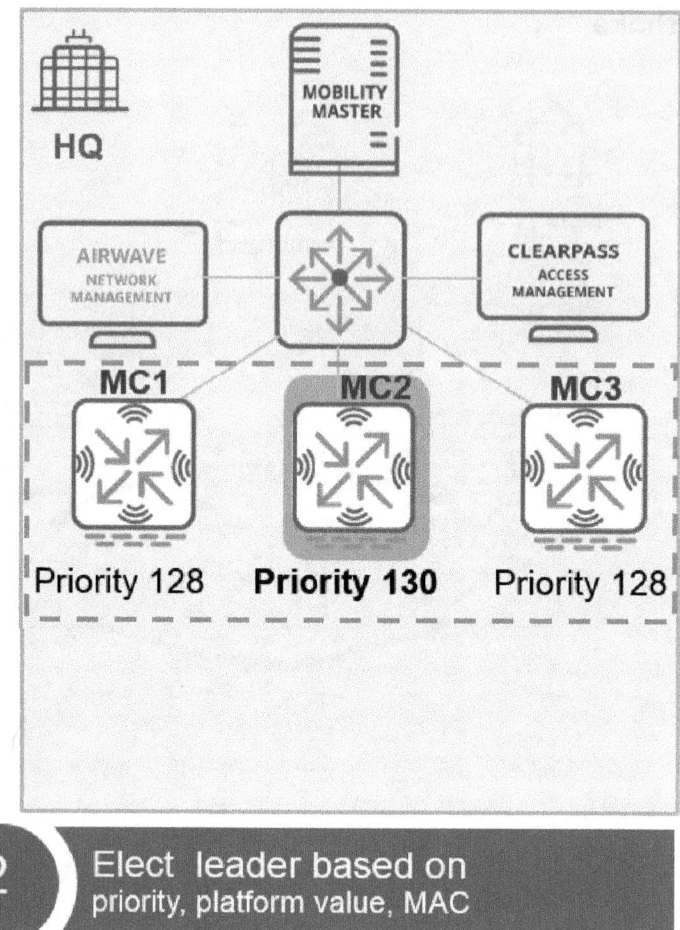

Figure 5-4 Cluster leader election

Using the handshaking mechanism, all cluster members become fully meshed, with a consistent view of the cluster. Then they elect a cluster leader. The cluster member with the highest effective priority becomes the cluster leader.

The effective priority is derived from a combination of:

- configured priority (128 by default)
- platform value
- controller MAC address

The priority value is calculated by the following formula:

effective_priority = (((configured_priority << 8) + platform_value) << 48) + controller_mac_addr

If priority and platform are the same, then the device with the highest MAC address wins the election. The "<<" symbol is a "left-shift" operator, which gives more weight to configured priority than to platform value. Further details of this calculation are beyond the scope of this course.

In the example shown in Figure 5-4, MC2 has the highest priority and so wins the election to become the cluster leader.

All MCs end up with fully meshed IPsec tunnels to other MCs.

Note

Although cluster members could be connected via a Layer 3 routed network, it is strongly recommended that all cluster members be placed in the same L2 broadcast domain.

Cluster leader role

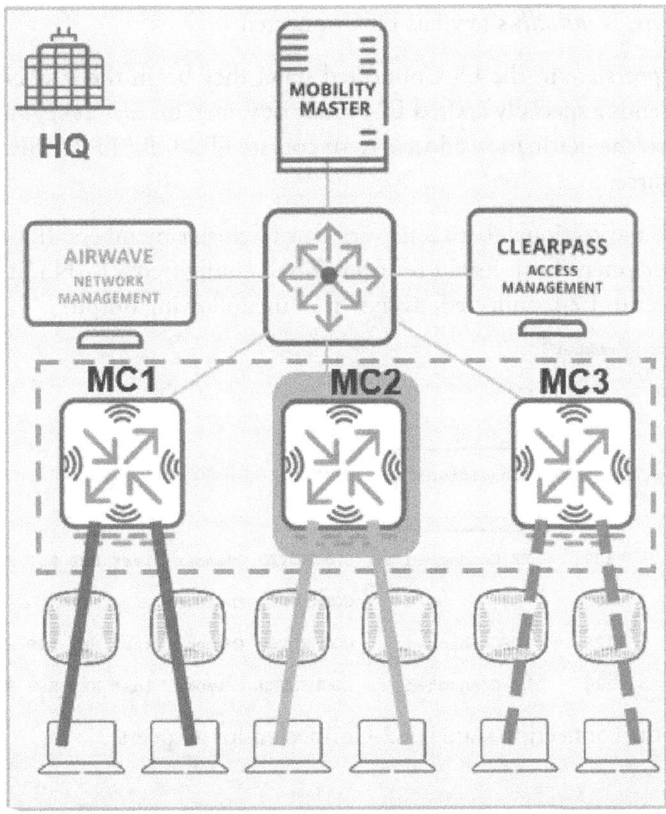

Figure 5-5 Cluster leader role

The cluster leader assumes several responsibilities.

Bucket map computation—One of these responsibilities is to map clients to a dedicated MC within the cluster. This is known as bucket map computation. Figure 5-5 shows two clients mapped to MC1, two to MC2, and two to MC3.

Dynamically load-balance clients—The cluster leader ensures that each cluster member services approximately the same number of clients. This balance is automatically maintained as the load increases, or as cluster members join and leave.

Identify standby MCs—The cluster leader must perform dynamic assignment of Standby AP Anchor Controllers (S-AAC) and Standby User Anchor Controllers (S-UAC). These entities facilitate user and AP redundancy. You will learn about AAC and UAC in later chapters of this course.

Cluster connection types

You have learned that cluster members form a full mesh. Once this state is achieved, the cluster member connection type is *initially* shown as L3-Connected.

Once all cluster peers are in the L3-Connected state, they begin the VLAN Probing process. Each cluster member sends a specially crafted L2 broadcast frame, on *each configured VLAN on the controller*. As a broadcast, the destination address is, of course, FF:FF:FF:FF:FF:FF. A special MAC address is used for the source.

VLAN probing is bidirectional, between every pair of cluster members. If a cluster member receives a probe acknowledgment from its cluster peer, for all configured VLANS, it changes its connection state with that peer to L2-Connected, as shown in the following output:

```
show lc-cluster group-member

Cluster Info Table

------------------

Type  IPv4 Address  Priority  Connection-Type  STATUS

----  ------------  --------  ---------------  ------

peer  10.1.10.101     150     L2-Connected     CONNECTED (Member, last HBT_RSP 29ms ago, RTD = 0.495 ms)

self  10.1.10.100     151              N/A     CONNECTED (Leader)

peer  10.1.10.102     128     L2-Connected     CONNECTED (Member, last HBT_RSP 29ms ago, RTD = 0.495 ms)

peer  10.1.10.103     128     L2-Connected     CONNECTED (Member, last HBT_RSP 30ms ago, RTD = 1.005 ms)
```

You can see that the connection state is L2-Connected for all peers.

In the following output, cluster members do not share the same VLAN, and so their status remains as L3-connected:

```
show lc-cluster group-member

Cluster Info Table

------------------

Type  IPv4 Address   Priority Connection-Type  STATUS

----  ------------   -------- ---------------  ------

peer  10.1.10.104    128      N/A              CONNECTED (Member)

self  192.168.19.26  128      L3-Connected     CONNECTED (Leader, last HBT_RSP 76ms ago, RTD = 1.491 ms)
```

Cluster members also send periodic heartbeat messages to each other, to speed failure discovery. The heartbeat scheme is dynamic and takes into account the Round Trip Delay (RTD) between each pair of cluster members.

Note

Remember the italicized statement above—cluster member MCs probe on *every* configured VLAN. This fact will become important for configuration and troubleshooting efforts, to be discussed later in this chapter.

L2 versus L3 cluster member connections

Table 5-1 highlights the differences between L2 and L3-connected cluster members.

Table 5-1 L2 versus L3 cluster member connections

L2 Connection	L3 Connection
Fully redundant	Not fully redundant
APs and clients are fully replicated	Only APs are fully replicated
Users are fully synced between Active and Standby UAC nodes	Users are not synced between Active and Standby UAC nodes
High value sessions are synced	High value sessions are not synced
Users are not de-authorized upon failover, even from Active to Standby UAC	Users are de-authorized upon failover, even from Active to Standby UAC. Users must do a full dot1X authentication

Notice that L2-connected members are fully redundant, while L3-connected members are not.

L2-connected members enjoy full replication of both AP and client sessions. For L3-connected members, only AP sessions are fully replicated.

For L2-connected cluster members, users are fully synchronized between the Active UAC and Standby UAC nodes. This is not the case for L3-connected clusters, and the same is true for high-value sessions.

For L2-connected cluster members, users are not de-authorized during failover events, even from Active UAC to Standby UAC. However, for L3-connected clusters, users are de-authorized. This means that they must perform a complete 802.1X authentication after they reassociate with the AP.

Cluster redundancy

Cluster role introduction

There are two main roles that cluster controllers can assume, as either active or standby:

- Active cluster roles
  - Active AP Anchor Controller (A-AAC)—Facilitates controller redundancy for APs. Should an AP's A-AAC fail, the AP is controlled from the Standby AAC (S-AAC).
  - Active User Anchor Controllers (A-UAC)—Serves a similar purpose, but for WLAN *users*, as opposed to APs.
- Redundancy cluster roles:
  - Standby AAC (S-AAC)
  - Standby UAC (S-UAC)

When redundancy is enabled (default), the cluster leader elects standby controller roles for every AAC and UAC in the cluster: S-AAC and S-UAC. The A-AAC and A-UAC are assigned based on your configuration, as described in the pages that follow.

If redundancy is disabled, the stateful failover feature will not be available. Thus, clients are de-authorized by the APs in the event of a cluster member failure. However, the load-balancing feature is maintained.

Cluster roles - AAC

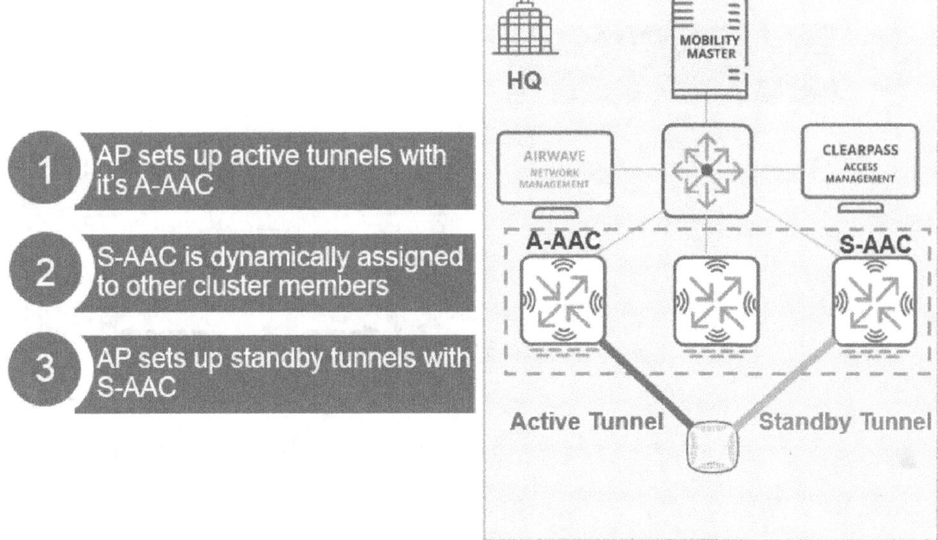
1 AP sets up active tunnels with it's A-AAC
2 S-AAC is dynamically assigned to other cluster members
3 AP sets up standby tunnels with S-AAC
HQ
MOBILITY MASTER
AIRWAVE
CLEARPASS
ACCESS MANAGEMENT
A-AAC
S-AAC
Active Tunnel
Standby Tunnel

Figure 5-6 Cluster roles—AAC

The A-AAC role is assigned to a cluster member MC (Figure 5-6). A-AACs facilitate controller redundancy for APs.

In AOS 8.0, the A-AAC is actually the AP Local Mobility Switch (LMS) controller. In other words, an AP group's system profile assigns its A-AAC, with the lms-ip option.

In AOS 8.1 a new feature called "AP active load balance" can assign the A-AAC automatically, according to MC loading. The lms-ip parameter is ignored when this function is enabled.

The A-AAC handles all AP and radio management functions, including the following:

- AP image upgrade
- CPSec tunnel setup
- Downloading configuration to the AP

With redundancy enabled, the cluster leader dynamically assigns the S-AAC role to another cluster member. The AP in turn builds a standby tunnel to the S-AAC.

 **Note**

AP load-balancing will be discussed in Chapter 6—"Advanced Clustering."

Cluster roles—AAC failover

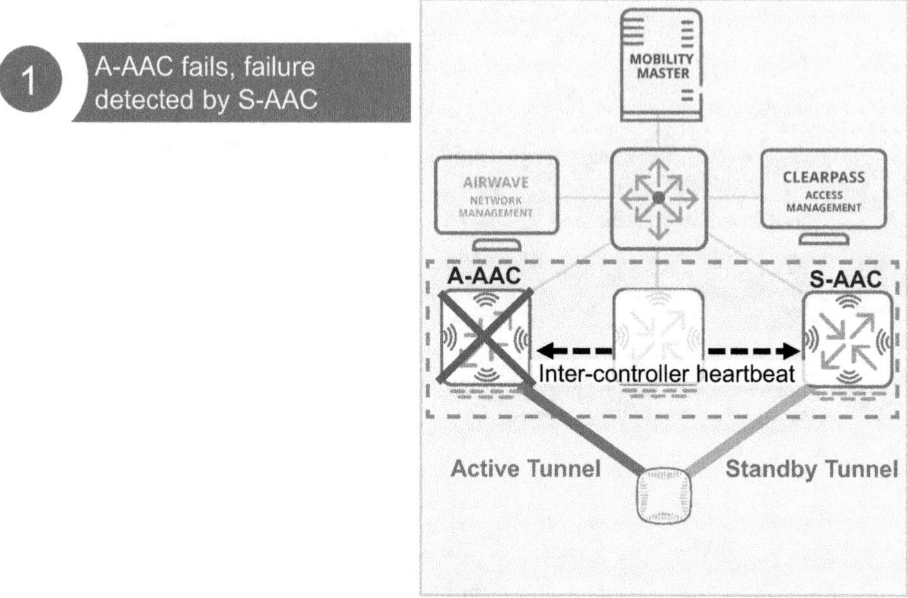

Figure 5-7 A-AAC fails

Figure 5-7 through 5-9 show what happens in the event of an A-AAC failure. You see the Active AAC has failed. Due to inter-controller heartbeat messages, the Standby AAC quickly detects the outage.

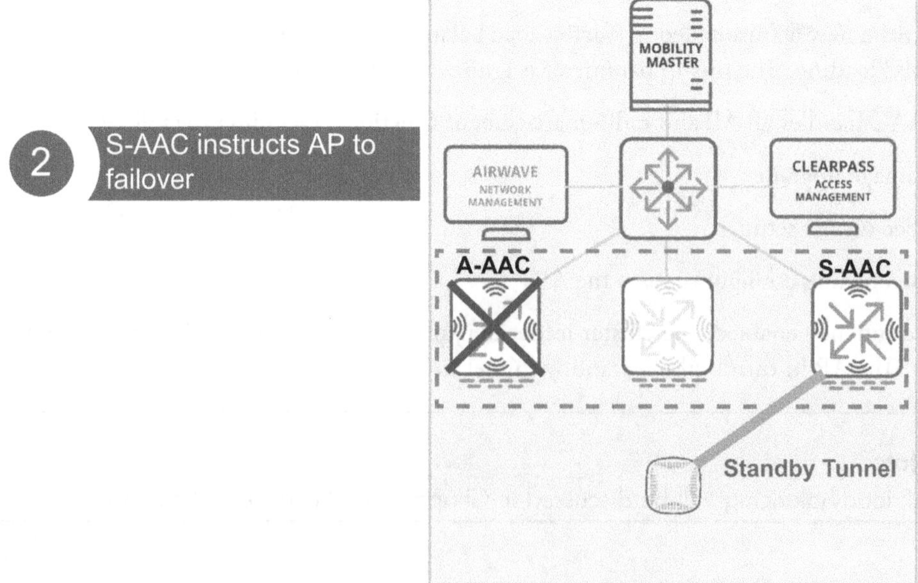

Figure 5-8 AP fails over

The S-AAC instructs the AP to failover immediately (Figure 5-8).

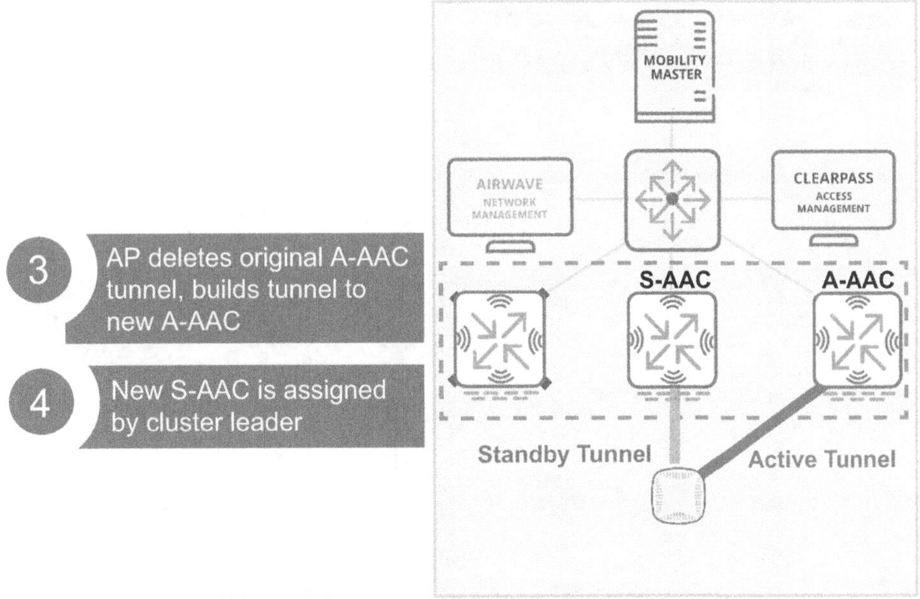

Figure 5-9 Active tunnel to new A-AACCluster roles—AAC failover

Figure 5-9 shows what happens next. The AP tears down its tunnel with the current A-AAC and changes the status of its S-AAC tunnel from standby to active.

Then the S-AAC becomes the new A-AAC for that AP, and the cluster leader promptly assigns a new S-AAC among the remaining cluster members.

Cluster roles—UAC

The User Anchor Controller (UAC) role is assigned to cluster members. This facilitates redundancy for end users.

The A-UAC Mobility Controller handles all wireless client traffic:

- Association/Disassociation notification
- Authentication
- All unicast traffic between the MC and its clients
- Roaming clients among APs

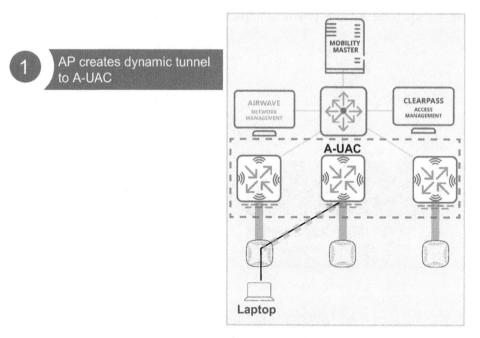

1 AP creates dynamic tunnel to A-UAC

Figure 5-10 AP creates dynamic tunnel to A-UAC

Upon associating with the AP, a client A-UAC MC is determined. The AP uses the existing GRE tunnel to push client traffic to its A-UAC. If no GRE tunnel exists, the AP creates a dynamic tunnel to that client's A-UAC. (Figure 5-10)

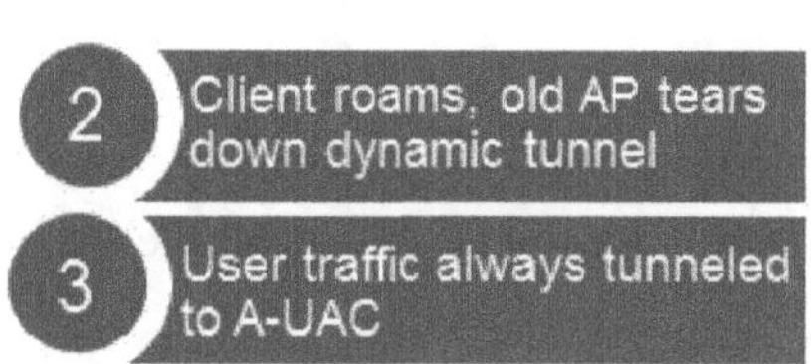

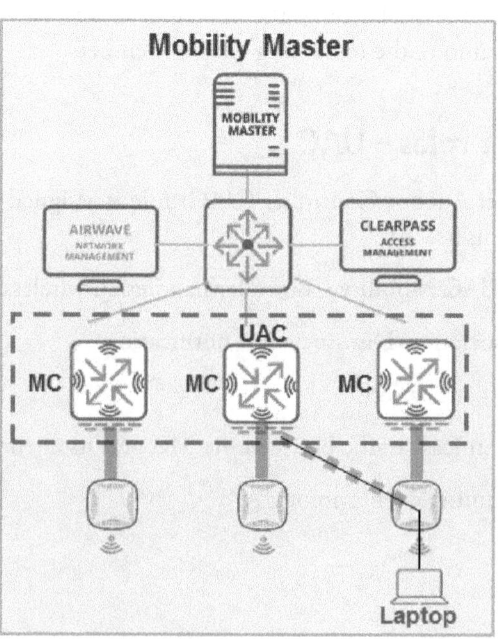

Figure 5-11 Client roams

When that client roams to a different AP, the original AP tears down the dynamic tunnel if no other clients are using it. The newly roamed-to AP follows the same tunnel guidelines as described above, forwarding traffic to the same A-UAC (Figure 5-11).

Cluster roles—UAC anchoring

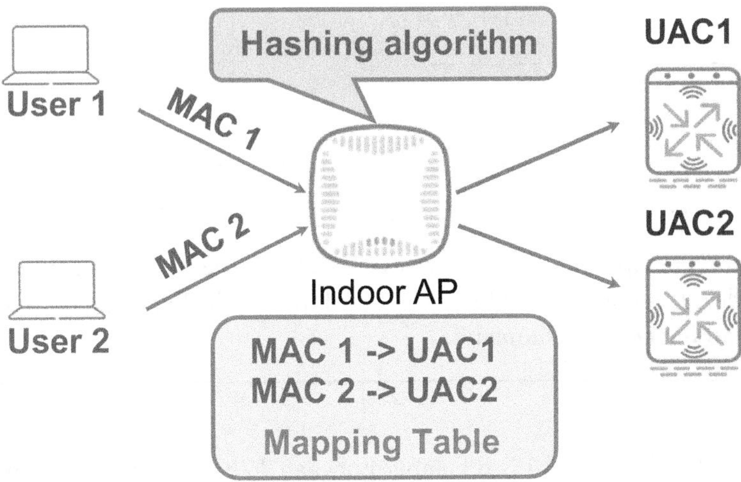

Figure 5-12 Cluster roles—UAC anchoring

You have learned that a user's traffic always terminates to the same A-UAC (Figure 5-12). This is regardless of which AP the user is connected to (within the controller clustering domain).

The APs go through the following steps to maintain a consistent A-UAC for each user:

- When a client associates with an AP, its Wi-Fi MAC address is run through a hashing algorithm. This produces a decimal number between 0 and 255.
- That decimal number acts as an index to a mapping table. This table indicates each client's A-UAC controller. This mapping table is also known as a bucket map.
- This bucket map is computed by the cluster leader on a per ESSID basis. This is pushed to all APs in the clustering domain.
- If redundancy is enabled, both A-UAC and S-UAC are assigned at the same time.

Cluster roles—mapping table

The following is an actual example of a client's A-UAC assignment. The client's MAC address is 48:e9:f1:37:95:27. Using a simple algorithm, this address is hashed at the AP, to a bucket index 133, as shown in the following output from the **show aaa cluster essid-all users** command.

```
(MC-1)# show aaa cluster essid-all users.

Active Users for ESSID : employee1

----------------------------------

BUCKET  MAC                IP           Active UAC   Standby UAC

------  ---                --           ----------   -----------

133     48:e9:f1:37:95:27  10.1.11.55   10.1.10.100  10.1.10.103
```

The AP scans its bucket map for the client's connected ESSID. The AP finds index 133, which points to the A-UAC index 01 and the S-UAC index 00, as shown in the following output from the **show aaa cluster essid-all bucketmap** command.

Note

In the map output below, 133 is a number between 128–159, and so the fifth row from the top is relevant. Now start at the left-most column, which is for whichever AP has been hashed to 128. The next column is for AP 129, and so on. The sixth row is our target AP, hashed to index number 133.

AS highlighted below, you can see that the A-UAC with an index of 01 is assigned to AP 133. This corresponds to MC 10.1.10.100. (This is revealed in the output of **show aaa cluster esside-all users** above.) For the S-UAC, index 00 corresponds to MC 10.1.10.103.

```
(MC-1)# show aaa cluster essid-all users.

Bucket map for employee1, Rcvd at : Wed Apr 12 09:01:24 2017

------------------------------------------------------------

Item               Value

----               -----

Essid              employee1

UAC0               10.1.10.103

UAC1               10.1.10.100

UAC2               10.1.10.101

UAC3               10.1.10.102
```

```
Active Map [0-31]     00 01 02 03 00 01 02 03 00 01 02 03 00 01 02 03 00
01 02 03 00 01 02 03 00 01 02 03 00 01 02 03

Active Map [32-63]    00 01 02 03 00 01 02 03 00 01 02 03 00 01 02 03 00
01 02 03 00 01 02 03 00 01 02 03 00 01 02 03

Active Map [64-95]    00 01 02 03 00 01 02 03 00 01 02 03 00 01 02 03 00
01 02 03 00 01 02 03 00 01 02 03 00 01 02 03

Active Map [96-127]   00 01 02 03 00 01 02 03 00 01 02 03 00 01 02 03 00
01 02 03 00 01 02 03 00 01 02 03 00 01 02 03

Active Map [128-159] 00 01 02 03 00 01 02 03 00 01 02 03 00 01 02 03 00
01 02 03 00 01 02 03 00 01 02 03 00 01 02 03

Active Map [160-191] 00 01 02 03 00 01 02 03 00 01 02 03 00 01 02 03 00
01 02 03 00 01 02 03 00 01 02 03 00 01 02 03

Active Map [192-223] 00 01 02 03 00 01 02 03 00 01 02 03 00 01 02 03 00
01 02 03 00 01 02 03 00 01 02 03 00 01 02 03

Active Map [224-255] 00 01 02 03 00 01 02 03 00 01 02 03 00 01 02 03 00
01 02 03 00 01 02 03 00 01 02 03 00 01 02 03

Standby Map [0-31]     01 00 03 02 01 00 03 02 01 00 03 02 01 00 03 02
01 00 03 02 01 00 03 02 01 00 03 02 01 00 03 02

Standby Map [32-63]    01 00 03 02 01 00 03 02 01 00 03 02 01 00 03 02
01 00 03 02 01 00 03 02 01 00 03 02 01 00 03 02

Standby Map [64-95]    01 00 03 02 01 00 03 02 01 00 03 02 01 00 03 02
01 00 03 02 01 00 03 02 01 00 03 02 01 00 03 02

Standby Map [96-127]   01 00 03 02 01 00 03 02 01 00 03 02 01 00 03 02
01 00 03 02 01 00 03 02 01 00 03 02 01 00 03 02

Standby Map [128-159] 01 00 03 02 01 00 03 02 01 00 03 02 01 00 03 02
01 00 03 02 01 00 03 02 01 00 03 02 01 00 03 02

Standby Map [160-191] 01 00 03 02 01 00 03 02 01 00 03 02 01 00 03 02
01 00 03 02 01 00 03 02 01 00 03 02 01 00 03 02

Standby Map [192-223] 01 00 03 02 01 00 03 02 01 00 03 02 01 00 03 02
01 00 03 02 01 00 03 02 01 00 03 02 01 00 03 02

Standby Map [224-255] 01 00 03 02 01 00 03 02 01 00 03 02 01 00 03 02
01 00 03 02 01 00 03 02 01 00 03 02 01 00 03 02
```

Cluster GRE tunnels

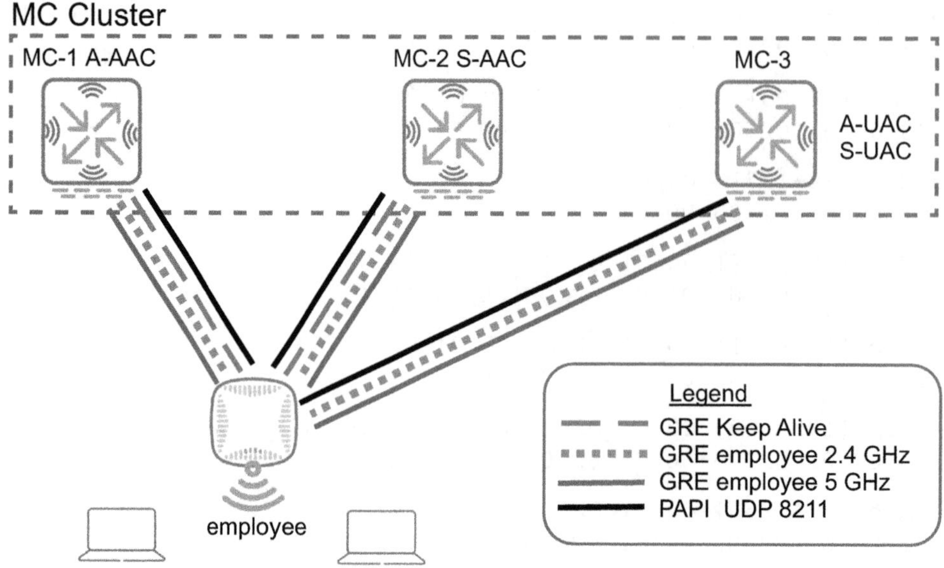

Figure 5-13 Cluster GRE tunnels

Each BSSID forms a GRE tunnel to the A-AAC and to the S-AAC (Figure 5-13).

If users associate with:

- employee 5 GHz SSID and the A-UAC or S-UAC is MC3, a GRE is built to MC3
- employee 2.4 GHz SSID and the A-UAC or S-UAC is MC3, a GRE is built to MC3
- voice 5 GHz SSID and the A-UAC or S-UAC is MC3, a GRE is built to MC3
- voice 2.4 GHz SSID and the A-UAC or S-UAC is MC3, a GRE is built to MC3

APs form a tunnel for PAPI communication with all MCs in the cluster.

Client stateful failover

Stateful failover conditions

A stateful failover within a cluster is defined as a seamless failover of users from their A-UAC to their S-UAC. This occurs with no disruption of service—no application time-outs or frame drops.

Two conditions are required to achieve a cluster stateful failover:

- Redundancy mode must be enabled
- Cluster members are L2-connected

You can use the **show lc-cluster group-membership** command to confirm these conditions, as shown in the following example:

```
(MC-1) #show lc-cluster group-membership
Cluster Enabled, Profile Name = "cluster1"
Redundancy Mode On
Active Client Rebalance Threshold = 50%
Standby Client Rebalance Threshold = 75%
Unbalance Threshold = 5%
AP Load Balancing: Enabled
Active AP Rebalance Threshold = 50%
Active AP Unbalance Threshold = 5%
Active AP Rebalance AP Count = 10
Active AP Rebalance Timer = 5 minutes
Cluster Info Table
------------------
Type  IPv4 Address    Priority  Connection-Type  STATUS
----  ------------    --------  ---------------  ------
peer  10.1.10.101      150       L2-Connected  CONNECTED (Member, last
HBT_RSP 77ms ago, RTD = 1.013 ms)
self  10.1.10.100      151                N/A  CONNECTED (Leader)
peer  10.1.10.102      128       L2-Connected  CONNECTED (Member, last
HBT_RSP 77ms ago, RTD = 1.013 ms)
peer  10.1.10.103      128       L2-Connected  CONNECTED (Member, last
HBT_RSP 77ms ago, RTD = 1.013 ms)
```

Stateful failover functionality

The stateful failover is possible thanks to the following features:

- Client state information is synchronized to the S-UAC, where multiple Global Share Memory (GSM) objects are copied over. This includes values related to the endpoint (sta), its MAC and IP addresses, key cache, and PMK cache.
- L2- and L3-connected are MC states within a cluster. The L2_user and L3_user refer to all data pertaining to a user in the controller's data and control plane. This specifically refers to the data-path station, bridge, user, and route entries in respective tables. It also refers to the control plane user-table entries. In the output of the command show user-table standby below, you can see that both clients have an L2-connected status, on VLAN 11.
- High-value sessions such as FTP and DPI-modified sessions are duplicated.

Note
If a session's priority/Type-of-Service (TOS) changes, the session is DPI-modified, and becomes a high-value session.

Note
More than two million sessions can exist in the system at any time—syncing all these would be wasteful. Some sessions are short-lived, so syncing these does not make sense.

```
(MC-2) #show user-table standby

Dormant Mac Hash Table
----------------------

IP            MAC                l2role         l3role  vlan   ua_done
--            ---                ------         ------  ----   -------
10.1.11.54    7c:fa:df:b5:f0:8b  authenticated           11    0
10.1.11.51    f0:43:47:c4:da:d8  authenticated           11    0

Essid/Bssid/Tunnelid                  Counts(User/PTK)  UUID                         Active UAC IP
--------------------                  ----------------  ----                         -------------
employee1/00:24:6c:13:c7:a8/0x10012   3/2               000c29159a410000000c0006     10.1.10.102
employee1/94:b4:0f:a0:bf:d0/0x10018   1/1               000c29159a410000000c000c     10.1.10.102
Total Entries: 2
```

Each client can have a maximum of ten sessions synchronized to the standby. This is independent of platform. If there is an eleventh session, it will not be synced until one of the other sessions is deleted.

Due to these enhancements, clients are not de-authenticated during UAC failover events.

Clustering (8.X) versus AP Fast Failover (6.X)

Table 5-2 compares AOS 8.x clustering with AOS 6.x Fast Failover. As you can see, several clustering features are not supported with Fast Failover.

Table 5-2 Clustering (8.X) vs AP Fast Failover (6.X)

Feature	AOS 8.x Clustering	AOS 6.x HA
Stateful failover	Yes	No
Client state sync	Yes	Yes (dot1x only)
Seamless roaming	Yes	No
Load balancing	Yes	No
AP active/standby tunnels	Auto	Manual
User de-authenticated (upon failover)	No	Yes

Roaming and load balancing will be discussed in the next chapter.

Learning check

2. Which two conditions must be setup to support stateful failover?
    a. L2 connection between cluster members.
    b. L3 connection between cluster members.
    c. The redundancy option is enabled in a clustering profile.
    d. The AP load balance option is enabled in the clustering profile.
3. What sessions can be synced to S-UAC?
    a. All traffic
    b. FTP session
    c. DPI qualified sessions
    d. Ping traffic

Clustering configuration and monitoring

Cluster configuration—Step 1

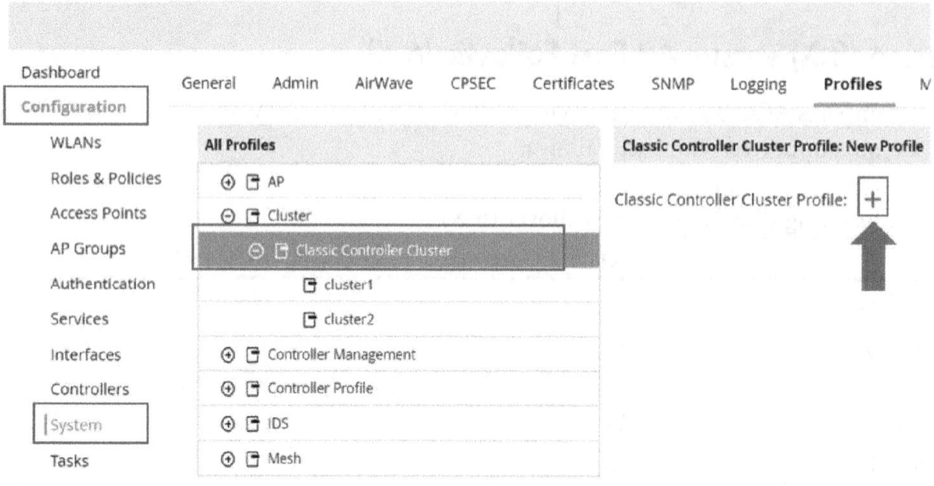

Figure 5-14 Cluster configuration—Step 1

Figure 5-14 shows the first task in a cluster configuration, where you create a cluster profile.

Navigate to **Managed Network > Configuration > System > Profiles**, and then under All Profiles, expand Cluster. Choose Classic Controller Cluster, then click on "+" to add a new cluster profile.

Cluster configuration—Step 1 (cont.)

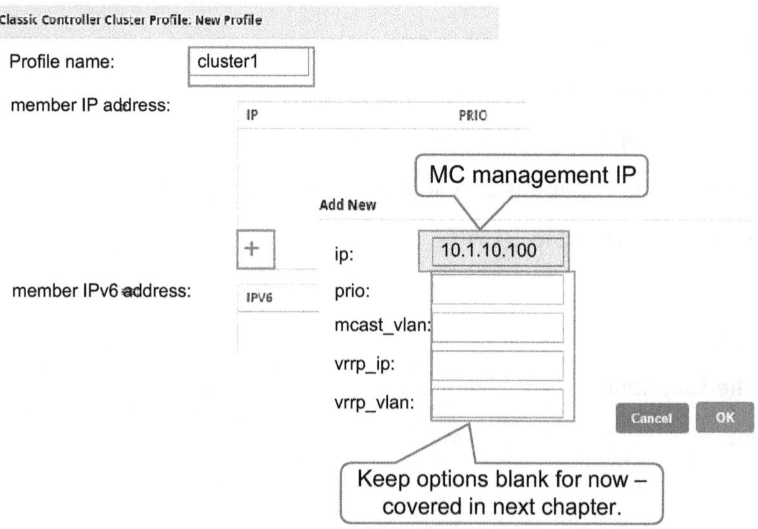

Figure 5-15 Cluster configuration—Step 1 (cont.)

Enter a name for the cluster profile, then click on "+" to add each cluster member, one by one. You will use each MC's management IP address for this purpose (Figure 5-15). The other options will be covered in the next chapter.

Cluster configuration—Step 2

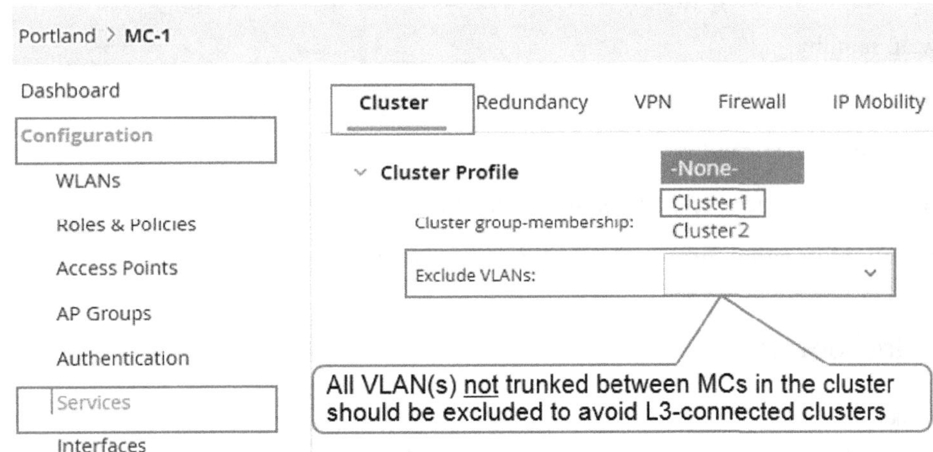

Figure 5-16 Cluster configuration—Step 2

You must attach the created profile to each of the cluster nodes. Figure 5-16 shows this process for the device named MC-1.

To start, select the appropriate device—MC-1 in this example. Then navigate to **Configuration > Services > Cluster**. Then choose the appropriate cluster.

Typically, you will leave the "Excluded VLANs" option blank. However, if VLAN-probing cannot be heard by the other VLANs, the nodes will report L3 connectivity.

For example, two nodes in a cluster are both on management VLAN 10. However, you configured an uplink port on MC-1 to permit VLAN 1 in the trunk port, but MC-2 does not permit VLAN 1. Do you recall what you learned earlier? Cluster members send probes on every VLAN for which they are configured. Even though VLAN 1 is not relevant to clustering, MC-1 sends a probe on this VLAN. Since MC-2 is not even configured for this VLAN, it does not receive this probe, and so does not respond.

In this example, the connection type will be L3 because the two nodes cannot hear VLAN-probing on VLAN 1. Once you exclude VLAN 1, the connection will immediately become an L2 connection.

Basic cluster show commands

The following lists the important show commands related to clustering.

- show lc-cluster group-membership
- show lc-cluster vlan-probe status
- show lc-cluster heartbeat counters
- show ap standby
- show user-table standby
- show datapath user standby
- show aaa cluster essid <essid name> mac <client mac address>

For additional information, refer to the *CLI Reference Guide*.

Cluster dashboard

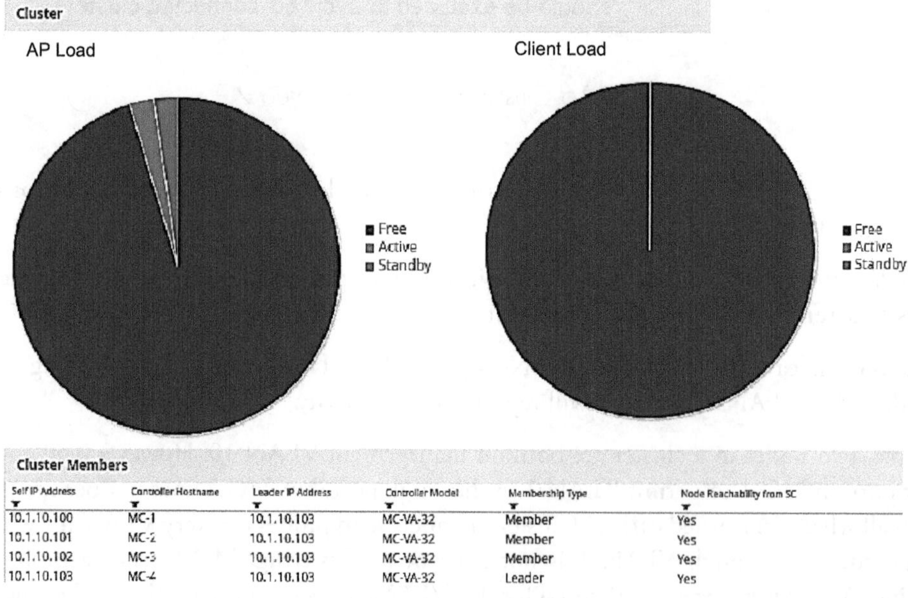

Figure 5-17 Cluster dashboard

The cluster dashboard highlights the AP and client load per cluster, as well as the list of cluster members. This includes the cluster leader. To access the cluster dashboard, choose Managed Networks > Dashboard > Cluster. Figure 5-17 shows the two pie charts that appear, as described below.

AP Load—Displays the proportional distribution of active, standby, and free APs for the selected cluster member. Hover your mouse above a section of the pie chart to view the count for that AP type.

Client Load—Displays the proportional distribution of active, standby, and free stations (clients) for the selected cluster member. Hover your mouse above a section of the pie chart to view the count for that station type.

Monitor A-AAC/S-AAC cluster roles

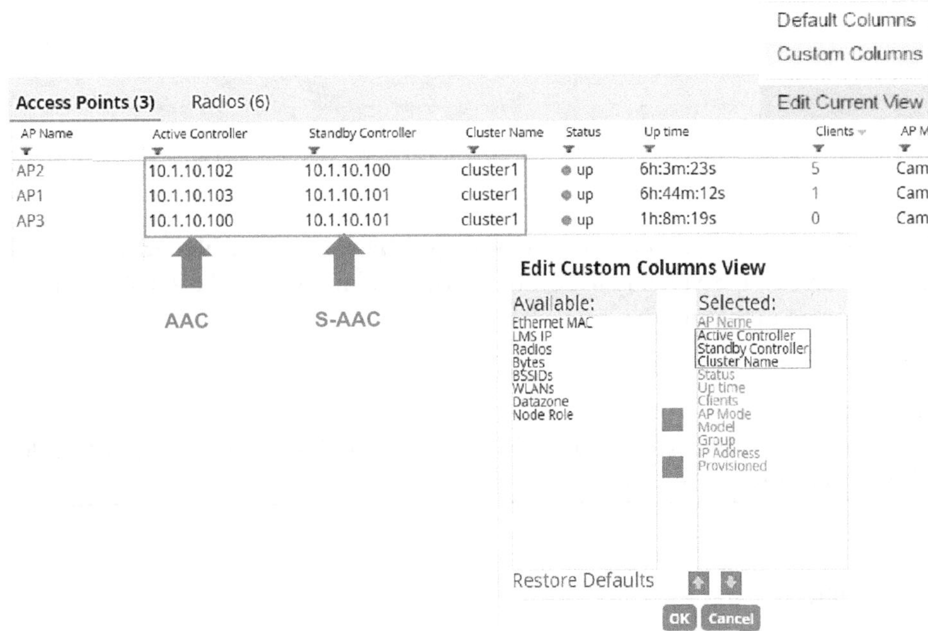

Figure 5-18 Monitor A-AAC/S-AAC cluster roles

By default, active and standby controllers would not be displayed in the dashboard. You must edit "Current View" to select the column options needed. Figure 5-18 shows how to do this, by navigating to **Managed network > Dashboard > Access Points**. Then edit the custom view to add Active Controller, Standby Controller, and Cluster Name.

Monitor A-UAC/S-UAC cluster roles

CONTROLLERS 6 1 | ACCESS POINTS 3 - | CLIENTS 5 | ALERTS 0 | admin

Search

Clients (5)

Custom Columns

Client	IP Address	Active Controller	Standby Controller	Role	Health(%)	Band	Radio PHY
10.1.11.51	10.1.11.51	10.1.10.102	10.1.10.101	authenticated	100	5 GHz	VHT 80 MHz
10.1.11.55	10.1.11.55	10.1.10.101	10.1.10.102	authenticated	100	5 GHz	VHT 80 MHz
10.1.11.52	10.1.11.52	10.1.10.102	10.1.10.103	guest	100	5 GHz	VHT 80 MHz
10.1.11.54	10.1.11.54	10.1.10.102	10.1.10.101	guest	100	5 GHz	HT 40 MHz
10.1.11.56	10.1.11.56	10.1.10.102	10.1.10.103	authenticated	100	5 GHz	VHT 80 MHz

Figure 5-19 Monitor A-UAC/S-UAC cluster roles

Figure 5-19 shows that you have navigated to **Managed network > Dashboard > Clients**. You see the global client table on the Mobility Master dashboard. Columns show the A-UAC and S-UAC for each client connected to the cluster.

Note

As shown in the previous slide, you also need to edit the "Custom Column" to display A-UAC and S-UAC in the dashboard screen.

Learning check

4. From the options below, which are the correct clustering configuration steps?
    a. Create a cluster profile in MM level.
    b. Create a cluster profile in Managed-Devices level.
    c. Attach the created profile to the cluster group membership in MM level.
    d. Attach the created profile to the cluster group membership in MC level.

6 Advanced Clustering

LEARNING OBJECTIVES

- ✓ The chapter continues the discussion of clustering from the previous chapter. You will learn about the cluster feature's ability to perform load balancing (LB) for both clients and APs. Then you will explore AP termination and redundancy flow, before moving on to advanced features.
- ✓ This includes the AP move feature and authorization server interaction. The chapter concludes with a discussion of cluster troubleshooting.

Cluster load balance overview

In this chapter, you will learn about both Client and AP load balancing. This includes a discussion of why you should use LB features, LB calculations, and LB configurations.

Client load balancing

Reason for client LB

With the bucket mapping scheme and the randomness of client MAC hashing, there will inevitably be disproportionate client distribution among cluster members. This is shown in Figure 6-1—MC1 is servicing two clients, MC2 has five clients, and MC3 has two clients. As the load increases, this imbalance creates disproportionate losses in system performance.

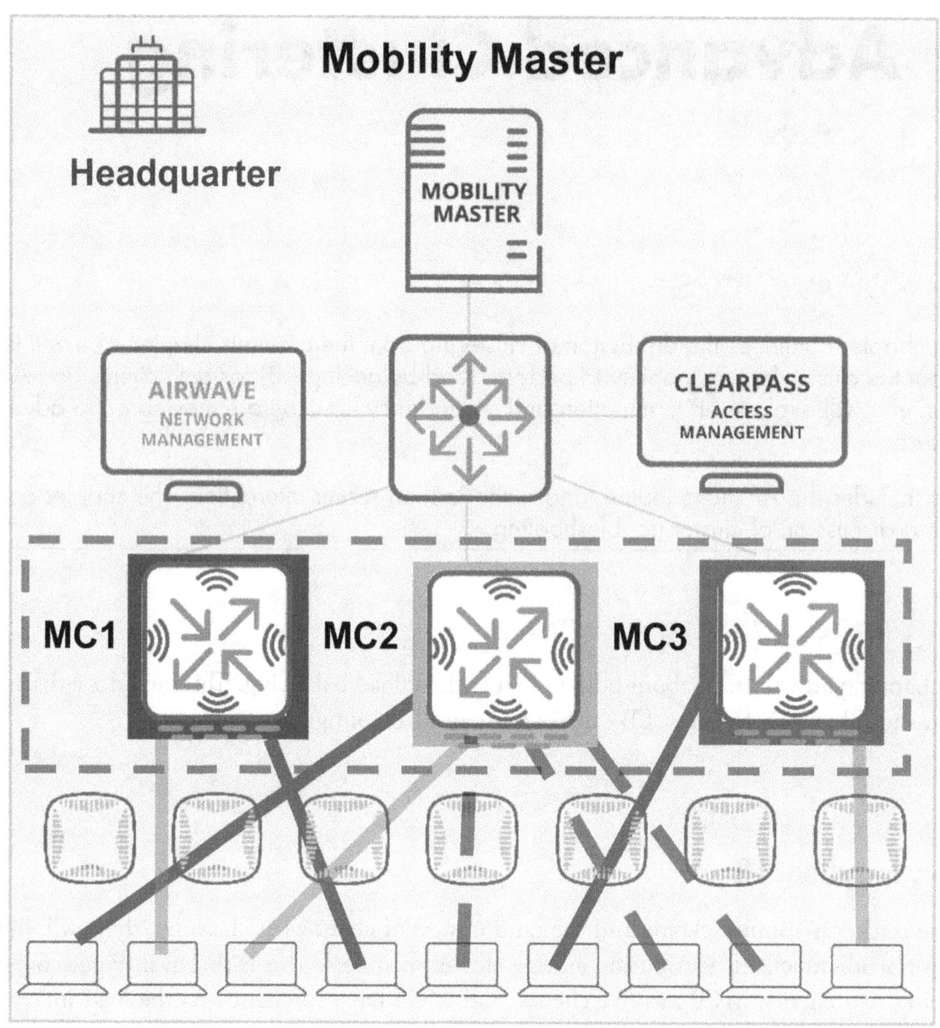

Figure 6-1 Reason for Client LB

Reason for Client LB (cont.)

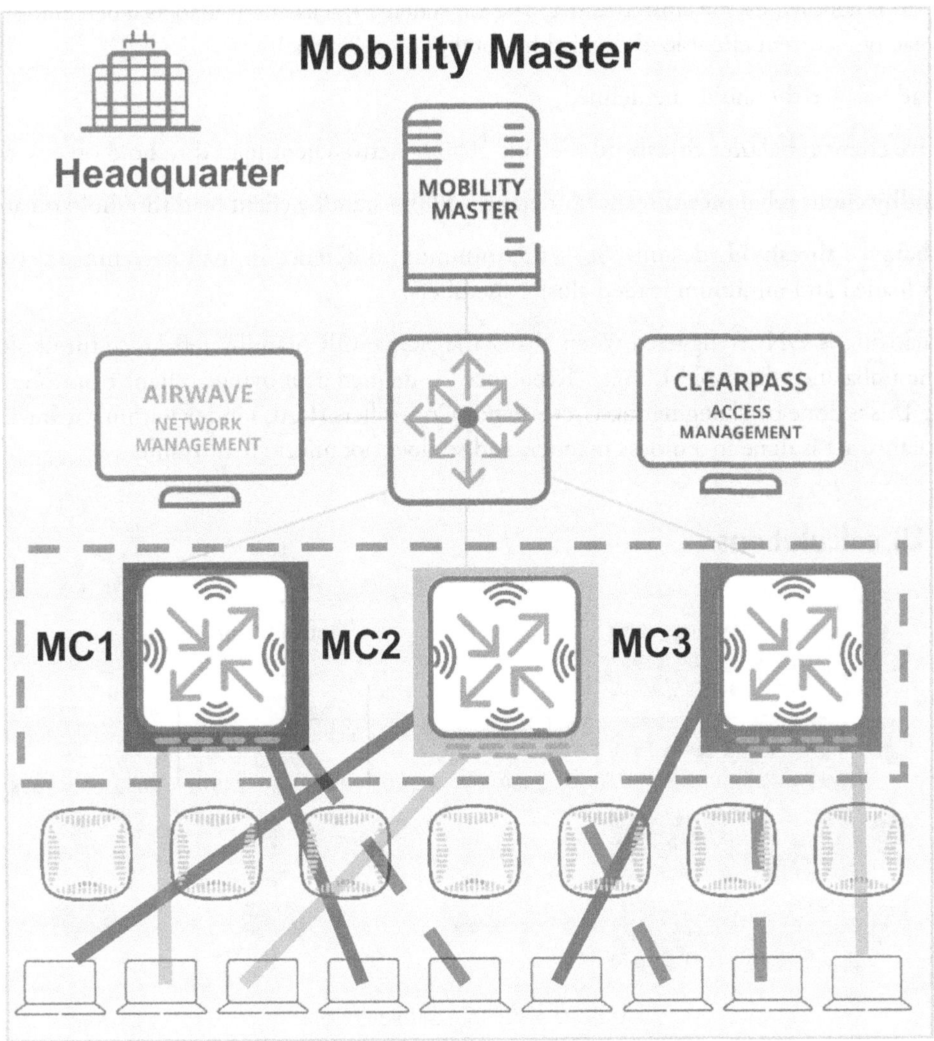

Figure 6-2 Reason for Client LB (cont.)

The goal of Cluster LB is to optimally distribute client loads across all cluster members. This is shown in Figure 6-2, where each controller services an equal number of clients. With the load balanced across cluster members, system performance improves dramatically. In fact, if the load is cut in half, system performs more than doubles.

Client LB triggers

Cluster LB is handled by the cluster leader. The LB scheme tracks client load as a percentage of platform capacity—current client load divided by total platform capacity.

Three load balance thresholds are defined:

- **Active client rebalance threshold** (default 50%)—active client load threshold on any node.
- **Standby client rebalance threshold** (default 75%)—standby client load threshold on any node.
- **Unbalance threshold** (default 5%)—the minimum difference in load percentage between the max loaded and minimum loaded cluster members.

Load balancing is ONLY triggered when either the Active OR Standby rebalance threshold is met AND the unbalance threshold is met. "Rebalance" is defined as moving a client from one node to another. This is done by changing the User Anchor Controllers (UAC) index within the bucket-map. The rebalance act is done in a hitless manner, and so does not affect client traffic.

Client LB calculations

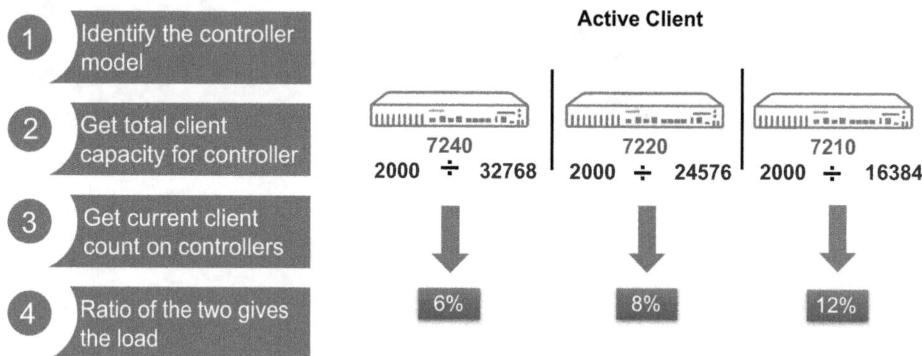

Figure 6-3 Client LB calculations

The goal of client LB is to balance the percentage of load across all cluster member controllers, regardless of platform type. Remember, % Load = client count/total platform capacity (Figure 6-3).

For example, assume two thousand clients are active on the 7240 controller, and another two thousand clients are on the 7220. From the load perspective, 7240 is only about 6% loaded, while the 7220 is about 8% loaded. A 7210 with 2000 clients is about 12% loaded.

Platform capacity for various models is listed below:

Model	Max concurrent devices
7005	1024
7008	1024
7010	2048
7024	2048
7030	4096
7205	8,192
7210	16,384
7220	24,576
7240XM	32,768

Client LB trigger example

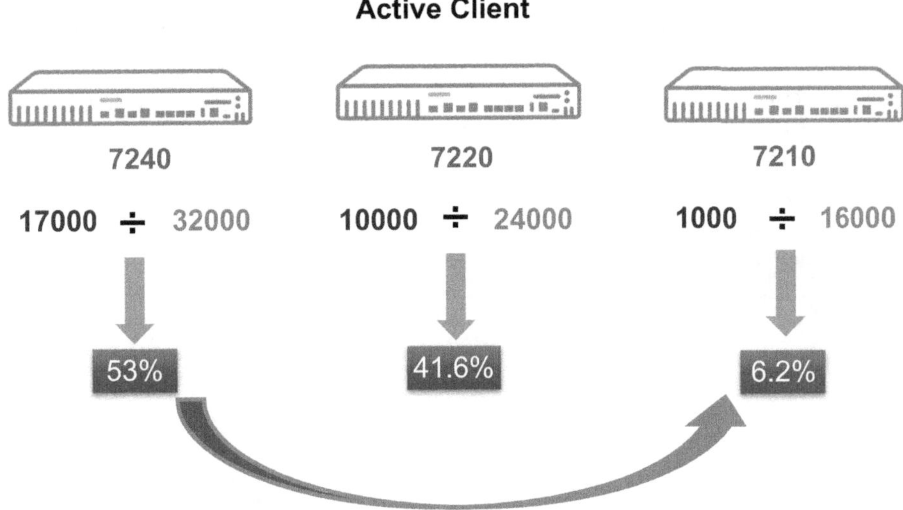

Figure 6-4 Client LB trigger example

Figure 6-4 shows a scenario where both rebalance conditions are met. The active client threshold is greater than 50%, and the unbalance threshold is greater than 5%; therefore, clients will be balanced from 7240 to 7210.

Two additional case studies are shown below. Please note that we will use 10% of the active-client-rebalance-threshold and 5% of unbalanced-threshold.

Case 1

7240: 3000 clients

7220: 2000 clients

Result: No LB because neither threshold is met (7240 is 9% and 7220 is 8%)

Case 2

7240: 500 clients

7220: 0 clients (node just rebooted)

Result: No LB because neither threshold is met (7240 is 1.5% and unbalance is < 5%)

Client LB configuration

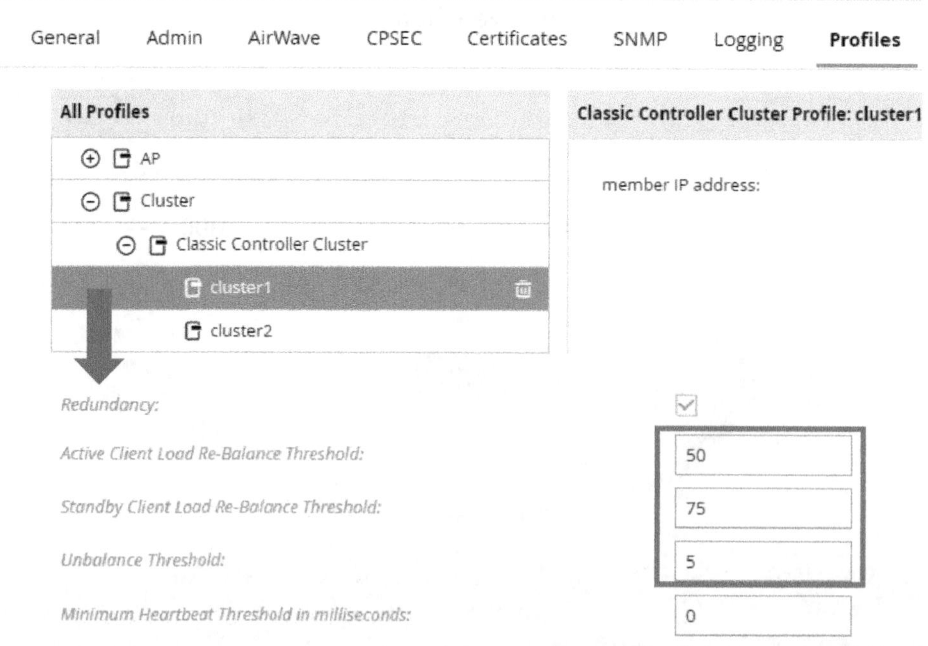

Figure 6-5 Client LB configuration

LB is enabled by default when a cluster is configured. The threshold parameters can be configured in a cluster group profile by navigating to **Managed Network > Configuration > Profiles**, as shown in Figure 6-5. You can also configure it via CLI, as described below.

```
(config) #lc-cluster group-profile "cluster name"

(Classic Controller Cluster Profile "Clust1")#active-client-rebalance-threshold 60

(Classic Controller Cluster Profile "Clust1")#unbalance-threshold  10
```

To show the client LB parameters:

```
show lc-cluster group-profile "cluster name"

Redundancy: No

L2-Connected: No

Active Client Rebalance Threshold:50%

Standby Client Rebalance Threshold:75%

Unbalance Threshold:5%
```

Client LB validation

You can use the `show lc-cluster load distribution client` command to check the client load distribution.

```
#show lc-cluster load distribution client

Cluster Load Distribution for Clients

-------------------------------------

Type      IPv4 Address    Active Clients        Standby Clients

----      --------------- --------------        ---------------

Self        10.1.10.100             1001                979

peer        10.1.10.101             890                 1005

peer        10.1.10.102             975                 980

peer        10.1.10.103             1020                1004

Total: Active Clients 3886 Standby Clients 3886
```

In the output, you can see that the peer on which you entered this command (Type column = self) has one active client and no standby clients.

The peer at address 10.1.10.101 has zero active clients. This peer is acting as the standby for the one active client shown.

Learning check

1. In one cluster, the client numbers and platform models are as shown. Is LB triggered?
   - 7240 (Capacity 32,000): 4000 clients
   - 7220 (Capacity 24,000): 700 clients
   a. Yes
   b. No

AP load balancing

AP LB overview

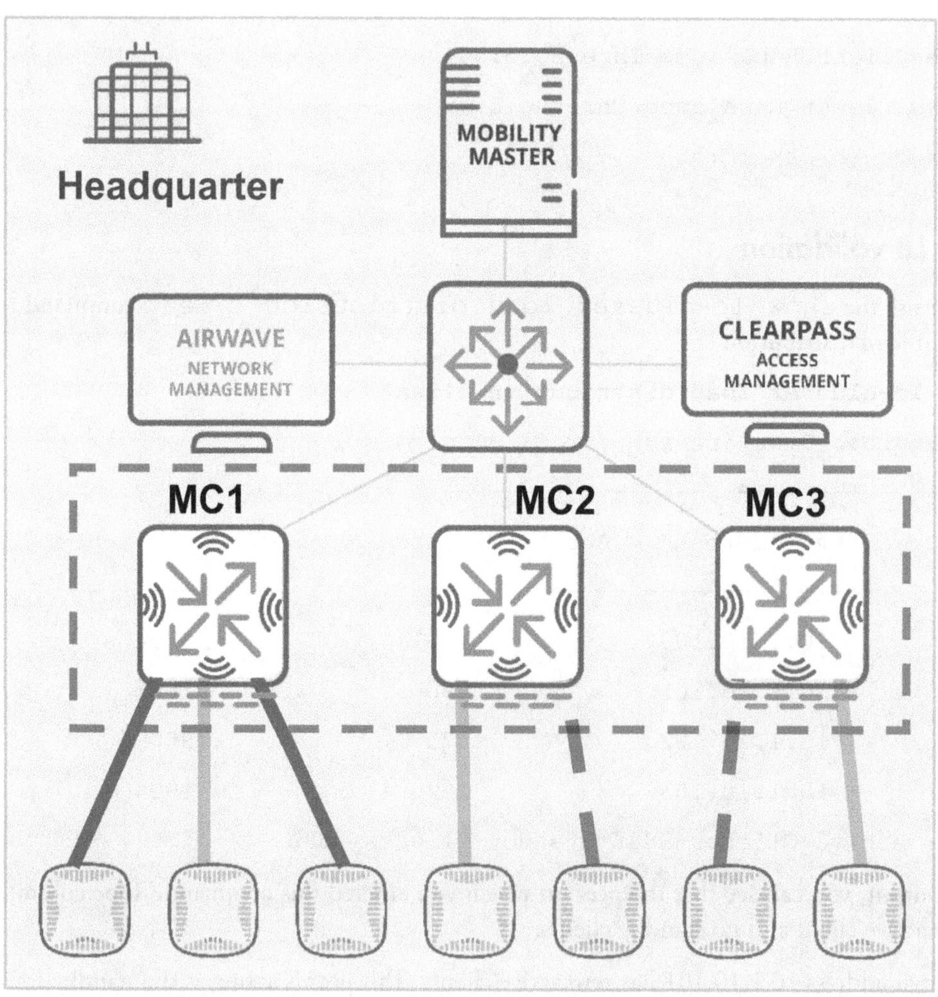

Figure 6-6 AP LB overview

As of ArubaOS 8.1, load balancing can be performed for active APs in a cluster setup.

Traditionally in AOS, the Local Mobility Switch (LMS) IP in the AP system profile acts as the AP's A-AAC. This creates customer difficulty, related to planning AP distribution in the cluster. You must carefully choose the AP's LMS IP and backup LMS IP—a time-consuming and tedious process.

The AP LB feature automatically assigns an AP's Active AAC (A-AAC) based on the load. The AP terminates on this assigned A-AAC. That means the lms-IP is ignored when AP LB is enabled. In Figure 6-6, the AP load is fairly balanced between the three cluster member controllers.

New AP distribution in a cluster

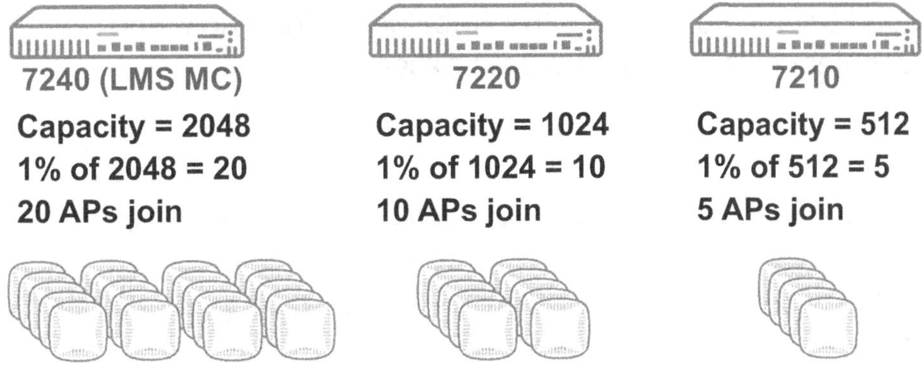

Figure 6-7 New AP distribution in a cluster

APs are originally distributed among cluster members based on 1% of each MC's capacity. The first 1% goes to the active-master/LMS controller, then that master/LMS controller distributes the second 1% to another member, third 1% to yet another member.

Figure 6-7 shows three cluster members. On the left, this particular 7240 can handle 2048 APs. One percent of 2048 is 20 APs. Assuming that the 7240 is the LMS MC, the first 20 APs join this controller. For the 7220, 1% of 1024 is 10 APs, and for the 7210, 1% of 512 is 5 APs.

Once all APs are connected to the cluster, LB thresholds activate and adjust as needed. The APs are notified of their Active AAC via the node list. The node list sent to each AP depends on the 1% rule.

AP LB triggers

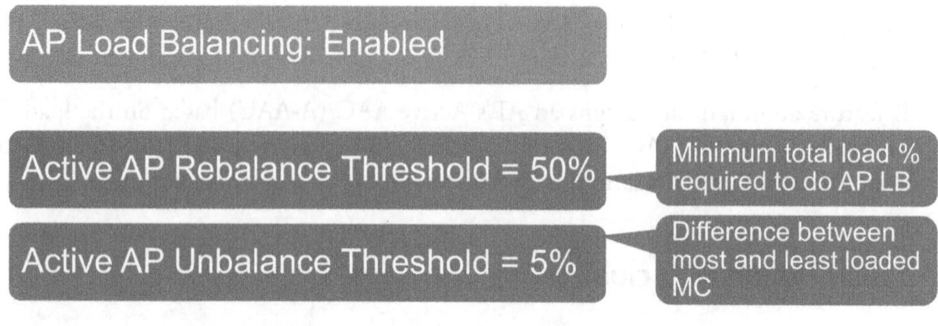

Figure 6-8 AP LB triggers

AP LB is disabled by default. Therefore, you must enable the feature to use it (Figure 6-8).

ClientMatch balances the load periodically, when total load exceeds the minimum load threshold, and the difference between the most and least loaded controller is greater than the Unbalance Threshold.

You control LB triggering by configuring the following cluster profile threshold parameters:

- Active AP Rebalance Threshold
- Active AP Unbalance Threshold

During rebalance, a certain order is used. First, the standby load is redistributed across cluster members, then the active load is redistributed, until the total load is balanced.

Internally, active AP rebalance is achieved using AP-Move functionality. The new A-AAC becomes the target controller for the AP.

APs are redistributed in a phased manner. The number of APs redistributed, and the rebalance timer can be configured from the cluster profile. AP LB has no impact on users.

AP LB configuration

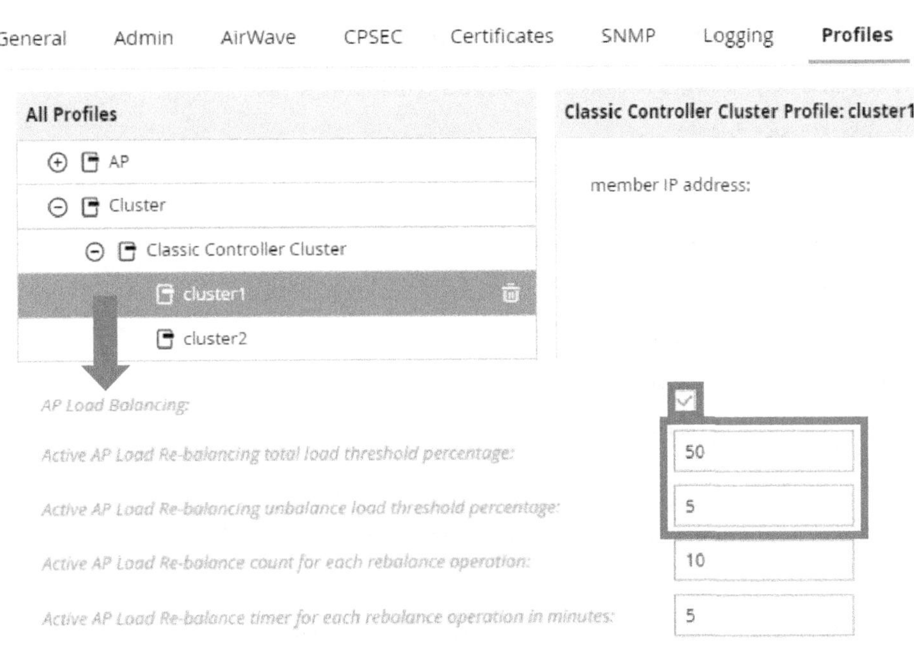

Figure 6-9 AP LB configuration

Figure 6-9 shows how to configure the AP LB feature, by navigating to **Managed Network > Configuration > Profiles**. Expand the cluster, choose the cluster profile, and click the box labeled AP LB. If desired, you can change the default triggers and timers.

You also can configure AP load balancing parameters via CLI, as shown below:

```
(MM1) [md] (config) #lc-cluster group-profile cluster1
      active-ap-lb
      active-ap-rebalance-threshold 50
      active-ap-unbalance-threshold-percentage 5
      active-ap-rebalance-ap-count 10
      active-ap-rebalance-timer 5
      write memory
```

AP LB validation

The following shows the output from the command `show lc-cluster group-membership`:

```
(MC1) #show lc-cluster group-membership

Cluster Enabled, Profile Name = "cluster1"

Redundancy Mode On

Active Client Rebalance Threshold = 50%

Standby Client Rebalance Threshold = 75%

Unbalance Threshold = 5%

AP Load Balancing: Enabled

Active AP Rebalance Threshold = 50%

Active AP Unbalance Threshold = 5%

Active AP Rebalance AP Count = 10

Active AP Rebalance Timer = 5 minutes

Cluster Info Table

Type IPv4 Address Priority Connection-Type STATUS

---- --------------- -------- --------------- ------

self 10.1.10.100 128    N/A CONNECTED (Member)

peer   10.1.10.101   128   L2-Connected   CONNECTED(Member,last   HBT_
RSP33msago,RTD= 0.989 ms)

peer   10.1.10.102   128   L2-Connected   CONNECTED(Member,last   HBT_
RSP33msago,RTD= 0.989 ms)

peer   10.1.10.103   128   L2-Connected   CONNECTED(Leader,last   HBT_
RSP33msago,RTD= 0.989 ms)
```

You can see members of the cluster, as configured in the profile named "cluster1," along with each member's connection-types. In this case, all cluster members are L2-connected with MC1.

You can also see the trigger and timer settings.

Note

Do you recall how important it is for cluster members to be L2-connected? If not, review this concept, as previously described in Chapter 5.

AP LB—validate AP load distribution

To validate how APs are distributed among the cluster, use the command `show lc-cluster load distribution ap`.

```
(MC) # show  lc-cluster load distribution ap

Cluster Load Distribution for APs

---------------------------------

Type IPv4 Address    Active APs     Standby APs

---- --------------- -------------- ---------------

peer   10.1.10.101             131          176

peer   10.1.10.102             153          142

self   10.1.10.100             204          103

peer   10.1.10.103             112          179

Total: Active APs 600 Standby APs 600
```

This example shows 600 total APs are distributed in the cluster. You see each cluster member and how many APs it servers, either as the A-AAC or S-AAC.

Learning check

2. By default, what is the status of the AP LB and client LB feature, respectively?
    a. Enabled/disabled
    b. Enabled/enabled
    c. Disabled/disabled
    d. Disabled/enabled

AP termination

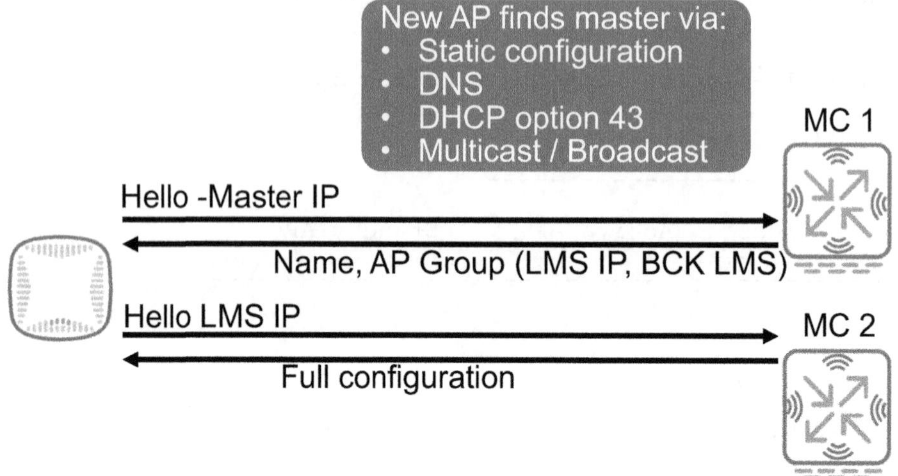

Figure 6-10 AP termination

A new AP finds the master IP address in one of several ways:

- Static configuration
- DNS
- DHCP Option 43
- Multicast or broadcast replies

The AP sends a hello message to the master IP (Figure 6-10). The master sends a configuration with the AP name and AP group, along with the LMS and Backup LMS from the master.

If there was no node list, then the AP sends a hello packet to the LMS IP. The MC with this LMS IP then replies with the AP group configuration. The AP then creates GRE tunnels based on configured SSIDs and radios.

AP termination in cluster—Part 1

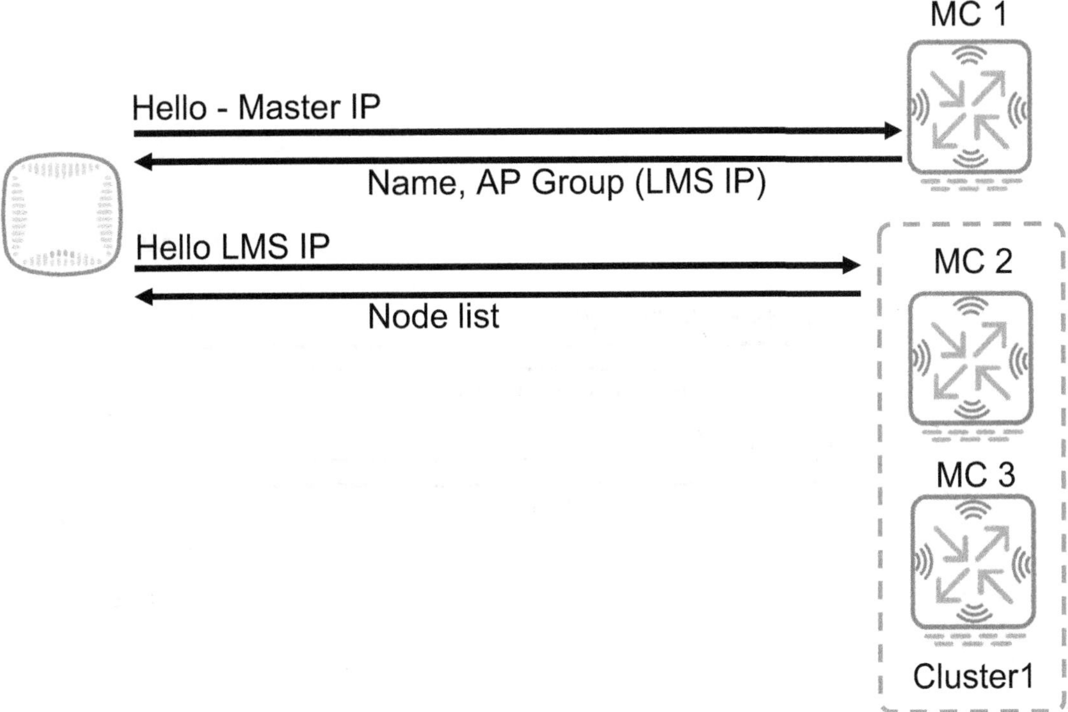

Figure 6-11 AP termination in cluster—Part 1

New APs find the master as described above (Figure 6-11). An MC sends the AP its name and AP group as well as the LMS IP. The LMS IP could be an MC or a cluster of MCs. If the AP received a node list, then it is part of a cluster. The AP then attempts to communicate with the LMS IP. If a node list is returned by the MC, then the AP is part of a cluster. The LMS parameter is thus ignored, since the node list now takes priority.

AP termination in cluster—Part 2

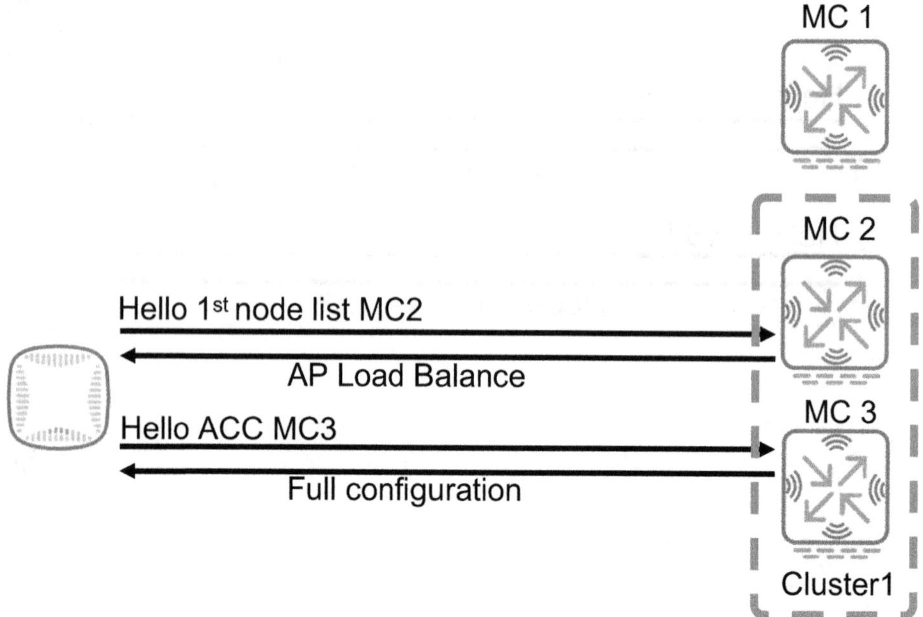

Figure 6-12 AP termination in cluster—Part 2

Once in communication with an MC in the cluster, the AP may terminate to that MC, or be redirected to its A-AAC (Figure 6-12). The AP sends a hello packet to the designated A-AAC, and receives its full configuration.

If there is no reply from any MC in the node list, the AP tries the LMS IP. If the LMS IP does not respond, the AP tries the backup LMS IP.

Configured AP

What about deployed APs that experience a power failure or are decommissioned? These APs always remember the following:

- AP Name: Either the default MAC address name, or the configured name.
- AP group: Either the default group or configured AP group name.
- Master IP: If the AP was setup with a static IP address. By default is the “aruba-master” pre-curser DNS name to use with the domain name for DNS lookup.
- CFG-LMS IP: The configured LMS IP. This is configured in the AP group AP system profile as the LMS IP.
- Server IP
- backup_vap_init master IP

- Node list: This will be all the IP addresses of all the MCs in the cluster. If the AP belongs to an AP group that is part of a cluster.
- Password: If the password was changed, the AP will remember the new password.

NOTE

If an AP reboots, it will search for an MC using DNS, DHCP 43, multicast, and broadcast. If not successful, the AP will continuously reboot.

AP termination—validation

The following output shows that you have connected to an AP's console port, interrupted the APs boot process, and are now at the apboot prompt. Your objective is to gather information about how this AP terminates to a controller, so you issue the `print` command.

In this first output, you can tell that this AP terminates to a cluster, since there is a node list in the apboot parameter.

```
apboot> print
servername=aruba-master
name=AP1
group=apgroup1
cert_cap=1
backup_vap_init_master=10.1.10.100
cfg_lms=10.1.10.101
num_total_bootstrap=14
backup_vap_password=53FFDA786630C9...
nodelist=10.1.10.100,10.1.10.101
stdin=serial
.......
```

If all nodes in the cluster are unavailable, this AP will terminate on the LMS (if the LMS is not in a cluster). At this point the AP is not terminated to a cluster member, and so there will no longer be a node list. The print command shows the previous_lms parameter, but not a nodelist parameter. This is shown in the following output:

```
apboot> print
servername=aruba-master
name=AP1
```

```
group=apgroup1
cert_cap=1
backup_vap_init_master=10.1.10.100
num_ipsec_retry=85
backup_vap_password=3A28B643D862568...
backup_vap_opmode=0
backup_vap_band=2
rap_tftp_upgrade=0
cfg_lms=10.1.10.101
stdin=serial
......
```

Of course, the AP will terminate on the previous_lms directly.

Redundancy example

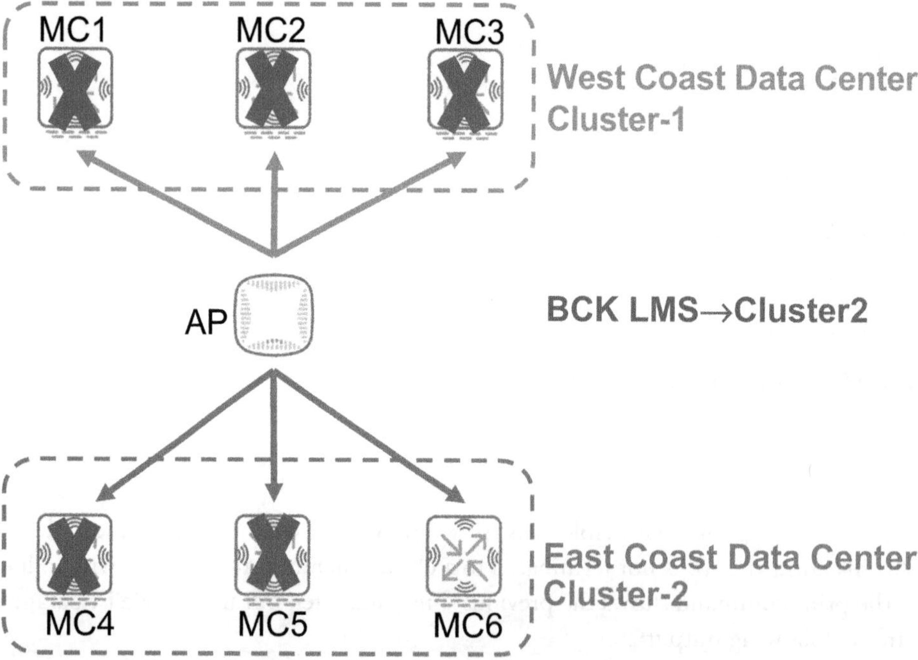

Figure 6-13 Redundancy example

If the entire node list is not reachable, then the AP does a "legacy rebootstrap." In other words, it first contacts the LMS, and then the backup LMS.

Figure 6-13 shows that three-node clusters are deployed in both the West Coast and East Coast data centers. The AP shown is configured for primary termination to the West Coast data center and backup to the East Coast data center.

If a West Coast cluster member fails, the AP moves to another West Coast cluster member MC. But if the entire West Coast data center is down, the AP terminates to the East Coast data center. And if the entire East Coast data center is also down? It is probably a zombie apocalypse—run! Meanwhile, the AP will try to terminate to its configured backup LMS.

Cluster and AP groups

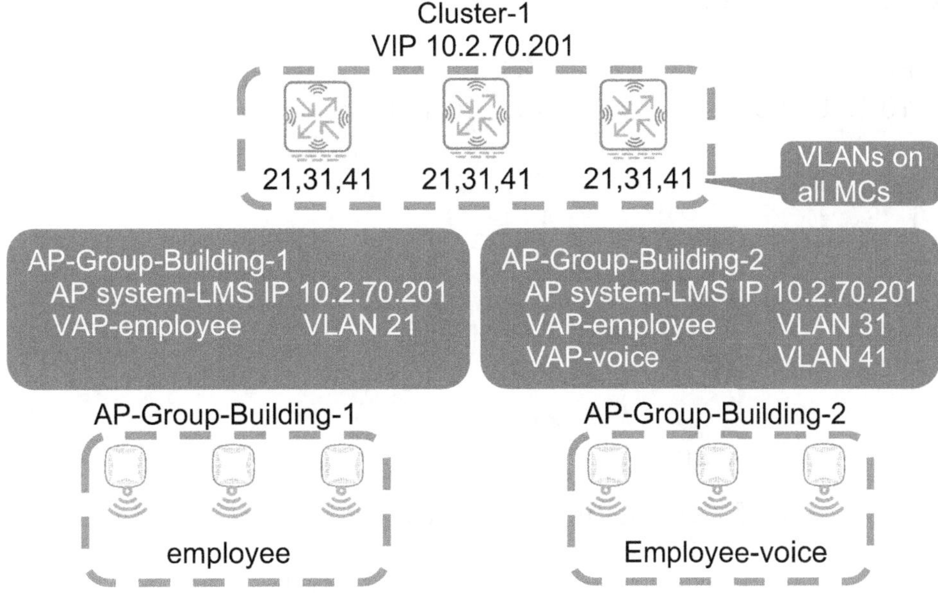

Figure 6-14 Cluster and AP groups

You may need to have another area advertise different SSIDs, or place users in different VLANs. To do this, simply create a new AP group (Figure 6-14).

You may configure all AP groups with an LMS IP set to an MC in the cluster. These groups will be in every MC in that cluster. Once an AP group is in the cluster, the node list takes over. Simply select the APs that should advertise specific SSID and place them into the proper AP group.

The example above shows an MC cluster with several APs in Building 1. You have different needs in Building 2. Therefore, you created a second AP group, and placed all APs in Building 2 in this group.

In the cluster, all APs could be load-balanced across several of the MCs. This is good, since both AP groups run in every MC in the cluster. In this way, you get all the advantages of a cluster—redundancy, AP load balancing, user balancing, and seamless upgrades.

Learning check

3. The cluster node-list has the highest priority for AP termination.
   a. True
   b. False

Additional advanced features

The apmove command

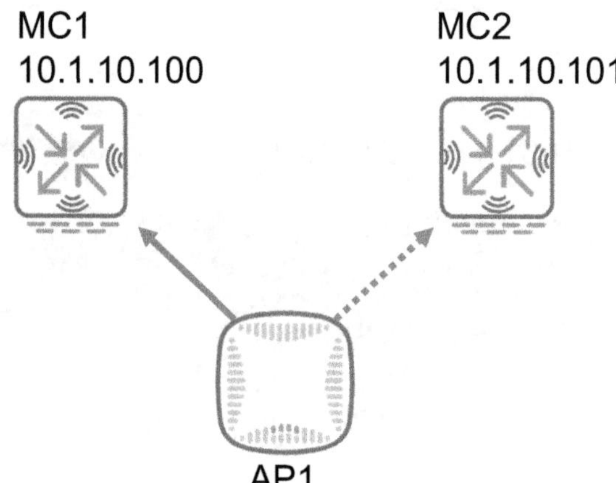

Figure 6-15 The apmove command

The `apmove` command allows you to manually reassign an AP or AP group to any managed device. You might do this when you want to move some specific APs to another managed device, without changing any configuration (Figure 6-15).

Another reason is when there is no failover/rebootstrap configuration between the current managed device and the target managed device. Use `apmove` to send a specific AP to a specific managed device.

apmove example

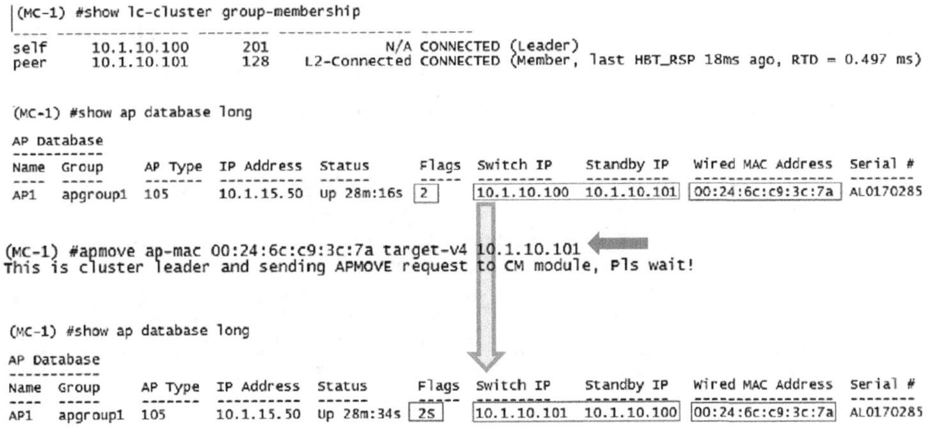

```
(MC-1) #show lc-cluster group-membership
---- -------------- -------- -------------- ------
self      10.1.10.100      201              N/A CONNECTED (Leader)
peer      10.1.10.101      128     L2-Connected CONNECTED (Member, last HBT_RSP 18ms ago, RTD = 0.497 ms)

(MC-1) #show ap database long

AP Database
-----------
Name  Group      AP Type  IP Address   Status       Flags  Switch IP    Standby IP   Wired MAC Address  Serial #
----  -----      -------  ----------   ------       -----  ---------    ----------   -----------------  --------
AP1   apgroup1   105      10.1.15.50   Up 28m:16s   2      10.1.10.100  10.1.10.101  00:24:6c:c9:3c:7a  AL0170285

(MC-1) #apmove ap-mac 00:24:6c:c9:3c:7a target-v4 10.1.10.101
This is cluster leader and sending APMOVE request to CM module, Pls wait!

(MC-1) #show ap database long

AP Database
-----------
Name  Group      AP Type  IP Address   Status       Flags  Switch IP    Standby IP   Wired MAC Address  Serial #
----  -----      -------  ----------   ------       -----  ---------    ----------   -----------------  --------
AP1   apgroup1   105      10.1.15.50   Up 28m:34s   2S     10.1.10.101  10.1.10.100  00:24:6c:c9:3c:7a  AL0170285
```

Figure 6-16 apmove example

Figure 6-16 shows an example of manually moving an AP.

You begin by issuing the command `show lc-cluster group-membership`. This reveals that MC1 (10.1.10.100) is the cluster leader, so this is where you will execute the `apmove` command. If you are moving an AP to another MC in the same cluster group, you must run `apmove` on the cluster leader.

You issue the command `show ap database long`. This establishes the current state for AP1. You can see that its current "Switch IP" is 10.1.10.100.

Then you issue the `apmove` command, as shown in Figure 6-16, followed by `show ap database long`. This verifies that the AP has indeed been moved to a new switch IP of 10.1.10.101.

If this were a High-Availability (HA) scenario, you would enter the `apmove` command on the HA-Active node. The AP will failover to HA standby. For more information on this, refer to the fast failover feature in the user guide.

If this were noncluster setup, you can enter the `apmove` command on the MC to which the AP is currently terminated.

Authorization without Authorization Server Interaction (ASI)

You have learned that clustering supports redundancy for both APs and clients. Client ACL and role names are synchronized across cluster members, as are AP data paths.

The UAC controller role facilitates end user redundancy. The UAC handles all wireless client traffic—association/disassociation, authentication, and all unicast traffic between itself and the client. Regardless of where clients roam, their UAC remains consistent.

Should the A-UAC fail, the user seamlessly connects to the S-UAC, which, of course, has a different IP address. This is where the challenge lies.

The Authorization module authenticates clients on the A-UAC and sets the A-UAC IP address as the NAS-IP. External RADIUS servers set the NAS-IP as the A-UAC IP in the client database (Figure 6-17). This NAS-IP is used later to change client states or attributes.

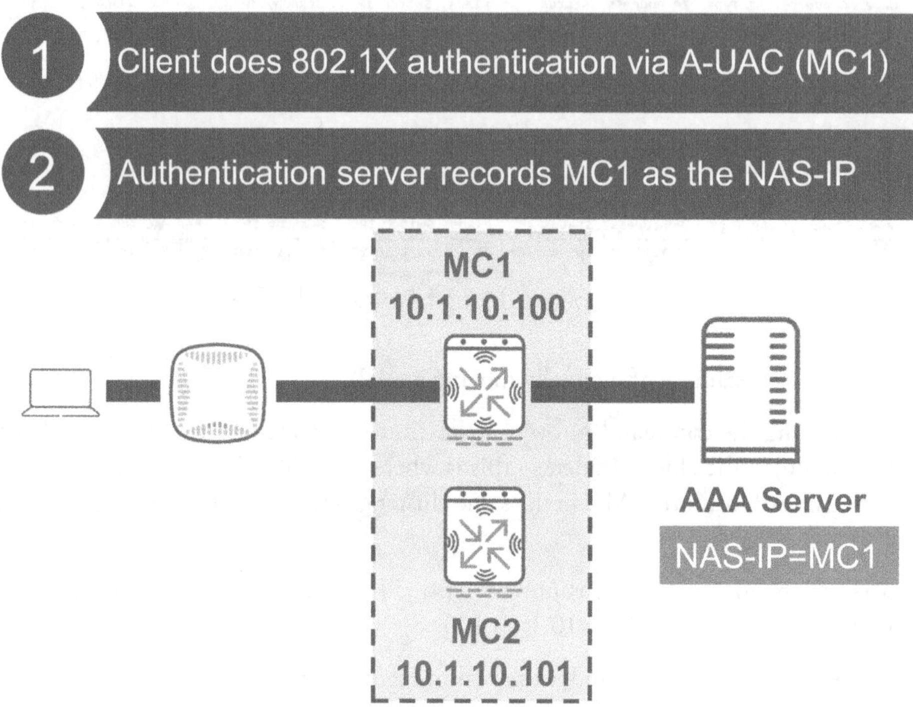

Figure 6-17 Authorization without ASI

However, when the client moves to a new UAC, the authentication server is not updated. This means that transactions initiated by the authorization server will fail (Figure 6-18).

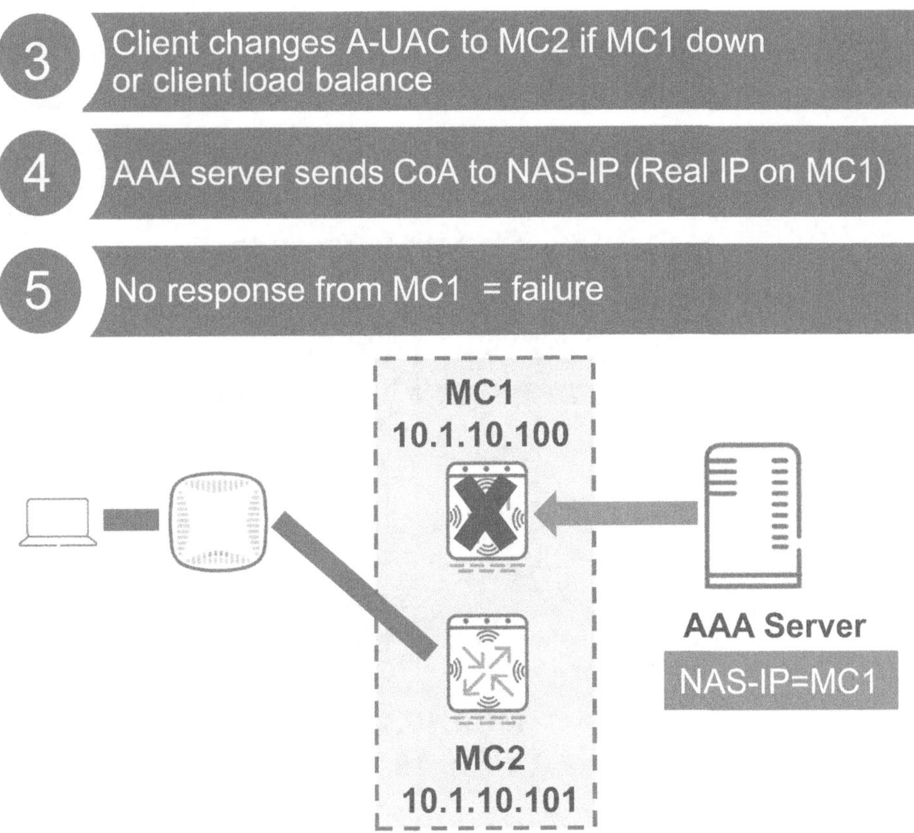

Figure 6-18 Authorization without ASI (Cont.)

To resolve this issue, you should configure each cluster member to use the Virtual Router Redundancy Protocol (VRRP), as described below. This enables interaction between the cluster and the authorization server. The Aruba User Guide refers to this as Authorization Server Interaction (ASI).

Authorization with ASI

Figures 6-19 and 6-20 demonstrate how VRRP enables the ASI feature and resolves the previously described challenge. In Figure 6-19, MC1, 2, and 3 are all configured to use VRRP, with MC3 acting as the VRRP active device.

The AAA server sets the NAS-IP to this VRRP IP address (Figure 6-19).

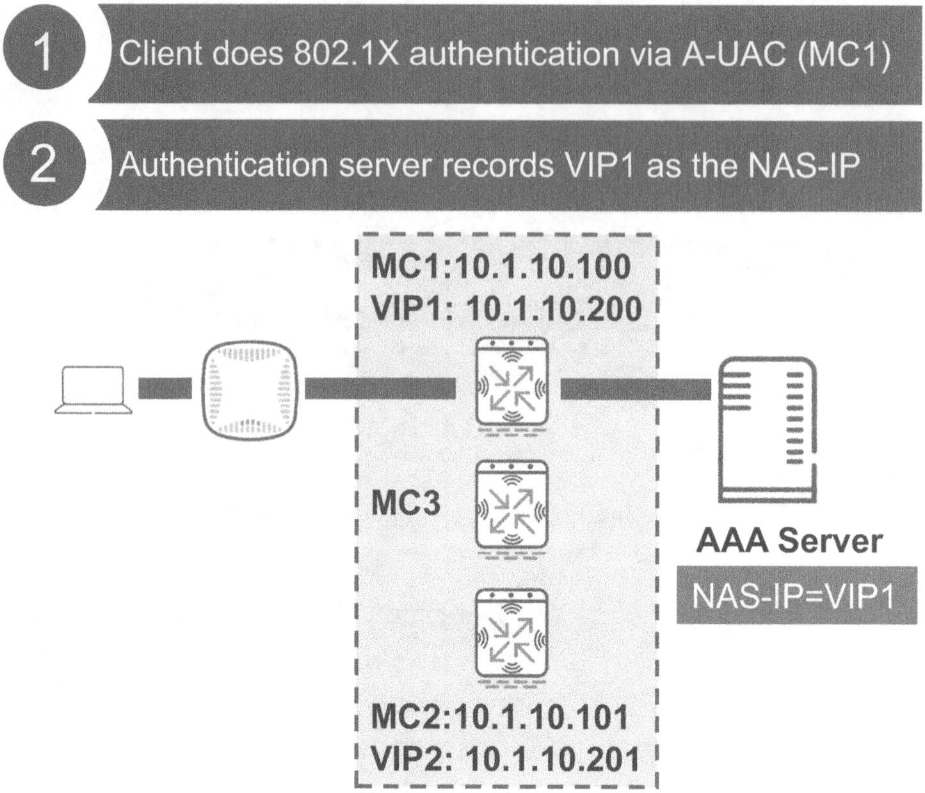

Figure 6-19 Authorization with ASI

So when the user must move to a new UAC, the AAA server contacts the VRRP IP address, served by MC3. MC3 redirects this authorization action to the A-UAC of the client (MC2) according to the bucket map (Figure 6-20). Thanks to the ASI feature, the challenge previously described is resolved.

3
Client changes A-UAC to S-UAC (MC2) if MC1 down or client load balance
4
AAA server sends CoA to NAS-IP (VIP1)
5
MC3 (VIP1) redirects the CoA to new A-UAC (MC2). Thank you ASI
MC1:10.1.10.100
VIP1: 10.1.10.200
MC3
AAA Server
NAS-IP=VIP1
MC2:10.1.10.101
VIP2: 10.1.10.201

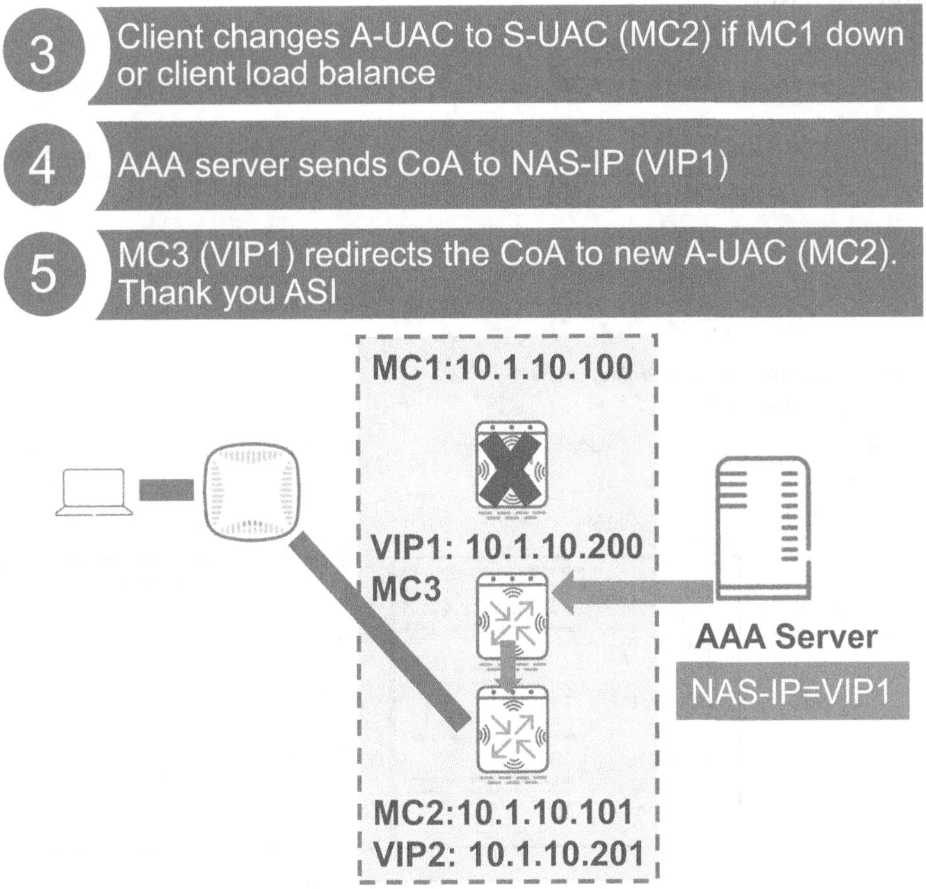

Figure 6-20 Authorization with ASI (Cont.)

Each MC needs one VRRP IP as its NAS-IP. You will learn more about the NAS-IP later in this chapter.

Configuring VRRP

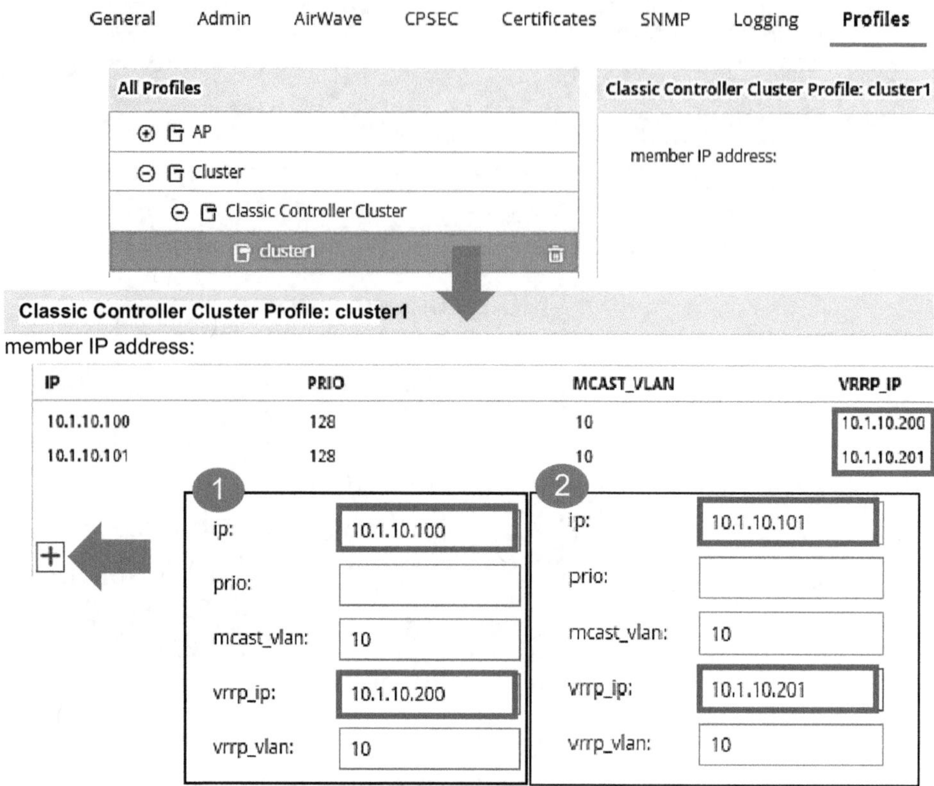

Figure 6-21 Configuring VRRP

Figure 6-21 shows how to configure VRRP, which enables ASI. Navigate to **Managed Network > Configuration > System > Profiles > Cluster > cluster profile.** Then click the "+" symbol.

1. Now add the actual IP address of the cluster node. In this example, you are adding cluster node1. Its *physical* IP address is 10.1.10.100, and its *virtual* VRRP IP address is 10.1.10.200.
2. Add another node. In this example, the physical IP is 10.1.10.101 and VRRP IP is 10.1.10.201

The syntax is described below.

- <ip>: controller to be made part of this cluster. The IPv4 Address is the value of the controller-ip
- <prio>: defines the priority level for the managed devices.
- <mcast-vlan>: enter the multicast VLAN.
- <vrrp-ip>: the virtual IP address that will be owned and serviced by the elected VRRP master.
- <vrrp-vlan>: specifies the VLAN ID of the VLAN on which the VRRP will run.

VRRP validation

The following output shows validating a VRRP configuration with the command `show vrrp`:

```
(MC-1)show vrrp
virtual router 220:
  Description
  Admin State UP, VR State MASTER
  IP Address 10.1.10.200 MAC Address 00:00:53:00:01:dc, vlan 10
  Priority 255, Advertisement 1 sec, Preemption Enable Delay 0
  Auth Type NONE ********
  tracking is not enabled
virtual router 221:
  Description
  Admin State UP, VR State BACKUP
  IP Address 10.1.10.201 MAC Address 00:00:53:00:01:dd, vlan 10
  Priority 235, Advertisement 1 sec, Preemption Enable Delay 0
  Auth Type NONE ********
  tracking is not enabled
(MC-2)show vrrp
virtual router 220:
  Description
  Admin State UP, VR State BACKUP
  IP Address 10.1.10.200 MAC Address 00:00:53:00:01:dc, vlan 10
  Priority 255, Advertisement 1 sec, Preemption Enable Delay 0
  Auth Type NONE ********
  tracking is not enabled
virtual router 221:
  Description
  Admin State UP, VR State MASTER
```

```
IP Address 10.1.10.201 MAC Address 00:00:53:00:01:dd, vlan 10
Priority 235, Advertisement 1 sec, Preemption Enable Delay 0
Auth Type NONE ********
tracking is not enabled
```

On MC1, you can see that two VRRP instances are configured. For virtual router 220, MC-1 is the master, it will respond to packets sent to IP address 10.1.10.200. Should MC-1 fail, MC-2 will "play the role" of IP address 10.1.10.200, taking over for MC-1. The opposite is true for the second VRRP instance—Virtual Router 221.

Each MC in a cluster is configured with one VIP address in the same subnet. Suppose you have four MCs in a cluster. The configuration would look like this:

```
lc-cluster group-profile "72xx-cluster"
controller 10.15.28.12 priority 128 vrrp-ip 10.15.28.22 vrrp-vlan 28
controller 10.15.28.13 priority 128 vrrp-ip 10.15.28.23 vrrp-vlan 28
controller 10.15.28.14 priority 128 vrrp-ip 10.15.28.24 vrrp-vlan 28
controller 10.15.28.15 priority 128 vrrp-ip 10.15.28.25 vrrp-vlan 28
```

Since the cluster size is four, Cluster Manager creates four VRRP instances. It starts with VRID: 220 to 223 on each cluster member and assigns VRRP priority of 255 for its own VRRP (ex: 10.15.28.22, corresponding to C1). It subsequently subtracts 20 from the previous priority and assigns this to the next VIP.

VRIDs 220 to 255 are reserved for internal purpose. Do not use these VRIDs when enabling this feature.

- Each cluster member inserts its own VRRP IP in a RADIUS packet's NAS-IP field and sends this to the RADIUS server, for each client connecting to it. For C1, it is 10.5.28.22; for C2, it is 10.15.28.23, and so forth. The same NAS-IP is synced to a standby controller, as part of standby user entry replication.
- Suppose C1 is the A-UAC and C3 is the S-UAC for some client. AUTH on C1 uses 10.15.28.22 as the NAS-IP in the RADIUS packets. C1also updates C3—"the NAS-IP for this client is 10.15.28.22."
- When C1 goes down, C3 activates, and AUTH on C3 uses 10.15.28.22 as NAS-IP for all subsequent RADIUS packets. A C1 failure engages the VRRP failover process - C4 takes the ownership of vrrp-ip 10.15.28.22, since it has the next highest priority (235).
- Now, RADIUS server CoA/Disconnect/XML-API messages sent to 10.15.28.22 arrive at C4. C4 forwards the RADIUS message to ALL controllers in the cluster (except a down controller). C2 also receives and processes the message. Thus, CoA/XML-API messages are successfully processed, even when the original A-UAC is down.

VRRP validation (cont.)

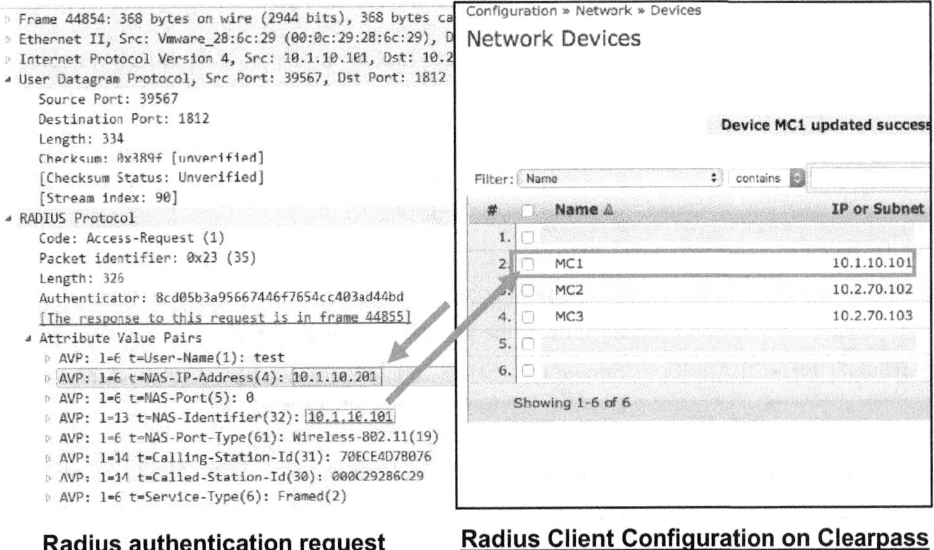

Figure 6-22 VRRP validation (cont.)

Figure 6-22 shows a packet capture, from NAS IP address 10.1.10.201. This is a RADIUS request from MC2 (10.1.10.101). Notice that the NAS-IP is the VRRP IP address—10.1.10.201.

The RADIUS client IP should be the real IP of the MCs.

Learning check

4. The RADIUS client IP should be VRRP IP address in VRRP configuration.
   a. True
   b. False

Clustering troubleshooting

Cluster formation issue

You have learned about the command `show lc-cluster group-membership`. It is especially useful for troubleshooting the status of cluster connections. Table 6-1 summarizes how to interpret the status output from this command.

Table 6-1 Cluster formation issue

Status	Reason
CONNECTED	All is good
INCOMPATIBLE	1. If two managed devices run different ArubaOS versions, a build string mismatch is found, and the managed devices are not part of the cluster. 2. There are four managed devices in a cluster (including a RAP), and you try to add another managed device, the "RAP cluster limit reached" error is displayed.
DISCONNECTED	1. No cluster members are in the CONNECTED state. 2. Physical connectivity issue between cluster members. 3. One of the ports is an untrusted node.
SECURE TUNNEL NEGOTIATING	Shown very briefly, until the IPsec tunnel is setup. If the status persists, there is an IPsec tunnel setup issue.
CONNECTED FROM SELF DISCONNECTED FROM PEER	MD1 and MD2 are connected. MD3 is later introduced in the cluster. MD1 and MD3 are connected, but MD2 and MD3 are not connected.

You see an actual output example below.

```
(host) [mynode] #show lc-cluster group-membership

Mon Dec 21 17:30:51.952 2015

Cluster Enabled, Profile Name = "6NodeCluster"

Redundancy Mode On

Active Client Rebalance Threshold = 50%

Standby Client Rebalance Threshold = 75%

Unbalance Threshold = 5%

Cluster Info Table

------------------

Type IPv4 Address Priority Connection-Type STATUS

---- --------------- -------- --------------- ------

self 10.15.116.3 128 N/A ISOLATED (Leader)

peer 10.15.116.4 128 L3-Connected CONNECTED-FROM-SELF-DISCONNECTED-FROM-PEERS

peer 10.15.116.5 128 L3-Connected CONNECTED-FROM-SELF-DISCONNECTED-FROM-PEERS
```

peer 10.15.116.8 128 L3-Connected CONNECTED-FROM-SELF-DISCONNECTED-FROM-PEERS

peer 10.15.116.9 128 N/A SECURE-TUNNEL-NEGOTIATING

Cluster not L2-connected

(MC)#show lc-cluster vlan-probe status

```
(MC-4) #show lc-cluster vlan-probe status

Cluster VLAN Probe Status
-------------------------
Type IPv4 Address     REQ-SENT REQ-FAIL ACK-SENT ACK-FAIL REQ-RCVD ACK-RCVD VLAN_FAIL CONN-TYPE
---- ---------------- -------- -------- -------- -------- -------- -------- --------- ---------
peer      10.1.10.100        0        0        1        0        1        0         0   L3 Conn
peer      10.1.10.101        0        0        1        0        1        0         0   L3 Conn
peer      10.1.10.102        0        0        1        0        1        0         0   L3 Conn
```

(MC)(config)# lc-cluster exclude-vlan <vlannumber>

Used to exclude unnecessary VLAN communications. This resolves "not-L2-connected" issues

Figure 6-23 Cluster not L2-connected

The `show lc-cluster vlan-probe status` command is used to check the VLAN probing status. Perhaps you are trying to deploy cluster members to be L2-connected, per best practices. However, although the members are on the same VLAN, the connection type shows as L3 connected. You see this in Figure 6-23, in the "CONN-TYPE" column.

Indeed, all cluster nodes are on management VLAN 10. However, an uplink port from one node permits VLAN 1 in the trunk port, but the other node does not. By default, cluster nodes test ALL VLANs for being on the same subnet. In this scenario, the connection type will be L3 because the two nodes cannot hear VLAN-probing on VLAN 1.

If you do not actually need VLAN 1 support, you can simply remove it from the configuration. However, if you do need VLAN 1 support on one of the controllers, you can use the command `lc-cluster exclude-vlan`, as shown in Figure 6-23. Once you exclude VLAN 1, the connection will immediately become an L2 connection.

Learning check

5. If the cluster member status is "INCOMPATIBLE", which two statements could be true?
   a. Cluster limit reached
   b. MCs run different ArubaOS versions
   c. MCs can hear heartbeat packet from peers
   d. Just a short period temporary status

7 Mobility

LEARNING OBJECTIVES

- ✓ This chapter provides an overview of mobility, before delving into legacy mobility. This includes Layer 2 and Layer 3 mobility solutions, configuration, and monitoring.
- ✓ You will then learn about cluster mobility examples and configurations, before exploring 802.11r technology and configuration.

Mobility overview

Roaming is what happens when a WLAN client device moves from one AP to another. This seamless movement is facilitated by 802.11 mobility standards. However, mobility becomes more complex when endpoints connect with tighter security mechanisms, based on 802.11i and 802.1X standards.

This is why Aruba introduced Layer 2 and Layer 3 mobility. This technology supports mobility within a single controller and mobility between multiple controllers.

It is well known that some WLAN endpoint devices simply do not roam very well, even when using a very high-quality WLAN solution. To alleviate this, the IEEE committee released the 802.11r standard, which relies on a technology called "BSS fast transition." HPE Aruba solutions support this standard. However, for this to work, client devices must also support the standard.

Mobility (roaming) overview

In the cellular world, there have always been handoff standards. Radios communicate with each other and coordinate handoffs. Base stations and handsets come from a small number of manufacturers and have tightly defined standards.

The 802.11 world evolved very differently. This is because early WLAN devices were computers and were not very mobile. In today's world, with smart phones and other devices, this has all changed. However, the standard 802.11 protocols have no provisions for roaming. The amendments in 802.11r were created to simplify roaming, for those end devices that support this standard.

Standard 802.11 mobility

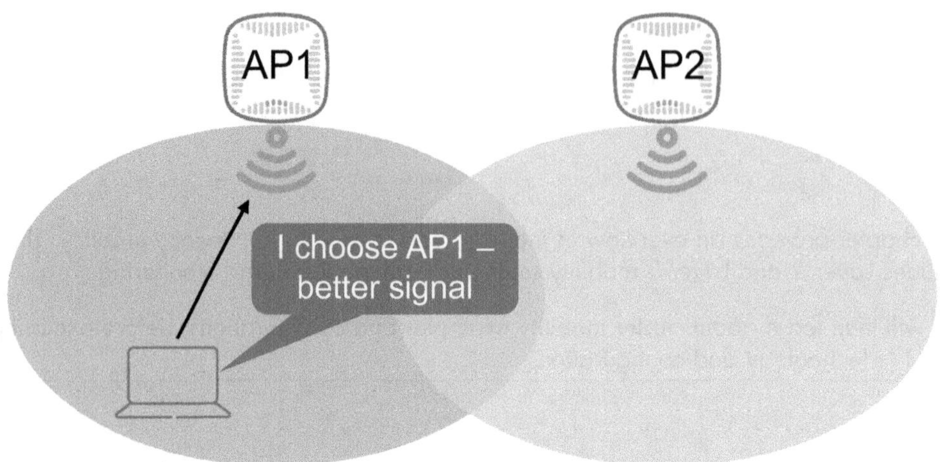

Figure 7-1 Initial client connectivity

With standard 802.11 roaming, clients form an initial AP association. This is typically to the closest AP—the one with the healthiest signal (Figure 7-1). Client devices often hold this AP association for as long as possible.

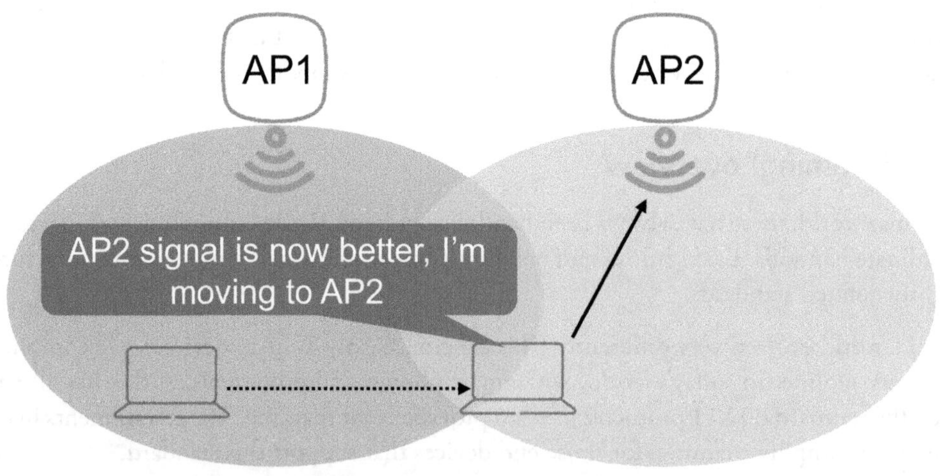

Figure 7-2 Standard 802.11 mobility

After this initial association, suppose the client begins to walk along a corridor. As this occurs, the signal to AP1 weakens, while the signal to AP2 grows stronger. When the error rates climb high enough, the client decides to drop the association with AP1 and associate with some new AP—AP2 in this example (Figure 7-2).

This example depicts a successful mobility event. This particular client device, like many client devices, was designed to roam well. Before the signal from their original AP becomes too weak, they re-associate to another AP.

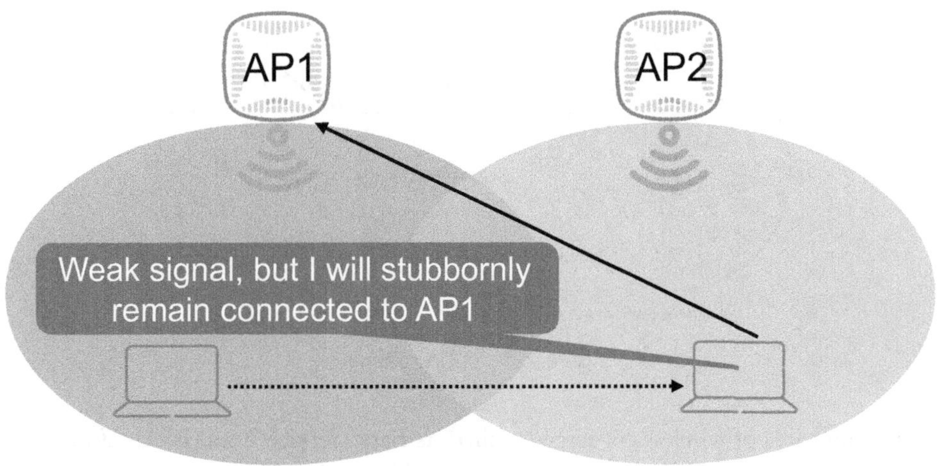

Figure 7-3 Some devices do not roam well

However, some devices lack such a design. In Figure 7-3, although the signal to AP1 is very weak, and the signal to AP2 is very strong, the client device simply refuses to move to another AP.

When roaming is not successful, clients can lose their connection, and all data sessions are interrupted. Clients must re-authenticate, get a new IP address, and so forth. This can be frustrating for end users. Many years ago, some vendors tried to improve this process by requiring proprietary software and/or clients.

Note

For many years, most Windows/Intel-based devices tended to roam quite well. However, certain smartphones and tablet devices did not roam very well at all. With standard 802.11 mobility, this can still hold true today. Later in this chapter, you will learn how this issue is being mitigated with newer standards.

Aruba mobility

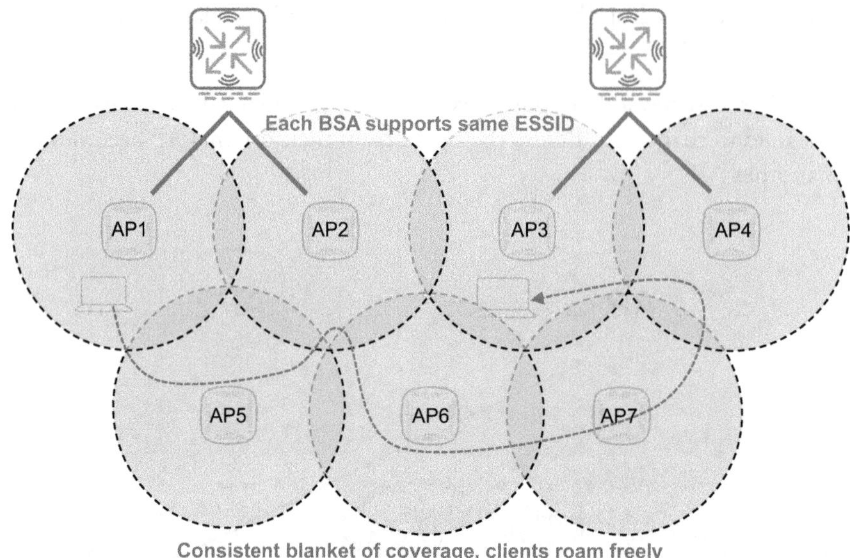

Figure 7-4 Aruba mobility

A single AP radio's area of wireless coverage is called its Basic Service Area (BSA). When installing a corporate-wide wireless network, you should position APs so that their BSAs overlap (Figure 7-4). Then make sure you configure the APs consistently, to support the same ESSID (commonly referred to as simply the SSID). In this way, you create an uninterrupted "blanket" of coverage. Clients can travel from one BSA to the next BSA without losing connectivity.

As the wireless client's signal to one AP weakens, the signal to another AP strengthens. At some point, the endpoint decides to move (roam) to the new AP. Service is uninterrupted, and there is little or no packet loss. For well-engineered client devices, on a well-designed WLAN system, this should reliably occur. Remember, the decision of whether and when to roam is made solely by the client device.

Some wireless devices may not be so well-engineered. The signal to their original AP has weakened, and there are other APs nearby with a very strong RF signal. Stubbornly, these devices will not roam to the new AP. Wireless Network Interface Cards (WNIC) that behave in this manor are referred to as "sticky".

Learning check

1. Which entity decides when a roaming event should occur?
    a. AP
    b. MM or Master
    c. MC or Local Controller
    d. The client device

Legacy mobility

Aruba centralized management

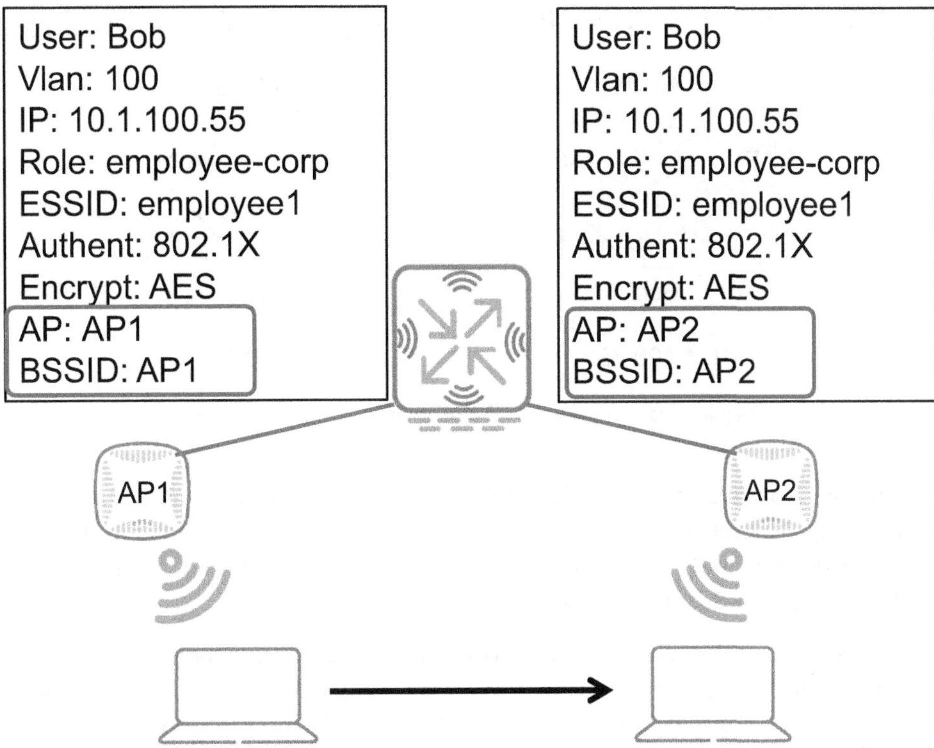

Figure 7-5 Aruba centralized management

Aruba's centralized management facilitates seamless client mobility. Therefore, when a client roams from one AP to another, it only changes radios. The controller maintains the state of authentication and encryption, while the client controls mobility (Figure 7-5).

In the previous two chapters, you learned how clustering facilitates redundant user mobility. You know that each client is assigned to a User Anchor Controller (UAC). Regardless of a client's connected AP, their traffic is always tunneled to the same controller—the A-UAC. This feature minimizes delays and packet drops associated with roaming events and makes for a more resilient solution.

Single controller mobility

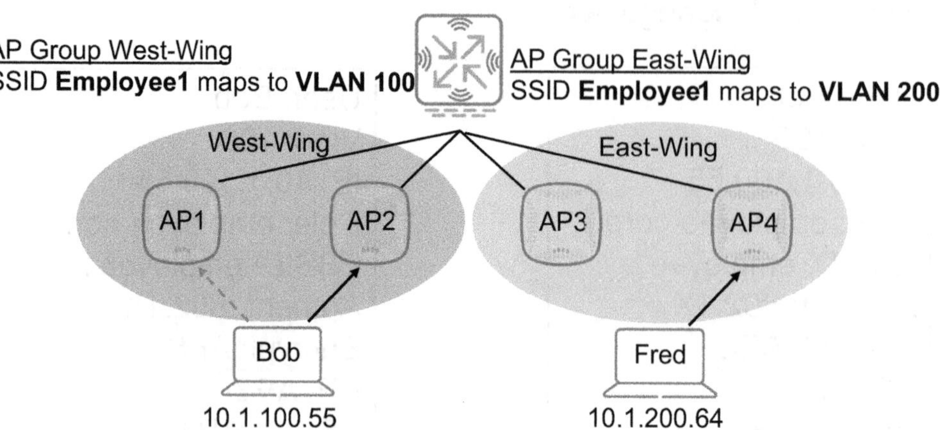

Figure 7-6 Single controller mobility—same AP group

When a client roams among one controller's APs, in the *same* AP group, that controller handles all mobility processing. The client retains its IP address, while the controller maintains Authentication, ACLs, flow classification, and state information. This is L2 roaming within a single controller. No special configuration is needed in this scenario.

Figure 7-6 shows that user Bob associated with AP1, then roamed to AP2, both in the West-Wing AP group. The record for Bob remains the same, other than being updated that he is now on AP2. The West-Wing AP group maps the employee1 SSID to VLAN 100. You can see that Bob has a VLAN 100 address of 10.1.100.55.

You also see that user Fred initially connected to an AP in the East-Wing group, which maps the same employee1 SSID to VLAN 200. Of course, Fred has a VLAN 200 address of 10.1.200.64.

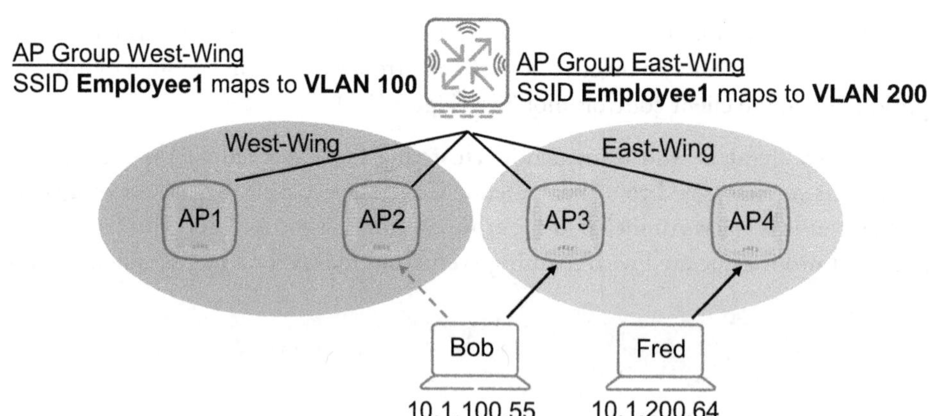

Figure 7-7 Single controller mobility—different AP group

Now, what if clients roam among one controller's APs in a *different* AP group. In Figure 7-7, Bob roams from AP2 to AP3, which is in the East-Wing group. This single controller has all client records, so there is no need to change Bob's subnet. Again, the controller changes nothing about Bob's record, other than indicating that he is now on AP3. Therefore, Bob retains the same VLAN and IP address, and seamless roaming is achieved.

Legacy inter-controller mobility

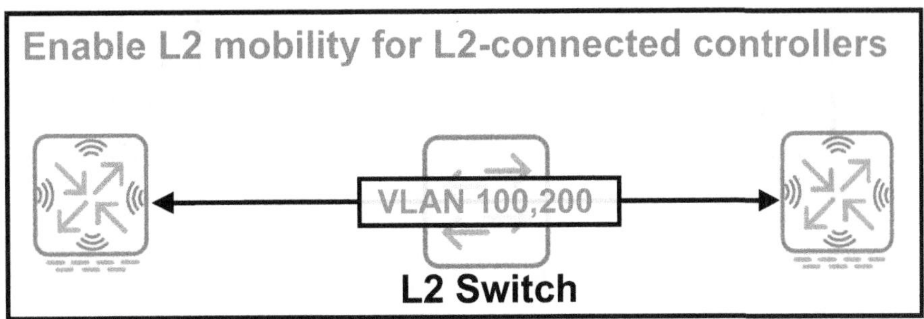

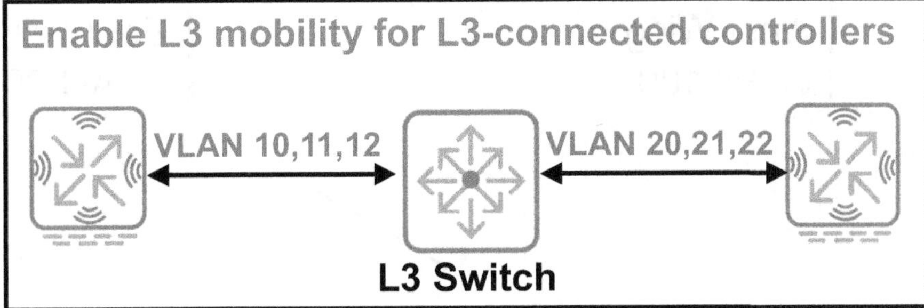

NEVER enable both L2 and L3 mobility on the same SSID

Figure 7-8 Legacy inter-controller mobility

AOS6.X and AOS8.0 both support legacy inter-controller mobility. You have two deployment options to support this scenario, as shown in Figure 7-8.

If all of your controllers are L2-connected, on the same subnet/VLAN, then you should enable L2 mobility. This may also be referred to as VLAN mobility. Today, it is less common that all controllers are L2-connected. This is because modern controllers are so scalable and can handle more APs. For example, the high-end 7200 controller can handle 2048 APs.

If controllers are deployed on different Layer 3 subnets, then you should enable L3 mobility. This is probably more representative of today's environments.

If you select L3 mobility, then you must disable L2 mobility. Both roaming scenarios should not run at the same time.

Legacy Layer 2 mobility

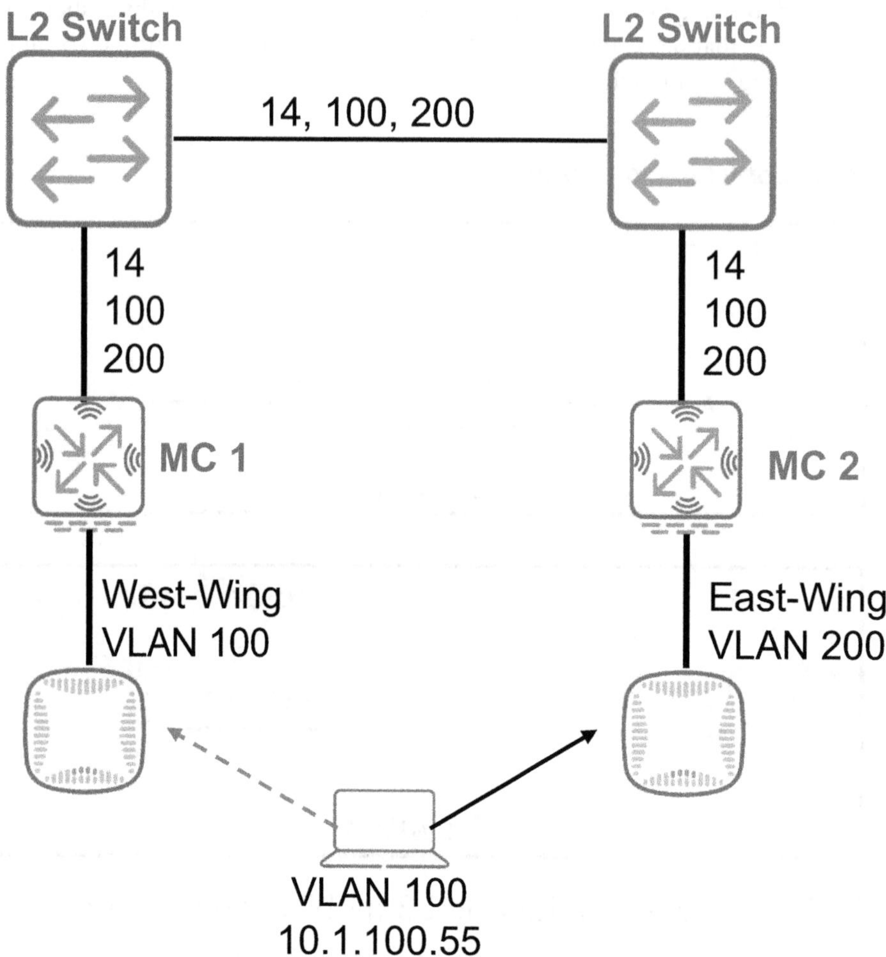

Figure 7-9 Legacy Layer 2 mobility

Figure 7-9 shows a legacy, L2 mobility scenario, with two controllers sharing the same subnets. Controller MC1's APs are members of the West-Wing group, and map the SSID to VLAN 100. Controller MC2's APs are members of the East-Wing group, and map the SSID to VLAN 200. VLANs 14, 100, and 200 are allowed to traverse the links between switches and MCs, as shown in Figure 7-9.

The client initially connects to the West-Wing AP and so is assigned a VLAN 100 address—10.1.100.55. This client then roams to an MC2 AP in the East-Wing group. The controller checks the ARP tables to determine the user's subnet. Assuming the controller finds the user, this is a seamless roaming event. The user maintains the same VLAN and subnet, and experiences no interruption of service.

Enabling legacy inter-controller L2 mobility

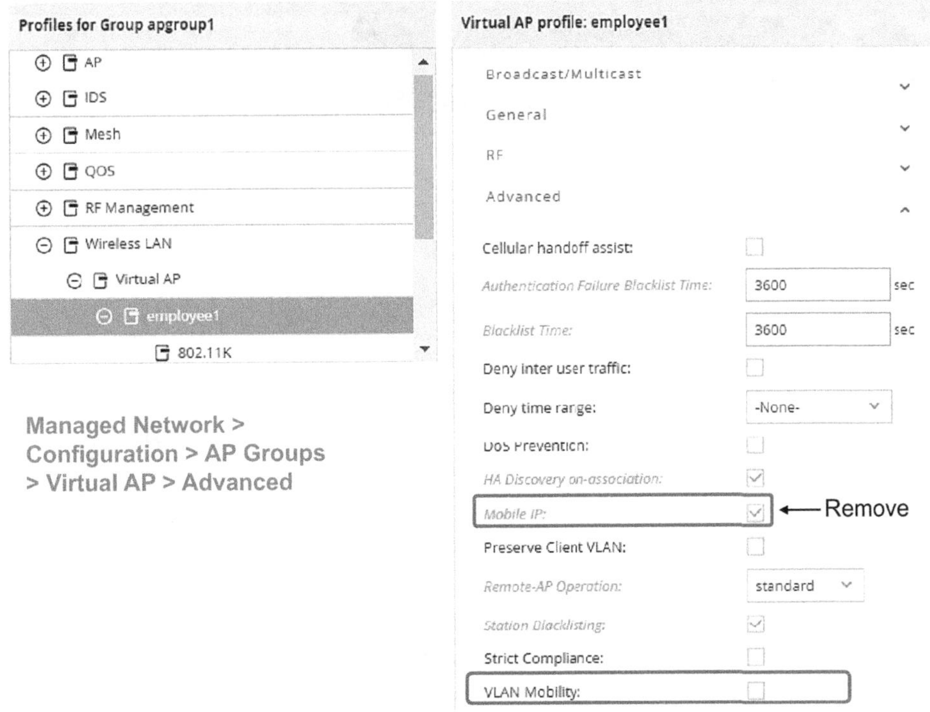

Figure 7-10 Enabling legacy inter-controller L2 mobility

You configure VLAN mobility between controllers on a per VAP basis (Figure 7-10). After all, you might want employees to be able to roam, but not guests.

In the VAP profile, enable VLAN mobility, and then remove the Layer 3 IP mobility. Remember, you should not have both L2 and L3 mobility enabled on the same VAP.

Legacy Layer 3 IP mobility

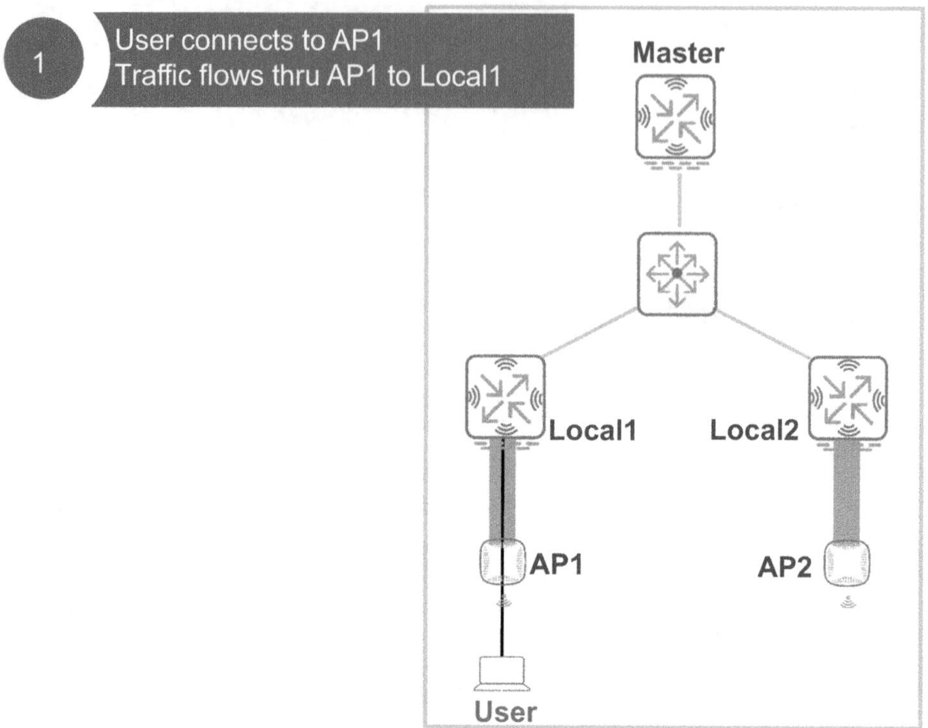

Figure 7-11 Legacy Layer 3 IP mobility

You should configure L3 mobility whenever your controllers are in different subnets. This is true if the controllers are not clustered. It is also true if they are clustered, but in different clusters.

In Figure 7-11, a user initially connects to an AP controlled by the Local1 MC. Local1 is, therefore, this user's "Home Agent" (HA). Suppose that the user's SSID maps to VLAN 100.

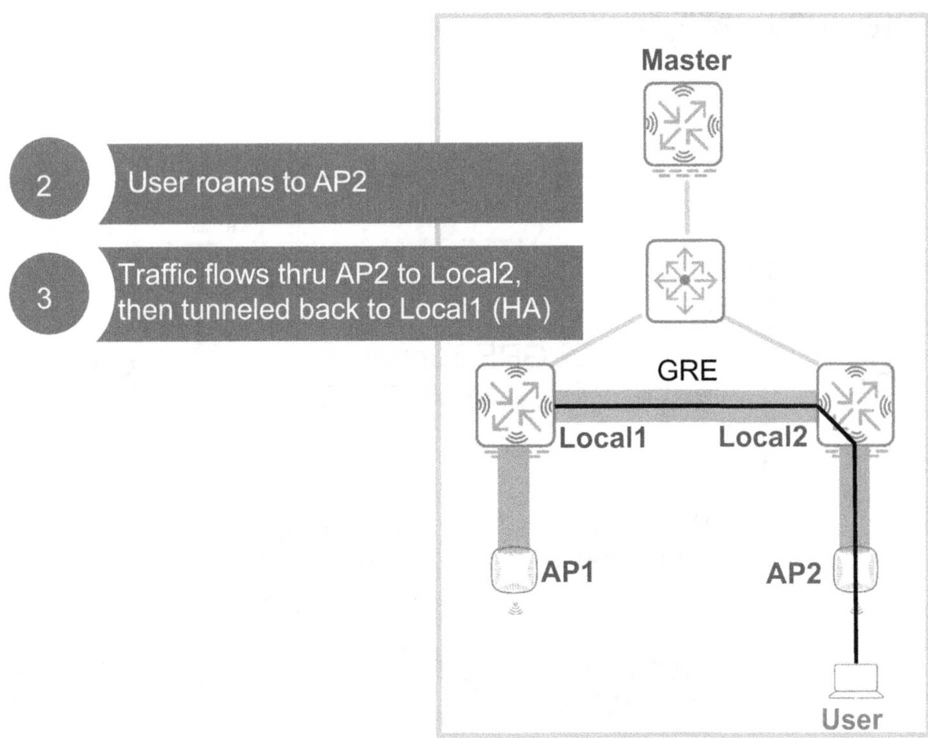

Figure 7-12 Legacy Layer 3 IP mobility

Then the user roams to AP2, controlled by the Local2 MC. Local2 serves as the "Foreign Agent" (FA) for this user (Figure 7-12). Local2 APs do not support VLAN 100 at all—they map the SSID to VLAN 200. Here is the issue. We must allow the user to keep their original IP address, or roaming will not be seamless. But how do we support a VLAN 100 user when they must exist on VLAN 200?

Local2 sees that the user has a VLAN 100 address, and from this determines that Local1 is this user's HA. Local2 and Local1 build mobile-IP tunnels, which are used to transmit client traffic back to the HA, where the user's VLAN is supported (Figure 7-12).

How does Local2 determine the user's HA as Local1? The FA discovers the HA by sending registration requests, "Who is the HA for VLAN 100?" The HA replies, "I am the HA for VLAN 100."

So a GRE tunnel is established between FA and HA. All this user's traffic is tunneled from AP2 to Local2, and then from FA Local2 to HA Local1. The HA unwraps the client's original frame and bridges the traffic toward its ultimate destination.

Legacy Layer 3 mobility example

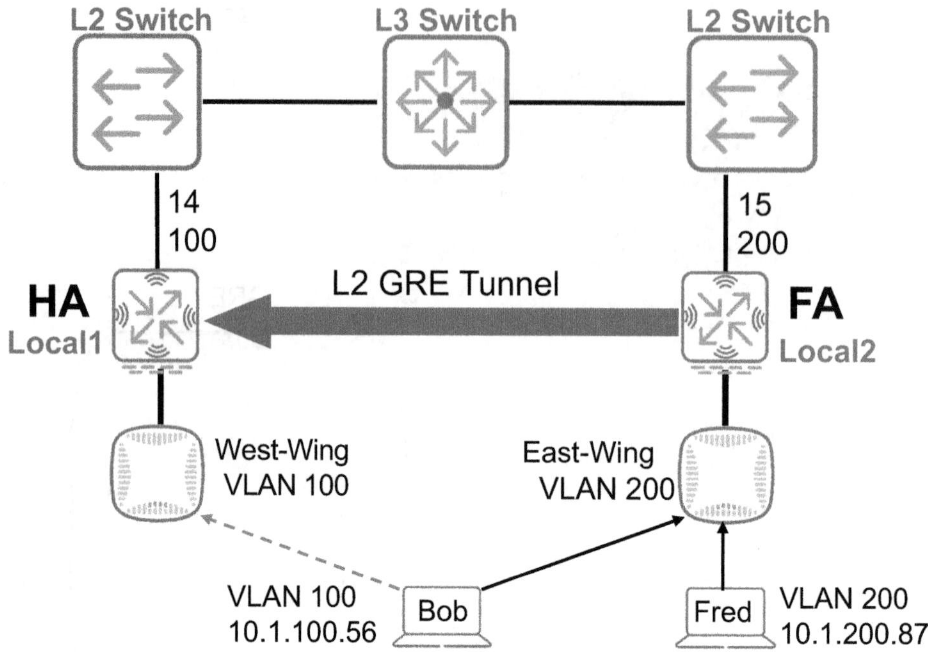

Figure 7-13 Legacy Layer 3 mobility example

Figure 7-13 shows an IP Mobility scenario in a legacy, AOS 6.x deployment. Bob initially connects to AP1, and so Local1 is the HA. Then Bob roams to AP2, and so Local2 becomes his FA.

To ensure seamless roaming, this user's traffic is tunneled from FA to HA. The HA then forwards the client's original packet on toward its ultimate destination.

To achieve this, both controllers must maintain L2 and L3 table entries for the user. This increases the load on each controller. Also, client traffic must first be forwarded to the HA and traverse the L2 GRE to or from the FA. This creates a suboptimal path with added delay.

Firewall rules on the HA are preserved—traffic tunneled from FA to HA is still run through the HA firewall policy.

Mobility domain roaming

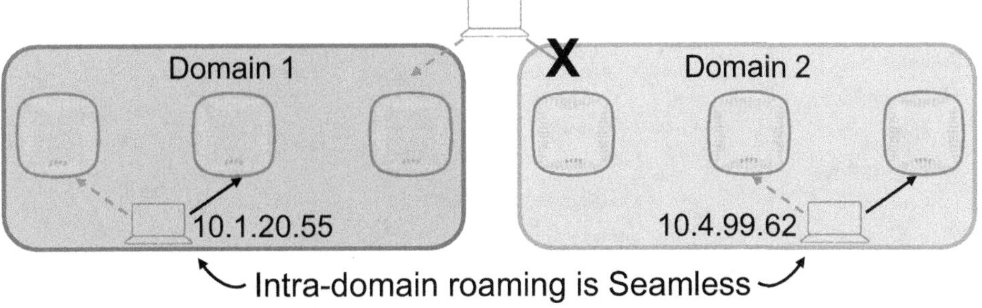

Figure 7-14 Mobility domain roaming

Mobility domains define a boundary for roaming clients. For large deployments, it may not be efficient (or even necessary) for users to roam the entire network. For example, suppose that a university has 5000 students. They awake in the morning and associate their devices to dorm room APs, which map them to dorm room subnets.

Later, they all roam to various areas of the main campus, maintaining their original subnet addressing. This may not be the best design. You could choose to ensure that roaming among the dorms is OK, and roaming about the campus is fine. However, roaming between the dorm and campus is not necessary.

To facilitate your design, you can define mobility domains, as shown in Figure 7-14. While a managed device *can* be part of multiple mobility domains, this is not recommended. A managed device should belong to only one domain. Devices in a mobility domain need not be managed by the same Mobility Master.

You configure mobility domains on a Mobility Master, which pushes this information to all its managed devices. You must configure each managed device with the active domain to which it belongs. Otherwise, it will be assigned to a predefined "default" domain.

In AOS6.4, you configure a mobility domain on the master controller. Please see the AOS6.X user guide for details.

Intra-domain roaming is seamless—users keep their IP addresses and access rules, without need for re-authentication.

However, inter-domain roaming is not seamless. When roaming between domains, the device is seen as a new device. It must re-authenticate, get a new IP address, and be reassigned to a firewall role.

Configure legacy inter-controller L3 mobility

Define L3 domain and Home Agents Table (HAT)

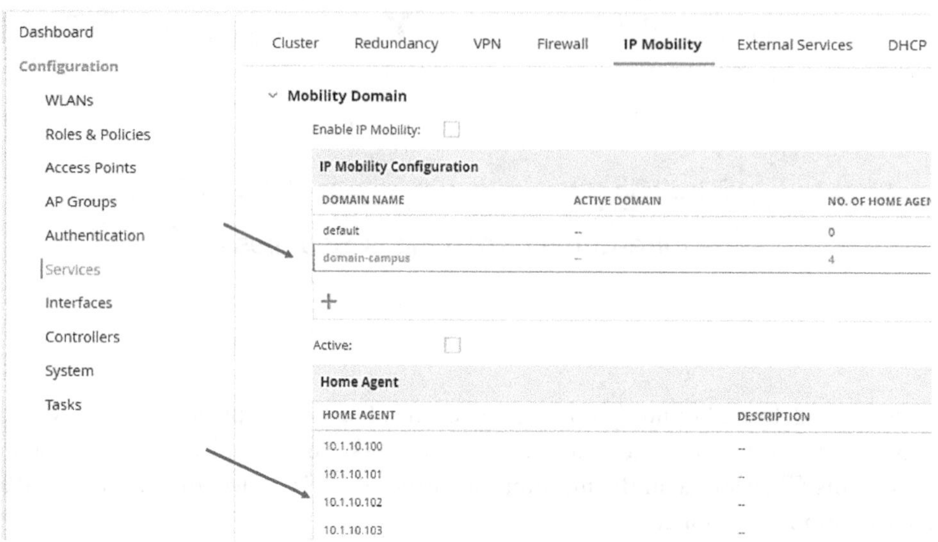

Figure 7-15 Define L3 domain and HAT

Figure 7-15 summarizes the configuration of legacy, inter-controller L3 mobility. You navigate to **Managed Network > Configuration > Services > IP Mobility**.

Then create a new IP mobility domain, and define the Home Agents Table (HAT). The HAT maps a set of VLANs to the correct HA. In our previous examples, you would configure the controller named "Local1" as the HA for VLAN 100, and Local2 as the HA for VLAN 200.

The domains are then pushed to every controller managed by this Mobility Master. Controllers receive the HAT when the feature is enabled. Thus, when a controller must act as an FA, it knows which controller is the HA for that client's VLAN.

Enable IP mobility per MC

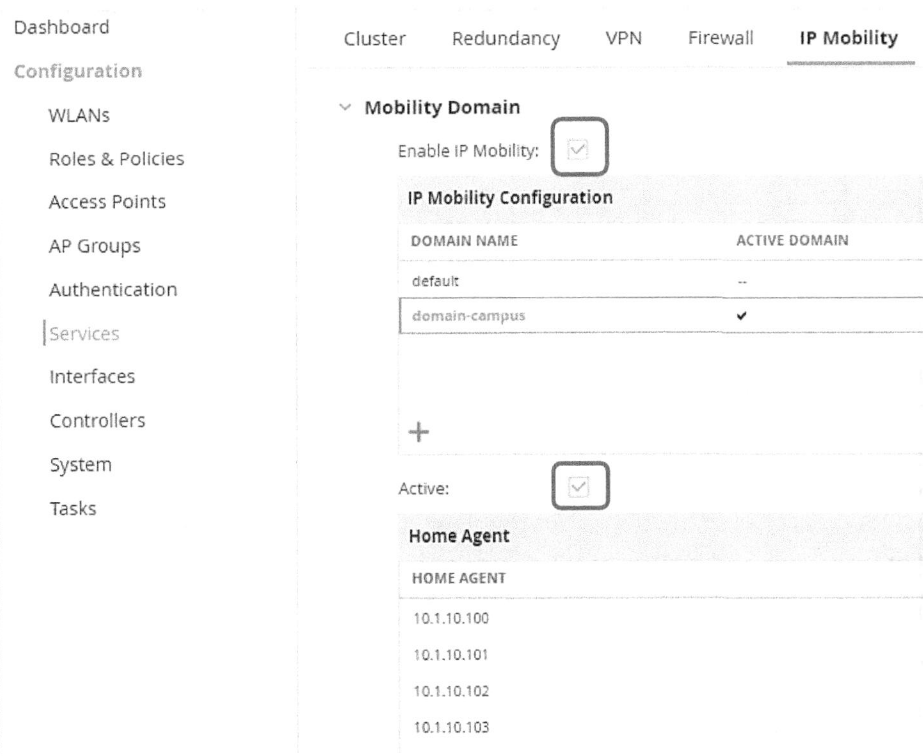

Figure 7-16 Enable IP mobility per MC

IP mobility must be enabled on EVERY MC (Figure 7-16). This feature is NOT enabled by default. You must enable all domains in the domain list on each MC.

Enable mobile IP per VAP

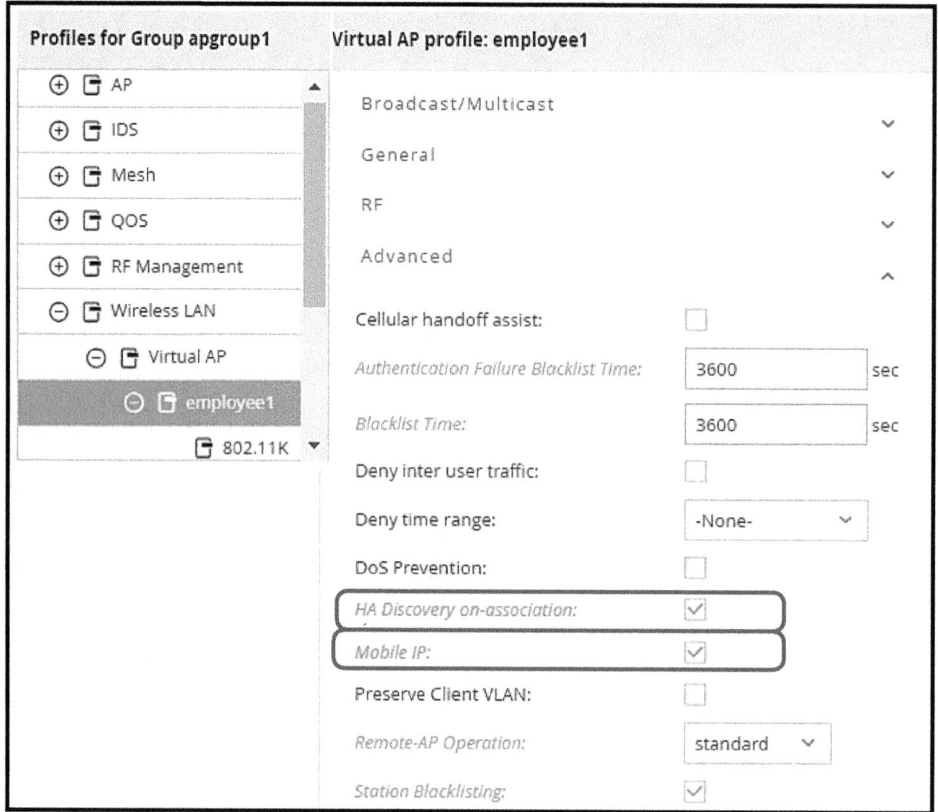

Figure 7-17 Enable mobile IP per VAP

You have configured domains and HAT tables and enabled the domains on each MC (Figure 7-17). Now you can select which VAPs (SSIDs) in each AP-group should use IP mobility. Simply navigate to **Managed Network > Configuration > AP Groups > Wireless LAN > Virtual AP**. Then check the Mobile IP checkbox.

In this example, you enable IP mobility on the employee VAP, in the AP-group named apgroup1. However, you will not enable it on the guest VAP.

Note that "HA discovery on-association" is enabled by default. This means that controllers automatically discover HAs in a more proactive manner. Here is how it works:

A device roams away from the HA and re-associates to an FA's AP. This roaming event triggers the FA to send a unicast request to all controllers in the domain. Thus, the FA finds the HA, which has the client's IP mobility state information. The FA-HA tunnel is thus formed, prior to the client generating traffic.

Without this "HA Discovery on-association" option, the FA waits to discovery the HA and form the tunnel until the device send an IP packet.

Note

Users in the deployment environment may have multiple devices, many of which are carried in their pockets. These devices connect, but rarely get pulled out of a user's pocket. This is often the case with students in a school that have a phone, a tablet, and a laptop. In special cases like this, you might consider leaving the "HA discovery on-association" feature disabled.

Monitor mobile clients

You can use the `show user` command to monitor client status. This command shows which clients are associated, along with their address information, assigned role, and connected AP. The "Roaming" column also indicates client roaming status.

In the following example, you can tell that MC-2 is the home agent, and that this client is not "home." The roaming status is "Away." Therefore, you know that a tunnel is formed from the FA to the MC-2 HA.

```
(MC-2)# show user

This operation can take a while depending on number of users. Please be
patient....

Users

-----

 IP          MAC                  Name       Role                   Age(d:h:m)    Auth

---------   ------------          -----      ----                   ----------    ----

10.1.11.50  48:e9:f1:34:c9:95                authenticated          00:00:17

VPN link    AP name               Roaming    Essid/Bssid/Phy

--------    -------               -------    ---------------

            AP2                   Away       employee1/94:b4:0f:a0:bf:d0/a-HT
```

In the following example, you can tell that MC-1 is the FA for this client. The client's addressing information is the same, and its roaming status is "Visitor."

```
(MC-1)# show user
```

```
This operation can take a while depending on number of users. Please be
patient....

Users

-----

   IP      MAC                  Name                    Role

--------- ------------         -----                   ----

10.1.11.50 48:e9:f1:34:c9:95                           sys_mip_role_43a894_24

Age(d:h:m) Auth    VPN link   AP name      Roaming   Essid/Bssid/Phy

---------- ----    --------   -------      -------   ---------------

00:00:17   AP2     Vistor     employee1/94:b4:0f:a0:bf:d0/a-HT
```

Clustering mobility

L2 clustering mobility overview

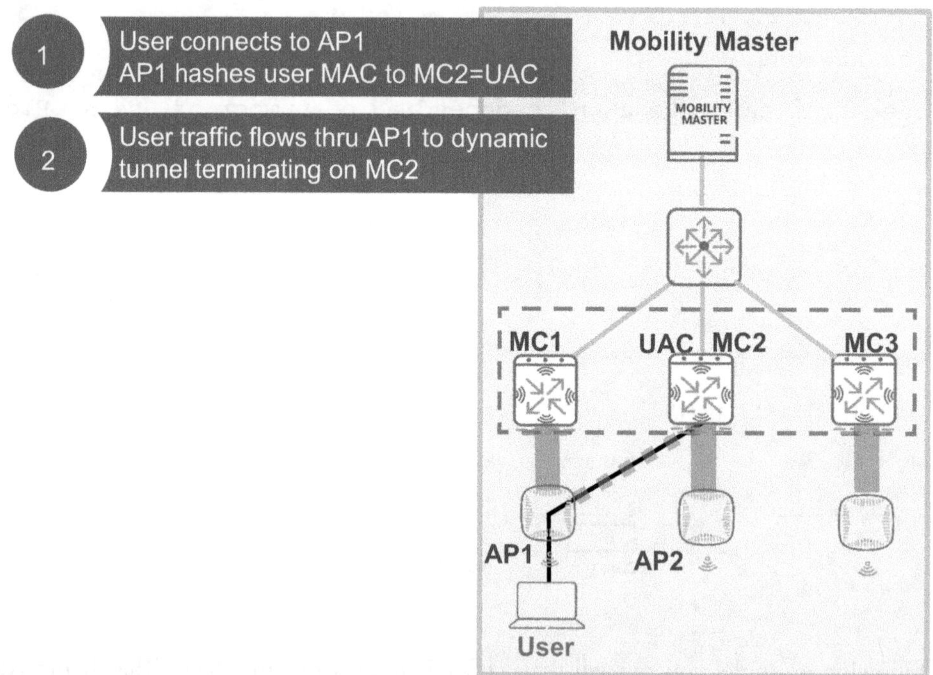

Figure 7-18 L2 clustering mobility overview

In 8.x, user state and traffic remain on the same controller, regardless of where they roam. Each user has a UAC to serve this purpose, as you learned in Chapters 5 and 6.

Suppose that the user originally connects to AP1. AP1 hashes the user MAC address and assigns MC2 as its UAC. Thus, AP1 forms a tunnel directly to MC2 for this user (Figure 7-18).

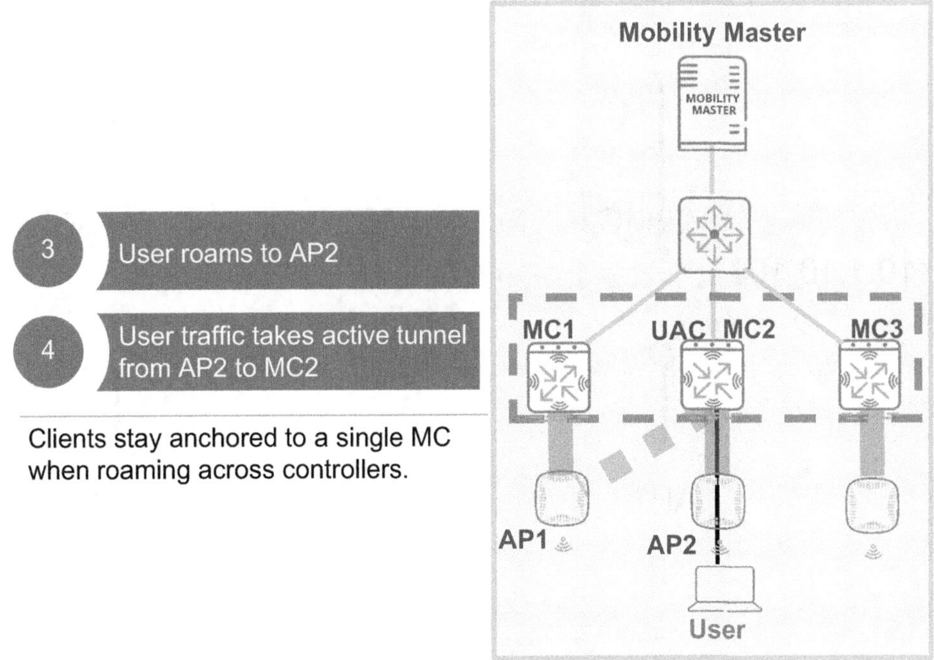

Figure 7-19 L2 clustering mobility overview (Cont.)

As the user roams to APs controlled by MC2 or MC3, nothing changes for the user. APs simply form a tunnel to MC2 for that user. MC2 (and only MC2) maintains that user's L2/L3 session information (Figure 7-19).

The path is always optimal, and delays are always minimal. Users have a stable, high-quality, seamless roaming experience, regardless of their point of attachment.

Note

Cluster configurations and legacy IP mobility are mutually exclusive.

Clustering mobility example (L2 or L3)

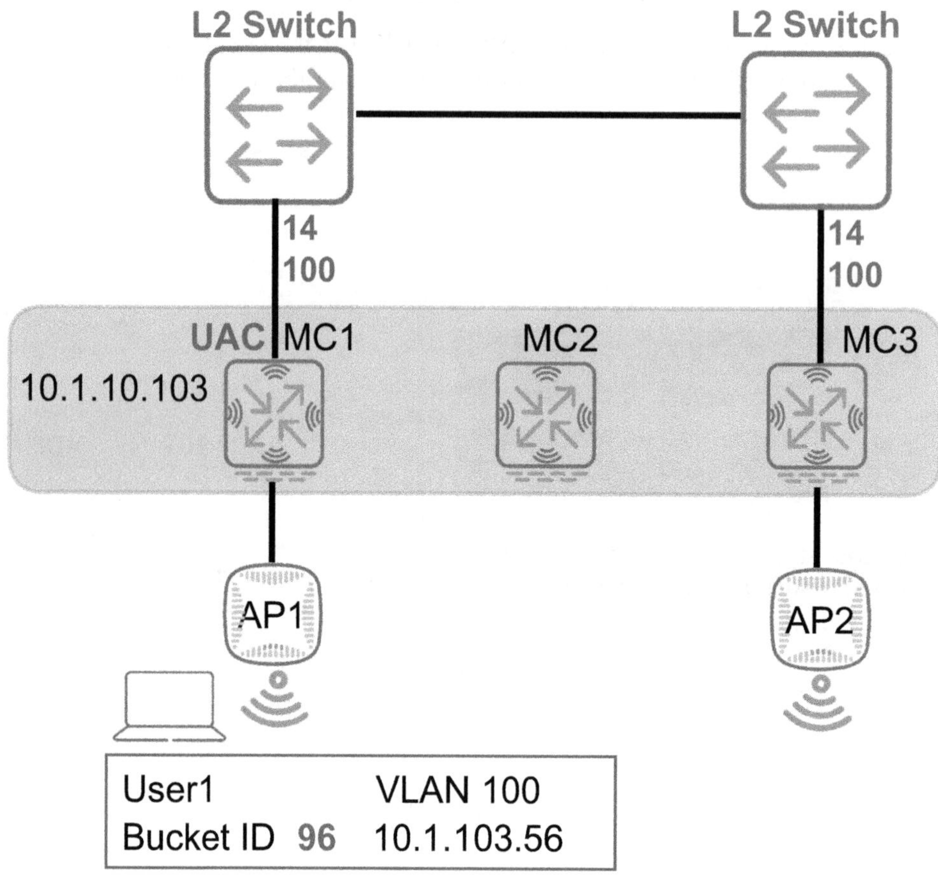

Figure 7-20 Clustering mobility example (L2 or L3)

In this scenario, User1 initially connects to AP1. AP1 hashes the client's MAC address, derives Bucket ID 96, and assigns MC1 to serve as this client's UAC (Figure 7-20).

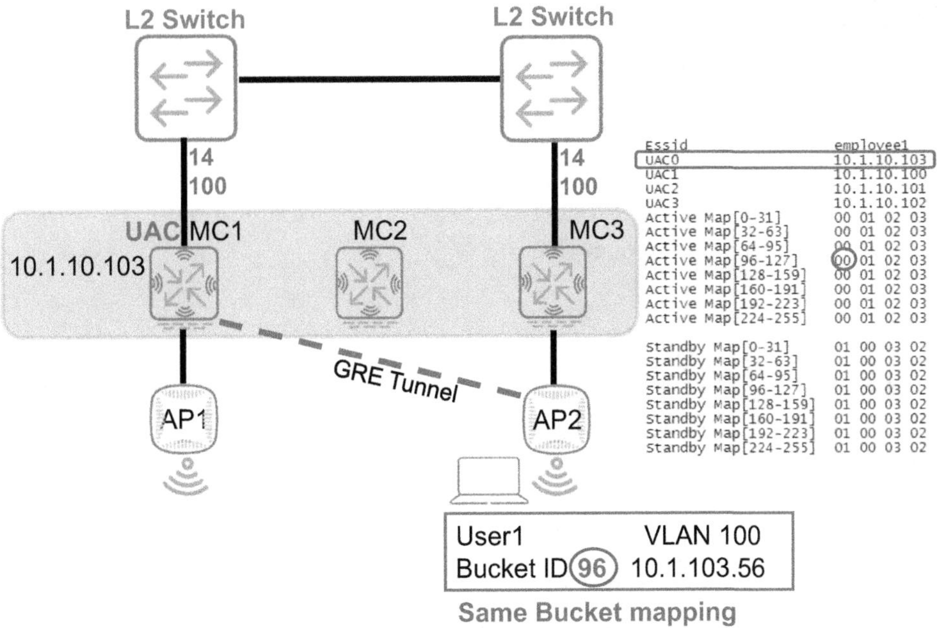

Figure 7-21 Clustering mobility example (L2 or L3)

Next, User1 roams from to AP2 which is controlled by MC3. MC1 and MC3 are in the same cluster, so they share an identical bucket map (Figure 7-21).

AP2 performs the same hash algorithm, and so derives the same BUCKET ID and UAC. Thus, AP2 establishes a GRE tunnel to MC1. All User1 traffic flows directly to MC1—its UAC. As shown, MC1's IP address is 10.1.10.103

Since MC1 and MC3 are L2-connected, this can be referred to as L2 mobility (roaming).

If MC1 and MC3 were L3-connected, roaming still functions. However, you would refer to this as L3 roaming.

Monitor clusters

```
show aaa cluster essid-all user
Active Users for ESSID : employee1
-----------------------------------
BUCKET  MAC                IP          Active UAC   Standby UAC
------  ---                --          ----------   -----------
66      a4:31:35:8d:63:ac  10.1.11.53  10.1.10.101  10.1.10.102
78      48:e9:f1:0a:ef:ab  10.1.11.55  10.1.10.101  10.1.10.102
94      a4:31:35:80:5b:85  10.1.11.54  10.1.10.101  10.1.10.100
206     7c:fa:df:b5:f0:8b  10.1.11.58  10.1.10.101  10.1.10.100
218     2c:1f:23:cc:c1:d7  10.1.11.56  10.1.10.101  10.1.10.103
226     2c:1f:23:bf:eb:b6  10.1.11.57  10.1.10.101  10.1.10.103

show aaa cluster essid-all bucketmap
------------------------------------------------------------
Item                 Value
----                 -----
Essid                employee1
UAC0                 10.1.10.103
UAC1                 10.1.10.100
UAC2                 10.1.10.101
UAC3                 10.1.10.102
Active Map[0-31]     00 01 02 03 00 01 02 03 00 01 02 03 00 01 02 03 00 01 02 03 00 01 02 03 00 01 02 03 00 01 02 03
Active Map[32-63]    00 01 02 03 00 01 02 03 00 01 02 03 00 01 02 03 00 01 02 03 00 01 02 03 00 01 02 03 00 01 02 03
Active Map[64-95]    00 01 02 03 00 01 02 03 00 01 02 03 00 01 02 03 00 01 02 03 00 01 02 03 00 01 02 03 00 01 02 03
Active Map[96-127]   00 01 02 03 00 01 02 03 00 01 02 03 00 01 02 03 00 01 02 03 00 01 02 03 00 01 02 03 00 01 02 03
Active Map[128-159]  00 01 02 03 00 01 02 03 00 01 02 03 00 01 02 03 00 01 02 03 00 01 02 03 00 01 02 03 00 01 02 03
Active Map[160-191]  00 01 02 03 00 01 02 03 00 01 02 03 00 01 02 03 00 01 02 03 00 01 02 03 00 01 02 03 00 01 02 03
Active Map[192-223]  00 01 02 03 00 01 02 03 00 01 02 03 00 01 02 03 00 01 02 03 00 01 02 03 00 01 02 03 00 01 02 03
Active Map[224-255]  00 01 02 03 00 01 02 03 00 01 02 03 00 01 02 03 00 01 02 03 00 01 02 03 00 01 02 03 00 01 02 03

Standby Map[0-31]    03 03 03 02 03 03 03 02 03 03 03 02 03 03 03 02 03 03 03 02 03 03 03 02 03 03 03 02 03 03 03 02
Standby Map[32-63]   03 03 03 02 03 03 03 02 03 03 03 02 03 03 03 02 03 03 03 02 03 03 03 02 03 03 03 02 03 03 03 02
Standby Map[64-95]   03 03 03 02 03 03 03 02 03 03 03 02 03 03 03 02 03 03 03 02 03 02 01 02 02 02 01 02 02 02 01 02
Standby Map[96-127]  02 02 01 02 02 02 01 02 02 02 01 02 02 02 01 02 02 02 01 02 02 02 01 02 02 02 01 02 02 02 01 02
Standby Map[128-159] 02 02 01 02 02 02 01 02 02 02 01 02 02 02 01 01 01 00 01 01 01 00 01 01 01 00 01 01 01 00 01 01
Standby Map[160-191] 01 00 01 01 01 00 01 01 01 00 01 01 01 00 01 01 01 00 01 01 01 00 01 01 01 00 01 01 01 00 01 01
Standby Map[192-223] 01 00 01 01 01 00 01 01 01 00 01 01 01 00 01 01 03 00 00 00 03 00 00 00 03 00 00 00 03 00 00 00
Standby Map[224-255] 03 00 00 00 03 00 00 00 03 00 00 00 03 00 00 00 03 00 00 00 03 00 00 00 03 00 00 00 03 00 00 00
```

Figure 7-22 Monitor clusters

To view a list of clients and with key cluster information, use the command `show aaa cluster essid-all user`. Figure 7-22 shows the users associated with the SSID named employee1. You see each user's MAC and IP addresses, their bucket ID, along with active and standby UAC.

You can see the actual bucket map with the command `show aaa cluster essid-all bucketmap`.

Learning check

2. Which statement is correct about the comparison between clustering mobility and legacy mobility?
    a. With L3 IP mobility, client traffic is tunneled to the same controller, regardless of connected AP
    b. VLAN mobility can keep user data terminated on same controller
    c. Clustering does not support L3 roaming
    d. Clustering mobility is seamless

802.11r (Fast BSS Transition)

IEEE 802.11r

- Initially, full 802.1X authentication
- Keys distributed to AP and client
- OKC or 802.11r caches these keys

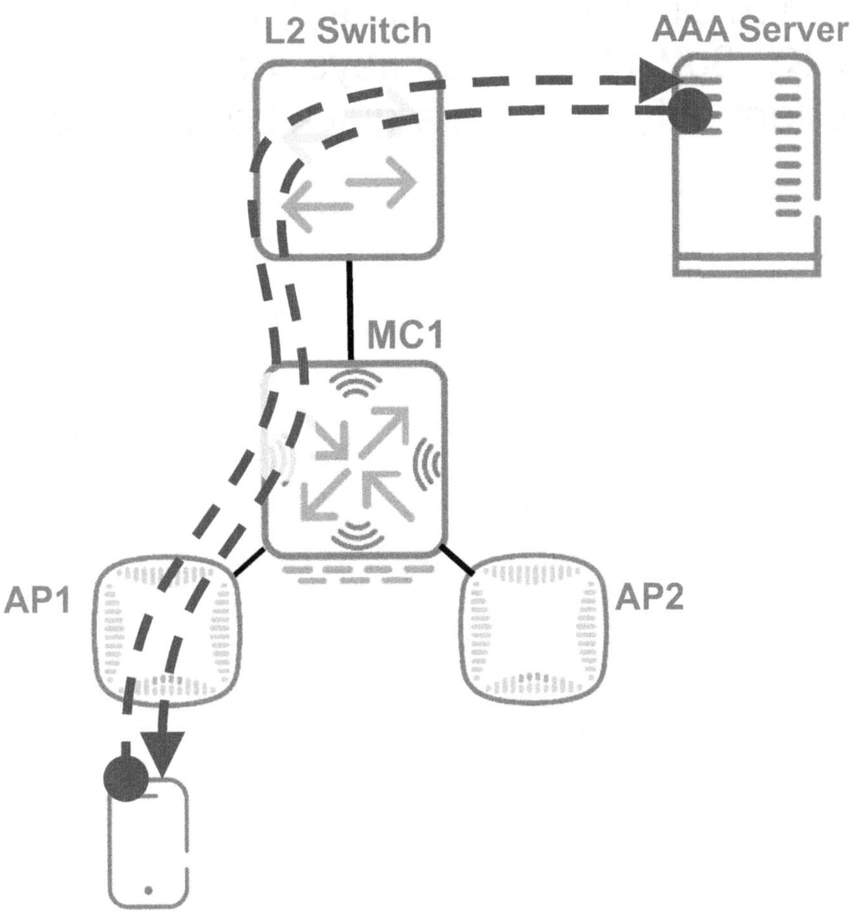

Figure 7-23 Keys are cached upon initial authentication

When clients roam between APs they must re-authenticate, which causes delays. These delays must be mitigated to provide seamless roaming.

Look at Figure 7-23. Upon initial client connection, full 802.1X or PSK authentication is performed, and keys are derived. These keys are distributed to endpoint and AP, to be used for frame encryption and hashing. A feature called Opportunistic Key Caching (OKC) caches these keys, in preparation for potential roaming events. OKC has been around for many years and often works fine. However, it is not standardized and has limitations.

This is why the IEEE committee defined the 802.11r standard, using a technology called BSS Fast Transition. Like OKC, it caches keys to facilitate fast roaming. Unlike OKC, it is a well-defined standard.

- When client roams, full auth not required
- OKC/802.11r cached keys are used
- Client only requires a quick handshake

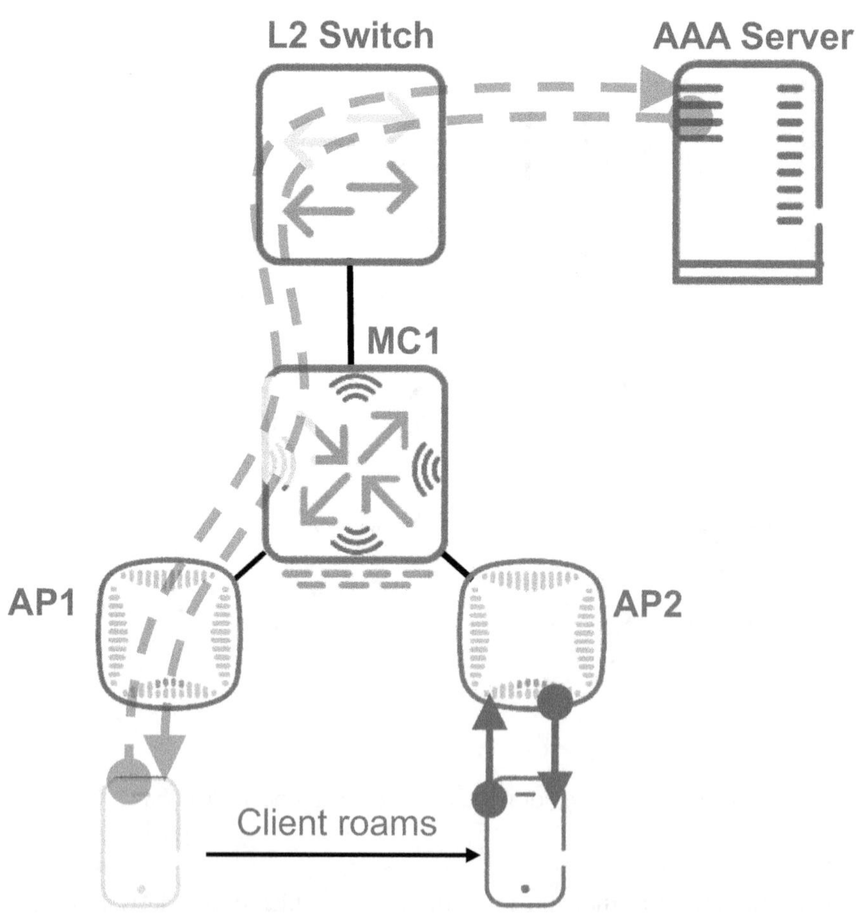

Figure 7-24 IEEE 802.11r

So OKC or 802.11r caches the keys generated from the initial authentication. Thus, when a client roams to another AP, they need not perform a full authentication. With just a quick four-way handshake they are accepted to the new AP. Seamless roaming = happy users.

However, OKC typically only functions for intra-controller roams. And while OKC is supported by most vendors, it is not a standard, so there could be device-to-network incompatibilities, which could cause unhappy users.

You might be able to deploy the 802.11r standard, instead of OKC, which can eliminate these issues and improve roaming performance. Standard 802.11r allows client stations to establish security and QoS at the target AP, prior to or during re-association. This reduces connection delays. You can research 802.11r standards online for additional information.

Note

Aruba only supports 802.11r for Tunnel Mode and Decrypt-Tunnel Mode. AOS only supports 802.11r Over the Air (OTA) mode. It does not support Over the Distribution System (OTDS) mode. (The term "Distribution System" merely means "the wired network"). Also, some client devices may not yet support 802.11r. The older the device, the less likely it is to support 802.11r.

802.11r configuration

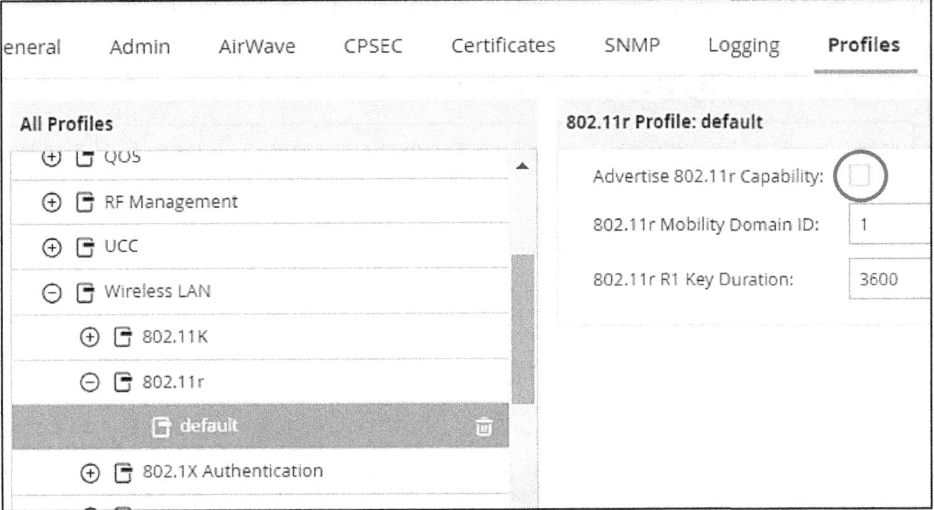

Figure 7-25 802.11r configuration

The following summarizes 802.11r configuration via the GUI.

1. Navigate to **Configuration > System > Profiles.**
2. In the All Profiles list, expand the Wireless LAN menu, then select 802.11r.
3. Select an existing 802.11r profile to edit. Click + to create a new Profile, enter a name.
4. Configure the following 802.11r radio settings:
   a. Choose the Advertise 802.11r Capability option to allow VAPs to advertise 802.11r capability (Figure 7-25).
   b. Enter the mobility domain ID (1-65535) in the 802.11r Mobility Domain ID field. Default = 1.

Note

Fast Transition roaming is only supported between APs in the same Mobility Domain on the same controller. You can configure the mobility domain in the 80.211r profile, and map it in the controller's SSID profile. Thus, all clients connected to the same SSID, roaming among APs on the same controller, are a part of the same Mobility Domain.

5. Enter the R1 Key timeout value in seconds (60-86400) for decrypt-tunnel or bridge mode in the 802.11r R1 Key Duration field. The default value is 3600.
6. Click Save. Then click Pending Changes.
7. In the Pending Changes window, select the check box and click Deploy Changes.

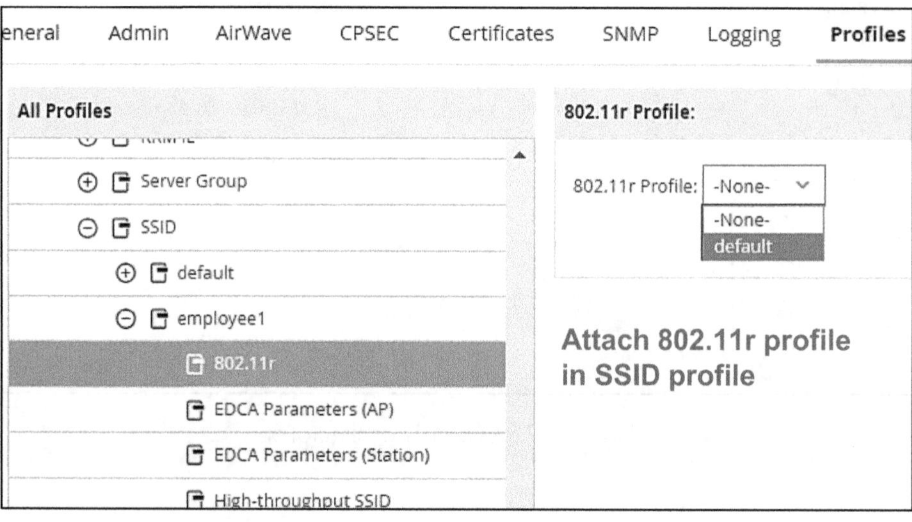

Figure 7-26 802.11r configuration (Cont.)

8. Navigate to SSID profile, choose the 802.11r profile under SSID profile. Click Submit (Figure 7-26).
9. Click Pending Changes.
10. In the Pending Changes window, select the check box and click Deploy Changes.

Note

802.11r supports Master-Local or Clustering deployment.

Validate client support for 802.11r

show ap association (On MC)

```
The phy column shows client's operational capabilities for current association

Flags: A: Active, B: Band Steerable, H: Hotspot(802.11u) client, K: 802.11K client, M: Mu beam formee, R: 802.11R client,

PHY Details: HT   : High throughput;      20: 20MHz;  40: 40MHz; t: turbo-rates (256-QAM)
             VHT  : Very High throughput; 80: 80MHz; 160: 160MHz; 80p80: 80MHz + 80MHz
             <n>ss: <n> spatial streams

Association Table
-----------------
Name  bssid              mac                auth  assoc  aid  l-int  essid      vlan-id  tunn       hy               assoc.
----  -----              ---                ----  -----  ---  -----  -----      -------  ----       --               ------
AP1   00:24:6c:13:c7:a8  a4:31:35:80:5b:85  y     y      4    20     employee1  11       0x10       -HT-40sgi-1ss    20s
AP1   00:24:6c:13:c7:a8  48:e9:f1:0a:ef:ab  y     y      2    20     employee1  11       0x10       -HT-40sgi-1ss    24s
AP1   00:24:6c:13:c7:a8  a4:31:35:8d:63:ac  y     y      3    20     employee1  11       0x1000d    a-HT-40sgi-1ss   24s
AP1   00:24:6c:13:c7:a8  2c:1f:23:bf:eb:b6  v     v      1    20     employee1  11       0x1000d    a-HT-40sgi-1ss   24s

 phy             assoc. time  num assoc  Flags  Band
 ---             -----------  ---------  -----  -----
 a-HT-40sgi-1ss  20s          1          WVRAB  0/0
 a-HT-40sgi-1ss  24s          1          WRAB   0/0
 a-HT-40sgi-1ss  24s          1          WVRAB  0/0
 a-HT-40sgi-1ss  24s          1          WRAB   0/0
```

Figure 7-27 Validate client support for 802.11r

Not all wireless clients support 802.11r. You might even experience different results for the same hardware running on a different OS version (Figure 7-27). To validate client 802.11r support, use the command `show ap association`.

If clients have an "R" in the flags column, they support 802.11r.

Learning check

3. 802.11r is also useful for a WPA2-personal SSID.
   a. True
   b. False

8 Advanced Security

LEARNING OBJECTIVES

✓ This chapter focuses on advanced security concepts and configuration. You will learn about RADIUS authentication and Extensible Authentication Protocols (EAP) termination options, before exploring machine authentication and client blacklisting.

✓ Next, you will engage with global firewall settings, Access Control Lists (ACL), and Authentication, Authorization, and Accounting (AAA) profiles. The chapter ends with a discussion of best practices, as relates to certificates.

Multiple RADIUS servers and AAA fast connect

Advantage of multiple RADIUS servers

For some deployments, a single RADIUS authentication server will suffice. However, many larger, more mission-critical deployments will benefit from multiple RADIUS servers. This can increase redundancy and scalability, with load balancing.

Server list order—fall through

To facilitate these redundancy and scalability advantages, you define a server group. You define server members in an ordered list. The first server in the list is always used by default, unless it is unavailable, in which case the next server in the list is used (Figure 8-1). In other words, the process "falls through" to the next server. You can use the WebUI to configure the server order. Select a server, then use the up or down arrows to position it.

Understand that in Figure 8-1, the first server, RADIUS-1, was unavailable and did not respond; therefore, the next server was used. However, if the first server is available and responds with a client authentication failure, there is no further processing for that client. The process does not "fall through" to the next server in the list.

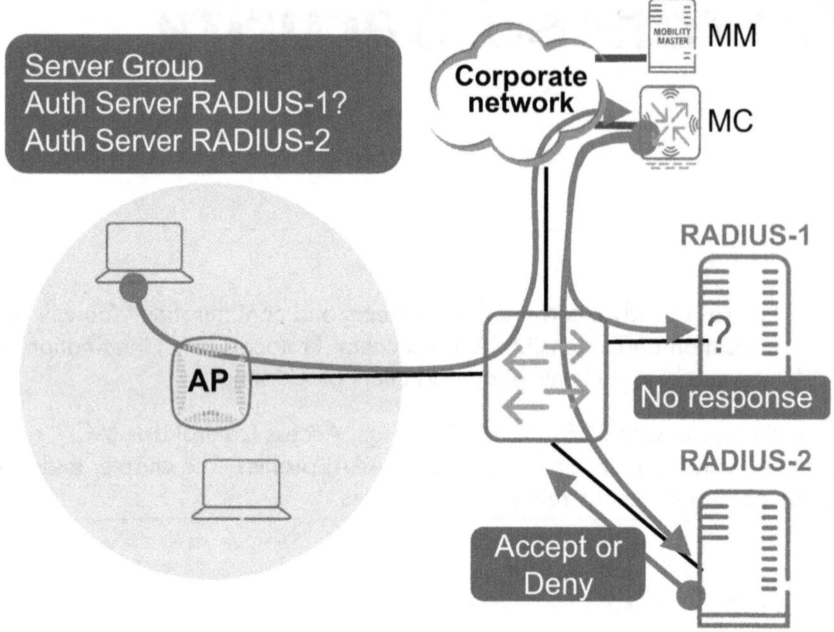

Figure 8-1 Server list order—fall through

Server list order—fail through

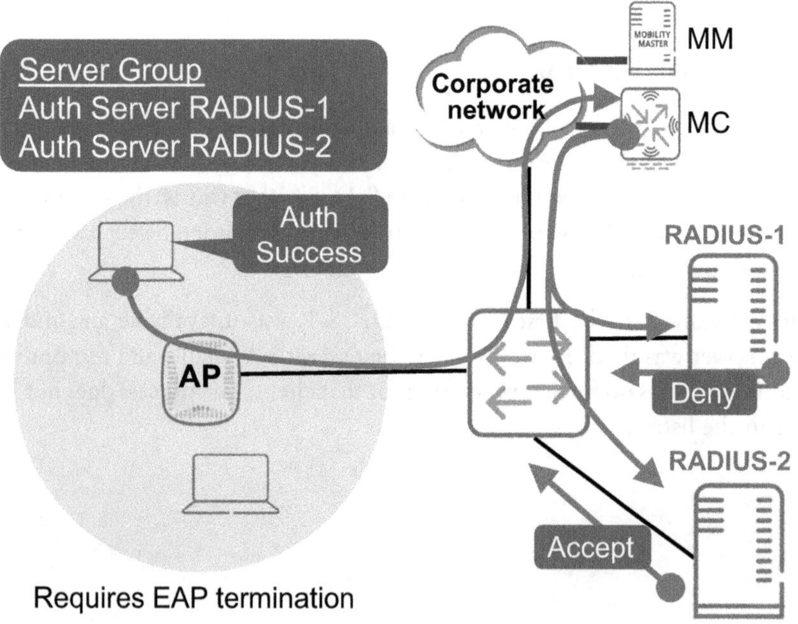

Figure 8-2 Server list order—fail through

The *fall*-through action as just described is fairly typical. In some cases, you might prefer to enable *fail*-through authentication for the server group (Figure 8-2). In this case, if the first server in the list denies authentication, the managed device attempts authentication with the next server in the list. The MC attempts to authenticate with each listed server until authentication succeeds, or the list of servers is exhausted.

Points to consider before enabling fail-through authentication:

- This feature is not supported for 802.1X authentication with a server group of external RADIUS servers. You can, however, use fail-through authentication when the 802.1X authentication is terminated on a managed device (AAA FastConnect).
- Certain servers, such as the RSA RADIUS servers, lock out the managed device if there are multiple authentication failures; therefore, you should not enable fail-through authentication with these servers.

Enabling fail-through and load-balancing

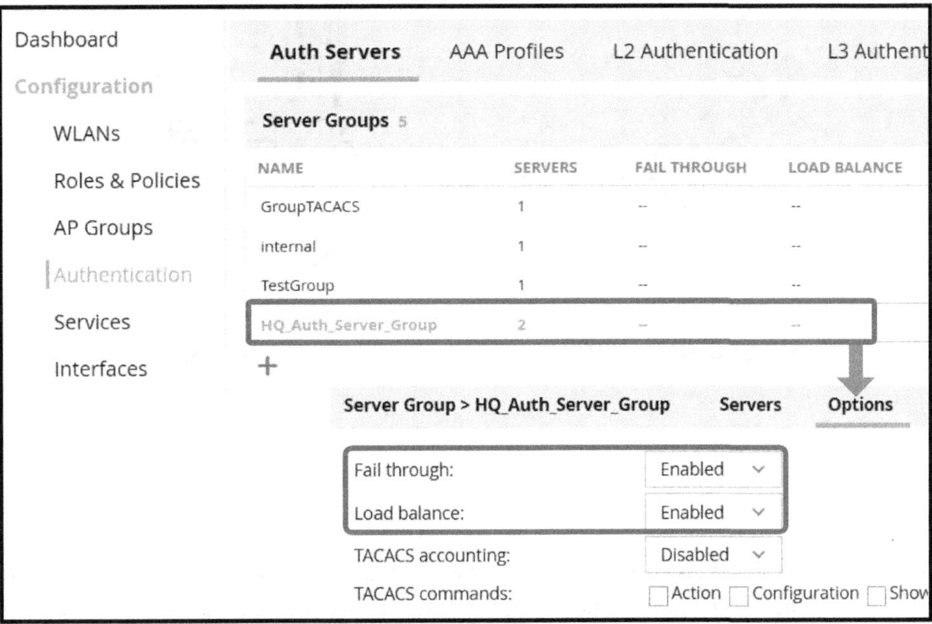

Figure 8-3 Enabling fail-through and load-balancing

Figure 8-3 summarizes how to configure fail-through and load-balancing.

1. In the Mobility Master (MM) node hierarchy, navigate to the **Configuration > Authentication > Auth Servers**.
2. Select the desired server group from the list.

3. Select Options.
4. Select Enabled for Fail through.
5. Select Enabled for Load Balance.
6. Click Submit.

Dynamic server selection

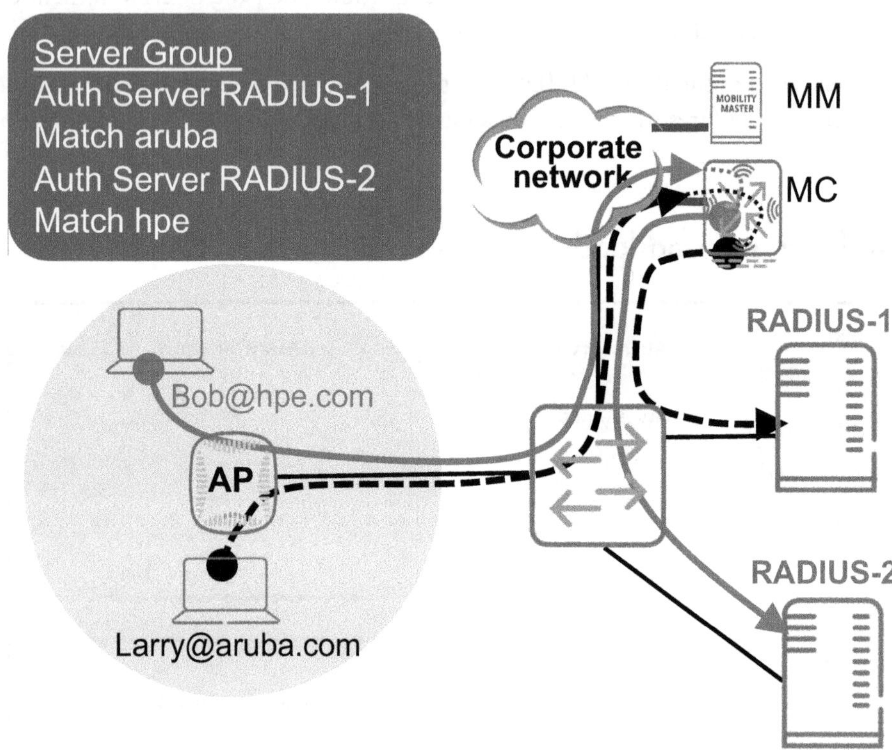

Figure 8-4 Dynamic server selection

MCs can dynamically select an authentication server from a server group, based on information sent by the client in an authentication request (Figure 8-4). For example, an authentication request can include client or user information in one of the following formats:

- <domain>\<user>: for example, arubanetworks.com\aarush
- <user>@<domain>: for example, aarush@arubanetworks.com
- host/<pc-name>.<domain>: for example, host/aarush.edservices.arubanetworks.com (this format is used with 802.1X machine authentication in Windows environments)

When you configure a server in a server group, you can associate the server with one or more match rules.

You could configure multiple match rules for the same server. The MC compares the client/user information with the match rules configured for each server, starting with the first server in the server group. If a match is found, the MC sends the authentication request to the server with the matching rule. If no match is found before the end of the server list is reached, an error is returned, and no authentication request for the client/user is sent.

RADIUS load-balancing was added in AOS 6.4. The goal of this feature is to reduce the response time for RADIUS requests by distributing them across several servers, based on their capacity. This increases RADIUS server availability and eliminates the need to deploy external load balancers for this purpose.

Basically, it keeps a running average of response times for each server. If response times are relatively similar, the load will be evenly distributed. A server with a quicker average response will get more requests (based on moving average response times). If a server has a lengthy delay on some authorizations, its utilization may skew downward. If a server has not been used for a period of 5 minutes, its moving average is reset to the default. This gets it back into the round-robin load balancer.

The server used for a given client will be "sticky" whenever possible to facilitate shorter re-authentications instead of full authorizations.

Writing server matching rules

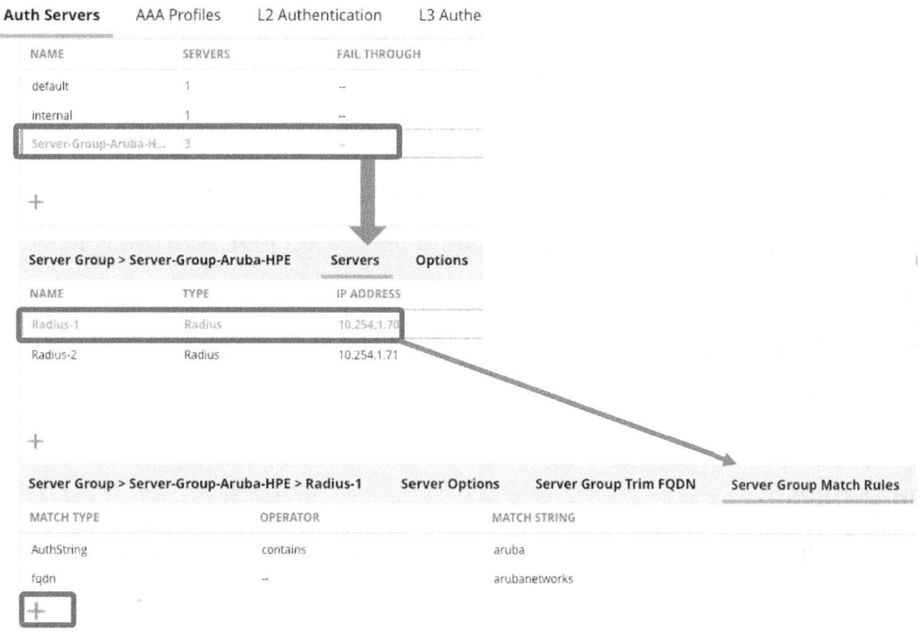

Figure 8-5 Writing server matching rules

Figure 8-5 summarizes how to configure server matching rules.

1. In the MM node hierarchy, navigate to **Configuration > Authentication > Auth Servers**.
2. Under the Server Groups table, select a server group.
3. Select Servers option.
4. Select desired authentication server from the list.
5. Select Server group match Rules option.
6. Click on + to add a new Rule.

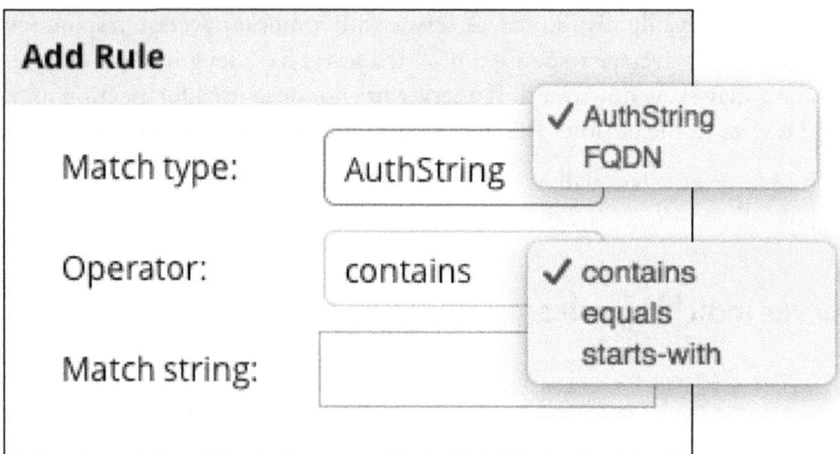

Figure 8-6 Configure the rule

Figure 8-6 shows how the process continues by configuring the actual rule.

7. Select AuthString from the Match Type dropdown list. (Select FQDN to configure FQDN rule).
8. Select the operator.
9. Enter the Match string.
10. Click Submit.

Matching rules

You just learned how authentication can be based on information from the client, in one of the following formats:

- <domain>\<user>: for example, arubanetworks.com\aarush
- <user>@<domain>: for example, aarush@arubanetworks.com
- host/<pc-name>.<domain>: for example, host/aarush.edservices.arubanetworks.com

You can then define server rules to match on this criterion.

You can also use the "match FQDN (domain name)" option for a server rule. With this rule, the server is selected if the <domain> portion of the user information exactly matches a specified string. It must be in the format of one of the first two bullets above—<domain>\<user> or <user>@<domain>.

The bullets below reiterate the caveats of using a match FQDN rule:

- This rule does not support client information in the host/<pc-name>.<domain> format, so it is not useful for 802.1X machine authentication.
- The match FQDN option performs matches on only the <domain> portion of the user information sent in an authentication request.

Trim FQDN option

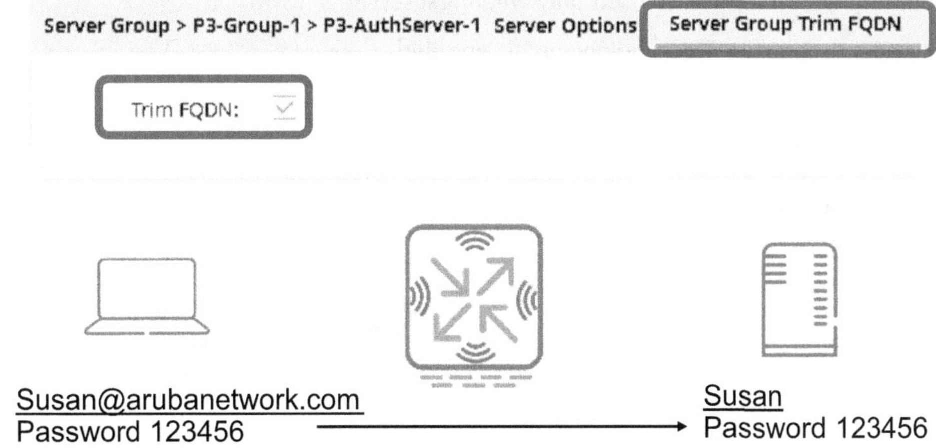

Figure 8-7 Trim FQDN option

You also have the option of trimming domain information from the requests (Figure 8-7).

Before a Mobility Controller (MC) forwards an authentication request to a specified server, it can truncate the domain-specific portion of the user information. This is useful when user entries on the authenticating server do not include domain information. You can specify this option with any server match rule.

This option is only applicable when the user information is sent to the managed device in the following formats:

- <domain>\<user> the <domain>\ portion is truncated
- <user>@<domain> the @<domain> portion is truncated

Learning check

1. When multiple servers are mapped to a server group, will all servers be used for validating the user credentials?
    a. Yes, all servers will be used from top to bottom.
    b. No, only first server will be used.
    c. Subsequent server will be used only when first server is down.
    d. If "Fail through" is enabled.
2. When multiple servers are mapped to a server group, can you distribute the authentication load among the servers?
    a. Yes, we can distribute based on the rules.
    b. No, only first server will be used.
    c. Subsequent server will be used only when first server is down.
    d. It depends whether "Load-balancing" is enabled.

EAP termination

EAP authentication

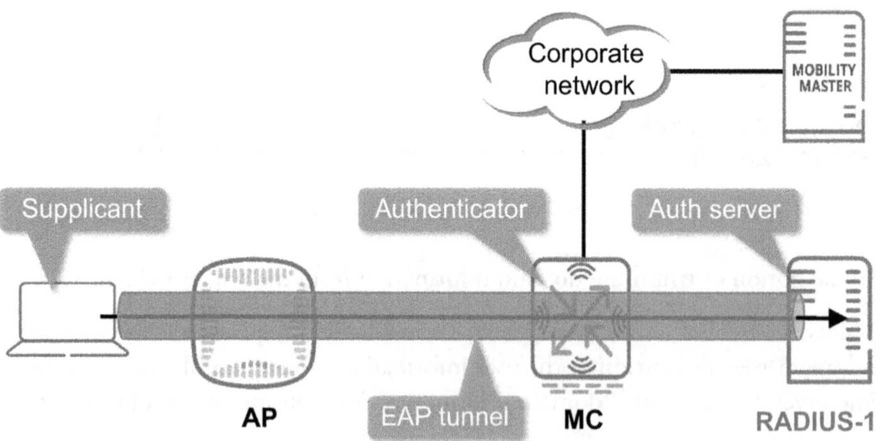

Figure 8-8 EAP authentication

EAP is an authentication framework, providing for the transport and usage of keying material, and other parameters generated by EAP methods (Figure 8-8).

There are many different EAP "flavors" or methods. Some are defined by RFCs and some are vendor-specific. EAP is not a wire protocol—it only defines message formats. Each protocol that uses EAP defines a way to encapsulate EAP messages for transport.

Normal EAP exchange is between the client supplicant and the RADIUS Authentication Server. The controller acts as the Authenticator, in the middle of this communication. It need not be familiar with the EAP type. It just forwards the traffic between the client and the authentication server.

AAA FastConnect/EAP Termination

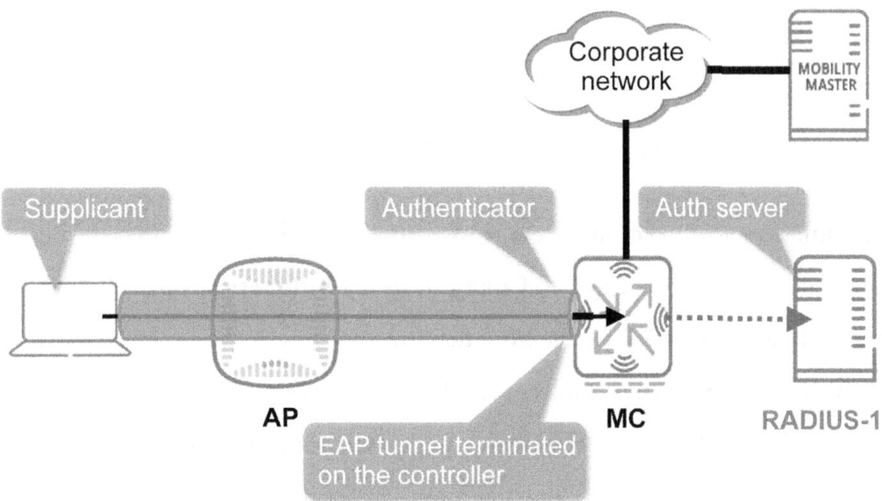

Figure 8-9 AAA FastConnect/EAP Termination

AAA FastConnect allows the encrypted portions of 802.1X authentication exchanges to be terminated on the controller (Figure 8-9). A controller's hardware encryption engine dramatically increases scalability and performance.

The feature supports PEAP-MSCHAPv2, PEAP-GTC, and EAP-TLS. It removes the requirement for external authentication servers to be 802.1X-capable. FastConnect increases authentication server scalability by permitting hundreds of authentication requests per second. This becomes ever more important, as the proliferation of mobile devices accelerates.

Some enterprise RADIUS servers become overwhelmed with authentication requests. This can decrease authentication response times to minimize user complaints.

Enabling AAA FastConnect

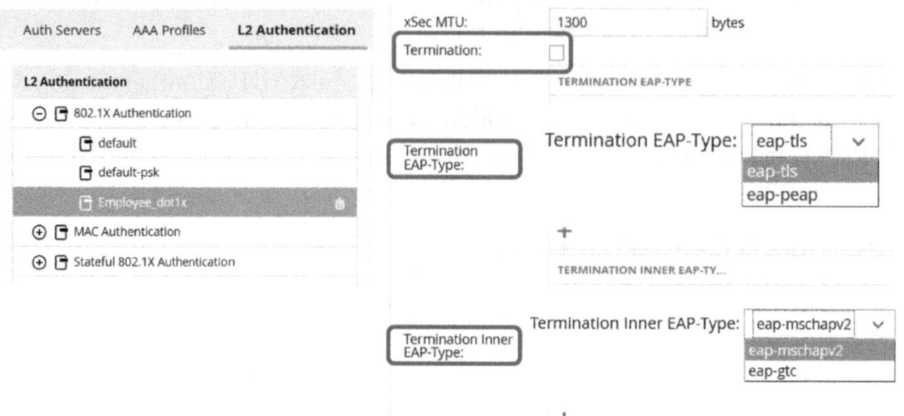

Figure 8-10 Enabling AAA FastConnect

Figure 8-10 summarizes how to configure the AAA FastConnect feature.

1. In the MM node hierarchy, navigate to **Configuration > Authentication > L2 Authentication.**
2. Select the dot1x authentication profile from the list.
3. Select the **Termination** check box to enable AAA FastConnect.
4. Select the Termination EAP-Type (Click on + to get the dropdown list).
5. Select the Termination inner EAP-Type (Click on + to get the dropdown list).
6. Click Submit.

Machine authentication

Configuration > Authentication > L2 Authentication

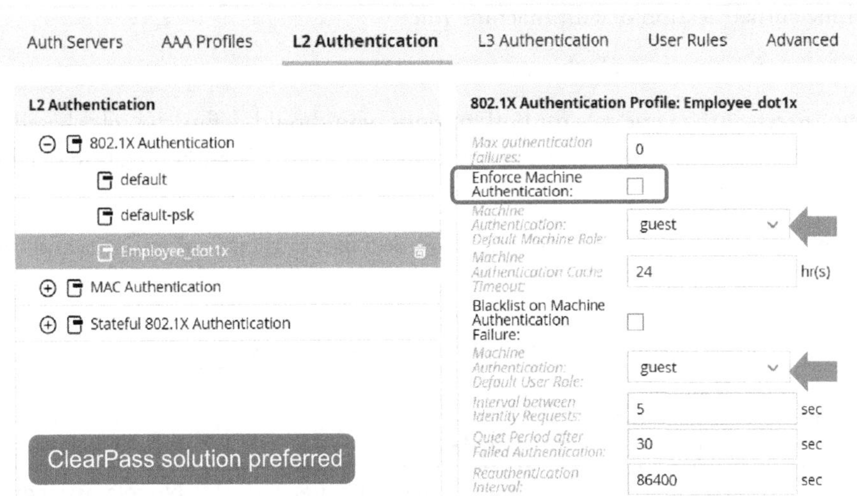

Figure 8-11 Machine authentication

When a Windows device boots, it can be configured to log onto the network domain using a machine account (host/<pc-name>.<domain>). Within the domain, the device is authenticated before computer group policies and software settings can be executed. This process is called machine authentication. Machine authentication ensures that only authorized devices are allowed on the network.

You can configure 802.1X for both user and machine authentication by selecting the option Enforce Machine Authentication. This process is shown in Figure 8-11, and described below.

1. In the MM node hierarchy, navigate to **Configuration > Authentication > L2 Authentication**.
2. Select the dot1x authentication profile from the list.
3. Select the Enforce Machine Authentication check box to enable the Machine Authentication.
4. Select the Machine Authentication default machine role.
5. Select the Machine Authentication default User role.
6. Click Submit.

Role assignment with machine authentication enabled

When you enable machine authentication, there are two additional roles you can define in the 802.1X authentication profile:

- Machine authentication default machine role
- Machine authentication default user role

While you can select the same role for both options, you should define the roles based on the polices to be enforced. Also, these roles can be different from the 802.1X authentication default role configured in the AAA profile.

Table 8-1 shows various combinations of machine and user authentication status and shows the resultant roles that are applied.

Table 8-1 Role assignment with machine authentication enabled

Machine Authentication Status	User Authentication Status	Description	Role assigned
Failed	Failed	Both machine and user authentication failed. L2 authentication failed.	No role assigned. Network access denied.
Failed	Passed	Machine authentication fails and user authentication succeeds. Server-derived roles do not apply.	Machine authentication default user role configured in 802.1X authentication profile.
Passed	Failed	Machine authentication succeeds and user authentication has not been initiated. Server-derived roles do not apply.	Machine authentication default machine role configured in the 802.1X authentication profile.
Passed	Passed	Successful machine and user authentication. If there are server-derived roles, the role assigned via the derivation takes precedence. This is the only case where server-derived roles are applied.	A role derived from the authentication server takes precedence. Otherwise, the 802.1X authentication default role configured in the AAA profile is assigned.

Blacklist

Blacklist due to failed authentication

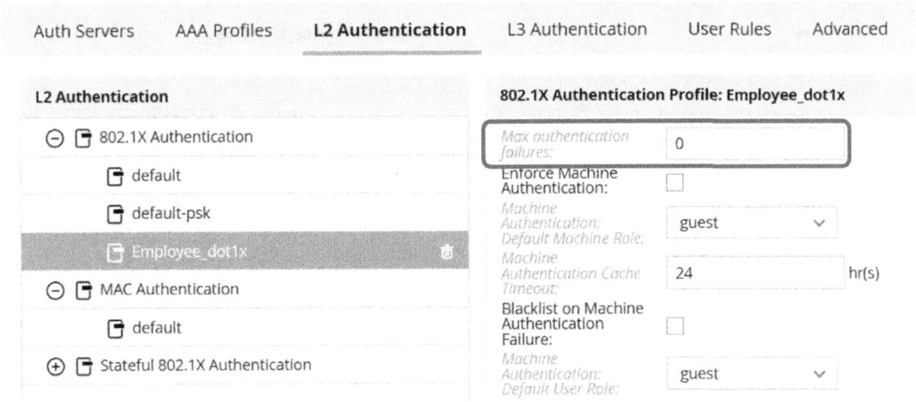

Figure 8-12 Blacklist due to failed authentication

Users that fail authentication can be blacklisted for a defined time period. During this time, the user device remains completely disconnected from any SSID on the controller. The Authentication Failure Blacklist Time is for authentication failures within the set time period and Blacklist Time is how long the user will be disconnected from the WLAN.

Figure 8-12 shows how to configure 802.1X authentication failure blacklisting.

1. In the MM node hierarchy, navigate to **Configuration > Authentication > L2 Authentication**.
2. Select the dot1x authentication profile from the list.
3. Enter a value for number of authentication failures before blacklisting at Max authentication Failure option.
4. Click Submit.

Notice that Max authentication failures is set to 0 in this example. This means there can be an unlimited number of authentication failures.

 **Note**

You can enable authentication failure blacklisting even for MAC authentication and Captive Portal authentication. Similar options are available in MAC and CP authentication profiles.

Setting authentication failure blacklist time

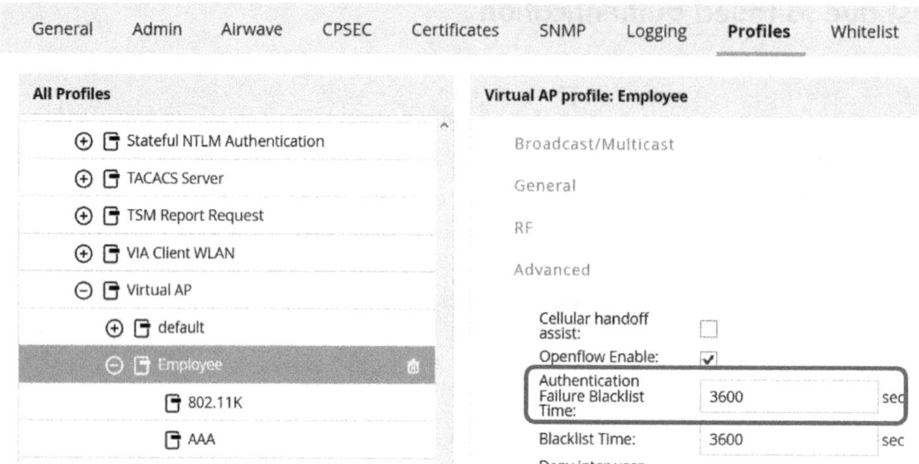

Figure 8-13 Setting authentication failure blacklist time

The default blacklist time is 3600 seconds (60 minutes) (Figure 8-13). You can select any value, based on your requirements. To modify this parameter, use the procedure described below.

1. In the MM node hierarchy, navigate to **Configuration > System > Profiles**.
2. Select the desired Virtual AP profile from the list.
3. Enter a value for Authentication Blacklist Time (seconds).
4. Click Submit.

Port and VLAN ACLs

Port ACLs versus VLAN ACLs

Table 8-2 summarizes a comparison between port and VLAN ACLs.

Table 8-2 Port ACLs vs VLAN ACLs

	Port-session-acl (P-ACL)	VLAN X-Session-acl (V-ACL)	Action
Trunk port	Present	Not Present	Apply **P-ACL** to all VLAN traffic
	Not Present	Present	Apply **V-ACL** to VLAN X traffic
	Present	Present	Apply **P-ACL** to all VLAN traffic except VLAN x to which **V-ACL** is applied
	Not Present	Not Present	**No** ACLs will be applied
Access Port	Present	Not Present	Apply **P-ACL** to incoming traffic
	Not Present	Present	Apply **V-ACL** to incoming traffic assuming port belongs to VLAN X
	Present	Present	Apply **V-ACL** to incoming traffic if port belongs to VLAN X else ps_acl
	Not Present	Not Present	**No** ACLs will be applied

You can apply a firewall policy to the port itself, or to the port's VLAN. The VLAN policy overrides the port policy. On a trunk port with many VLANs the port policy applies to all traffic. However, should one of those VLANs have a policy applied, it overrides the port policy for that specific VLAN.

For example, say Port 1 is configured as a trunk with three VLANs—1, 2, and 3. An applied port policy blocks pings. However, a policy applied to VLAN 2 allows pings. All devices on VLAN 2 could ping but devices on VLAN 1 and 3 could not.

Additionally, Port 2 is configured as an access port in VLAN 2. An applied port policy blocks ping. The devices on this port cannot ping. The VLAN 2 policy that allows pings is configured on Port 1 so it does not apply to the VLAN 2 on Port 2.

This is an important distinction! VLAN ACLs are still applied to ports. This is different than what those trained in other vendor products may expect.

Remember, VLAN policy takes precedent over port policy.

Wired access control

Aruba controllers and APs have Ethernet ports. By default, controller ports are trusted. This means that devices connected to these ports need not authenticate, and their traffic does not pass through the firewall. The device can get an IP address and send traffic, unrestricted by the controller.

All campus AP ports are setup as uplinks by default. AP wired ports can be re-configured as access or even trunk ports. You can force devices connecting to a port to authenticate via captive portal or even with 802.1X authentication. If no authentication is required but restrictions are needed, simply apply an Initial role.

If simple restrictions are needed, then you can apply firewall policies to ports or VLANs.

Controller ports

Depending on the model, controllers have between 4 and 16 ports. The controller acts like a Layer 2 switch, or it can be a Layer 3 router. By default, controller ports are trusted access ports in a VLAN—connected devices are not restricted by the controller, as previously described.

If you need more security, a simple firewall policy can be added to the port or the VLAN. If the port is configured as nontrusted, then users must authenticate and their traffic passes through the firewall. A AAA profile is associated with the port. This determines the connected device's role assignment. The AAA profile also determines the authentication required.

Wired AAA profile examples

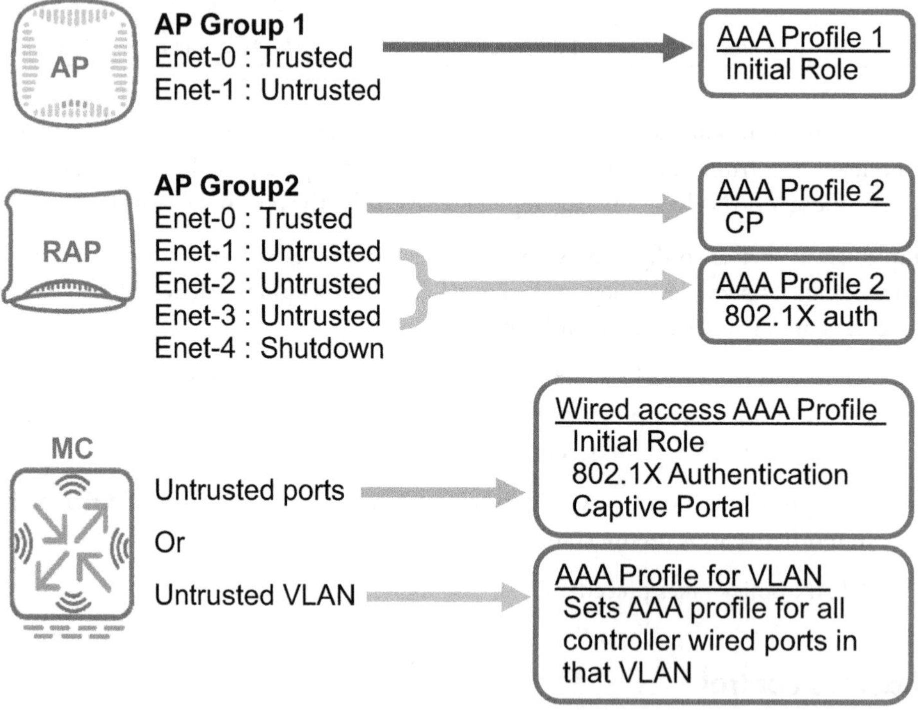

Figure 8-14 Wired AAA profile examples

Within an AP group, you can configure ports as trusted or untrusted, and assign AAA profiles for authentication. Figure 8-14 shows an example for AP-Group1, with Ethernet port 0 and Ethernet port 1. Port 0 defaults as an uplink port, so any configuration here is ignored. Port 1 is set to untrusted and assigned an AAA profile that puts the devices in an initial role.

Note that all the APs in this AP group get the same port configuration. If this is not desired, create several AP groups to vary the configuration, or do a specific AP configuration.

In AP Group2, Ethernet port 1 is untrusted. It is given an AAA profile that forces Captive Portal authentication. Ports 2 and 3 are assigned an AAA profile that enforces 802.1X authentication. Port 4 is shut down. All APs in this AP group get the same port configuration. Controller ports or VLANs can be set as untrusted. An AAA profile can be assigned to the VLAN.

If a port on the AP or the controller is set as untrusted, but no AAA profile is assigned, then the wired access AAA profile is assigned. The wired access AAA profile is a default setting for all untrusted ports.

Wired port settings in AP

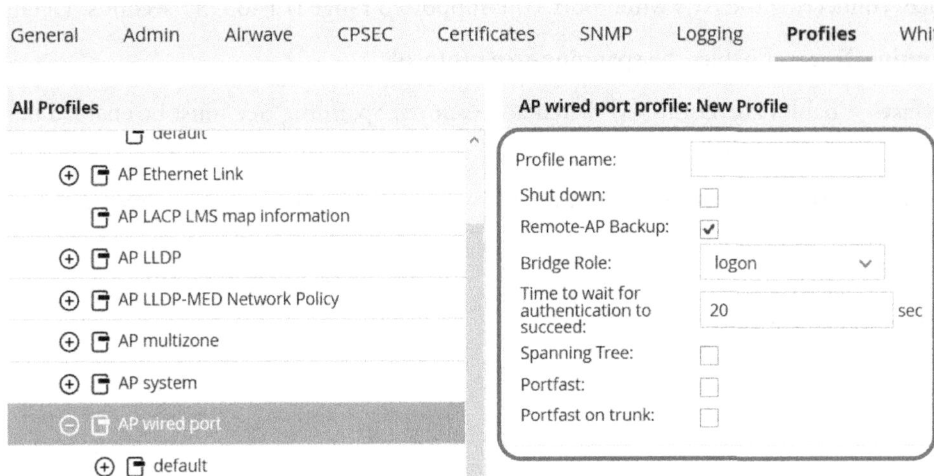

Figure 8-15 Wired port settings in AP

This configuration is only applicable to APs with Ethernet ports (Figure 8-15). Use a wired AP profile to enable or disable the wired port, define an AAA profile, and associate the port with an Ethernet link profile. Link profiles define speed and duplex values.

 **Note**

Basic AP wired port settings can be configured via the WebUI, while some additional advanced settings are available only in the CLI.

In the WebUI

1. Navigate to **Configuration** > **System** > **Profiles**.
2. Select **AP** > **AP Wired Port**. Select the target AP wired port profile to modify.
3. Set the parameters as required.
4. Click Submit.

Possible parameters to be modified are listed below.

- **Shut down**—Disable the wired AP port.
- **Remote AP Backup**—Enable this option to use the wired port on a Remote AP for local connectivity, or for troubleshooting when the AP cannot reach the managed device. If the AP is not connected to the managed device, no firewall policies are applied when this option is enabled. The AAA profile is applied when the AP connects to a managed device.
- **Bridge Role**—Assigned to a user if split-tunnel authentication fails.
- **Time to wait for authentication to succeed**—Authentication timeout value, in seconds, for devices connecting the AP's wired port. The supported range is 1–65535 seconds. Default = 20.
- **Spanning Tree**— Enables the spanning-tree protocol.
- **Portfast**—Enables Portfast for AP wired access ports. Spanning tree must be enabled before this command can be used.
- **Portfast on trunk**—Enables Portfast for AP wired trunk ports. Spanning tree must be enabled before this command can be used.

Mapping AAA profile

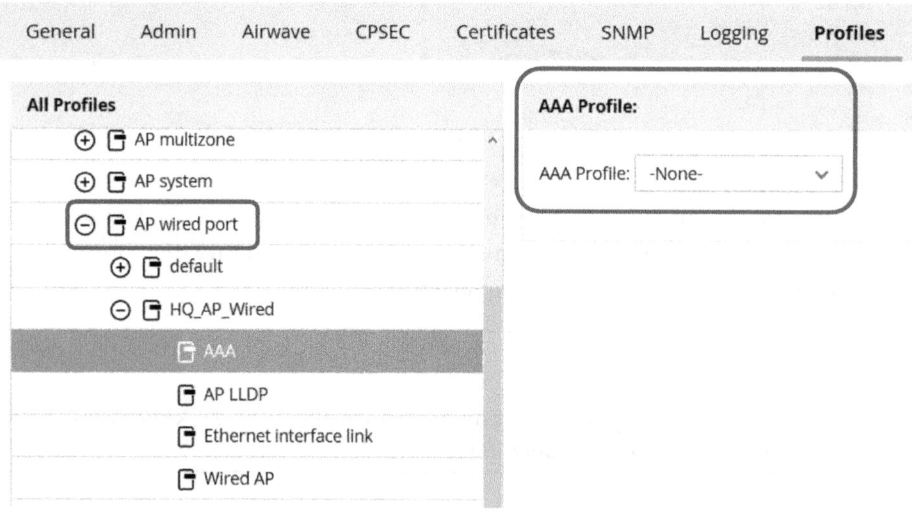

Figure 8-16 Mapping AAA profile

The AAA profile selected for the port determines the authentication method. A dot1x authentication profile along with an Authentication server group initial role should be mapped to the AAA profile.

Navigate to **Configuration > System > Profiles**. Then expand the AP wired port to access the AAA profile, as shown in Figure 8-16.

To define a captive portal service, create an AAA profile that has guest-Logon for the initial role. This should launch the captive portal service.

Mapping Ethernet link and wired AP profiles

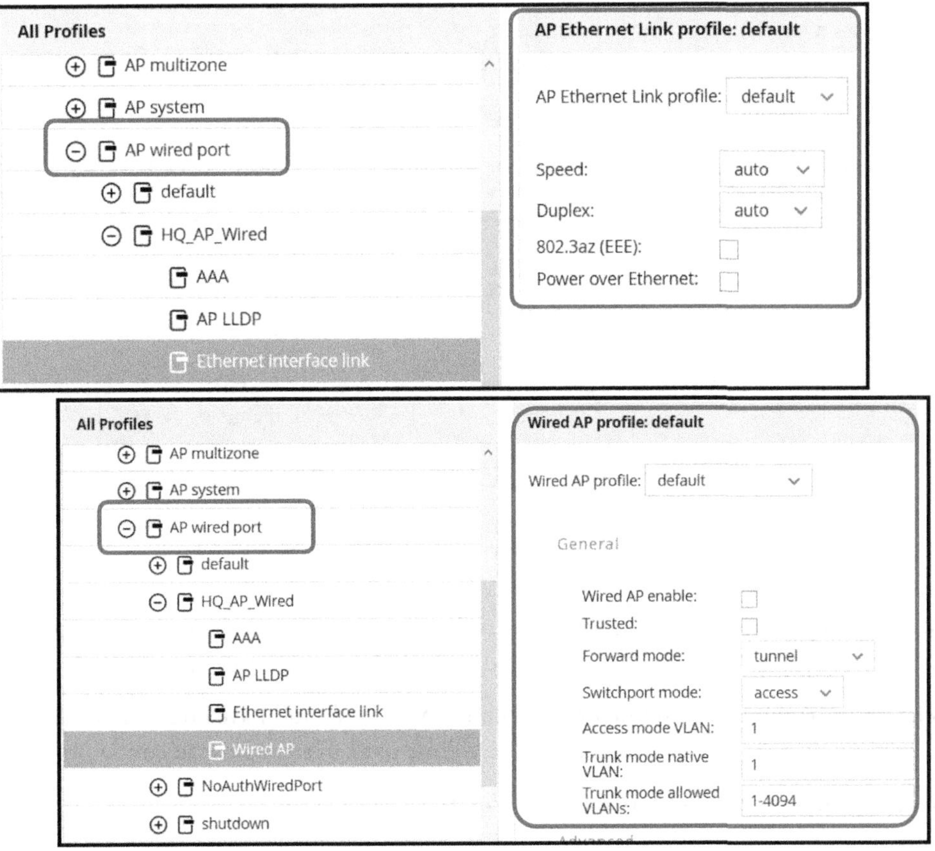

Figure 8-17 Mapping Ethernet link and wired AP profiles

You can assign a profile to an Ethernet link, as shown in Figure 8-17.

The AP Ethernet Link Profile allows you to configure speed, duplex, and PoE.

The wired AP profile enables the AP interface. Trusted or untrusted can be set on the port. You can configure the forwarding mode—tunnel, split-tunnel, or bridge mode. The switch port mode allows you to set access port or trunk port operation.

Wired port controller settings

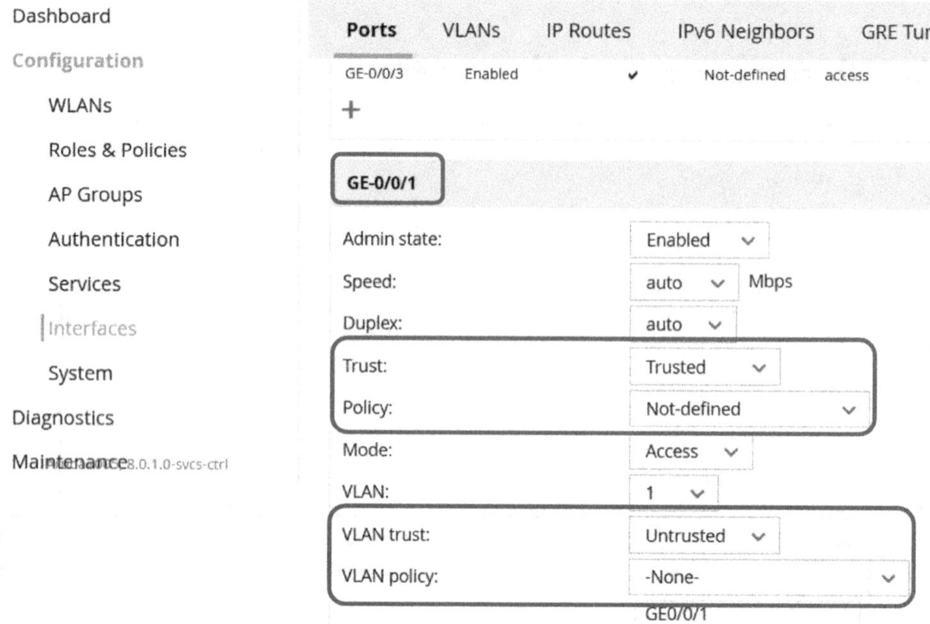

Figure 8-18 Wired port controller settings

When configuring wired controller ports, you can set the port or VLAN to untrusted (Figure 8-18). You can also keep the port and VLAN as trusted and still apply a port policy.

If the VLAN or the port is set to untrusted, then the VLAN should have an AAA profile. If no AAA profile has been set, then the global AAA profile will be used. Here is how to configure this.

1. Navigate to **Configuration > Interface > Ports.**
2. Select the target port to modify.
3. Set the target parameters as desired.
4. Click Submit.

Mapping AAA profile to a VLAN interface

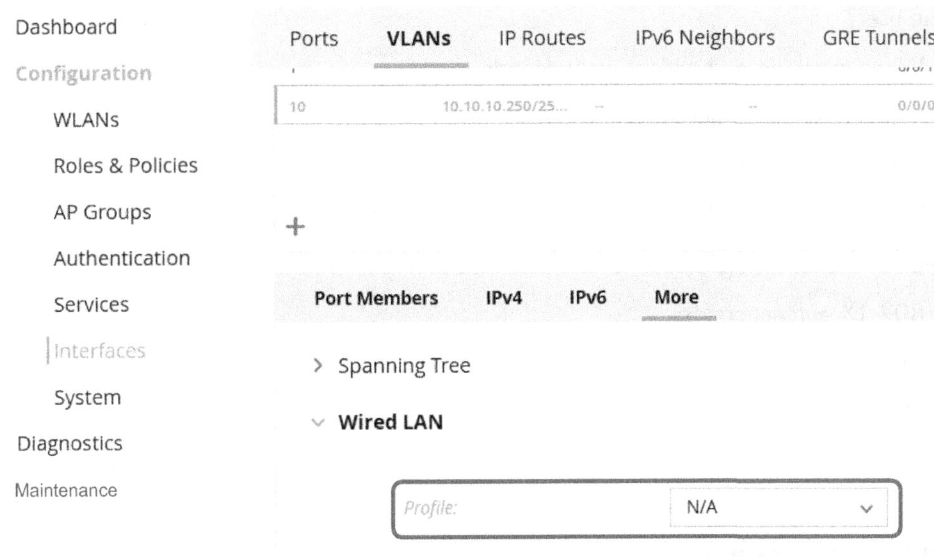

Figure 8-19 Mapping AAA profile to a VLAN interface

You have the choice to setup the port or the VLAN to untrusted. You can also keep the port and the VLAN as trusted and still apply a port policy.

If the VLAN or the port is set to untrusted, then the VLAN should have an AAA profile. If no AAA profile has been set, then the global AAA profile will be used. Here is how to configure this (Figure 8-19).

1. Navigate to **Configuration > Interface > VLANs**.
2. Select the target VLAN to map the AAA profile.
3. Select More menu
4. Select Wired LAN
5. Select the AAA profile from the dropdown list.
6. Click Submit.

Learning check

3. With machine authentication set, when will the AAA authentication default role be assigned to the user?
   a. When machine authentication succeeds.
   b. When user authentication succeeds.
   c. When machine and user authentication both succeed.
   d. When machine authentication failed and user authentication succeeds.
4. Which of the following authentications can be configured on a controller port?
   a. 802.1X authentication
   b. Captive Portal
   c. SIP authentication
   d. MAC authentication

Global firewall settings

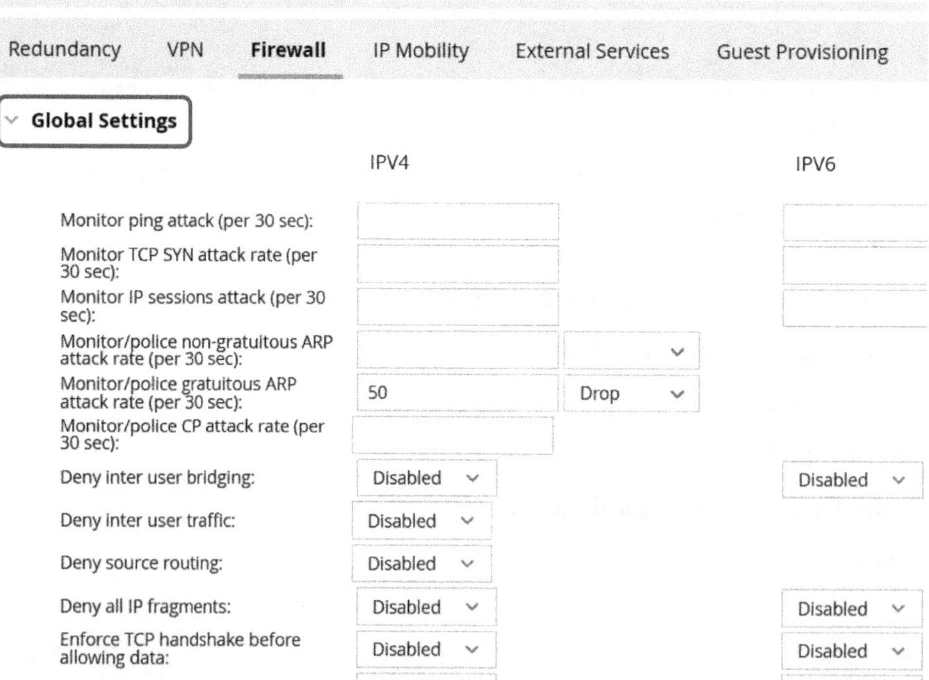

Figure 8-20 Global firewall settings

Figure 8-20 shows optional firewall parameters you can set on managed devices, for IPv4 traffic. These settings will affect the entire system. Be very careful when changing these parameters. To set these global parameters, navigate to **Configuration > Services > Firewall > Global Settings**. Some example parameters are listed below.

Deny inter user bridging—Prevents the forwarding of L2 traffic between wired or wireless users. You can configure user role policies that prevent L3 traffic between users and networks, but this does not block L2 traffic. This option can be used to prevent traffic, such as AppleTalk or IPX, from being forwarded.

Deny inter user traffic—Denies traffic between untrusted users by disallowing L2 and L3 traffic. This parameter does not depend on the deny-inter-user-bridging parameter being enabled or disabled.

Deny source routing—Permits the firewall to reject and log packets with the specified IP options—loose source routing, strict source routing, and record route. Note that network packets are permitted if the IPv6 source or destination address of the network packet is defined as a "link-local address (fe80::/64)."

Deny all IP fragments—Drops all IP fragments.

Do not enable this option unless instructed to do so by an HPE Aruba representative.

Prohibit IP spoofing—Enables detection of IP spoofing, where an intruder sends messages using the IP address of a trusted client. When this option is enabled, source and destination IP and MAC addresses are checked for each ARP request/response. Traffic from a second MAC address using a specific IP address is denied, and the entry is not added to the user table. Possible IP spoofing attacks are logged and an SNMP trap is sent.

Prohibit RST replay attack—When enabled, closes a TCP connection in both directions if a TCP RST is received from either direction. You should not enable this option unless instructed to do so by an Aruba representative.

Session idle timeout (sec)—Set the time, in seconds, that a non-TCP session can be idle before it is removed from the session table. Specify a value in the range 16–259 seconds. You should not set this option unless instructed to do so by an Aruba representative.

Broadcast-filter ARP—Reduces the number of broadcast packets sent to VoIP clients, thereby improving the battery life of voice handsets. You can enable this option for voice handsets in conjunction with increasing the DTIM interval on clients.

Prohibit ARP spoofing—Detects and prohibits ARP spoofing. When this option is enabled, possible ARP spoofing attacks are logged and an SNMP trap is sent.

Enforce TCP sequence numbers—Enforces the TCP sequence numbers for all packets.

Certificates

Client and server certificates

As of ArubaOS 8.0.1, MM and managed devices generate a controller-issued server certificate. This can be used to demonstrate authentication for captive portal and WebUI management access. The controller-issued server certificate is used as the default certificate for WebUI authentication, 802.1X termination, and Single Sign-On (SSO).

HPE Aruba strongly recommends that you replace the default certificate with a custom certificate, issued for your site or domain by a trusted Certificate Authority (CA). This section describes how to generate a Certificate Signing Request (CSR) to submit to a CA, and how to import the signed certificate received from the CA into the managed device.

During certificate-based authentication, the managed device provides its server certificate to the client for authentication. After validating the managed device's server certificate, the client presents its own certificate to the managed device for authentication. To validate the client certificate, the managed device checks the Certificate Revocation List (CRL). This is maintained by the issuing CA.

Obtaining server certificates

As a best practice, always replace the default server certificate in the managed device with a custom certificate, issued for your site or domain by a trusted CA. To obtain a security certificate for the managed device from a CA, follow these high-level steps:

1. Generate a Certificate Signing Request (CSR) on the managed device using either the WebUI or CLI.
2. Submit the CSR to a CA. Copy and paste the output of the CSR into an email and send it to the CA of your choice.
3. The CA returns a signed server certificate and the CA's certificate and public key.
4. Install the server certificate.

Generate and submit CSR

1. In the Managed Network node hierarchy, navigate to **Configuration > System > Certificates.** Click the CSR section.
2. Enter the required information and then click Generate New.
3. Click View Current to display the generated CSR. Select and copy the CSR output between the BEGIN CERTIFICATE REQUEST and END CERTIFICATE REQUEST lines, paste it into an email, and send it to the CA of your choice.

Import certificate to controller

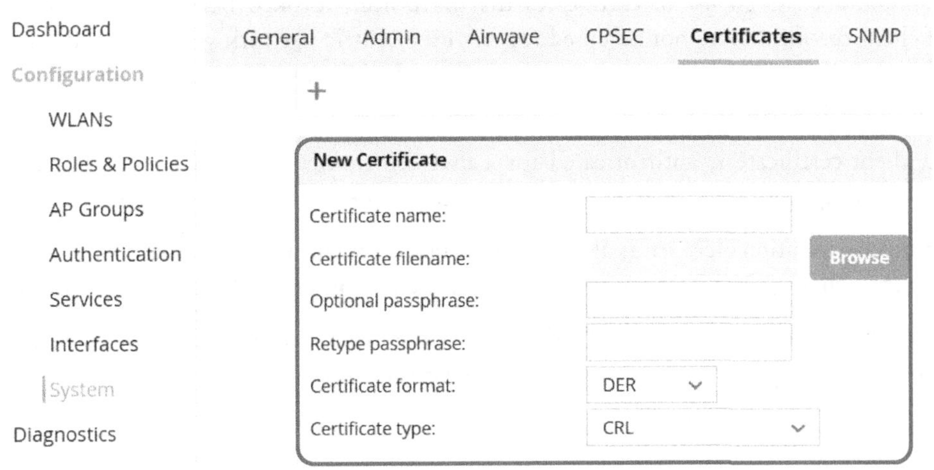

Figure 8-21 Import certificate to controller

You can import the following types of certificates into the managed device (Figure 8-21):

- Server certificate signed by a trusted CA. This includes a public and private key pair.
- CA certificate used to validate other server or client certificates. This includes only the public key for the certificate.
- Client certificate and client's public key.

In the WebUI

1. In the Managed Network node hierarchy, navigate to **Configuration > System > Certificates**.
2. In the Import Certificates table click +.
3. For Certificate Name, enter a user-defined name.
4. For Certificate Filename, click Browse to navigate to the appropriate file on your computer.
5. If the certificate is encrypted, enter and repeat the passphrase.
6. Select the Certificate Format from the drop-down list.
7. Select the Certificate Type from the drop-down list.
8. Click Submit.

Checking CRLs and expiration alert

CAs maintain a CRL—a list of certificates that have been revoked before their expiration date. Expired client certificates are not accepted for any user-centric network service. Certificates may be revoked because a certificate key has been compromised or the user specified in the certificate is no longer authorized to use the key.

When a client certificate is authenticated for a user-centric network service, the managed device checks with the appropriate CA, to ensure that the certificate has not been revoked.

The certificate expiration alert sends alerts when installed certificates are about to expire. This corresponds to trust chains, OCSP responder certificates, and any other certificates installed on the device.

By default, the system sends this alert 60 days before the expiration of the installed credentials. This alert is then repeated periodically on a weekly or biweekly basis.

This alert consist of two SNMP traps:

- wlsxCertExpiringSoon
- wlsxCertExpired

Learning check

5. It is best practice to replace the default certificates with custom certificates?
   a. True
   b. False
6. What is the default certificate expiration alert period?
   a. One week
   b. 15 Days
   c. 30 Days
   d. 60 Days

9 Role Derivation

LEARNING OBJECTIVES

✓ This chapter is focused on role derivation—the process of determining and assigning appropriate user roles. We begin with a review of HPE Aruba firewall features and functions, including policies and rules. Then you will explore policy assignments and bandwidth limitations.

✓ Next, the discussion will focus on user rules, server derivation, and default roles. We end with some ideas for troubleshooting these areas, with a focus on the Access Tracker feature.

Roles, policies, and rules

Aruba firewall review

In an Aruba network, the client is associated with a user role. This determines the client's network privileges. Each role is associated with a set of policies, which control user access. These policies are enforced by Aruba's stateful firewall.

Stateful firewalls keep track of each user session and are aware of bi-directional traffic. It analyzes outbound traffic, determines what the appropriate return traffic should be, and allows that return traffic to enter. No rules are needed for the returning traffic.

Conversely, statically defined router ACLs lack this intelligence. You would typically need to define rules to allow traffic to exit your network, and create additional rules to allow returning ingress packets.

The firewall performs Deep Packet Inspection (DPI)— it is application aware and can permit or deny traffic based on this criterion. The Aruba firewall is also dynamic. A policy rule's address information can change as the policies are applied to users. When moving from subnet to subnet, user role and policy assignments remain consistent.

The firewall includes extended features. It can blacklist users who attempt certain actions, or apply Quality-of-Service (QoS) to the traffic.

These features are applied to connected users, based on their role assignment. This assignment can be derived from a configuration on the local controller, or from a RADIUS server. The RADIUS standard includes attributes that can facilitate this. The standard also allows for Vendor Specific Attributes (VSA). Aruba VSAs enhance role derivation capabilities.

The HPE Aruba ClearPass product can also be used for role derivation. ClearPass integrates with Aruba controllers to provide for more advanced, dynamic environments. This provides for role derivation, Change-of-Authorization (CoA), and downloadable roles.

Aruba firewall

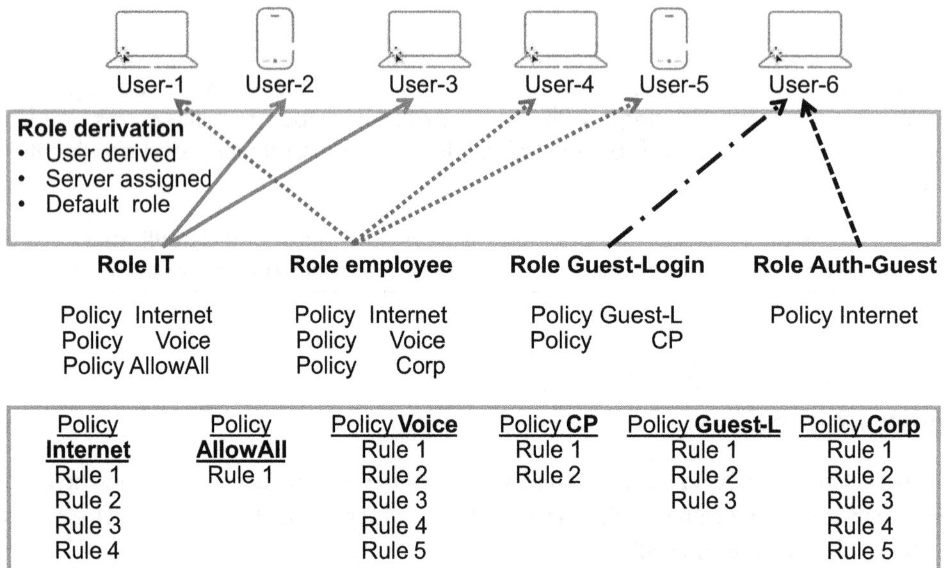

Figure 9-1 Aruba firewall

Roles are created for groups with similar access needs. These access needs are controlled by a policy. Figure 9-1 shows the use of intuitive policy names, so you can easily see that users assigned the IT role will have access to the Internet, VoIP, and everything else. Users assigned to the Auth-Guest role only have internet access.

These policies are comprised of rules, which allow or deny traffic. You will see actual rules soon. For now, Figure 9-1 simply shows a generic "Rule 1," "Rule 2," etc. You can imagine rule 1 of the Internet policy saying, "If Internet access is attempted, then permit" and rule 2 saying, "if corporate access is attempted, then deny."

If traffic matches a rule, then an action is taken. No other policy rules are examined. Possible rule actions include allow traffic, deny traffic, and apply QoS policy to the traffic.

Note

Each of the first few frames are inspected, a match is found, and then an action is applied. This action information is cached. Therefore, no lookup is required for subsequent frames—the action is simply applied. This improves performance of the Aruba solution.

When users attach, the system must determine what roles to apply. This is called role derivation. This can be performed based on local configuration, or indicated by an external server. If neither occurs, then the default authentication role is applied.

Identity-based Aruba firewall

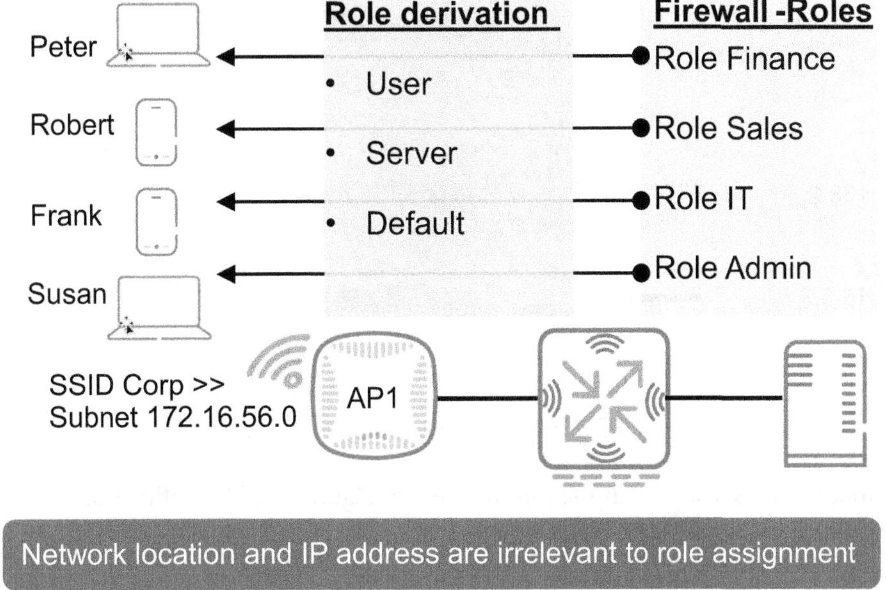

Figure 9-2 Identity-based Aruba firewall

Regardless of a user's connected AP, SSID, or subnet, role derivation determines their network access levels—their role.

Figure 9-2 shows that four roles are defined in the controller—Finance, Sales, IT, and Admin. As users connect, they are assigned to a role via the controller's role derivation process. For example, Peter, Robert, Frank, and Susan have all connected to the same SSID, and are assigned to the same subnet. However, each is assigned to a unique role.

Figure 9-2 also shows how roles are determined. A user's role could be assigned directly to their user account, or their role could be determined by an external RADIUS server. If there is no locally derived role and no server-derived role, then the user falls into the authentication default role.

Your location, attached AP, and IP address is usually irrelevant to your role assignment. However, rules are available that can base role assignment on connected AP or VLAN assignment.

Centralized and consistent security

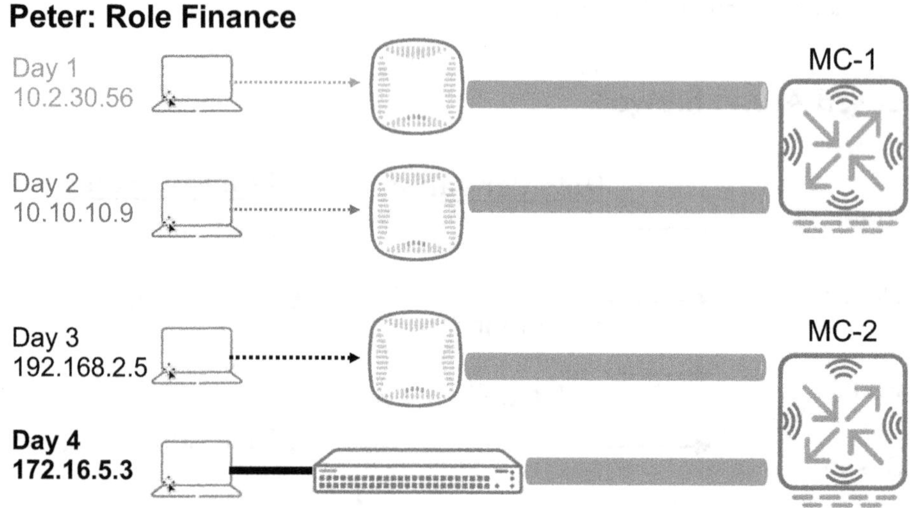

Figure 9-3 Centralized and consistent security

In this scenario, Peter associates with the top-most AP in Figure 9-3. His traffic is bridged to subnet 10.2.30.0, and he is assigned to the Finance role.

As Peter moves from one AP to another, he may be mapped to a different subnet, but his assignment to the Finance role is unaffected.

This can also apply to wired connections. Tunneled Node is an HPE Aruba feature in which a switch creates GRE tunnels to a dedicated MC. The wired user is treated like any other wireless user. You will learn about the tunneled node feature in a later chapter.

This ensures that you have central control over a consistent security policy.

Aruba role derivation example

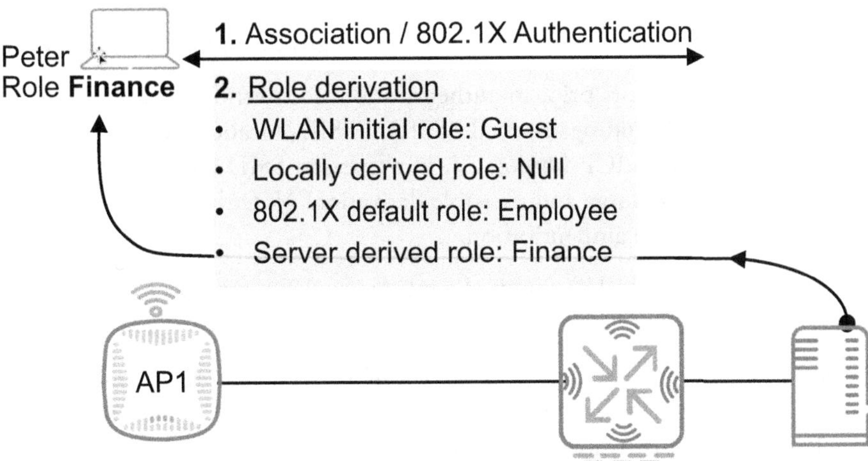

Figure 9-4 Aruba role derivation example

The controller's role derivation process determines a user's role. This can be done in many ways. Upon initial association, a user is given the initial role. If no other derivation is configured, then that role is applied.

There can be locally derived roles, which take precedence over the initial role. If the SSID was setup with an authentication type, then there would be an authentication default role.

If a RADIUS or a ClearPass server returns a role, it takes precedence. This is shown in Figure 9-4. Peter did not connect as a guest, and so that initial role does not apply. There also was no locally derived role for Peter. Now, although others that connect to AP1 might be assigned the 802.1X default role of Employee, perhaps Peter is a member of a special group. For this group, the external RADIUS server overrides this assignment with the Finance role.

Learning check

1. What role derivation trumps all other role assignments?
   a. Initial role
   b. Server-derived role
   c. Authentication method default role
   d. Controller default role

Role derivation sequence

The role derivation sequence is as follows:

1. As a user associates with the network, the controller assigns the initial, pre-authenticated role.
2. A user-derived role also occurs prior to authentication, to override the initial role. This can be based on several factors, including attached BSSID, ESSID, location, MAC Address, encryption type, DHCP-Option, or DHCP-Option-77. However, an SSID configured for authentication will override both the initial role and user-role derivation. Note that the DHCP options are L3 options—only used with L3 authentication.
3. You have learned that RADIUS standard and Aruba VSA attributes can be used for role assignment.
   a. After authentication, the RADIUS or the ClearPass server can return role assignment attributes. Upon receipt of Aruba VSAs, the controller automatically places the user in the specified role or VLAN. If Aruba VSAs have not been configured in the RADIUS server, the server sends standard RADIUS attributes.
   b. These attributes can specify the role and/or VLAN, but the controller must be configured to look for that RADIUS attribute. This server rule configuration is required.
4. If a RADIUS role is not specified or does not exist, the default authentication role is used. There are separate default roles for captive portal, 802.1X, MAC, and VPN authentication methods. The role is assigned based on which authentication method is configured on the SSID.

Role assignment

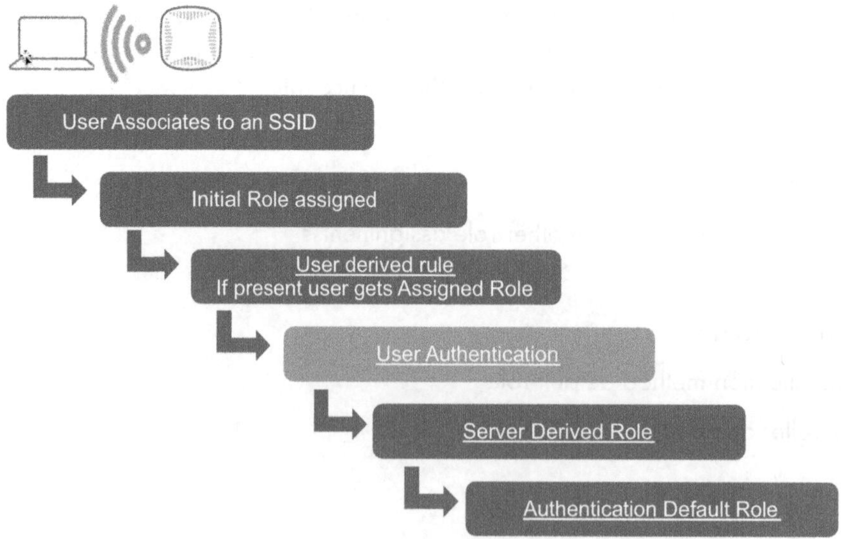

Figure 9-5 Role assignment

Figure 9-5 offers us additional information about the role derivation process.

- A user associates and is placed in the initial role. This is often used for guest access. When associating with the guest SSID, the client is placed in a guest login role and presented with a Captive Portal page.
- Next, the process checks for a user-derived role. This can be used when you need to base the role on user location, connected SSID, VLAN, or encryption methods.
- If a user rule is not created, then authentication is required.
- During authentication, a server-derived role can be applied, if one has been configured.
- If you configure the RADIUS server to return attributes, you must configure the controller with server rules. If there is a RADIUS server with Aruba VSAs or a ClearPass, then no server rules are needed.
- Lacking any server-derived roles, the authentication method's default role is assigned.

User rules

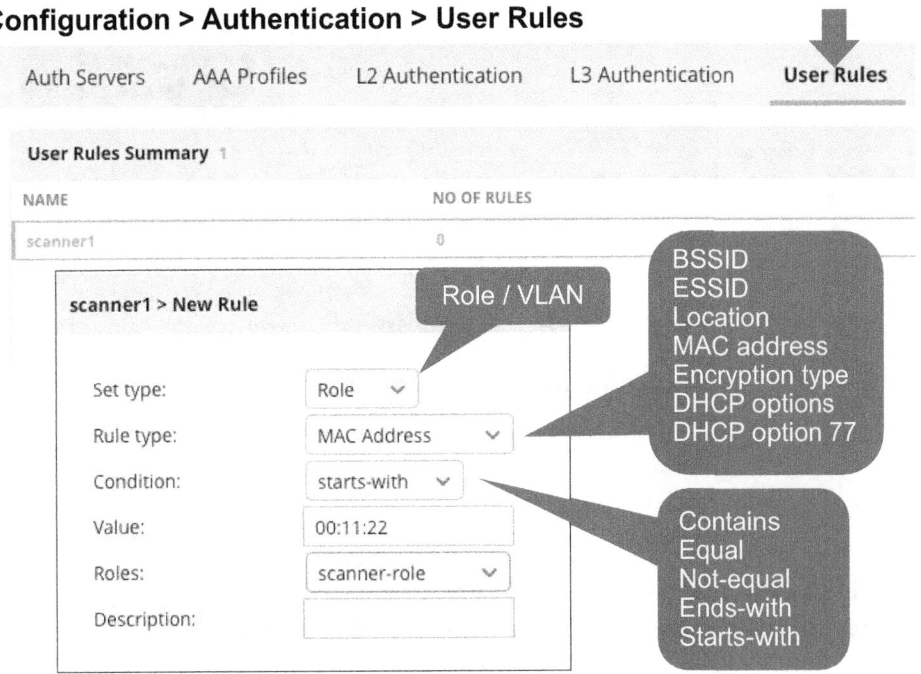

Figure 9-6 User rules

User role and VLAN assignment can be based on conditions defined in a user rule. The conditions can be based on location, BSSID, ESSID, MAC address, encryption type, or DHCP options. You can choose an operator value of contains, equal to, not-equal to, ends-with, or starts-with.

For example, a company has several handheld scanners, which are limited to MAC authentication. However, you do not have an inventory of these devices and their MAC addresses. This is required for MAC authentication, and so this authentication technique seems impractical.

However, the devices are all from the same vendor, and so have the same OUI—00:11:22. You can simply create a scanner SSID, and configure the rule shown in Figure 9-6:

Set the Role—if MAC address—starts with—00:11:22—then assign the "scanner-role."

You have already defined "Scanner-role" with policies that permit all required communications with the server.

The technique described above works well. However, with the advent of ClearPass profiling, user rules have become somewhat obsolete.

WLAN and user rules

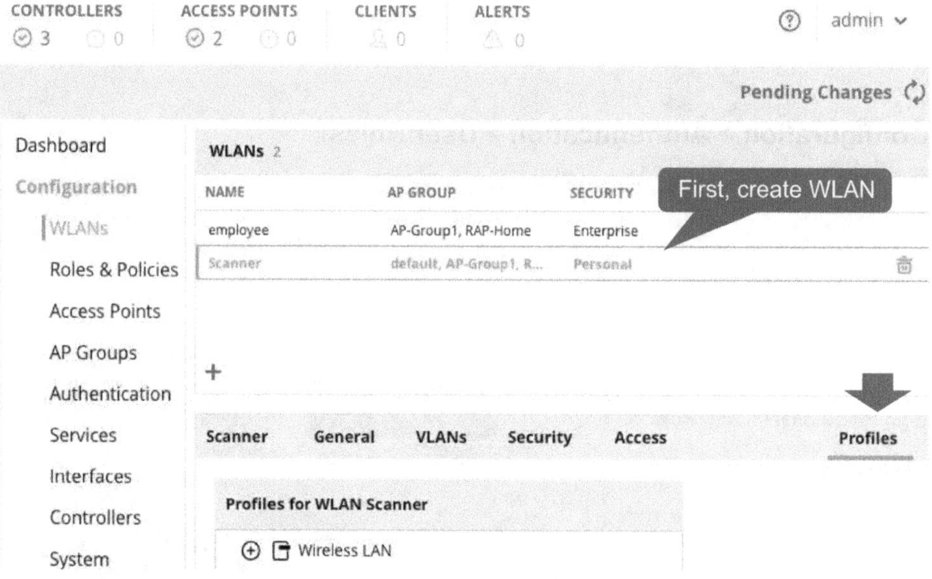

Figure 9-7 WLAN and user rules

After user rule creation, you can create the WLAN. In this scenario, the SSID is configured to use a PSK passphrase. This is because your scanners support PSK authentication.

Now you need to *apply* the user rule to this WLAN. Figure 9-7 shows that you have navigated to **Configuration > WLANs.** Now click on the scanner WLAN to edit it. Select the Profiles tab to apply the User Rule.

WLAN and user rules (cont.)

Scanner General VLANs Security Access Profiles

Profiles for WLAN Scanner

- Wireless LAN
  - Virtual AP
    - Scanner
      - 802.11K
      - AAA
      - Anyspot
      - Hotspot 2.0
      - SSID
      - WMM Traffic management

AAA Profile: Scanner

AAA Profile:	Scanner
Initial role:	logon
MAC Authentication Default Role:	guest
802.1X Authentication Default Role:	guest
Download Role from CPPM:	
Set username from dhcp option 12:	
L2 Authentication Fail Through:	
Multiple Server Accounting:	
User idle timeout:	seconds
Max IPv4 for wireless user:	2
RADIUS Roaming Accounting:	
RADIUS Interim Accounting:	
User derivation rules:	scanner1

Figure 9-8 WLAN and user rules (cont.)

Once in Profiles, expand and click on the AAA profile (Figure 9-8). Here is where you set the User derivation rules. Users that associate to the scanner WLAN must meet the criteria specified in the scanner User Rule. If not, they denied access.

However, you can enable the L2 Authentication Fail Through option, if desired. Thus, if the rule-based OUI authentication fails, they can “fail through” to another authentication mechanism, such as 802.1X.

Learning check

2. What is NOT a valid rule type for a User Rule?
   a. BSSID
   b. ESSID
   c. Location
   d. AP type
   e. MAC Address
   f. Encryption type
   g. DHCP Options
   h. DHCP Option 77

Server derivation

MC–Server communication

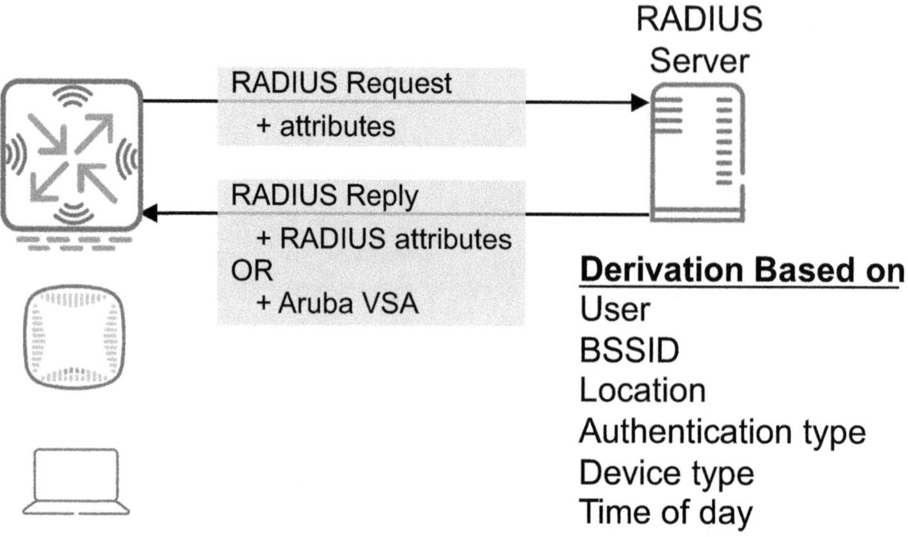

Figure 9-9 MC—Server communication

For server-derived roles, the controller and server must exchange information. The actual exchange depends on server type and whether the VSAs have been installed on that RADIUS server.

During any RADIUS-based authentication, the client requests authentication. The controller receives this request, and sends a RADIUS request to the server. This request includes appropriate attributes (Figure 9-9).

This server uses this information to derive a role. It replies to the controller with Aruba VSAs or RADIUS attributes.

If this RADIUS reply includes an Aruba VSA, the controller puts the user in the specified role or the VLAN. The controller can find and apply the correct VSA without need for additional configuration. If a RADIUS attribute is returned, controller configuration is required.

MC and ClearPass

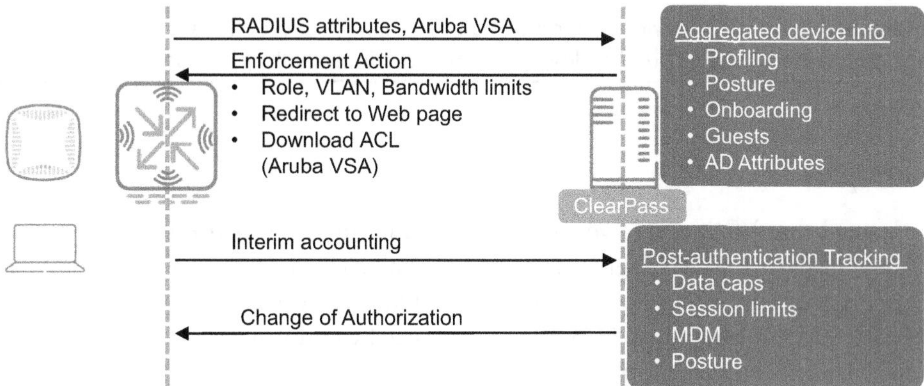

Figure 9-10 Server derivation

Authentication and authorization processes require enforcement information (Figure 9-10). ClearPass can select specific attributes to return to the Network Access Device (NAD), based on certain conditions. This includes the following:

- The machine authenticates to an AD.
- A certain set of users authenticate via 802.1X.
- Users have tablets or smartphones that require secure connections, with certain access control policies.
- Temporary workers, contractors, and guests are identified that require different access levels.
- Device health status

If a condition above is met, some action can be taken:

- Implement a simple "allow access" RADIUS attribute.
- Apply a VSA to assign the user to a specific VLAN.
- Apply an ACL, or in the case of Aruba controllers, apply user roles via RADIUS attributes.
- Issue CLI commands (in certain situations).
- Redirect users to a web page, for guest login.
- Send session-based attributes that restrict bandwidth or active session count. The user session is terminated when assigned limits are reached.
- Apply SNMP-based enforcement actions for VLAN steering.

 **Note**

Enforcement can also be via Change-of-Authorization (CoA) actions. For example, a message can be sent to the NAD to lower or raise a client's authorization level.

VSA examples

You have learned that VSAs enable vendor-specific communication between NADs and RADIUS servers. For third-party RADIUS servers, you can download and deploy a dictionary file of Aruba VSA's. Supported products include Free RADIUS; Juniper Steel Belted RADIUS, Juniper Steel Belted RADIUS MMS, and Cisco ACS. There is no need to implement VSA's on the ClearPass as they are automatically implemented.

Here is a list of Aruba VSA's

- **Aruba-User-Role**—Assigns the post-authentication user role. User access is based on role attributes.
- **Aruba-User-VLAN**—Assigns the user VLAN. This is an integer, from 1 – 4094.
- **Aruba-Priv-Admin-User**—If set in a RADIUS accept message, the enable prompt is bypassed.
- **Aruba-Admin-Role**—Assigns management role, post management authentication. View this role with the command `show mgmt-role`.
- **Aruba-Essid-Name**—ArubaOS sends the client SSID
- **Aruba-Location-Id**—Sent in Access Request or Access Accept packets, to define/identify the AP name
- **Aruba-Port-ID**—String 7
- **Aruba-Template-User**—String 8
- **Aruba-Named-User-Vlan**—Returns user VLAN name, which the controller could be map to one or multiple VLAN IDs.
- **Aruba-AP-Group**—Sent in Access Request to identify client AP's Group. Sent in Access Accept to identify the AP Group membership.
- **Aruba-Framed-IPv6-Address**—This attribute is used for IPv6-based RADIUS accounting.
- **Aruba-Device-Type**—ArubaOS sends client OS type, as determined by ArubaOS
- **Aruba-No-DHCP-Fingerprint**—Tells the controller not to base role and VLAN assignment on DHCP finger printing.
- **Aruba-Mdps-Device-Udid**—The Unique Device Identifier (UDID) is an input attribute to the Onboard application. This is used when device authorization is via the internal RADIUS server,

within the ClearPass Policy Manager (CPPM). The UDID is compared against role mappings or enforcement policies, to determine device eligibility for onboarding. The next two VSAs below are used for the same thing.

- **Aruba-Mdps-Device-Imei**—The International Mobile Equipment Identity (IMEI). See above.
- **Aruba-Mdps-Device-Iccid**—The Integrated Circuit Card Identifier (ICCID). See above.
- **Aruba-Mdps-Max-Devices**—Used by Onboard to define and enforce the maximum number of devices that can be provisioned by a given user.
- **Aruba-Mdps-Device-Name**—The device name is used as described above, as for the UDID, IMEI, and ICCID.
- **Aruba-Mdps-Device-Product**—Device Product is used as described above for UDID.
- **Aruba-Mdps-Device-Version**—Device Version is used as described above for UDID.
- **Aruba-Mdps-Device-Serial**—Device Serial number is used as described above for UDID.
- **Aruba-AirGroup-User-Name**—Device owner—username associated with the device.
- **Aruba-AirGroup-Shared-User**—Contains a comma-separated list of user names with whom the device is shared.
- **Aruba-AirGroup-Shared-Role**—Contains a comma-separated list of user roles with which this particular device is shared.
- **Aruba-AirGroup-Device-Type**—one for personal device and two for shared device.
- **Aruba-Auth-Survivability**—Used by Auth survivability feature for IAP to indicate CPPM server to send.
- **Aruba-AS-User-Name and Aruba-AS-Credential-Hash**—Attribute is just used as a flag and no specific value is used.
- **Aruba-AS-User-Name**—Used by Auth survivability feature for IAP, CPPM sends the actual username to the IAP that can be used by IAP to authenticate the user if the CPPM server is not reachable.
- **Aruba-AS-Credential-Hash**—Used by Auth survivability feature for IAP, CPPM sends the NT Hash of the password to IAP that can be used by IAP to authenticate the user if the CPPM server is not reachable.
- **Aruba-WorkSpace-App-Name**—Used by CPPM to implement per-APP-VPN and identify the application on controller. A container VM running on iPad, for example, houses multiple applications; whenever a particular application initiates an IKE/IPsec connection with the controller, provision is made to download role, VLAN, and more from CPPM, based on the client application name.

- **Aruba-Mdps-Provisioning-Settings**—Used as part of the ClearPass Onboard technology, this allows CPPM to signal back to the Onboard process. Thus, CPPM learns the context of the device provisioning settings. These are applied to the device based on applied role mappings.
- **Aruba-Mdps-Device-Profile**—Allows CPPM to signal back to the Onboard process. CPPM learns which device profile to apply, based on role mappings.
- **Aruba-AP-IP-Address**—The RADIUS server sends this to the controller when a RAP authenticates. It contains the static inner IP used for the RAP.
- **Aruba-AirGroup-Shared-Group**—Specifies the shared group list for the device, if known. This is a comma-separated list of group names. This attribute is omitted if the shared group list is not set or blank.
- **Aruba-User-Group**—Specifies a user's group memberships, if known. This is a comma-separated list of group names. This attribute is omitted if the group list is not set or blank.
- **Aruba-Network-SSO-Token**—Specifies the SSO token obtained as part of network level authentication from CPPM for a particular user.
- **Aruba-AirGroup-Version**—This attribute is a 32-bit integer in network byte order. The allowable values for this attribute are:
  - 1—For AOS release before 6.4 and CPPM release before 6.3.
  - 2—For AOS release 6.4 and CPPM release 6.3.
  - New values shall be defined in future releases.
- **Aruba-Auth-SurvMethod**—It is used internally between AUTH and Local Survival-Server in AOS 6.4.3.x and higher to support auth-survivability. AUTH will add this VSA with other RADIUS attributes in an auth-request to Auth-Server (for example, CPPM). If all servers are OOS in the server-group, this auth-request with all RADIUS attributes (including VSA-39) will be sent to Local Survival-Server.
- **Aruba-Port-Bounce-Host**—When this VSA is included with a DISCONNECT message, it will signal the Mobility Access Switch running AOS 7.4.0.3 or higher to shut down the port for the duration specified (0–60 seconds).
- **Aruba-Calea-Server-Ip**

Configure WLAN to use server-derived roles

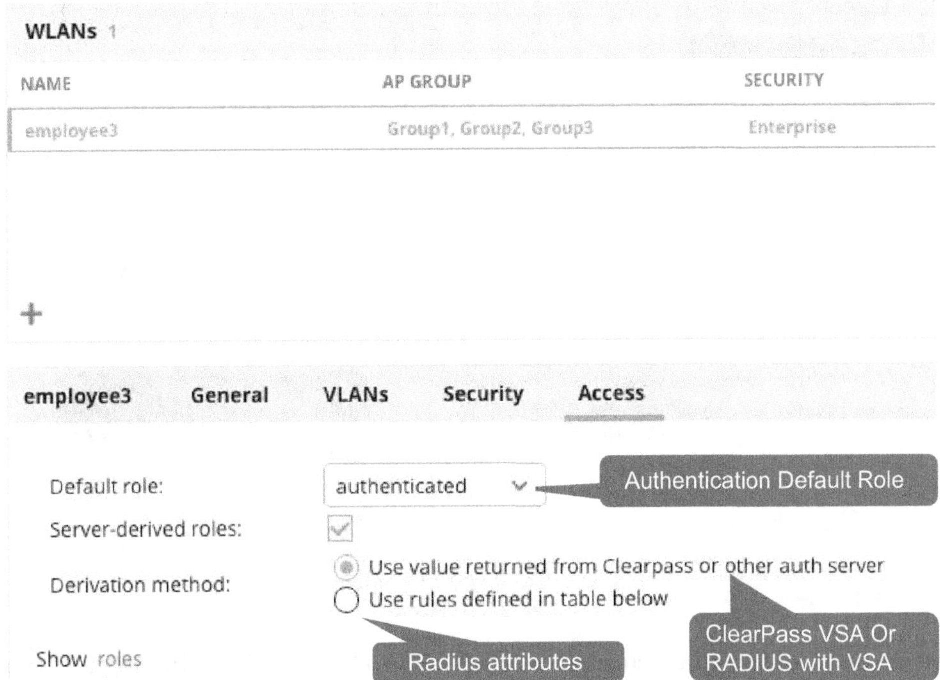

Figure 9-11 Configure WLAN to use server-derived roles

Like a RADIUS server that has Aruba VSAs, ClearPass will return the Aruba VSAs and a value; therefore, no server rules are needed.

The MC receives a reply from ClearPass with the Role or VLAN settings, and the user is placed in the specified Role and/or VLAN. If no value is returned from the servers, then the user will fall into the authentication default Role.

Figure 9-11 shows that the employee3 WLAN is configured to use server-derived roles. If that server-derivation fails, a default role is configured.

Aruba VSA in ClearPass

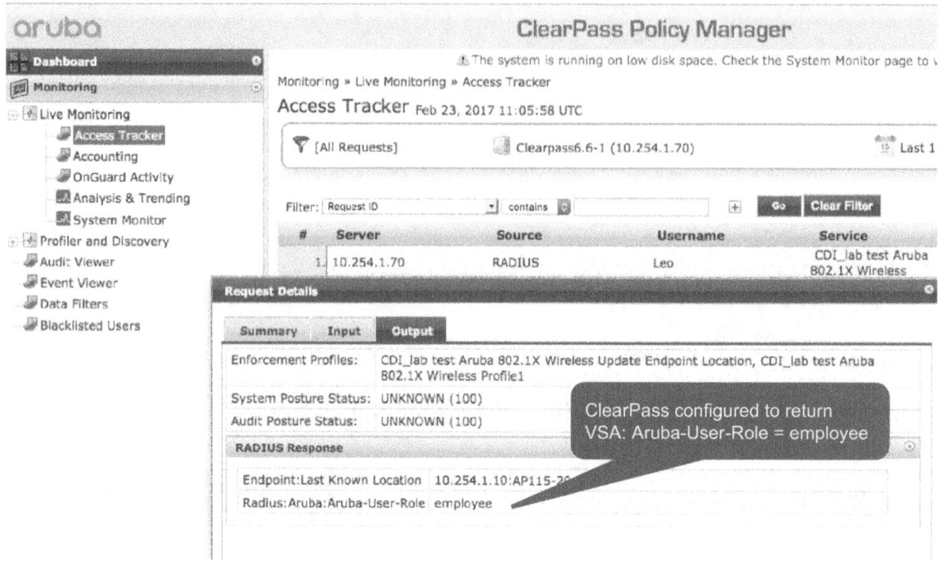

Figure 9-12 Aruba VSA in ClearPass

ClearPass has been configured to return the Aruba VSA "Aruba-User-Role." In this case, the user has authenticated via ClearPass, and the Role selected is "employee."

If no employee role was preconfigured on the MM, then user would get the 802.1X default Role.

RADIUS attribute—Windows NPS

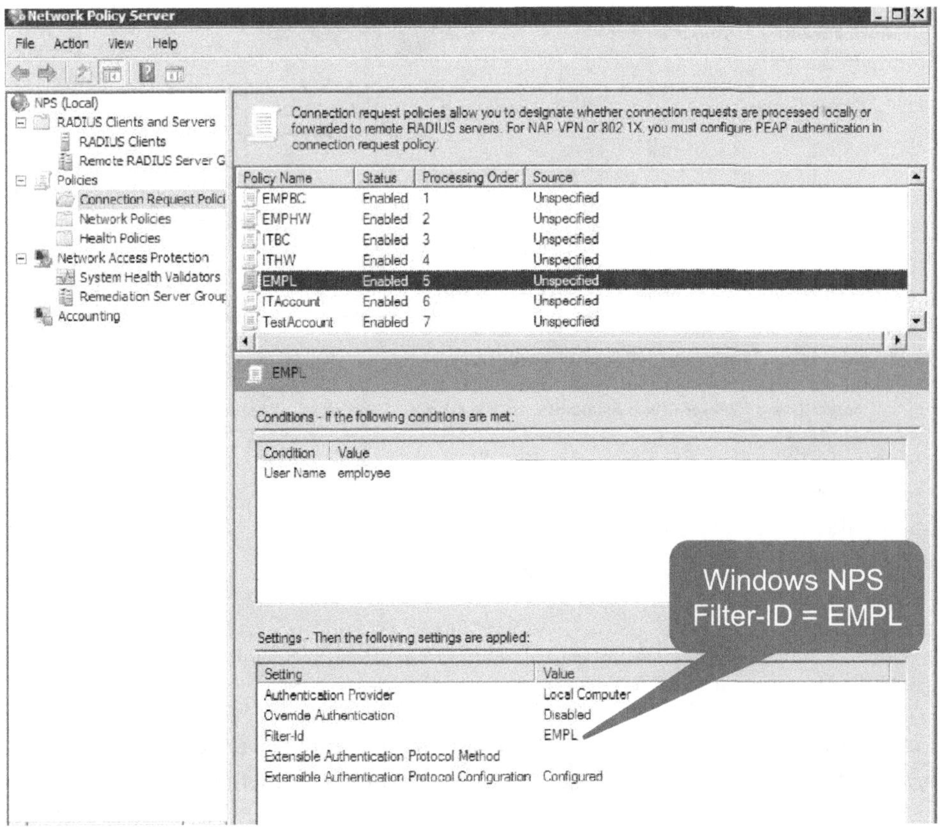

Figure 9-13 RADIUS attribute—Windows NPS

Figure 9-13 shows the configuration of a Microsoft-based RADIUS server, referred to as the Network Policy Server (NPS). In this scenario, the RADIUS server is configured with a connection request policy named EMPL. As configured, the RADIUS reply for some group of users will include a Filter ID value of EMPL.

You must configure the controller to look for the RADIUS reply's Filter-ID setting and map the value to a Firewall Role. If you fail to do so, the user is assigned to the authentication method default role.

Server role derivation—RADIUS attributes

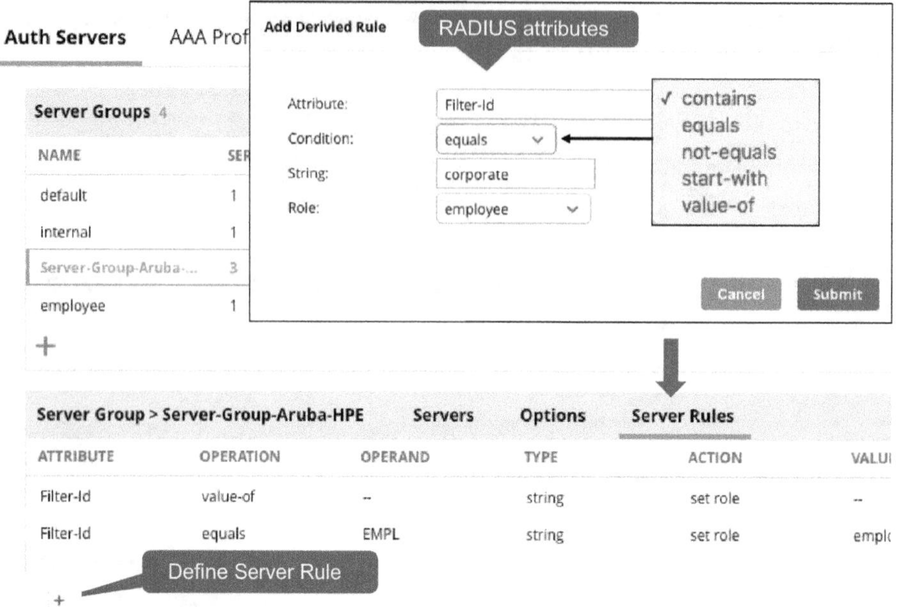

Figure 9-14 Server role derivation—RADIUS attributes

You just configured NPS to return a Filter-ID to the MC. Figure 9-14 shows how to configure the MC to leverage this Filter-ID, by navigating to Configuration > Authentication > Auth Servers.

A WLAN is configured to use a server-group, where you define the derivation method. This scenario uses a role derivation rule. The rule tells the controller to look for the Filter ID. If the Filter-ID is equal to EMPL, then assign the employee role. If not, then move to the next rule. This rule specifies that if the Filter-ID equals "corporate," then assign the role named "employee."

If the user authenticated, but the returned value does not correspond to any rule, then the authentication method default role is assigned.

Default roles

WLAN AAA profile—initial and authentication default role

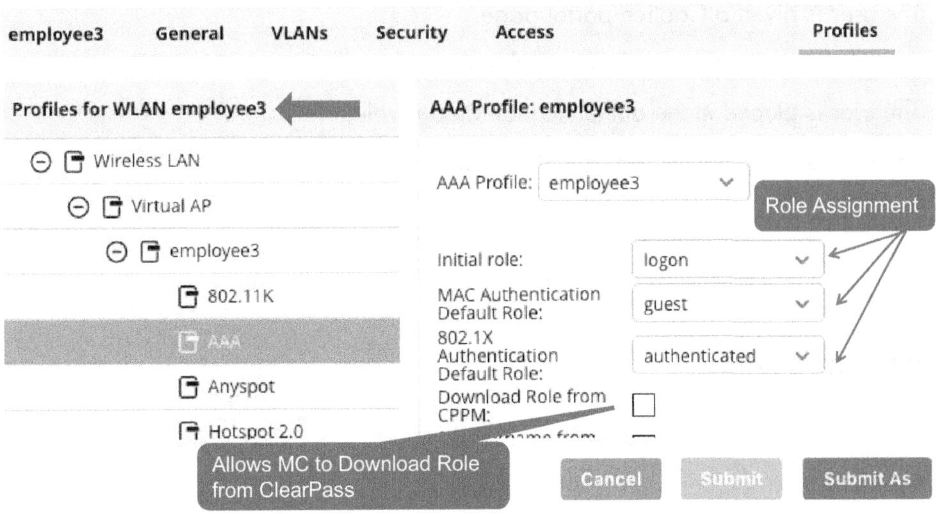

Figure 9-15 WLAN AAA profile—initial and authentication default role

Figure 9-15 shows that the empoyee3 role, selected in the last slide, was placed in the 802.1X authentication default role. This is because the WLAN is configured for 802.1X.

If the RADIUS server responds with a derived role, then the user will be placed in that role. If the RADIUS server simply confirms that the user is authenticated, the user is placed in the 802.1X default role. If the RADIUS returns a value that does not correspond to any MC-defined roles, the user is placed in the authentication type default role.

Understand that these are the default roles for THIS particular AAA profile. You can create another AAA profile with different defaults, applied to a different WLAN. Every WLAN can have a different AAA profile.

Note

ClearPass can download roles directly to the MC, if this option is enabled.

Learning check

3. A user authenticates, and ClearPass sends the VSA "Aruba-User-Role" with a value of Sales. There is no Sales Role in the MC. What happens?
   a. The user is given a Captive portal page.
   b. A Sales Role is automatically created in the MC.
   c. The user is placed in the authentication default role.
   d. The user is de-authenticated from the network.
   e. The user is blacklisted.

Bandwidth limits

Role bandwidth limits

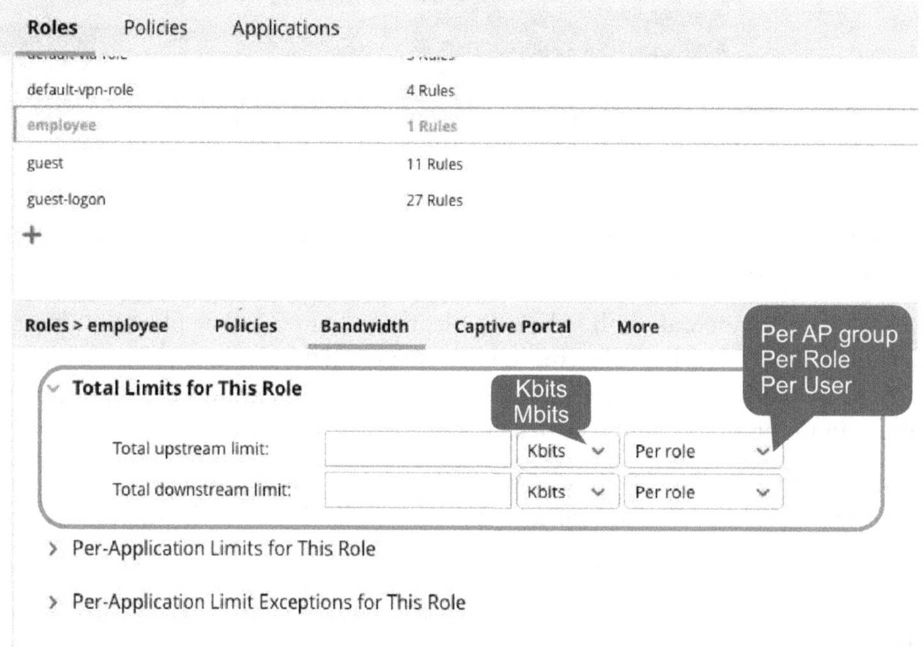

Figure 9-16 Role bandwidth limits

Figure 9-16 shows how to configure a role with bandwidth limits. This example uses the "Per role" option. Thus, bandwidth limits apply to all users in this role. Kbits option is currently selected. However, you can change to mbits if desired. Then enter, say 10 in both upstream and downstream limit fields. Of course, this would limit all users' combined traffic to 10 mbps in each direction.

The Per User option limits bandwidth on a per user basis. If set along with the same 10 kbits values as before, each user may use up to 10 mkbps in each direction.

If you choose the Per AP-group option, bandwidth used for all users in one ap-group is limited to an aggregate 10 kbps total.

Suppose there are six users in a role, and users A and B are connected to APs in ap-group1. Users C and D are in ap-group2. The sum of user A and B's bandwidth may not exceed the configured values. The sum of user C and D's bandwidth may not exceed the configured values.

Application-specific bandwidth contracts allow you to control or reserve rates for specific applications, on a per-role basis.

An optional exclusion list allows you to exclude applications or application categories from the bandwidth contract.

Role application bandwidth limits

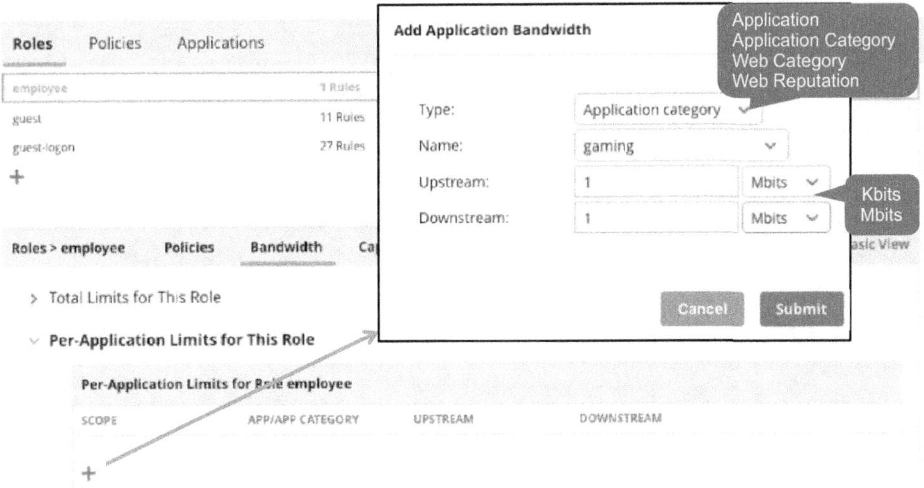

Figure 9-17 Role application bandwidth limits

Figure 9-17 shows the configuration of a role's per-application bandwidth limits, which can be broken down into four categories.

- Specific applications, such as Adobe, Apple-music.
- Application categories include gaming and streaming.
- Web Categories include home and garden, shopping.
- Web Reputation is categorized in levels, between "high risk" and "trustworthy."

The limits can be made for upstream and downstream in Kbits or Mbits.

Learning check

4. What methods can be used to assign user roles?
    a. Initial role
    b. Locally derived
    c. Authentication default role
    d. Server derived role
    e. AP derived role

Troubleshooting

Assess client roles

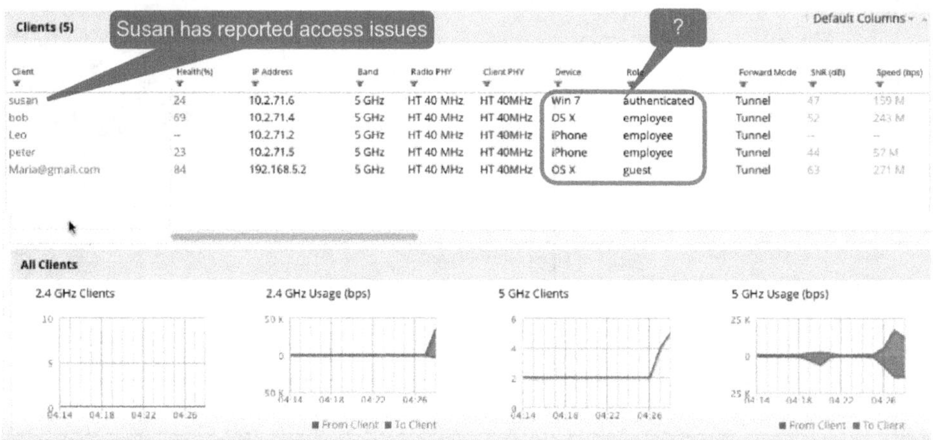

Figure 9-18 Assess client roles

Figure 9-18 shows the client dashboard output. You can see your clients and their assigned roles. All employees are assigned to the employee role, and there is a guest user assigned to the guest role.

Notice that Susan is assigned to the authenticated role, and not the employee role. This could be a problem. Perhaps no VSA or RADIUS attribute was returned for her, or the value returned did not match a configured role.

Now that you have discovered this issue, it is easier to investigate in the server's GUI page. If there is a discrepancy between what your server administrators tell you, as compared to what you see, a deep dive into the logs is necessary.

If the proper role is assigned, but users do not have proper access, you should analyze role and policy configuration. You may need to modify some rules. First, let us look at the client detail for Susan.

AirWave user role derivation command

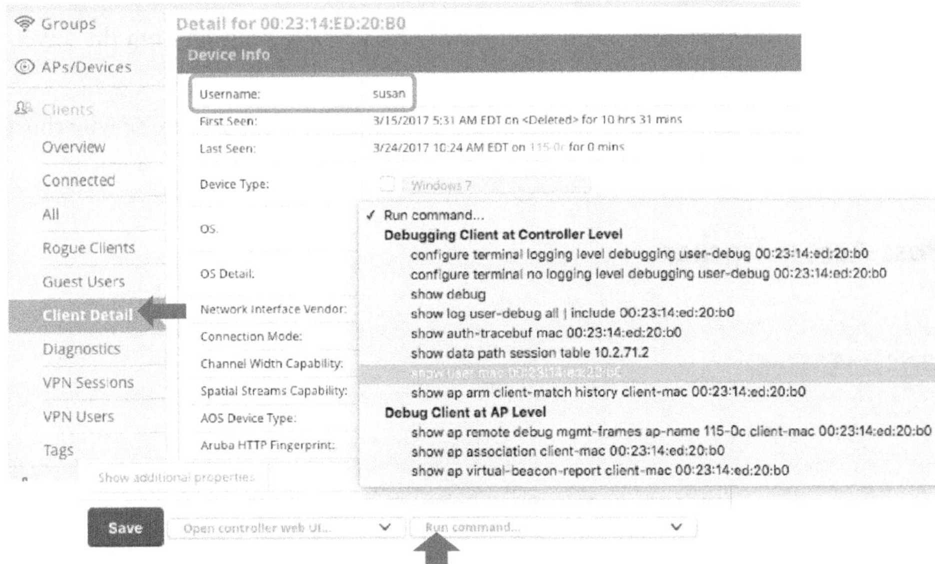

Figure 9-19 AirWave user role derivation command

In Figure 9-19, you are continuing your diagnostic efforts in AirWave. You have navigated to Susan's Client Detail page. In the drop-down menu for "Run command," choose the command `show user mac <mac address>`.

AirWave—Show user mac <mac_address>

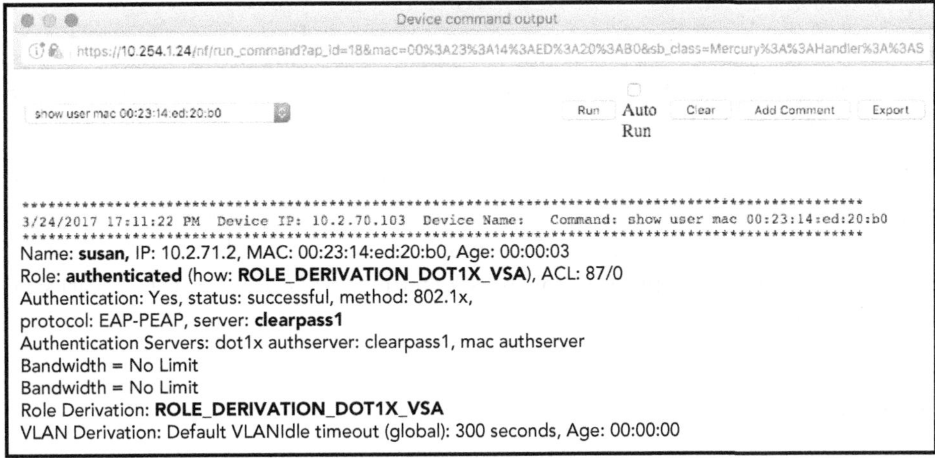

Figure 9-20 AirWave—Show user mac <mac_address>

When you run the command in AirWave, a pop up window shows the results. Figure 9-20 shows Susan's role and method of assignment.

The role was derived using the Role_Derivation_DOT1X_VSA, as returned from the server defined as clearpass1. The VSA assigns the authenticated role.

If this is not the desired assignment, you should access clearpass1, and determine why this role was assigned.

ClearPass Access Tracker

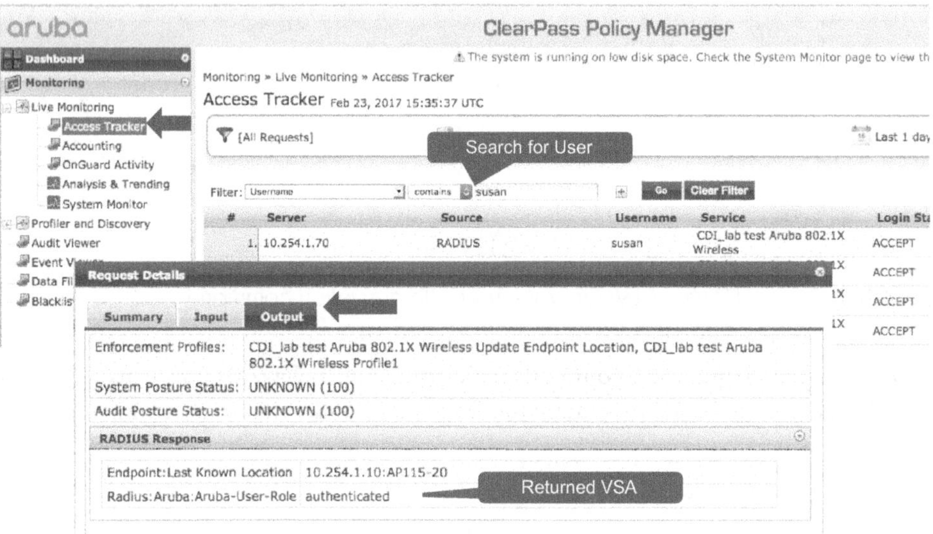

Figure 9-21 ClearPass Access Tracker

In ClearPass, navigate to **Monitoring > Access Tracker**. This is an excellent place to troubleshoot user authentication and role derivation.

Figure 9-21 shows you searching for user Susan. Several entries are found, and you click on the most recent entry. You know that Susan is getting authenticated, but is given the wrong role. Click on the Output tab. You can see that ClearPass is returning the "Aruba-User-Role" VSA, with a value of "authenticated." The ClearPass administrators must determine the reason for this. ClearPass diagnostics is beyond the scope of this course.

Role bandwidth limitation

Refer to the output below of the `show rights guest-auth` command as we explore this new scenario.

You noticed a strain on internet bandwidth. So, over the weekend, you decided to configure a bandwidth limit of 500 K per guest user. Now guests are complaining of a very bad service.

To analyze the guest-auth role, you decide to run the command `show rights guest-auth`. You notice that the limitation was placed on a per *role* basis, instead of a per *user* basis.

Also, a limitation on an application category has been implemented. In this case, gaming.

You might decide to access the controller GUI and configure per user bandwidth contracts, as previously described. Alternatively, you could raise the bandwidth limitation for the per role option.

```
(P1T1-MC) # show rights guest-auth
Derived Role ='guest-auth'
Up BW contract = guest-auth upstreamper-roleui(500000 bits/sec )
Down BW contract = guest-auth downstreamper-roleui (500000 bits/sec)
Name  Type
----  ----
Application BW-Contract List
----------------------------
Name     Type         BW Contract                Id  Direction
----     ----         -----------                --  ---------
gaming   appcategory  guest-authgamingdownstream  4   downstream
gaming   appcategory  guest-authgamingupstream    3   upstream
access-list List
Priority  Source  Destination   Service  Application  Action
TimeRange  Log  Expired  Queue  TOS
--------  ------  -----------   -------  -----------  ------
---------  ---  -------  -----  ---
1         user    corp-network  any                   deny
2         any     any           svc-dhcp              permit
3         user    dns-server    svc-dns               permit
4         user    any           any                   permit
```

10 Remote Access

LEARNING OBJECTIVES

- ✓ This chapter focuses on accommodating remote offices and users. We begin with an overview of the various options, including the use of Remote APs (RAP), Instant APs (IAP), the Virtual Intranet Access (VIA) client, and the use of branch office controllers.
- ✓ You will learn about the infrastructure, including RAP operation and the use of Internet Key Exchange (IKE) and Zero-Touch Provisioning (ZTP). Then you will learn how to use that infrastructure in support of remote client connectivity. In other words, you will learn how to deploy WLANs to use tunnel mode, bridge mode, and split-tunnel mode.
- ✓ In most cases, this remote connectivity is vital to the enterprise, so redundancy is wise. You will learn to achieve this redundancy by using a Local Mobility Switch (LMS), or perhaps via the use of 3G/4G/LTE cellular technology.
- ✓ The final section of this chapter is about HPE Aruba's VIA solution. You will learn how to download, install, configure, and troubleshoot VIA deployments.

Remote access options

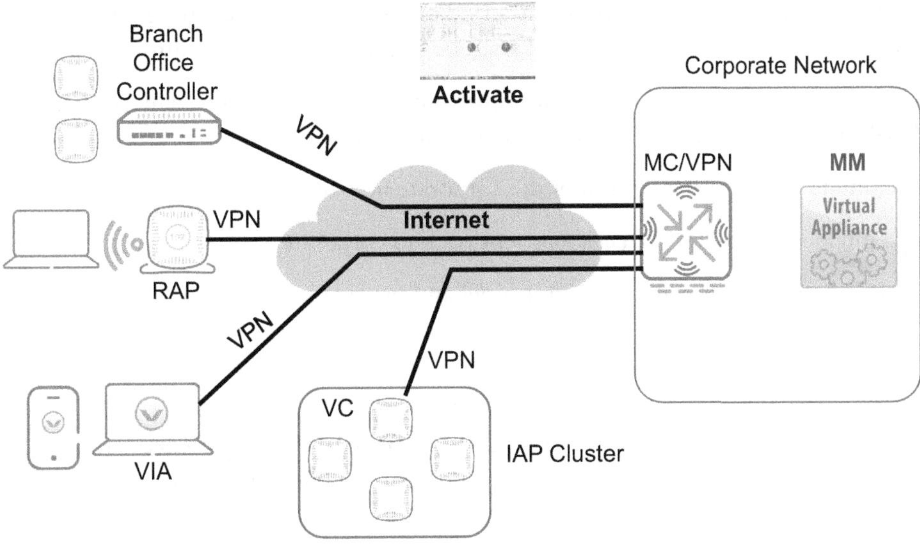

Figure 10-1 Remote access options

Figure 10-1 provides an overview of the various options for remote access. A small to medium-sized office may warrant the deployment of a branch office controller, installed on site. You could also opt to deploy an IAP in which the AP serves as its own controller. Multiple IAPs can form a cluster and elect a Virtual Controller.

Smaller offices may be able to get by with one or more RAPs, directly controlled by a controller at the corporate HQ. Traveling users can use the VIA client to connect to corporate resources, or you might opt for an IAP cluster. The cloud-based Activate service can be used in conjunction with ZTP to provide for easier deployments and reduced IT staffing load.

In all the scenarios described above, a VPN tunnel is formed over the Internet between managed device and controller. This ensures the secure transmission of both control and data plane traffic.

Soon, you will learn how VPN tunneling protects control and data plane traffic.

RAP introduction

RAP overview

RAPs must traverse the internet to get to a controller. Other than that, they function the same as Campus Access Points (CAP). RAPs advertise SSIDs based on their AP group membership, creating a remote extension of the corporate network. RAPS can advertise the exact same SSIDs as corporate HQ CAPs.

It is common to use RAPs to support home workers, branch offices, stores, restaurants, and kiosks. They are useful when small sites need access to the corporate network.

To connect to the controller, the RAP forms an L2TP/IPsec tunnel over the Internet. Some APs are preset as RAPs, but most are CAPs. All CAPs can be staged and converted into RAPs.

While RAPs operate like CAPs, remote locations do have some specific data forwarding requirements. RAPs support three types of SSID configurations to support these needs.

- Tunnel mode is a simple extension of the corporate network.
- Bridge mode is a local SSID that is not sent back to corporate.
- Split-tunnel mode is a combination of tunnel and bridge modes.

RAP advantages

One reason RAPs are very popular is the simplified, consistent user experience. The SSID, encryption, and access rights are consistent across all locations—whether a user connects to a CAP at HQ, or a RAP at a remote facility.

RAPs eliminate the need for VPN clients or additional user credentials. This simplifies the solution, reduces client mistakes, and reduces the load on IT staff.

IT staff also benefit from a single management interface and set of policies. Troubleshooting user issues is about the same, regardless of whether the connection is via RAP or CAP.

RAP encryption

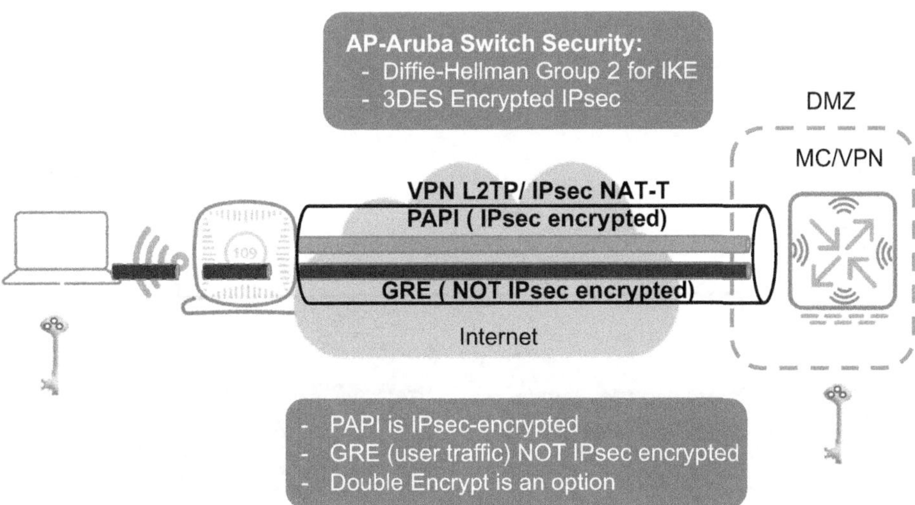

Figure 10-2 RAP encryption

You have learned that RAPS and controllers communicate over the Internet via a VPN tunnel. Figure 10-2 zooms in on the detail of this connectivity.

First, the RAP and controller form an IPsec tunnel. IPsec provides per-packet data origin authentication, data integrity, and data encryption. The IPsec tunnel endpoints (RAP and controller) authenticate each other via certificate or a PSK. Once the IPsec tunnel is established, the Layer 2 Tunneling Protocol (L2TP) connection is formed, and performs a user-level authentication. L2TP offers no protection, nor does it need to. It relies on the protection of the outer IPsec tunnel.

Note

Understand that the "user-level authentication" mentioned above is not related to end users. This refers to username/password authentication between the "users" of the tunnel—the RAP and the controller. This will be described on the next page.

These tunnels form to support control and data plane traffic between the RAP and the controller. Just like CAPs, RAP control plane traffic uses Protocol Application Programming Interface (PAPI). This traffic is encrypted inside an IPsec tunnel, as shown in Figure 10-2.

However, the RAP typically does not encrypt client traffic since it has already been encrypted by the client device. The user authenticates with, say, 802.1X to gain access to the network. Thus, user traffic is already encrypted with AES. It is simply placed inside an unsecured GRE tunnel and forwarded to the controller. However, you can enable the "double encrypt" option, which encrypts all user traffic (preencrypted or not) in the L2TP/IPsec tunnel.

RAP VPN IKE or certificate

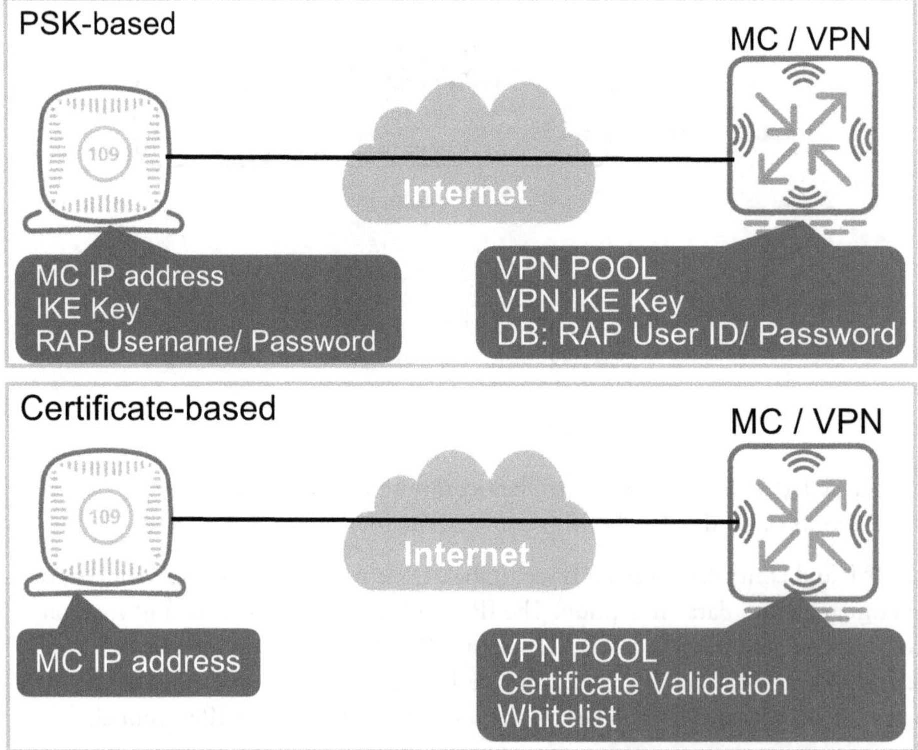

Figure 10-3 RAP VPN IKE or certificate

To form the IPsec tunnel, RAPs and controllers must authenticate to each other. Authentication can be based on either Pre-Shared Keys (PSK) or certificates. Figure 10-3 highlights key configuration settings required on the RAP and controller.

For the PSK method, you must configure matching PSKs on the RAP and controller. You must also configure username/password credentials. You can use the same credentials for all RAPs, but this is not recommended. Unique username/password credentials per AP is preferred. This makes it easier to revoke access for a single RAP. The username/password can be automatically generated. These credentials are placed in the controller's internal DB.

Certificate-based APs require certificate validation on the controller and must be included in the whitelist. All new Aruba APs ship with a factory certificate. The controller can be configured to automatically accept all CAPs and RAPs, or perhaps only APs from a certain subnet.

Deployment options

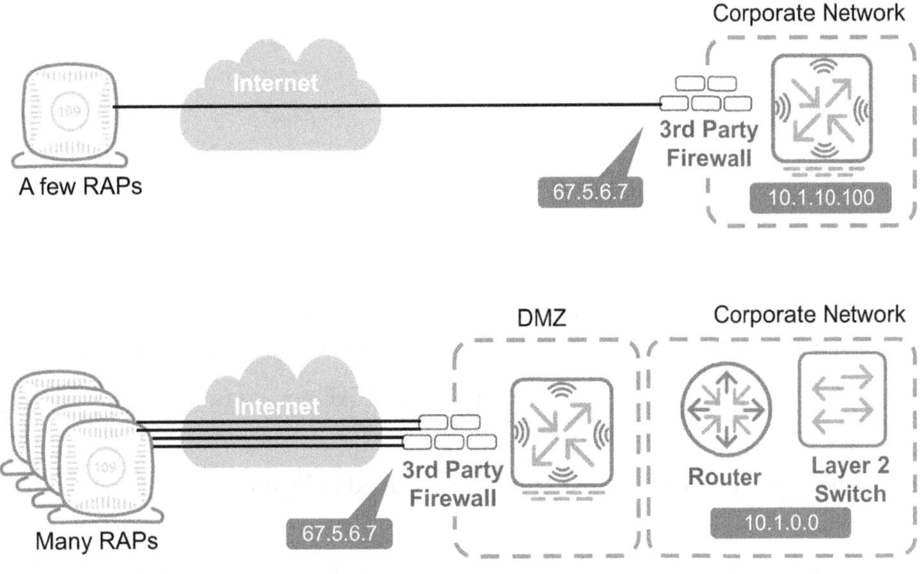

Figure 10-4 Deployment options

RAPs must communicate with a controller. For smaller deployments, the few needed RAPs may terminate directly to a corporate controller, via some third-party firewall. The gateway firewall must NAT the traffic back to the controller. This is shown in the top example of Figure 10-4. If your firewall lacks NAT support, RAPs can be configured to perform NAT.

For larger deployments, the top example shown is not appropriate. It is a best practice to place a separate controller in your De-Militarized Zone (DMZ), as shown in the bottom example of Figure 10-4.

RAP controller assignment

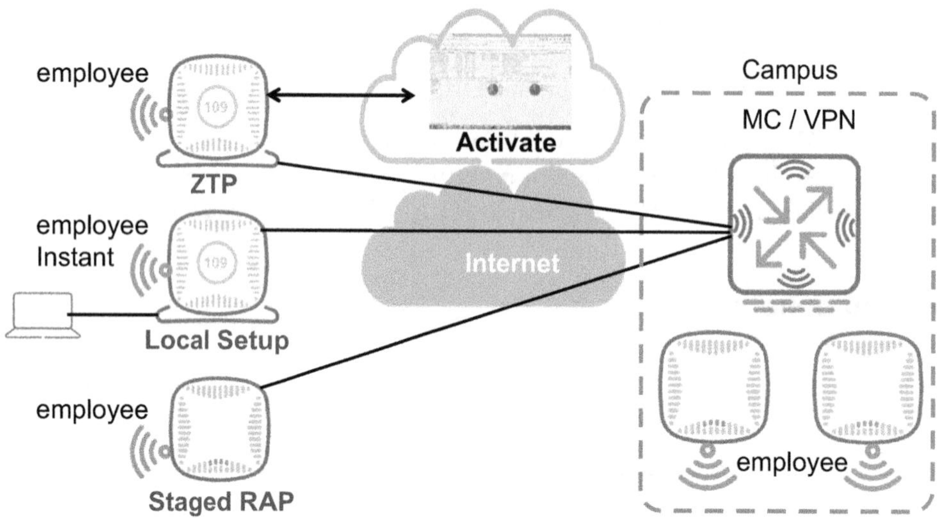

Figure 10-5 RAP controller assignment

RAPs and CAPs can offer identical SSIDs and authentication methods, for a transparent user experience. Whether at a campus or a remote location, the employee experience is the same.

All Aruba APs can function as RAPs, but the methods a RAP uses to find its controller depends on AP type. There are three methods.

Any CAP can be staged to become a RAP. This is represented in Figure 10-5 by the AP named "Staged RAP."

The RAP3/108/109/155 models boot up as IAPs, as depicted in the top-most AP, labeled ZTP. Then they will automatically attempt to communicate with the Aruba cloud-based Activate service. If an entry exists in Activate, it tells the IAPs to convert themselves into RAPs. The RAPs are then directed to an MC with VPN configuration.

IAPs can also be locally converted to RAPs, as represented in Figure 10-5 by the Local Setup AP. You can associate with the instant SSID or connect an Ethernet cable, then open the IAP GUI page and make the conversion to RAP.

Learning check

1. What are the two VPN deployment methods for RAPs?
   a. IKE/PSK
   b. RAP over VIA
   c. Certificate based
   d. Controller Activate
   e. MC in DMZ

RAP WLAN

RAP WLAN forwarding modes

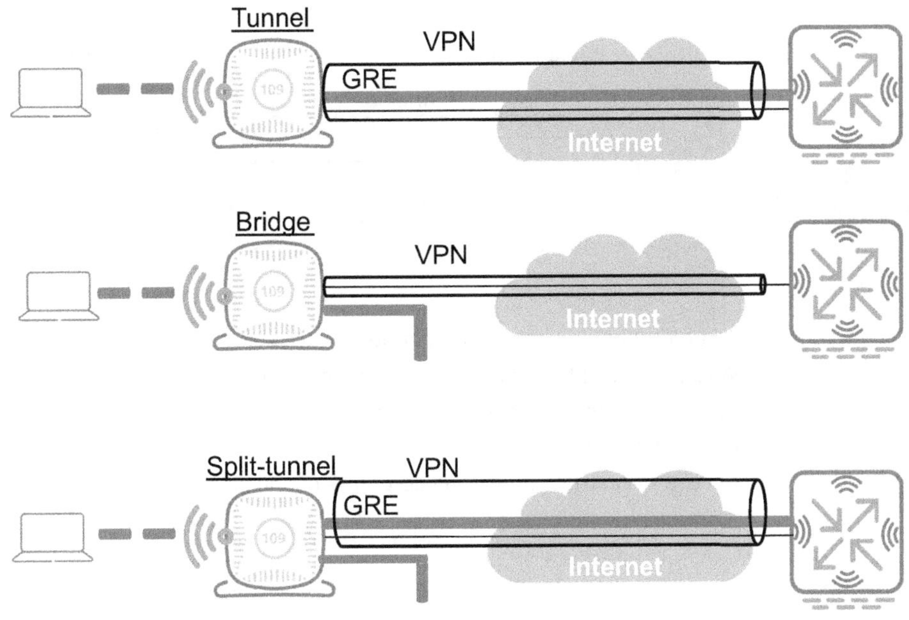

Figure 10-6 RAP WLAN forwarding modes

RAP SSIDs can be configured to forward user traffic in tunnel, bridge, or split-tunnel mode (Figure 10-6).

Tunnel mode—Data traffic is tunneled inside IPsec to the controller. Data is encrypted and unencrypted at the controller. Data traffic is not encrypted by the RAP since the user traffic is already encrypted. However, double encryption is an option. On the other hand, control traffic uses IPsec encryption to the controller. The RAP sends all 802.11 frames over a GRE tunnel to the controller. Clients obtain an IP address from a VLAN on the controller in the corporate network.

Bridge mode—The RAP encrypts and decrypts the traffic, but all traffic is locally bridged, directly toward its ultimate destination. The RAP converts each user's 802.11 frame to an Ethernet frame, and then bridges these frames to the local Ethernet LAN. The client acquires its IP address locally.

Split-Tunneling—This mode is used for employees that may need to tunnel corporate-related traffic to the controller but also have local requirements. You configure firewall roles and policies. This enables the RAP to decide which traffic is tunneled and which traffic is locally bridged. The client obtains an IP address from a VLAN on the controller in the corporate network.

RAP tunnel mode WLAN

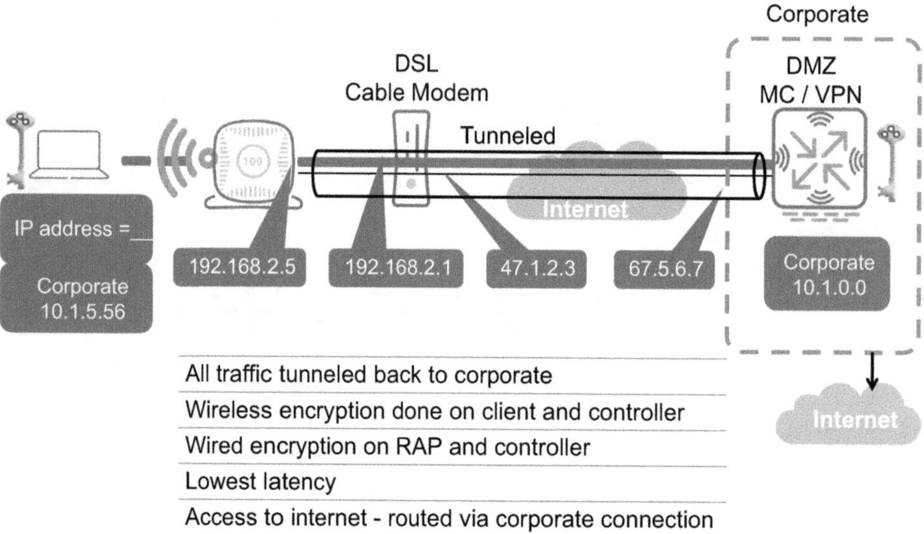

Figure 10-7 RAP tunnel mode WLAN

Figure 10-7 shows the process of a RAP forwarding WLAN traffic in tunnel mode:

- The client encrypts the traffic and transmits it to the RAP. The RAP forwards this pre-encrypted traffic over a GRE tunnel, to the MC.
- The MC decrypts this client-encrypted traffic. The MC encrypts all traffic destined to the user endpoint, where it is decrypted. Of course, this assumes the SSID was setup with encryption.
- The users are assigned a corporate IP address, from the corporate DHCP server.

- All traffic is tunneled to the controller, even if it is not ultimately destined for internal corporate subnets.
- The RAP may have extra wired ports, also configured in tunnel mode, to support end-user connectivity. These users are also assigned a corporate IP address. However, their traffic will be encrypted by the RAP with IPsec and decrypted by the MC.
- Lower latency is achieved since the RAP need not encrypt wireless traffic. It merely forwards it over the GRE tunnel.

RAP bridge mode WLAN

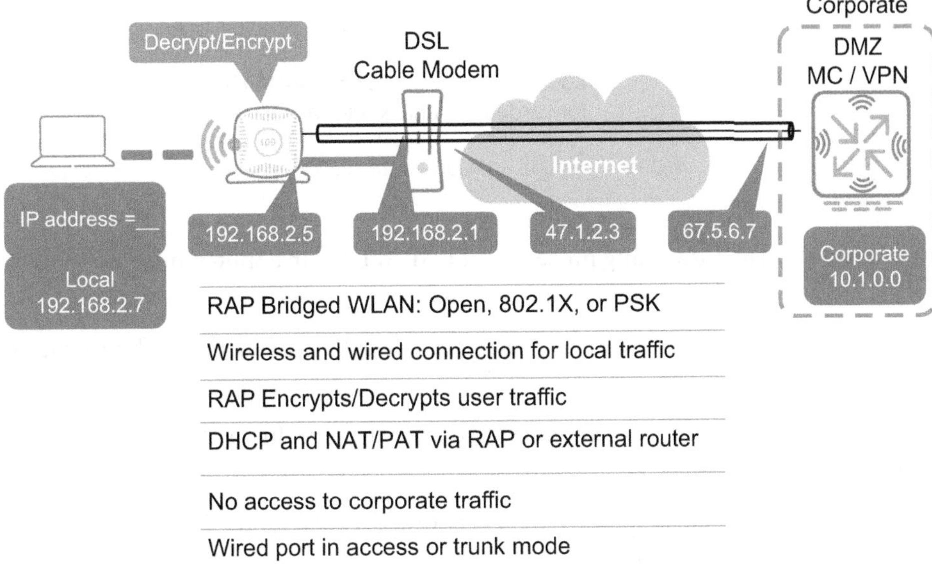

Figure 10-8 RAP bridge mode WLAN

Figure 10-8 shows the data forwarding process for a RAP WLAN in bridge mode, as described below.

- Bridged traffic is decrypted locally on the RAP.
- User IP addresses can be assigned from a local DHCP server or from the RAP, which can also perform NAT and PAT. Notice that the client has received a local address of 192.168.2.7.
- No traffic is sent to the corporate network. The traffic is only routed locally.

RAP split-tunnel mode WLAN

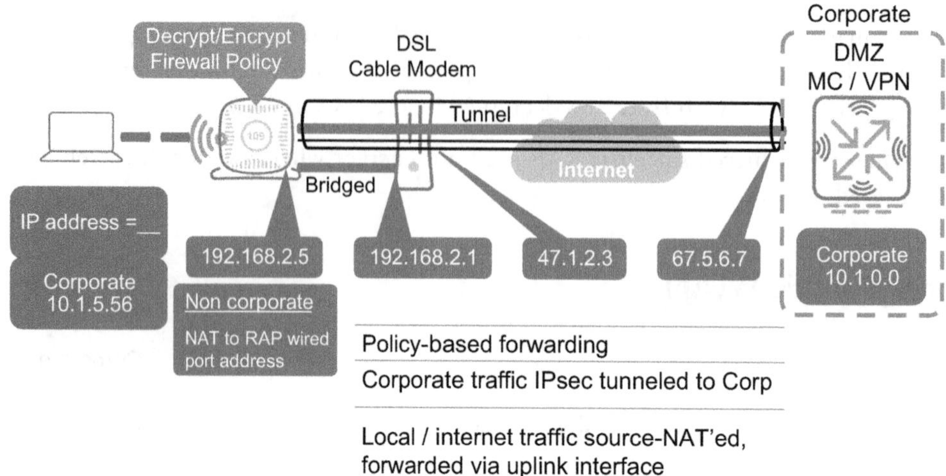

Figure 10-9 RAP split-tunnel mode WLAN

Figure 10-9 shows the data forwarding process for a RAP WLAN in a split-tunnel mode, as described below.

- Split-tunnel mode allows the RAP to route traffic locally or send the traffic to the corporate network.
- The RAP uses a configured firewall policy to decide if the traffic is destined for the corporate network.
- If the traffic is not destined for the corporate network, the RAP source-NATs the traffic to its own Ethernet address and routes it locally.
- The RAP decrypts packets from Corporate, and encrypts packets within IPsec for packets destined to the Corporate.
- The client is assigned a corporate IP address.

WLAN examples

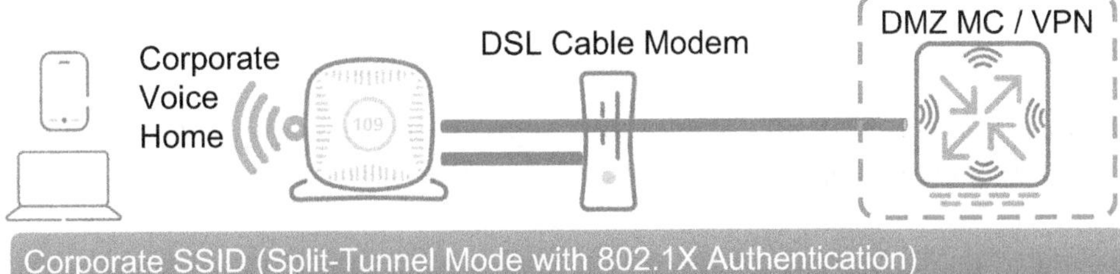

Corporate SSID (Split-Tunnel Mode with 802.1X Authentication)

- Employee laptop can reach corporate and local resources
- 802.1X authentication and security implemented at corporate
- RAP decrypts all packets. Corp packets re-encrypt for tunnel transport
- Local internet traffic is source-NAT'd at the AP

Voice SSID (Full-Tunnel Mode with PSK Authentication)

- AP handles association and authentication
- PSK refreshed periodically for low-latency re-association
- Traffic encrypted at phone, decrypted at corporate

Home SSID (Bridge Mode with PSK authentication)

- Peer-to-peer exchanges facilitate local printer sharing
- Traffic is locally bridged

Figure 10-10 WLAN examples

Figure 10-10 shows a scenario where a RAP is configured with three SSIDS. Each SSID uses one of the three forwarding modes.

The corporate SSID is configured for split-tunnel forwarding. A split-tunnel firewall policy has rules that identify corporate subnets. Traffic destined for these subnets is tunneled to the Corporate. Local or Internet-bound traffic will not appear in the list of corporate subnets. Thus, this traffic is source-NAT'ed and locally bridged.

The voice SSID is in tunnel mode. The voice application requires corporate access to reach the SIP server. Otherwise, the voice solution is broken. Therefore, all traffic is tunneled to the Corporate.

The home SSID is in bridge forwarding mode. Users authenticate to this SSID using a PSK, which is sent from the controller via the secured L2TP/IPsec tunnel. All traffic is locally forwarded directly to its ultimate destination.

RAP WLAN operation mode

SSIDs support four operating modes, as described below:

- **Standard Mode**—The SSID requires controller connectivity to function.
- **Always Mode**—The SSID operates regardless of controller connectivity.

- **Backup Mode**—The SSID is only advertised if controller connectivity is lost, or if the RAP has never communicated with the controller.
- **Persistent Mode**—The SSID is only advertised upon after initial controller connectivity is established. However, if this connectivity is lost, the SSID remains functional.

Tunnel and split-tunnel *forwarding* modes only support the standard *operating* mode. Only the bridged forwarding mode supports all four operating modes.

Learning check

2. In split-tunnel mode, the device will receive an IP address from which of the following?
   a. From the RAP DHCP
   b. From the local network DHCP server
   c. Corporate DHCP
   d. Will get a public IP address
   e. Laptop own DHCP server

Configuring RAP

RAP configuration steps

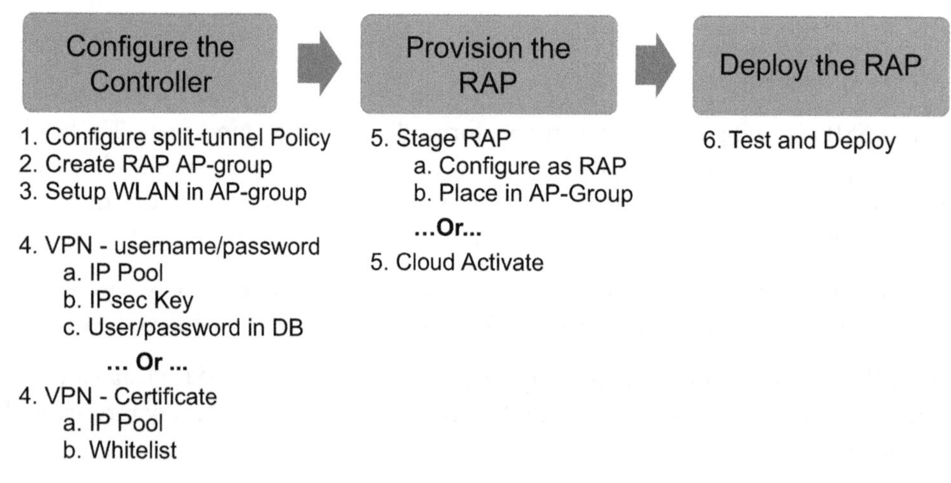

Figure 10-11 RAP configuration steps

Here are the steps for creating a RAP (Figure 10-11):

1. Configure the appropriate policy for the forwarding mode. For example, you need a split-tunnel policy for the corporate SSID, which uses the split-tunnel forwarding mode.
2. Configure a new AP group for the RAP. This is not required, but is highly recommended.
3. Create or assign a specific WLAN to the new RAP group.
4. For a VPN using username/password-based authentication:
    a. Configure the VPN server on the controller, and add an IP address pool.
    b. Configure an IPsec key (unless you use certificates).
    c. For L2TP/PAP authentication, configure username/password credentials in the internal data base.
    d. Configure the authentication server, for username/password validation.
4. For a VPN using certificate-based authentication:
    a. Configure the VPN server on the controller, and add an IP address pool.
    b. Configure the AP whitelist.
5. Stage the RAP
    a. Provision the AP to be a RAP.
    b. Place it in the right AP group with the controller IP and matching IPsec settings.
    c. If configuring AP certificates, add the RAP into the whitelist.
5. If you are using Activate, RAP staging is not necessary. Activate redirects the RAP to a specific controller and an AP group.
6. Finally, test the RAP. If IPsec is up, then test the SSID connectivity. You can now deploy RAPs.

Configuring WLAN & role

Split-tunnel policies

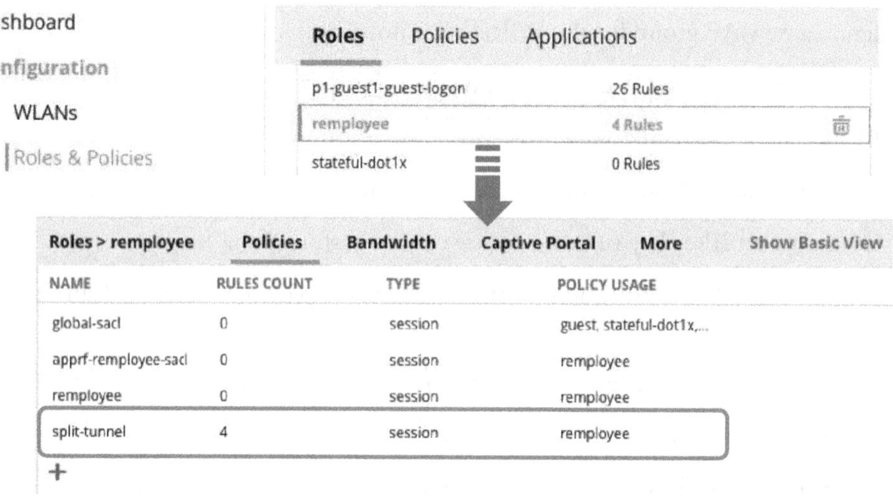

Figure 10-12 Configuring WLAN & Role

Figure 10-12 shows that you have navigated to **Configuration > Roles & Policies**. This scenario involves a split-tunnel policy for the role named "remployee." Within this role, all global and SSID-based policies are executed before the split-tunnel policy. In this case, the preceding policies have no rules.

Split-tunnel policy

```
split-tunnel
------------
Pri  Source          Destination     Service    App  Action
1    any             any             svc-dhcp        permit
2    user            corporate-net   any             permit
3    corporate-net   user            any             permit
4    user            any             any             src-nat
                                                     pool dynamic-srcnat
```

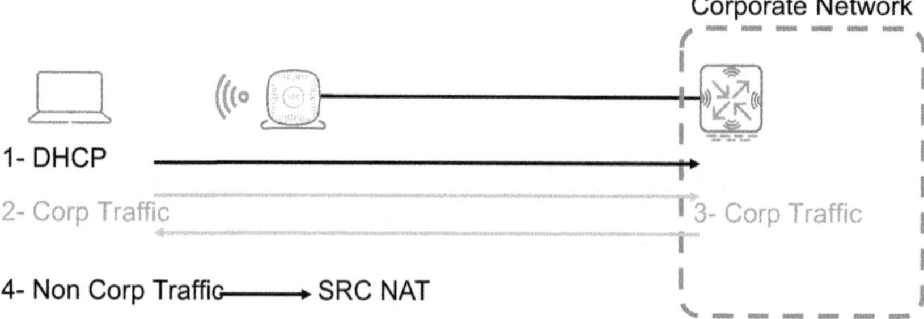

Figure 10-13 Split-tunnel policy

The purpose of a split-tunnel policy is to determine which traffic is allowed to access the corporate networks.

In Figure 10-13, the first rule in this policy allows DHCP to the corporate network. The next two rules allow traffic from users to the corporate subnets.

The actual subnets are defined in an alias, which is a best practice. The use of aliases enhances your workflow. You simply modify the subnets specified in the alias, and every policy that references this alias is automatically updated.

The fourth rule is for noncorporate traffic. All this traffic is source-NAT'ed to the RAP's local IP address and routed out of the RAPs Ethernet port, as local traffic.

WLAN configuration

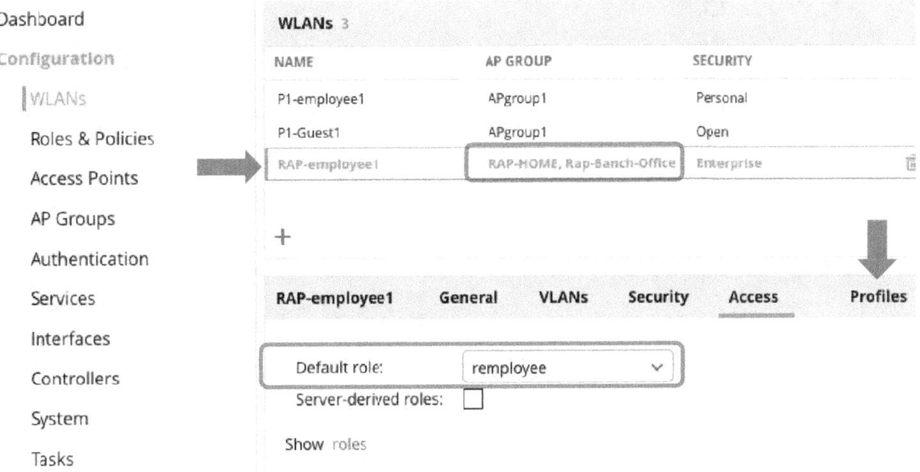

Figure 10-14 WLAN configuration

This example shows creation of the RAP-employee1 WLAN. This WLAN is assigned to two AP groups—RAP-HOME and Rap-Branch-Office. This WLAN is configured with 802.1X authentication and placed in VLAN 73. The remployee role, with the split-tunnel policy, is assigned as the default role for this WLAN. Initially, the WLAN was created to use the tunnel-forwarding mode. To configure the WLAN to use split-tunnel mode, you must edit the WLAN profile.

VAP forward mode—Split-tunnel

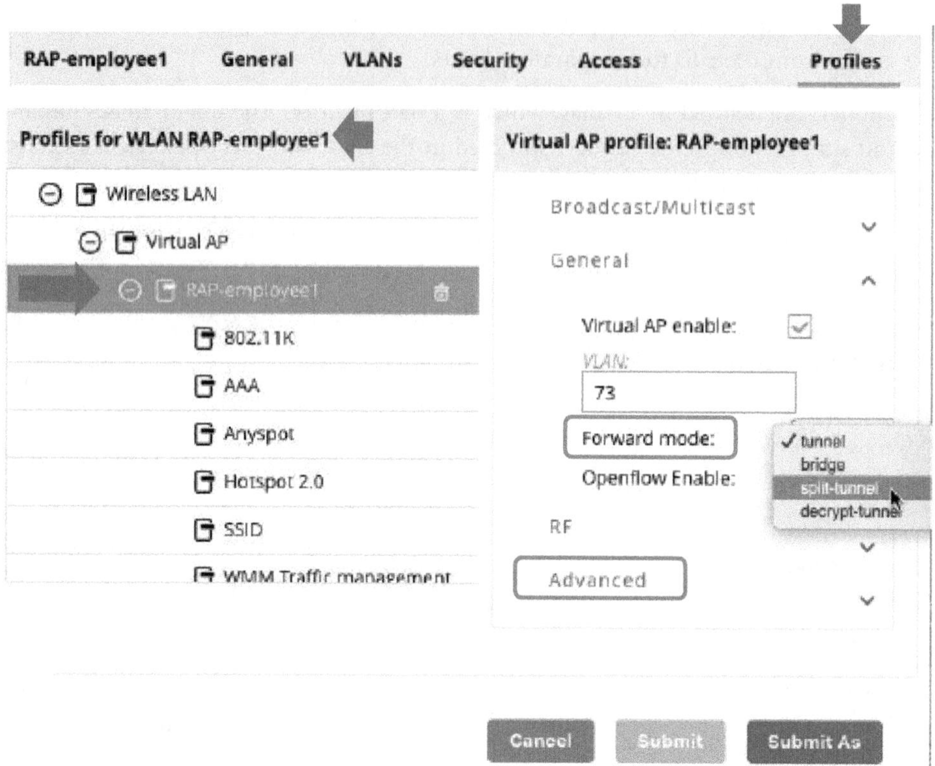

Figure 10-15 VAP forward mode—Split-tunnel

Figure 10-15 shows how to edit the WLAN forwarding mode. Originally set to tunnel mode, the objective is to change it to split-tunnel mode, by navigating to the profiles tab.

1. In the WLAN profile, expand the WLAN and virtual AP and select the VAP.
2. In the General section, select the forwarding mode.
3. Choose split-tunnel from the drop-down menu.
4. If the intent was to use the bridge-forwarding mode, no specific role is needed—simply select the bridge-forwarding mode.

Note

Decrypt tunnel mode is only for campus APs and is not recommended for RAPs.

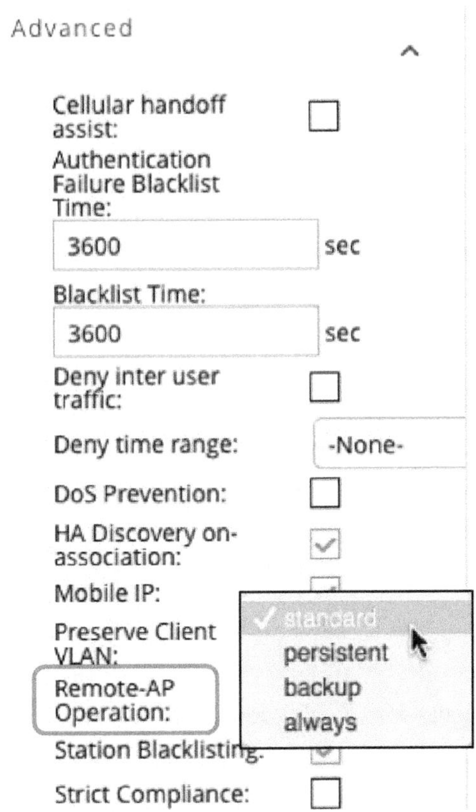

Figure 10-16 VAP forward mode—Split-tunnel (Cont.)

5. Expand the Advanced section to set the Remote-AP operation mode (Figure 10-16).
   a. For split-tunnel, only the standard option is a valid choice.
   b. If a bridge WLAN is created, then you have the choice of persistent, backup, and always.

VPN IKE setup

VPN address pool and IKE key

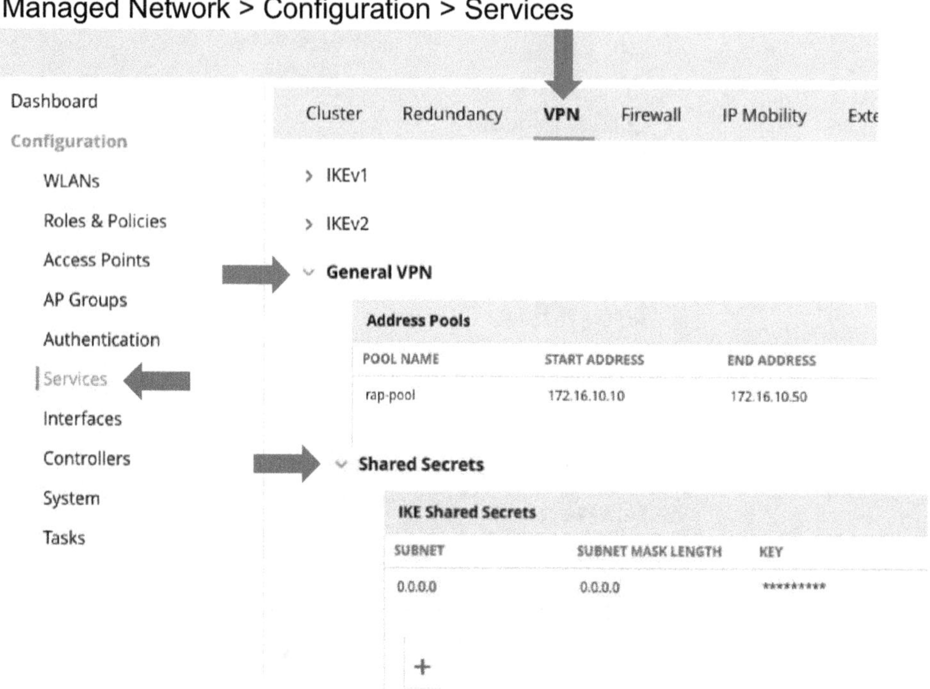

Figure 10-17 VPN address pool and IKE key

The VPN server is preconfigured with the requirements for the RAP. To see and edit these settings navigate to **Managed Networks > Configuration > Services**, then select the VPN tab.

Under the VPN tab, you can select to enable the RAP connection. PAP uses a shared secret between the RAP and controller tunnel. Next, configure the VPN IP pool of addresses as required. These address pools are used for the RAP's inside address.

The IPsec protocol suite includes IKE. IKE establishes secure communication channels called Security Associations (SA). For the RAP solution, SA authentication requires matching shared secrets on the RAP and the VPN server. Figure 10-17 shows that an IKE-shared secret key has been configured to be used for connecting devices on any subnet, with any mask.

Assuming the RAP has a matching key, the SA will form, and then the IPsec tunnel can be established. Remember, IKE-shared secret keys are not required for certificate-based RAPs.

If you intend to use the internal database for authentication, be sure to add the RAPs username/password credentials.

Note

The IPsec protocol uses "transforms." This is a collection of protocols used to "transform" your clear, unprotected data into encrypted, protected transmissions. The default transforms used by the Aruba solution are cryptographically strong, and need not be modified.

RAP staging

RAP staging review

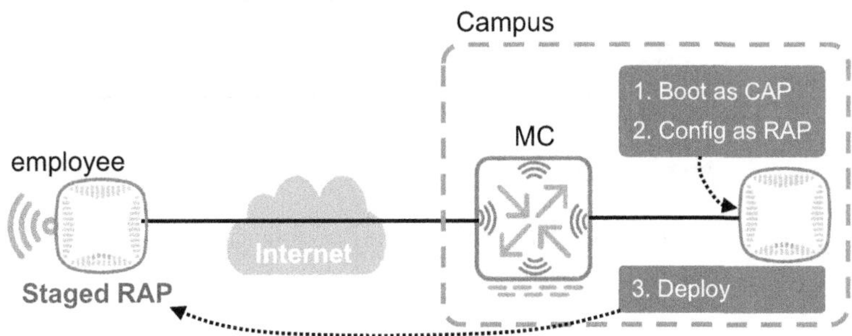

Figure 10-18 RAP staging review

You have learned that all HPE Aruba APs can function as a RAP, and that RAPs form tunnels with a controller. Recall that, other than static configuration, there are two methods for a RAP to find the controller—staging and ZTP. The method used depends on the AP type.

In Figure 10-18, a CAP is staged to become a RAP. First, the AP boots up as a CAP. Then you manually configure, or stage it, to become a RAP. Finally, you deploy the RAP to the desired location. Read on to find out how.

RAP staging configuration

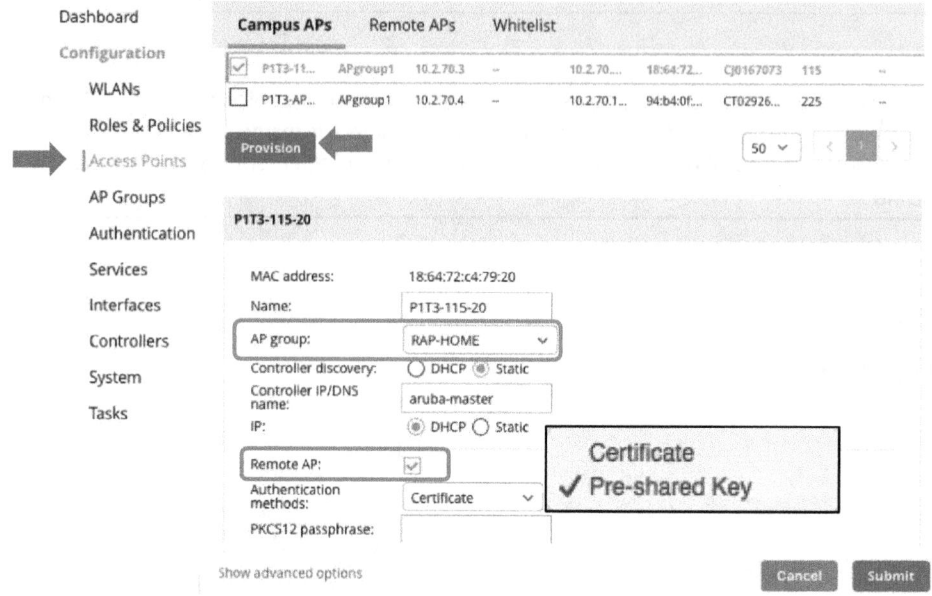

Figure 10-19 RAP staging configuration

To stage an AP to become a RAP, it must first join the network as a CAP. Figure 10-19 shows that you have navigated to **Configuration > Access Points**.

- Select the CAP from the Access Points tab and click on provisioning.
- Place the CAP in the proper AP group and then select the RAP option.
- The authentication methods can be Certificate- or PSK-based.

This configuration continues below.

RAP staging configuration (cont.)

- If you are using the PSK option (as opposed to certificates), you must configure the RAP's IKE PSK to match that configured on the VPN server.
- For the credential assignment, you could select Global User Name, but all RAPs would use the same usernames and passwords. This is not recommended as it would be difficult to revoke a single RAP.

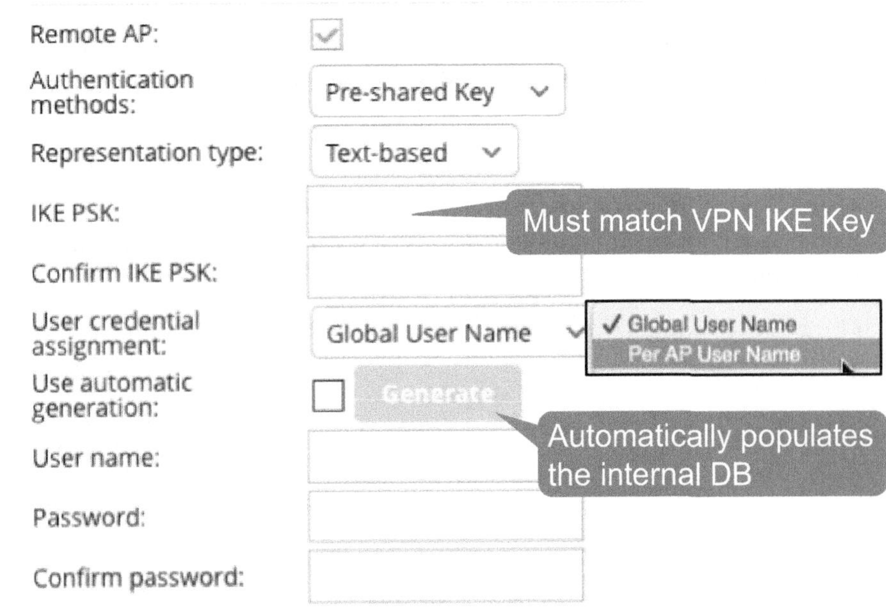

Figure 10-20 RAP staging configuration (cont.)

- Instead, select the Per AP User Name option. You can enter your own user names and passwords, or simply click **Use automatic generation** to have matching credentials created for you.

RAP ZTP

ZTP

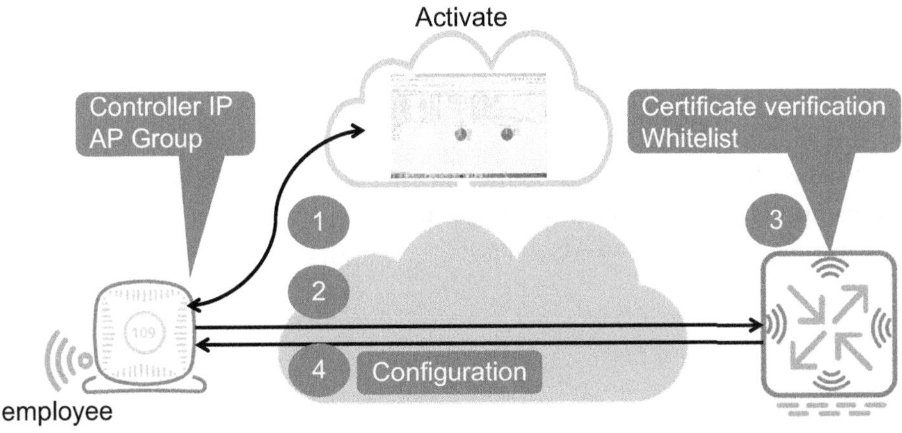

Figure 10-21 ZTP

ZTP makes deployments very easy, as shown in Figure 10-21. The RAPs initially boot up as IAPs. If the IAP has an Ethernet connection to the Internet, it communicates with the Activate cloud-based service. The IAP identifies itself with a MAC address, serial number, and type. If listed, Activate tells this IAP to convert itself to a RAP and to communicate with an MC. Activate also provides the AP group name.

Now that the IAP is a RAP, it communicates with the controller. The controller verifies the RAP certificate, and that it is included in the whitelist. If all is correct, the controller transmits the RAP's AP group configuration.

Whitelist

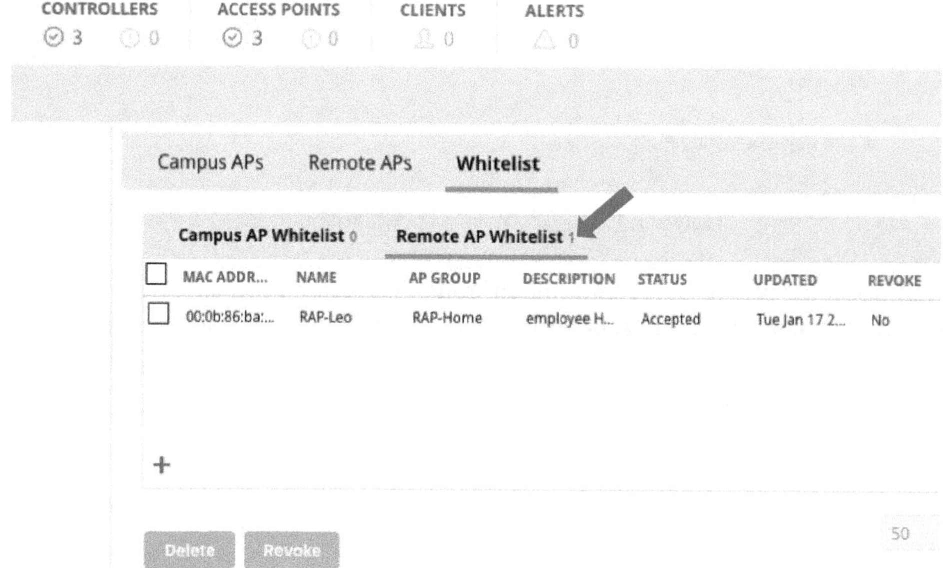

Figure 10-22 Whitelist

Figure 10-22 shows that a whitelist has been created for a certificate-based RAP, by navigating to **Managed Network > Configuration > Access Points**. This list can be automatically populated. The whitelist specifies the RAP name and AP group.

Aruba Activate

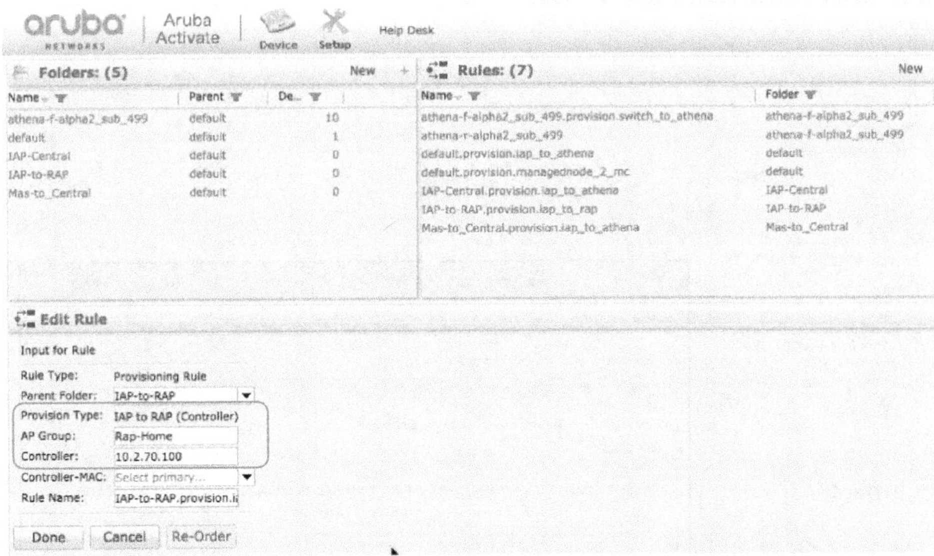

Figure 10-23 Aruba Activate

Figure 10-23 shows the user interface for an Activate account. Smaller networks will depend on the main Activate account. Large corporations may want their own account. If so, they can make a request to Aruba HPE.

This Activate account has a rule that will convert IAPs to RAPs. It specifies the AP-group and the MC IP address. All IAPs associated to this rule will be converted.

Local configuration

Local IAP GUI—Conversion to RAP

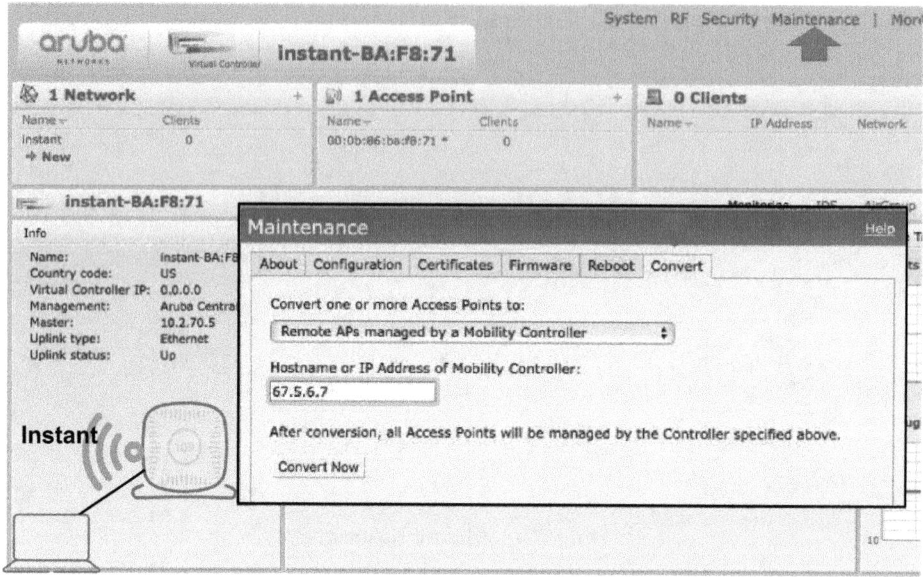

Figure 10-24 Local IAP GUI—Conversion to RAP

To use ZTP, all RAPs are initially IAPs. You have learned that Activate can convert and direct the RAP to a mobility controller. However, if Activate is not accessible or not configured, you can perform a local configuration (Figure 10-24).

To connect, associate to the Instant WLAN. Alternatively, connect an Ethernet port to the RAP/IAP and you will receive an IP address.

Login to the IAP GUI with a username/password of admin/admin. Proceed to the maintenance tab and click on the Convert tab.

In the drop-down menu select **RAPs managed by a Mobility controller**. Enter the IP address or the URL of the mobility controller.

Remember, this is not the IP address of the Mobility Master. It is the IP address of a mobility controller or a gateway firewall that will NAT the traffic to the MC.

RAP authentication (optional)

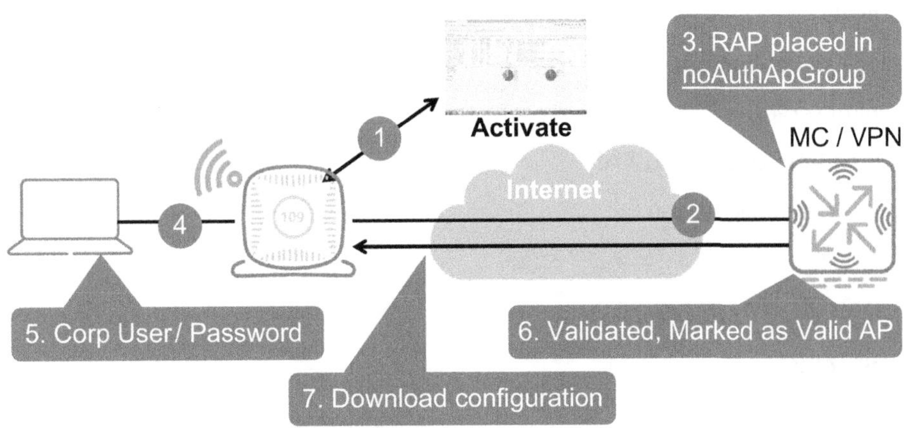

Figure 10-25 RAP authentication (optional)

You have the option to use RAP authentication (Figure 10-25). If enabled, a new RAP is initially assigned to the AP group named NoAuthApGroup. This means the RAP has been partially provisioned, but not yet authenticated at the remote site. This allows you to connect to an unauthorized RAP via a wired port and enter a corporate username and password. Once a valid user is authorized, the MC marks the RAP as authorized. The RAP then downloads the configuration from its assigned AP group.

Here are the steps for this process:

1. IAP/RAP boots and queries the activate server for the MC IP address.
2. The RAP now communicates with the MC.
3. The RAP is placed in the NoAuthApGroup. This allows the user to gain wired access.
4. You connect to the RAP via Ethernet.
5. You authenticate with a corporate username and password.
6. The MC validates these credentials against a RADIUS server.
7. If validated, the MC moves the AP to its proper AP group. Thus, the AP is configured and begins to advertise SSIDs.

Learning check

3. Name three ways a RAP can be directed to the MC/VPN.
   a. Activate
   b. IAP Local configuration
   c. Central server
   d. Staged from a CAP to a RAP
   e. RAP Local configuration

RAP troubleshooting

RAP monitoring

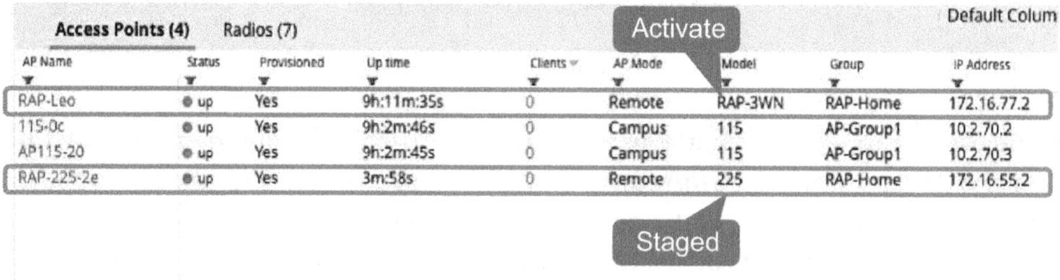

Access Points (4) Radios (7) Default Colum

AP Name	Status	Provisioned	Up time	Clients	AP Mode	Model	Group	IP Address
RAP-Leo	up	Yes	9h:11m:35s	0	Remote	RAP-3WN	RAP-Home	172.16.77.2
115-0c	up	Yes	9h:2m:46s	0	Campus	115	AP-Group1	10.2.70.2
AP115-20	up	Yes	9h:2m:45s	0	Campus	115	AP-Group1	10.2.70.3
RAP-225-2e	up	Yes	3m:58s	0	Remote	225	RAP-Home	172.16.55.2

Activate
Staged

Figure 10-26 RAP monitoring

Navigate to **Dashboard > Access Points** to monitor APs (Figure 10-26). This list shows four APs, two of which are RAPS. RAP-Leo is a RAP3 model that was either locally configured or used Activate. The AP named RAP-225-2e was staged. Both APs belong to the AP group RAP-Home. You also see the RAP's VPN inner IP address.

 **Note**

Nothing in the output shown in Figure 10-26 reveals whether the AP was locally configured, used Activate, or was staged. You would have known this because of your previous configuration efforts.

Certificate RAP/IKE RAP

You can monitor APs from the CLI with the command `show ap database`.

The output from this command is shown below, with a list of APs. Look at the "Flags" column. RAP-225-2e was staged. The "R" tells us that it is a RAP, and the lack of a "c" tells us that it is not certificate-based; therefore, it must be using IKE PSK.

```
(P1T1-MC) #show ap database

AP Database
-----------
Name        Group      AP Type  IP Address    Status          Flags  Switch IP     Standby IP
-------     -------    -------- ---------     ------          -----  ----------    -----------
115-0c      AP-Group1  115      10.2.70.3     Up 28m:1s              10.2.70.101   0.0.0.0
AP115-20    AP-Group1  115      10.2.70.2     Up 6h:17m:53s          10.2.70.101   0.0.0.0
RAP-225-2e  RAP-Home   225      172.16.55.8   Up 27m:16s      R      10.2.70.101   0.0.0.0
RAP-Leo     RAP-Home   RAP-3WN  172.16.55.7   Up 28m:10s      Rc2    10.2.70.101   0.0.0.0
Flags:
U = Unprovisioned; N = Duplicate name; G = No such group; L = Unlicensed
I = Inactive; D = Dirty or no config; E = Regulatory Domain Mismatch
X = Maintenance Mode; P = PPPoE AP; B = Built-in AP; s = LACP striping
R = Remote AP; R- = Remote AP requires Auth; C = Cellular RAP;
c = CERT-based RAP; 1 = 802.1X authenticated AP; 2 = Using IKE version 2
u = Custom-Cert RAP; S = Standby-mode AP; J = USB cert at AP
i = Indoor; o = Outdoor        M = Mesh node; Y = Mesh Recovery
z = Datazone AP
```

RAP-Leo is a certificate-based RAP. The flags show that it is a RAP, it is certificate-based, and it is using IKE version 2.

As with the previous GUI output, you also see the AP group, AP type, IP address, up time and what switch is servicing the RAPs.

Note that there is no standby IP for these RAPs. This means there is no failover controller for redundancy. You will learn about this in the next section of this chapter.

RAP VPN connection

The following shows the output for the command `show crypto ipsec sa`. You can see an IPsec SA for each of the RAP VPN tunnels.

```
(P1T1-MC) #show crypto IPsec sa

IPsec SA Active Session Information
-----------------------------------
Initiator IP Responder IP  InitiatorID     ResponderID Flags Start Time      Inner IP
------------ ------------  -----------     ----------- ----- --------------- --------
67.4.71.5    10.2.70.101   172.16.55.8/32  0.0.0.0/0   UT    Mar 10 13:00:33 172.16.55.8
```

```
IPsec SA (V2) Active Session Information
-----------------------------------
Initiator IP  Responder IP  SPI(IN/OUT)        Flags Start Time        Inner IP
------------  ------------  ----------------   ----- ---------------   --------
78.5.81.4     10.2.70.101   e5019e00/c3169d00  UT2   Mar 10 13:00:25   172.16.55.7
Flags:
T = Tunnel Mode; E = Transport Mode; U = UDP Encap
L = L2TP Tunnel; N = Nortel Client; C = Client; 2 = IKEv2
```

You see the tunnel initiator and responder IP addresses, which is verification that the VPN tunnel is up. You can tell that the entry with an inner IP address of 172.16.55.8 is the IKE RAP – it does not have a "2" in the Flags column. The entry with an inner IP address of 172.16.55.7 is the certificate based RAP3.

RAP redundancy

RAP redundancy

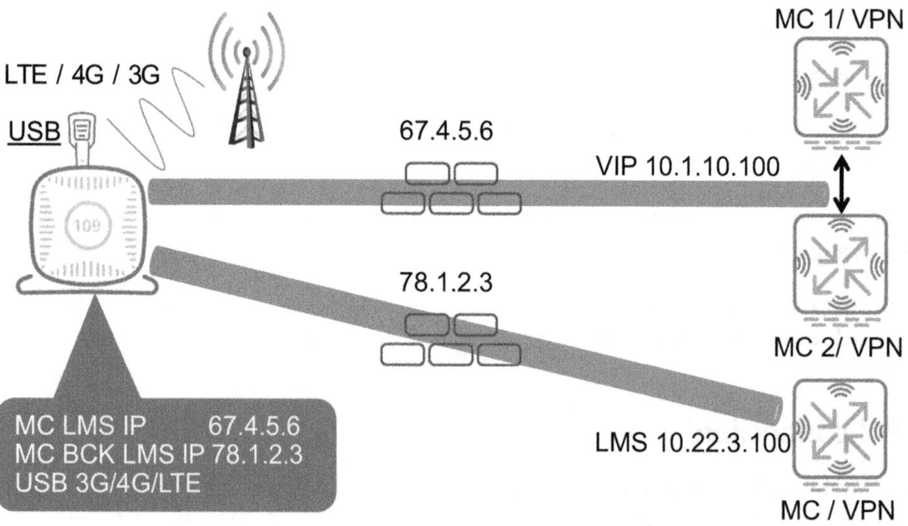

Figure 10-27 RAP redundancy

Figure 10-27 shows RAP redundancy options. The RAP may be configured with the Local Message Switch (LMS) IP address of the MC. Additionally, you can configure the RAP with a backup-LMS IP address. If the RAP loses contact with the LMS-IP, it attempts to contact the backup LMS IP.

You can also configure the RAP to use a USB-based 3G/4G/LTE device. If you do, and the RAP loses local connectivity, it attempts to use a cellular connection. If the USB supports multiple standards, then the technology with the highest speed is tried first.

RAP cluster redundancy

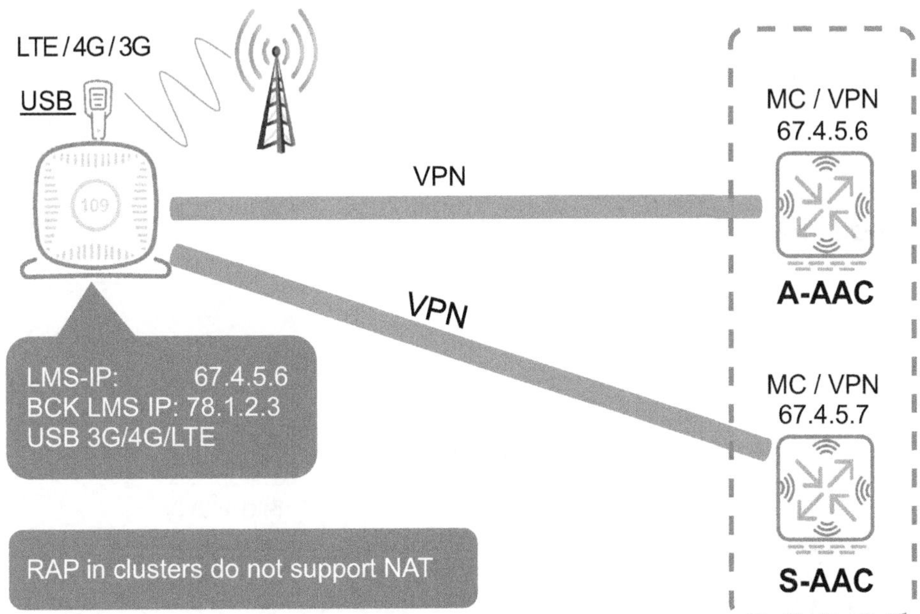

Figure 10-28 RAP cluster redundancy

RAPs may terminate on an MC cluster (Figure 10-28). This would require the cluster to have public IP addresses because NAT is not supported with RAPs in a cluster.

The RAP creates two VPN connections: one to the A-AAC and one to the S-AAC. The controller's IP address must be the public IP address

The Local Message Switch (LMS) IP address is one of the MCs, or the VIP in the cluster. You can also configure the RAP with a backup-LMS IP address. This could be another cluster or a single MC's address.

If the RAP loses contact with the LMS-IP, it attempts a connection to the backup LMS IP.

If the RAP loses its local connectivity, it attempts to use the USB 3G/4G/LTE stick (if so configured). If the USB supports multiple standards, then the highest will be tried first.

Learning check

4. Name two ways to provide redundancy for RAP.
    a. LMS Backup
    b. Activate can redirect
    c. AirWave can redirect
    d. USB 3G/4G/LTE
    e. Local redirect

Virtual Intranet Access (VIA)

VIA introduction

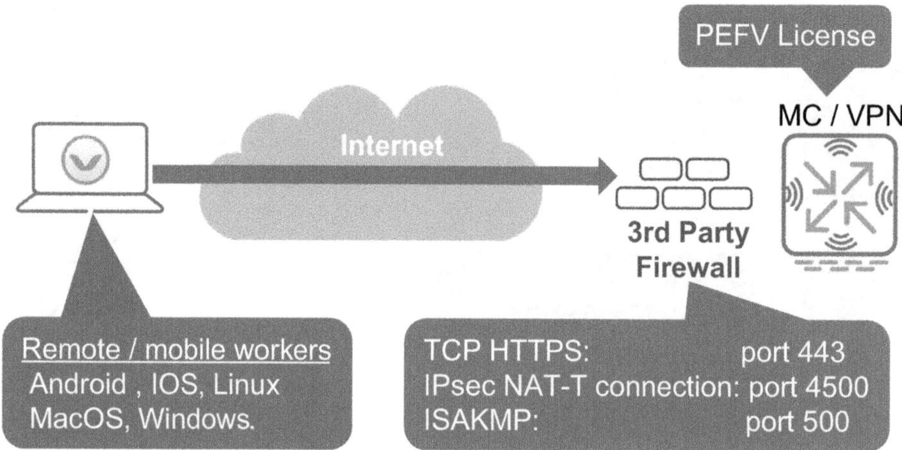

Figure 10-29 VIA introduction

VIA is software that you install on a client device. It enables remote user access to the corporate network. This is very useful for remote and mobile workers. VIA can be installed on many different end-user device types, as shown in Figure 10-29.

The Policy Enforcement Firewall Virtual (PEFV) license is mandatory for VIA implementations. You only need to install this license on the MC where VIA terminates.

As shown in Figure 10-29, any firewall between the client and MC must allow certain traffic.

- **TCP 443**—During initialization, VIA uses HTTPS port 443 connections to perform trusted network and captive portal checks.
- **UDP 4500**—This port is used for IPsec connection and NAT-Traversal (NAT-T).
- **UDP 500**—This port is used for Internet SA and Key Management Protocol (ISAKMP).

VIA configuration profiles

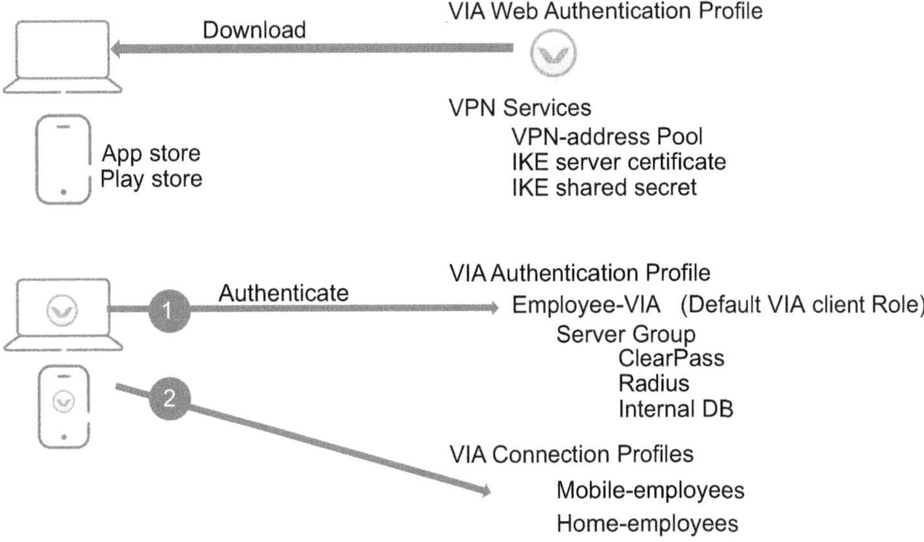

Figure 10-30 VIA configuration profiles

The web authentication profile is used by end-users to login to the VIA download page, at https://<corporateVIA>/via. If they are setup, they can download a VIA client. If more than one VIA authentication profile is configured, users can view this list and select a profile during client login (Figure 10-30).

The VIA authentication profiles contain server groups for authenticating VIA users. The server group contains the list of authentication servers where the user's VIA can authenticate. Servers can send back derived roles.

 **Note**

You can configure multiple VIA authentication profiles.

VIA connection profiles must be associated to a user role. Users logon and authenticate against the server group specified in the VIA authentication profile. Once authenticated, they are placed into a user role that associates them to a connection profile. The default VIA connection profile is used if the VIA configuration settings are derived from the VIA connection profile attached to the user role.

VIA MC configuration

Web authentication—downloadable VIA

Configuration > Services

Cluster Redundancy VPN Firewall IP Mobility External Services DH

› Site to Site

› DPD Details

⌄ VIA

VIA Installer Packages

Windows 64-bit anssetup.msi (Version : 3.0.0.0.87840)

Windows undefined-bit anssetup.msi (Version : 3.0.2.92324)

Windows 32-bit anssetup.msi (Version : 2.1.1.1.36296) Built-in

+

Logo: Browse Reset aruba

Upload your own logo: (Max size 128k)
(Logo dimensions must be 176px wide by 46px high or smaller)

Welcome Html: Browse Reset View

Login Banner: Browse Reset View

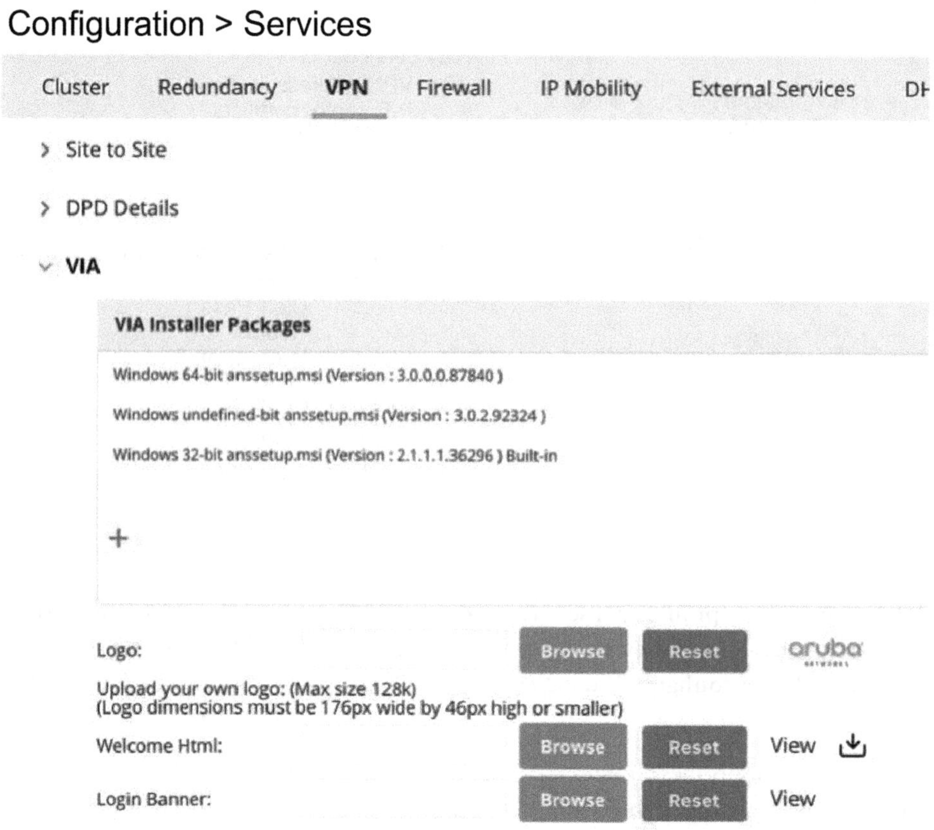

Figure 10-31 Web authentication—Downloadable VIA

Figure 10-31 shows how to prepare your MC with VIA installer packages, which can be downloaded to clients.

Navigate to **Configuration > Services > VPN**, then expand the VIA section. This is where you upload VIA installer packages for Windows 64-bit, Windows 32-bit, and Mac OS.

A user points their browser to controller's HTTPS URL. Once logged in, they can download the appropriate VIA package.

VIA client role

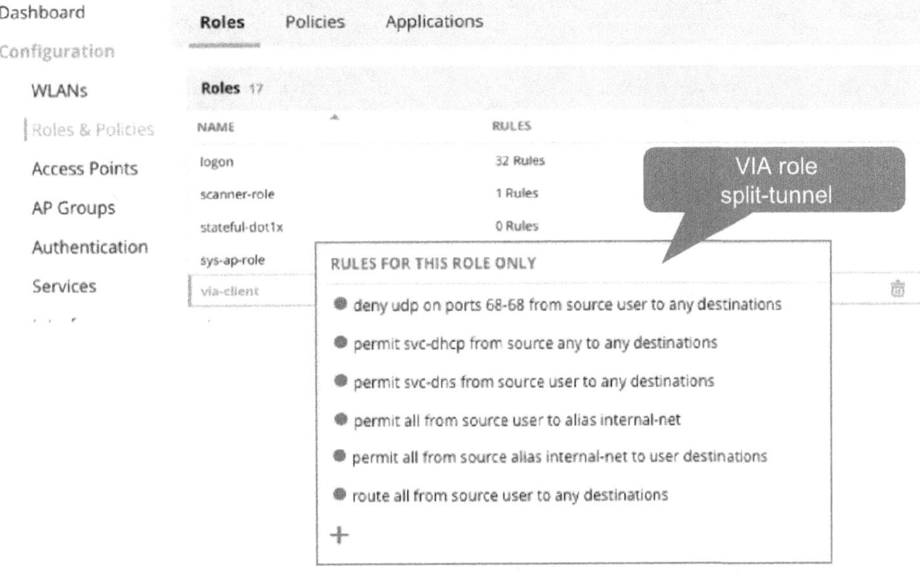

Figure 10-32 VIA client role

You must create a default client role for VIA (Figure 10-32). In this scenario, the VIA client role is created for split-tunnel requirements. This role permits the client to access DHCP and DNS services on the corporate network. It also allows general traffic to and from the corporate network. All traffic that is not destined for the corporate network will be NAT'ed to the VIA device local IP address.

Below, you can see the same policy configuration from the CLI.

```
ip access-list session via-client
 user any udp 68  deny
 any any svc-dhcp  permit
 user any svc-dns  permit
 user alias internal-net any  permit
 alias internal-net user any  permit
 user any any  route src-nat
```

VIA authentication profile

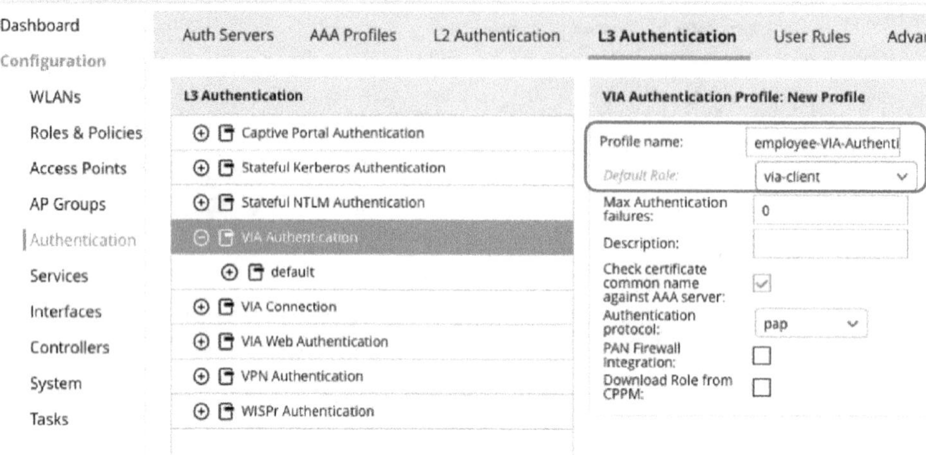

Figure 10-33 VIA authentication profile

The VIA authentication profile identifies what servers will be used to authenticate the VIA client and assign the default role. Figure 10-33 shows that you have navigated to **Configuration > Authentication > L3 Authentication**, to configure a profile name and assign the default role.

VIA authentication server group

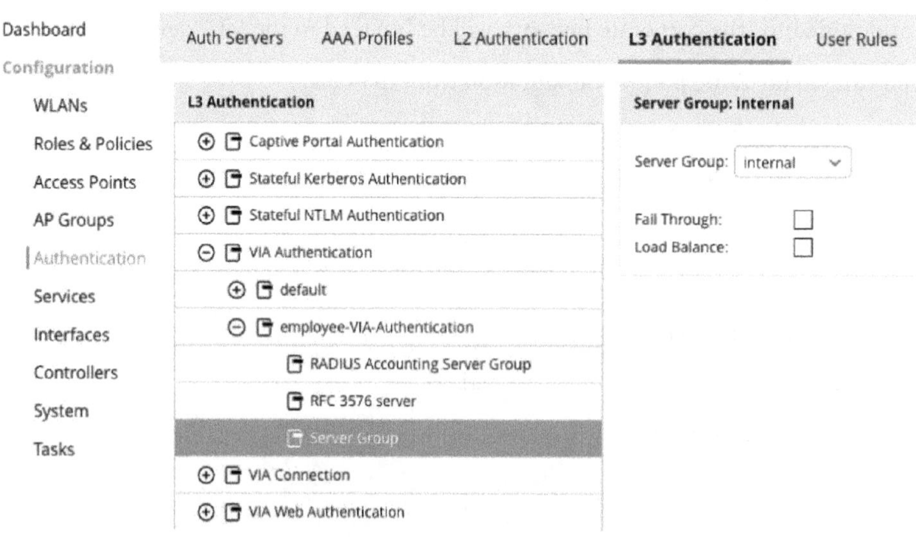

Figure 10-34 VIA authentication server group

Figure 10-34 shows that you have navigated to **Configuration > Authentication > L3 Authentication**, to configure a VIA authentication server group. This authentication profile uses the internal server group, which is appropriate for smaller VIA deployments. For larger deployments, a RADIUS server should be used.

VIA connection profile

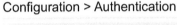

Configuration > Authentication

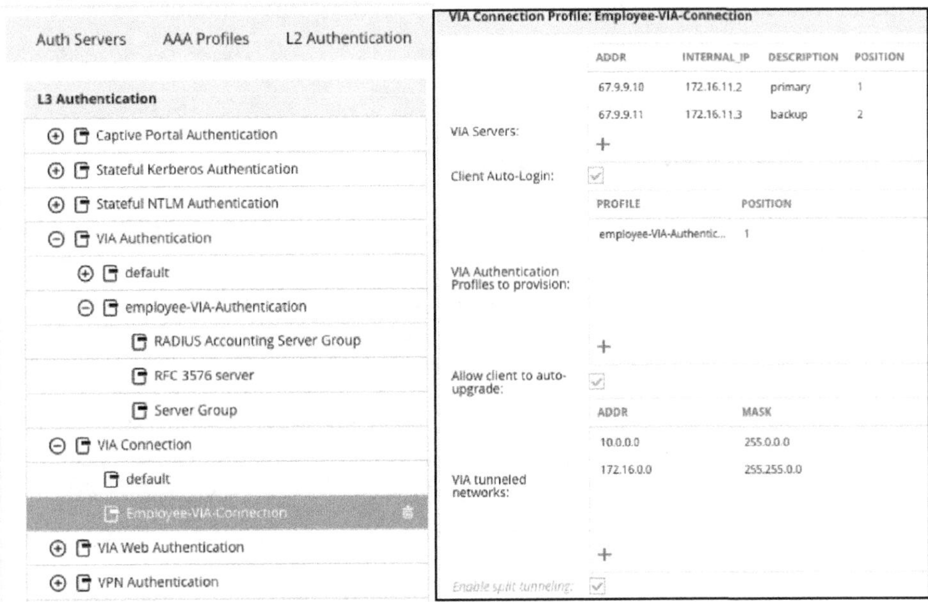

Figure 10-35 VIA connection profile

VIA configuration settings are derived from a VIA connection profile, as shown in Figure 10-35. This specifies the VIA server IP address, and which VIA authentication profiles to use. It also defines the internal network that can be used for split-tunnel.

Note

Many other VIA options can be configured in the connection profile. They are less relevant to this discussion and so they will not be covered here.

Learning check

5. What is the web authentication profile used for?
   a. To authenticate and download the installers
   b. To authenticate VIA via HTTPS
   c. To authenticate VIA certificate
   d. For authentication of RAPs
   e. Has the whitelist of authenticated VIAs

Client VIA download and install

Downloading VIA—MAC OS, Windows

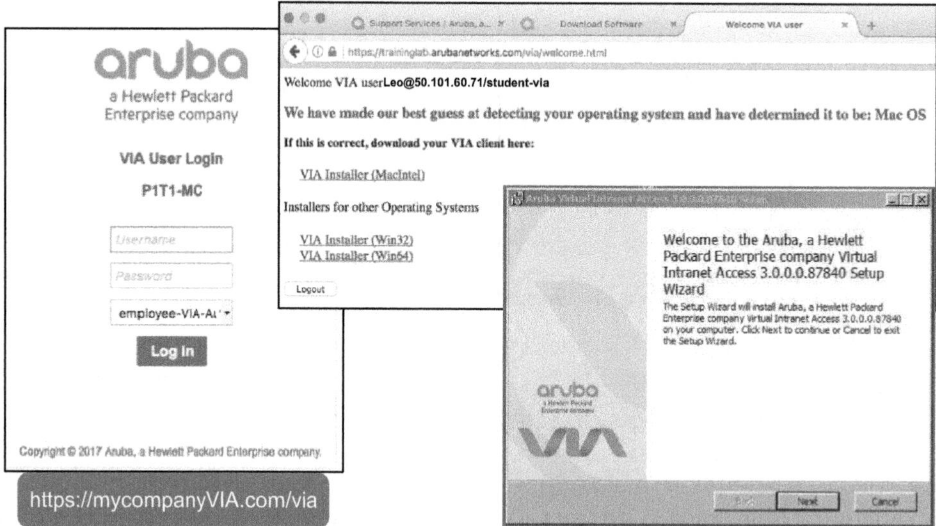

Figure 10-36 Downloading VIA—MAC OS, Windows

Once web authentication has been setup, you can access your controller via HTTPS and download VIA (Figure 10-36). You can do this for MAS OS, Windows 32K bits, or Window 64 Kbit devices.

You must login with the proper credentials and select VIA authentication profiles from the drop-down menu. The VIA web authentication profile automatically attempts to determine your OS and show you valid installers. Click on the installer for your OS and walk through the installation.

Smartphone download

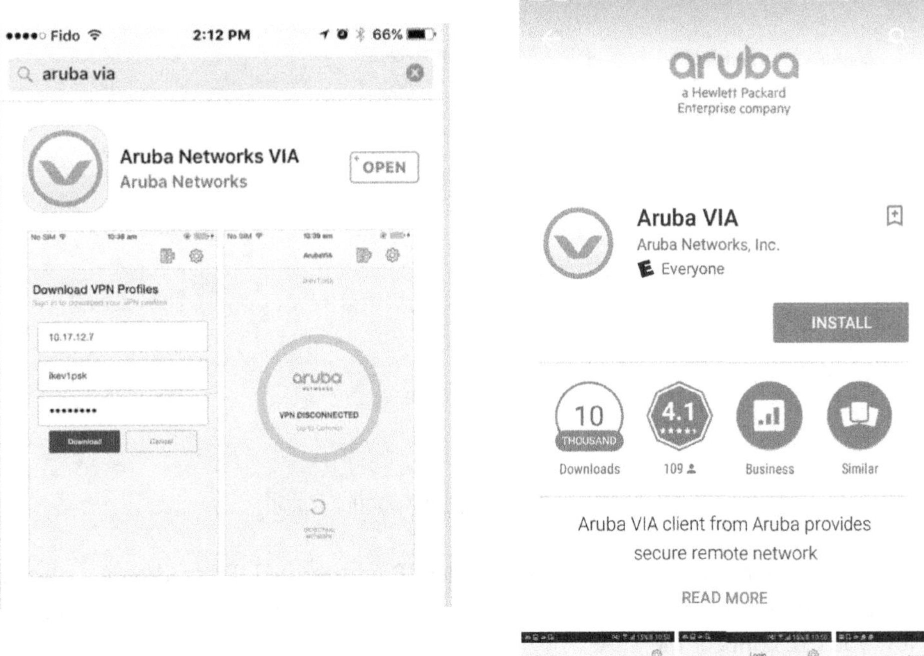

Figure 10-37 Smartphone download

iPhone users can download VIA in the app store (Figure 10-37). Just search for Aruba VIA. Android users can do the same thing from the Play store or Google Play store.

VIA client configuration

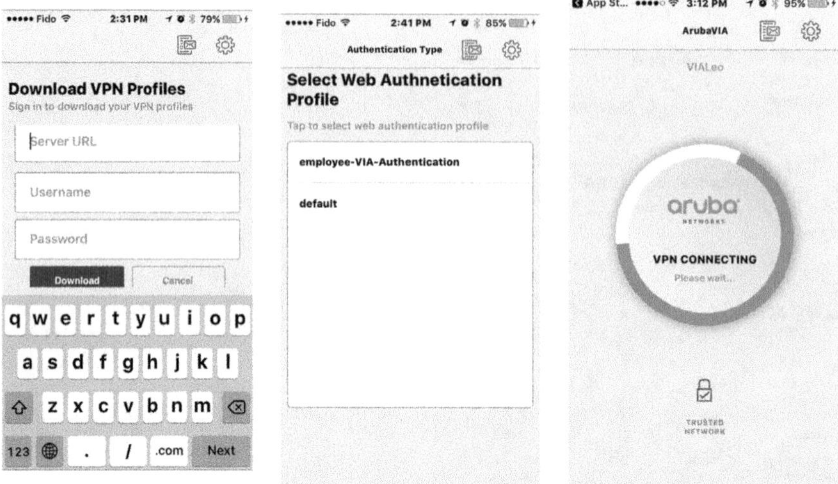

Figure 10-38 VIA client configuration

From a smartphone, you must specify the controller IP address or URL and enter valid corporate username/password credentials (Figure 10-38). Then select the VIA authentication profile you want to use. Now you can connect the VIA.

Troubleshooting VIA

MC—Troubleshooting

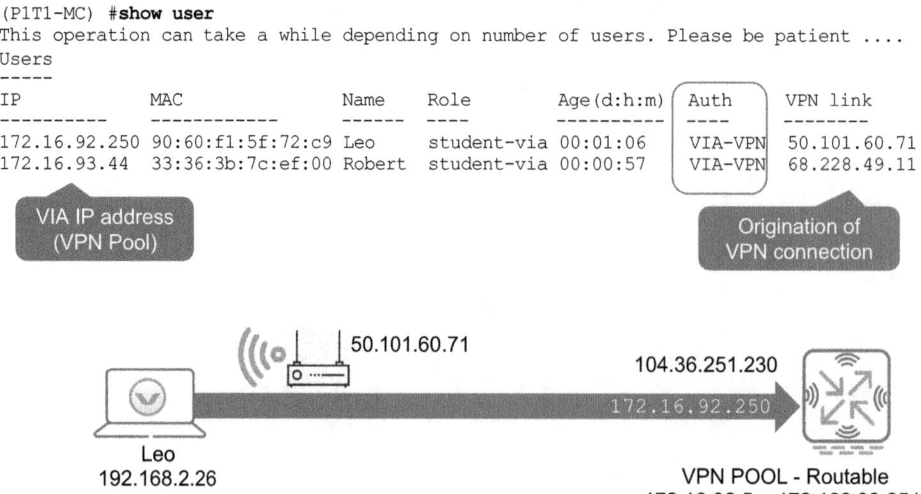

```
(P1T1-MC) #show user
This operation can take a while depending on number of users. Please be patient ....
Users
-----
IP             MAC                Name    Role         Age(d:h:m)   Auth     VPN link
----------     ------------       ------  ----         ----------   ----     --------
172.16.92.250  90:60:f1:5f:72:c9  Leo     student-via  00:01:06     VIA-VPN  50.101.60.71
172.16.93.44   33:36:3b:7c:ef:00  Robert  student-via  00:00:57     VIA-VPN  68.228.49.11
```


Figure 10-39 MC—troubleshooting

Figure 10-39 shows a typical scenario, in which a client uses VIA to connect to a remote site. User Leo is at some remote location and has been assigned a *local* IP address of 192.168.2.26. He uses his VIA client to connect to the MC, and a secure VPN tunnel forms. His device is assigned a *tunnel* IP address of 172.16.92.250, from the VPN pool.

This address came from the VPN pool of IP addresses, which must be routable in the network. To facilitate this, you must configure a VLAN on the MC and assign an IP address in this subnet. The DG can be the MC or an upstream router.

You have issued the command `show user` to assess end-user connectivity. You see that users Leo and Robert have been VIA-VPN authenticated. The IP column validates Leo's tunnel IP address. You also notice that although Leo's local address is 192.168.2.26, his end of the tunnel shows up as 50.101.60.71, in the "VPN link" column. This is probably because his local address is NAT'ed to an Internet-routable IP address.

It is best to assign authentication user names that reflect the actual user's name. This makes it easier to find and troubleshoot a specific user. However, if this is not the case, all is not lost. You can still help a user by asking them what IP address they have been assigned. The user simply looks at their VIA client configuration, as described below.

Client troubleshooting

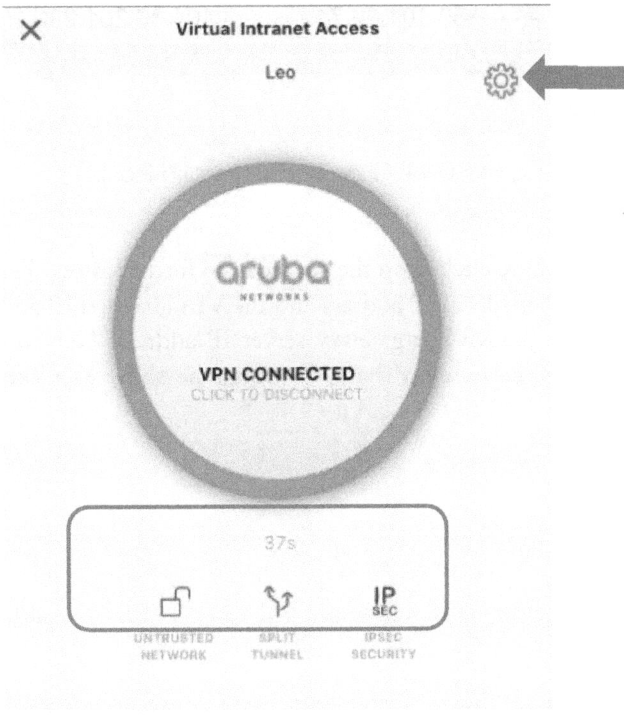

Figure 10-40 Client troubleshooting

From the client side, you can see that the VPN is connected and has been setup with split-tunnel (Figure 10-40). You can click on the gear icon to get more information, as shown in the next page.

Client troubleshooting (cont.)

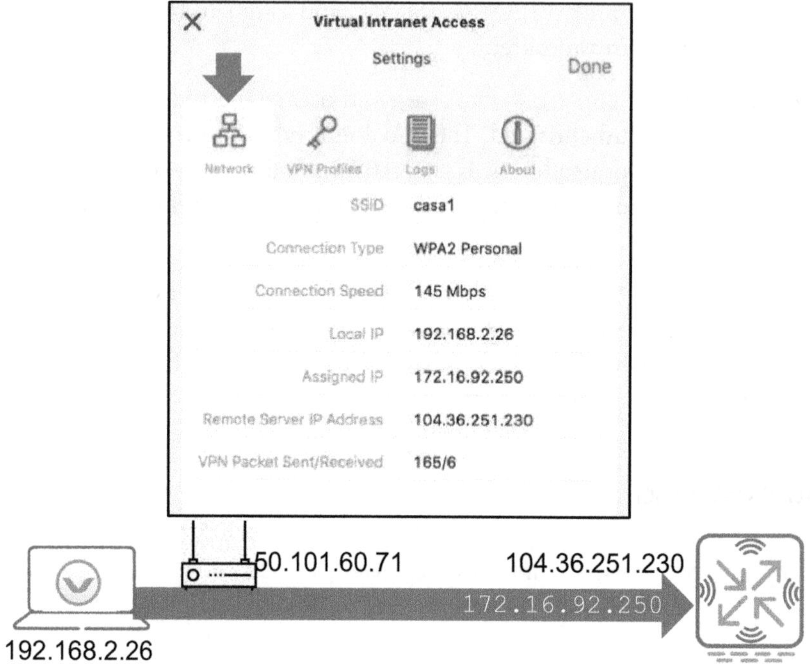

Figure 10-41 Client troubleshooting (cont.)

Figure 10-41 shows that you have clicked on the gear icon to further assess client connectivity. In the Network tab, you see the laptop's local IP address and the VIA assigned IP address, as assigned from the VPN pool. You also see the MC or gateway server IP address. Now you know this user's IP address, and so can identify the user on the MC, using the show user command, as previously described.

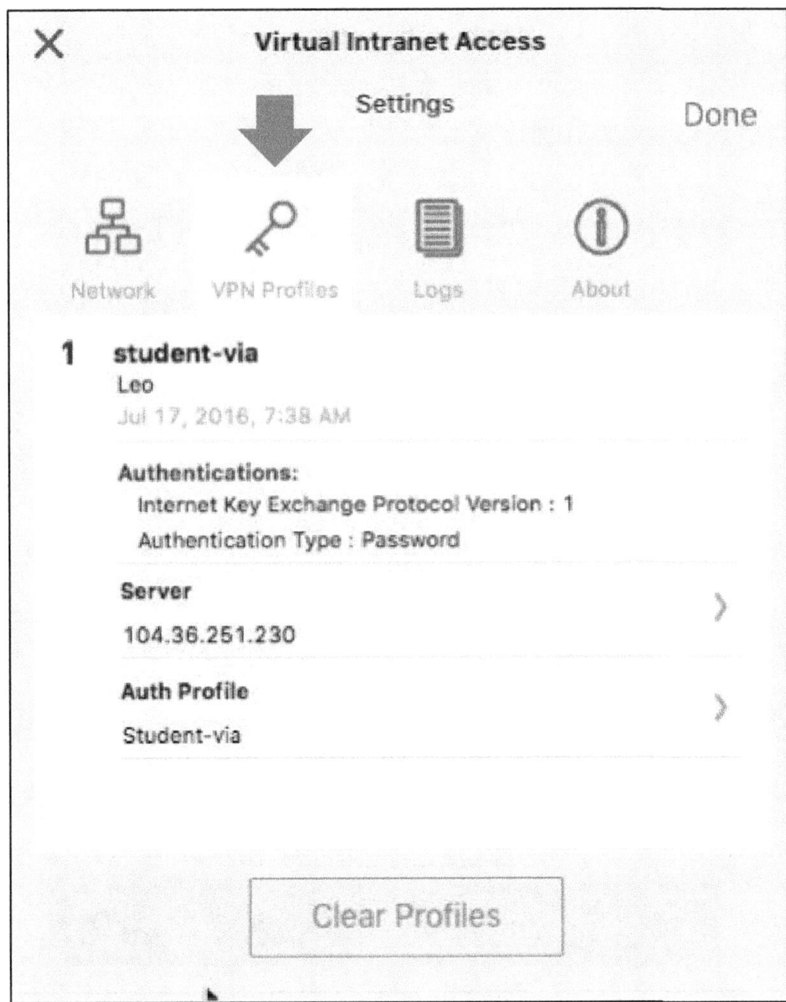

Figure 10-42 Client troubleshooting (cont.)

In the VPN Profiles tab (Figure 10-42), you see that Leo connected using the authentication profile named "student-via." This profile defines the corporate subnets, which should be sent through the tunnel. If you needed more information about how this profile should work, you can expand the Server and Auth Profile sections. You can also clear the profiles, but then you would need to re-enter the server IP address as well as your username and password.

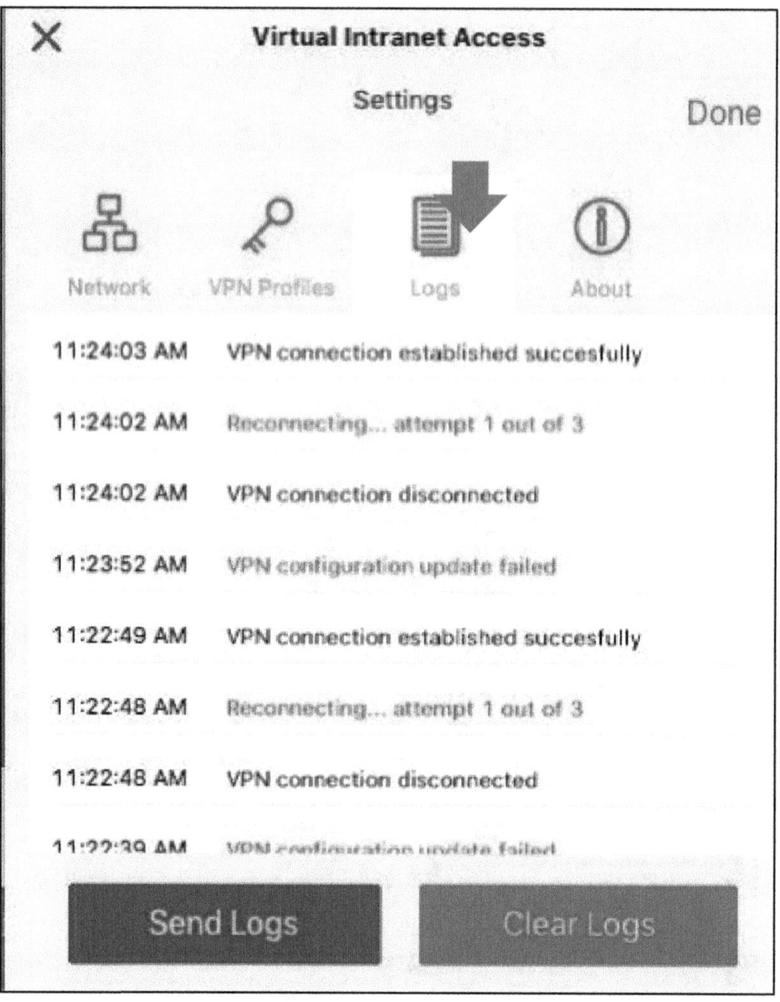

Figure 10-43 Client troubleshooting (cont.)

The logs tab (Figure 10-43) can reveal current and previous connectivity issues.

Learning check

6. What are the available options for remote access?
   a. VIA
   b. RAP
   c. Site-to-Site
   d. IAPs
   e. CAPs

11 Voice Optimization and UCC

LEARNING OBJECTIVES

- ✓ In this chapter, you will learn how to optimize voice traffic, starting with a discussion of Quality of Service (QoS) operation and mechanisms.
- ✓ Then you will learn about methods of accommodating voice traffic on an HPE Aruba deployment, before exploring Unified Communication and Collaboration (UCC).

Quality of Service (QoS)

What is QoS?

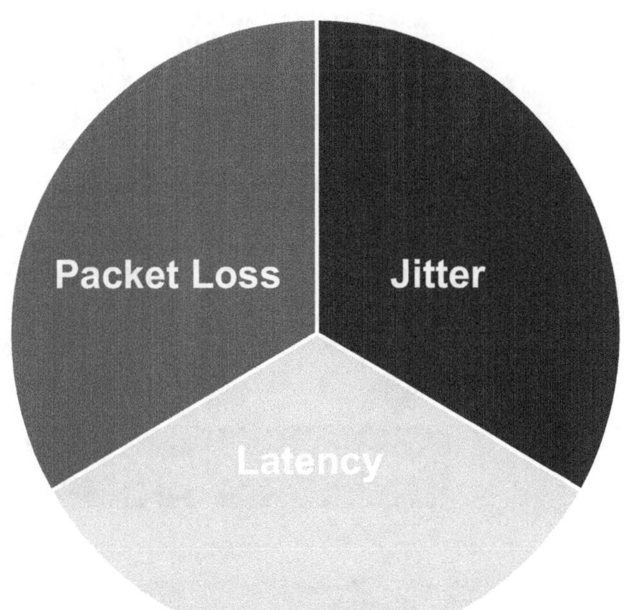

Figure 11-1 What is QoS?

QoS provides differentiated service to specific network traffic. Certain network services should be delivered within specific performance levels. For example, the quality of voice and video streams will break up if the bandwidth is inadequate or if transmission times are too long.

QoS prioritizes traffic to ensure defined performance levels are met. Real-time traffic streams require low packet loss, low latency, and controlled jitter (variations in latency). Even though high-priority traffic must take precedence, low-priority traffic flows must still be successfully sent and received.

Figure 11-1 refers to a Mean Opinion Score (MOS). This measures the overall quality of a VoIP call, based on the metrics of latency, packet loss, and jitter. The MOS lowers as these metrics degrade. An MOS degradation of less than 0.7 is considered a better-quality call. MOS also depends on the codec used, since each codec has a maximum achievable Network MOS.

Note

The word "codec" is a portmanteau, or a combination of two words – coder and decoder. It is an algorithm used to encode analog waveforms into a digital stream and then decode those digital streams back into analog waveforms for playback.

Why QoS?

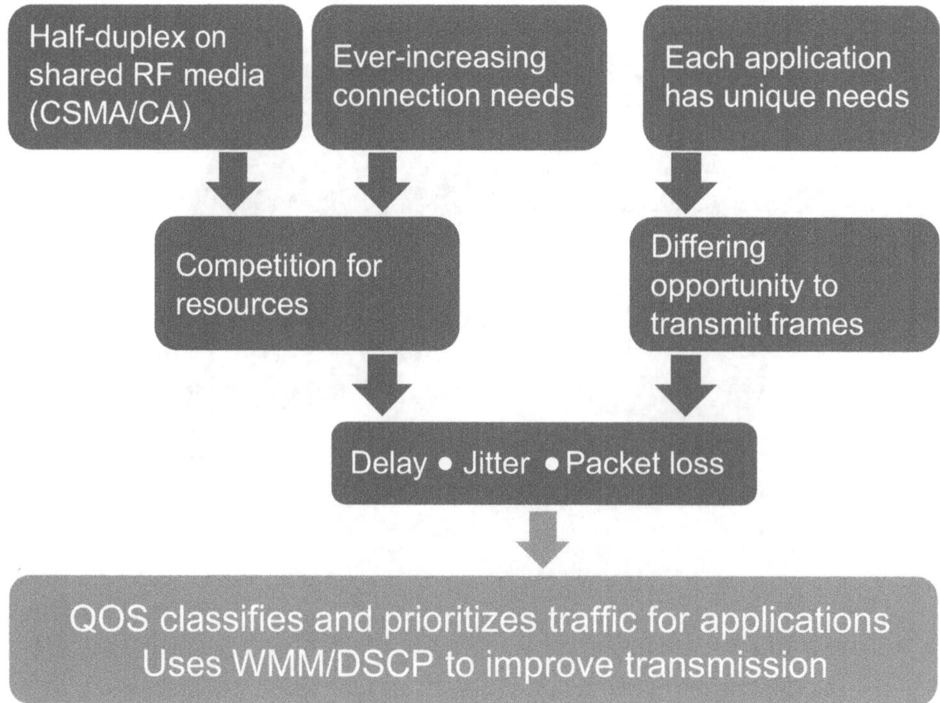

Figure 11-2 Why QoS?

QoS requirements differ by application (Figure 11-2). Voice and video are very sensitive to packet delay, but can tolerate low levels of packet loss. Many data applications are not sensitive to packet delay, but cannot tolerate any packet loss.

As packets traverse the network from source to destination, network congestion can cause packet drops, delays, and/or corruption. This results in retries and lost packets. Also, each packet in a stream of packets may experience varying amounts of delay (jitter), or arrive out of sequence. All of these scenarios cause issues for real-time traffic like voice and video.

802.11-based Wi-Fi traffic faces additional resource constraints, as compared to wired networks. WLANs operate in half-duplex mode on a shared media – like an old wired hub from the 1990s. Delay and interference in the air can increase retries, congestion, jitter, and dropped packets. This reduces the quality of the user experience.

Configuring QoS settings correctly on network components ensures that the various streams are given the correct levels of service. This improves the end-user experience. WLAN QoS mechanisms ensures that real-time traffic gets access to the media, with minimal delay. These mechanisms are discussed in the pages that follow.

Note

Within any given AP's BSS, one and only one device can transmit at a time. The mechanism used to facilitate this is called Carrier Sense Multiple Access/Collision Avoidance (CSMA/CA).

What is Wi-Fi Multimedia (WMM)?

The WMM standard provides a QoS mechanism for Wi-Fi networks. WMM defines four Access Categories (AC), called voice, video, best effort, and background. These are used to prioritize traffic. Thus, each application type gets appropriate network resources.

WMM is supported in all of Aruba's Wi-Fi wireless products, since they meet WMM prerequisites. HPE Aruba products are Wi-Fi certified for WMM. You just need to ensure that WMM is enabled, and that your client devices support WMM.

For a client application to receive WMM-based QoS, the application must also support WMM.

How WMM works

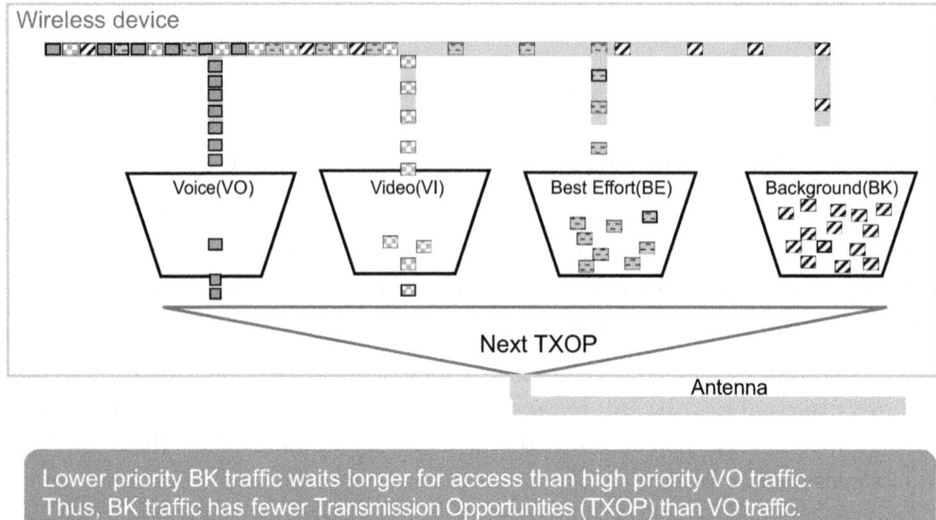

Figure 11-3 How WMM works

Figure 11-3 shows various frames that must be transmitted by a wireless device. The frames are categorized into WMM's four queues. Thus categorized, the frames can be serviced according to desired QoS. Generally, the higher priority voice traffic gets more frequent opportunities to be transmitted than the lower-priority background traffic.

This is because each queue has a different Transmission Opportunity (TXOP). The TXOP is a bounded time interval during which a station can send as many frames as possible. Lower priority BK traffic must wait longer for channel access than higher priority VO traffic. Thus, BK traffic has fewer opportunities to transmit than VO traffic. Notice that the BK queue is nearly full, with many packets waiting to be transmitted. Meanwhile, the VO and VI queues have very little traffic waiting to be transmitted. This high priority traffic gets sent very soon after it arrives in the queue.

What is Differentiated Services Code Point (DSCP)?

Type-of-Service Octet for DSCP

0	1	2	3	4	5	6	7
DSCP						*currently unused*	

Version	IHL	Type-of-Service	Total Length	
Identification			Flags	Fragment Offset
Time-to-Live		Protocol	Header Checksum	
Source Address				
Destination Address				
Options (+padding)				
Data				

IPv4 Packet Header

← 32 bits →

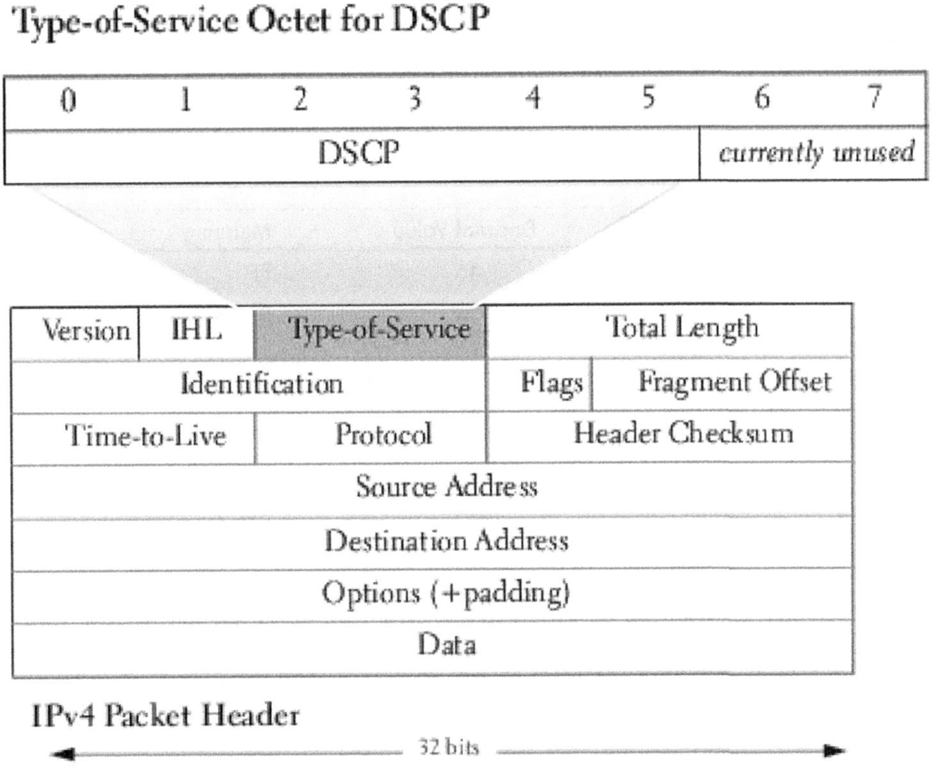

Figure 11-4 What is Differentiated Services Code Point (DSCP)?

You have learned that WMM is used for wireless networking. Differentiated Services Code Point (DSCP) is used for wired network QoS (Figure 11-4). Differentiated Services or DiffServ is a computer networking architecture that specifies a simple, scalable, and coarse-grained mechanism for classifying and managing network traffic. It provides QoS for modern IP networks.

For example, DiffServ can be used to provide low-latency service for critical network traffic, such as voice or streaming media. Meanwhile, noncritical services such as web traffic or file transfers get a best-effort service.

To classify packets, DiffServ uses the 6-bit DSCP field in the IP header. DSCP replaces the outdated Type of Service (TOS) field.

Note

The field in the IP header is nearly always labeled "TOS" in most documentation. Do not be confused. It is the same field as always. DSCP merely defines a new way to *use* these same bits that have always been in the TOS field of an IP header.

Since each device (router, Aruba controller, and so forth) can use the DSCP bits to decide how they will treat this traffic (how they will behave), we refer to this as a "Per-Hop Behavior" (PHB) mechanism. For example, a DSCP decimal value of 46 translates to an Expedited Forwarding (EF) behavior. This is typically used for very delay-sensitive traffic, like Voice-over-IP (VoIP). Other decimal values translate to various Assured Forwarding (AF) PHBs.

Table 11-1 lists the different DSCP values and their meaning.

Table 11-1 DSCP Values

DSCP Value	Decimal Value	Meaning
101 110	46	EF
000 000	0	Best effort
001 010	10	AF11
001 100	12	AF12
001 110	14	AF13
010 010	18	AF21
010 100	20	AF22
010 110	22	AF23
011 010	26	AF31
011 100	28	AF32
011 110	30	AF33
100 010	34	AF41
100 100	36	AF42
100 110	38	AF43

Note

For more details on DSCP, please see this link: https://en.wikipedia.org/wiki/Differentiated_services

End-to-end QoS

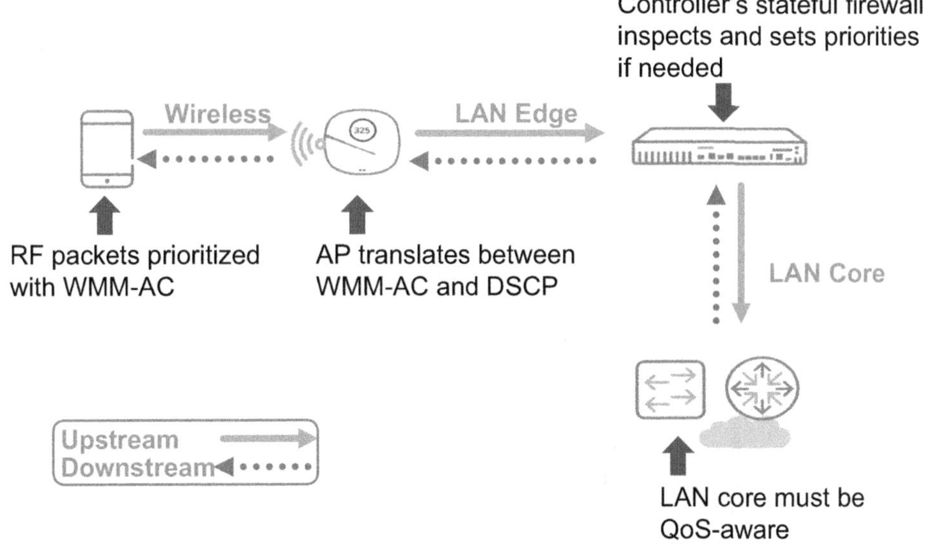

Figure 11-5 End-to-end QoS

The IEEE 802.11e standard defines the mapping between Wi-Fi WMM ACs and wired DSCP tags (Figure 11-5).

WMM is based on the IEEE 802.11e standard. It defines the basic QoS features for 802.11 networks. WMM references the 802.1p standard classification scheme. This scheme has eight priorities, which WMM maps to four ACs:

- Voice (AC_VO)
- Video (AC_VI)
- Best Effort (AC_BE)
- Background (AC_BK)

These ACs map to the four queues required by a WMM device.

Each wired L2 frame can be marked with an 802.1P value, and each L3 packet can be marked with a DSCP value. Aruba's DSCP WMM AC mapping commands allow you to customize the mapping between WMM ACs and DSCP tags, to prioritize various traffic types. You configure WMM AC mappings to a WMM-enabled SSID profile. If you do not define this mapping, default DSCP WMM AC mapping is used.

DSCP mapping for WMM AC configuration

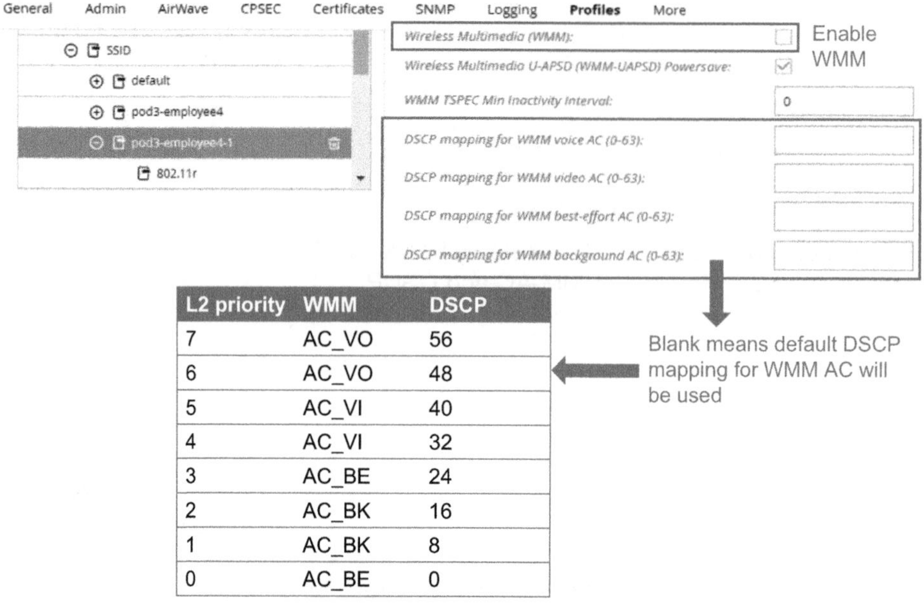

L2 priority	WMM	DSCP
7	AC_VO	56
6	AC_VO	48
5	AC_VI	40
4	AC_VI	32
3	AC_BE	24
2	AC_BK	16
1	AC_BK	8
0	AC_BE	0

Figure 11-6 DSCP mapping for WMM AC configuration

You can configure the controller to convert wireless WMM markings to wired DSCP markings, and back. Figure 11-6 shows the default DSCP-WMM mapping table.

You can enable WMM for wireless clients in the WebUI by following these steps:

1. In the Managed Network node hierarchy, navigate to **Configuration > System> Profiles**.
2. In All Profiles, expand **Wireless LAN > Virtual AP > default > SSID**. This example uses the default profile.
3. In the SSID Profile, select the Wireless Multimedia (WMM) check box.
4. You can customize the WMM AC mapping or use the default value, in which the options remain blank.

In a non-WMM or hybrid environment where some clients are not WMM-capable, non-WMM client traffic will continue using two queues. The voice (VO) queue for high priority traffic and the background (BE) traffic queue for the low priority traffic.

The IEEE 802.11e standard defines mapping between WMM ACs and Layer 3 DSCP tags. The WMM AC mapping commands allow you to customize the mapping between WMM queues and DSCP tags, as shown in Figure 11-6. This enables you to prioritize various traffic types.

You can apply and configure WMM AC mappings to a WMM-enabled SSID profile. Default WMM AC mapping will be used if the DSCP mapping is not configured.

Aruba recommends that you use a value of 40 for video traffic and 56 for voice.

DSCP EF-46 and WMM mapping problem

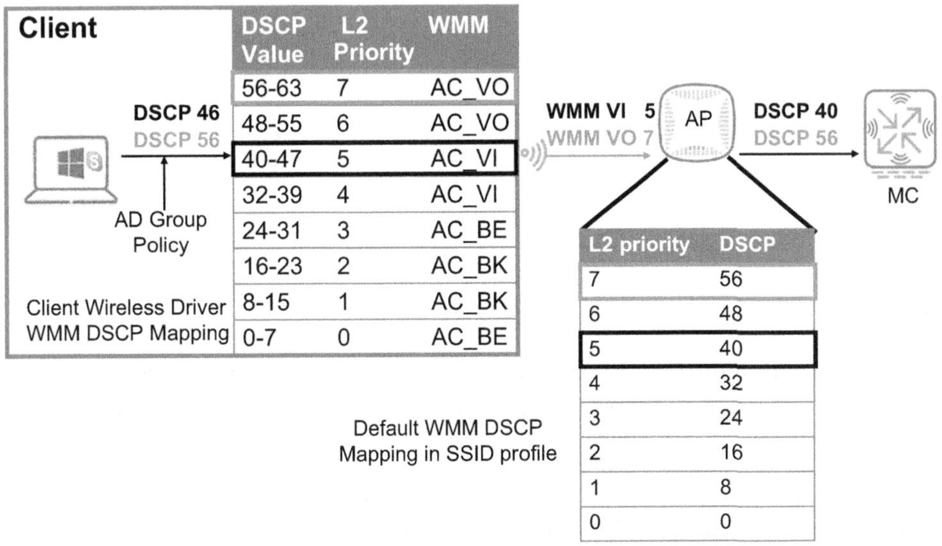

Figure 11-7 DSCP EF-46 and WMM mapping problem

When the WMM standard was defined, the L2 802.1p CoS model was used to define the eight WMM queues (Figure 11-7). Meanwhile, the Voice over IP (VoIP) community established a standard DSCP value for voice traffic. They used a DSCP value of 46, known as the Expedited Forwarding (EF) class. This can be referred to as EF-46. This results in Aruba devices mapping EF-46 traffic to the video class—AC_VI.

Inappropriate classification of upstream EF-46 traffic to WMM VI is a side effect of the general-purpose operating system on which Skype for Business runs. Client devices and APs that run on purpose-built operating systems are not classified inappropriately, as the mappings are set correctly by the manufacturer.

HPE Aruba recommends a solution to this upstream mistagging. You can apply higher DSCP values to wireless clients. In this example, the DSCP value is set to 56 for the voice client.

Learning check

1. An SSID profile's DSCP-WMM settings are only used by upstream traffic, from AP to MC.
    a. True
    b. False
2. How many Access Categories (AC) does WMM support?
    a. 4
    b. 6
    c. 8
    d. 64

UCC

What is UCC?

UCC is concerned with human interactions over a network infrastructure. This includes voice and video calls, conferencing, and desktop sharing. It identifies and re-marks real-time traffic with DSCP and WMM.

In AOS 8.X, UCC services run on MCs. This supports various protocols and applications such as Microsoft Lync/Skype for business, Cisco unencrypted Jabber, SIP, H.323, SCCP, Vocera, Wi-Fi calling, and more. The MM's UCC application implements the VoIP ALG to support both signaling- and heuristics-based Application Layer Gateways (ALG).

The UCC App uses the open flow infrastructure to receive the signaling messages from the managed nodes, and to install and delete flows on the managed nodes for calls made. This system improves media classification and prioritization, optimizes wireless access, and improves monitoring and troubleshooting.

Recommended deployment topology—AOS 8.x

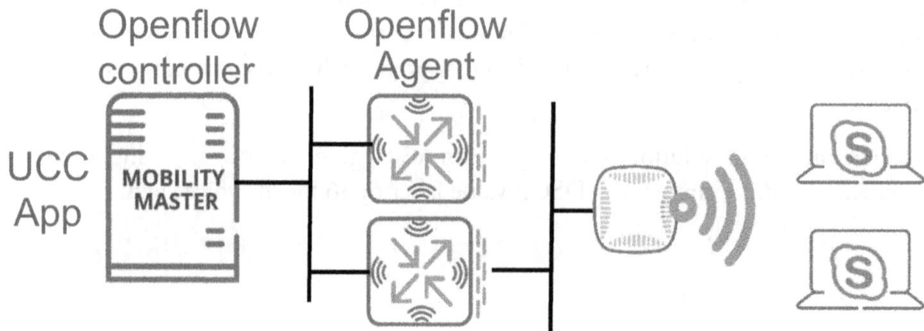

Figure 11-8 Recommended deployment topology—AOS 8.x

AOS 8.x supports two topologies—MM—MC and Standalone MC. These are described below.

MM—MC (Figure 11-8)

- The MM provides centralized visibility for all UCC calls made via its MCs.
- OpenFlow configuration is required.
- All UCC-relevant configurations must be done on the MM.

Standalone MC

- All ALGs run on the MC.
- OpenFlow is not required in this topology.

Configuration is done only on each MC node.

UCC deployment modes overview

This chapter describes use cases to demonstrate how QoS is translated for different call scenarios, using Skype for Business (SfB). The use cases apply to the deployment modes introduced below.

- WMM Only Mode (not UCC) is used for an easy deployment that does not involve UCC. For example, if you deploy a SIP application which is not supported by Aruba UCC, you must use WMM-Only mode.
- Heuristics Mode can be used for most UCC deployments, including SfB, Wi-Fi Calling, Jabber, and so forth. It also supports Aruba IAP products. Also, if Office365 online traffic priority is a consideration in your business scenario, you can use this mode.

Note

A heuristic algorithm is one that is designed to solve a problem in a more efficient manner, by focusing on the most important criteria.

- The Software Defined Networking (SDN) API Mode provides an interface to the Aruba MC. This enables access to SfB network diagnostic information about voice, video, desktop-sharing, and file-transfer, without having to inspect the traffic. This mode is recommended for SfB deployments, as many useful functions are available.
  - For example, the SDN API mode can classify and prioritize SfB desktop sharing and file transfer traffic.
  - It provides end-to-end call quality metrics, such as MOS. This enhances diagnostic efforts.
  - Detailed call statistics and reports are provided, which Heuristics mode cannot provide

WMM-only mode

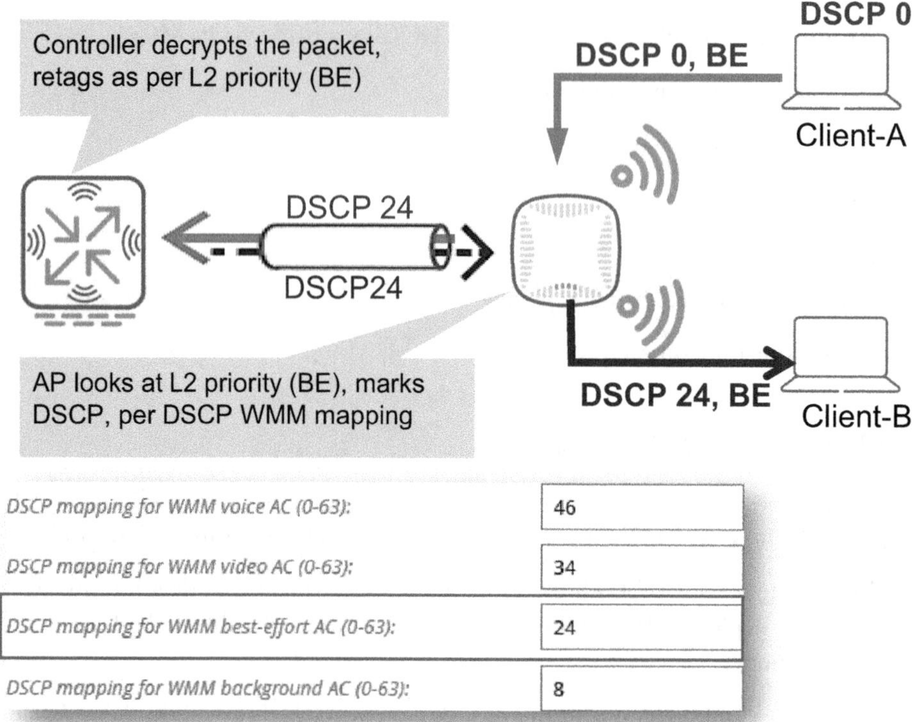

Figure 11-9 WMM-only mode

You can use a WMM-only deployment for applications that Aruba's UCC does not support, or when UCC is disabled (Figure 11-9). You simply define DSCP-WMM mapping on the controller, as previously described, and packets are marked accordingly.

In tunnel forwarding mode, traffic passes between the AP and the controller via 802.11 over GRE, and traffic is decrypted in the mobility controller. The AP and controller work in concert to identify the packet type. They mark the DSCP field, based on the DSCP-WMM mapping, as set in the MC.

In this example, Client A initiates a voice call to Client B. However, Client A does not tag voice traffic.

1. In the upstream direction (Client to Controller), Client-A sends untagged traffic (DSCP = 0 and WMM = BE). The AP looks at L2 priority (WMM – AC = BE) and sets DSCP 24, per the controller's DSCP-WMM mapping.
2. The controller decrypts the packet and uses L2 priority to assign DSCP 24 in the downstream direction (controller to client).
3. The AP assigns WMM – AC = BE, per the controller's DSCP-WMM mapping.

Note

In this case, we didn't use default DSCP-WMM-Mapping. If we use the default, the DSCP that AP sends to controller will be 0. Please refer back to Figure 11-7, which shows default mapping. Also, this discussion is focused on tunnel forwarding mode. If bridge mode was used, APs decrypt packets, then check L2 Priority to assign DSCP, per DSCP-WMM mapping in MC.

UCC heuristics mode

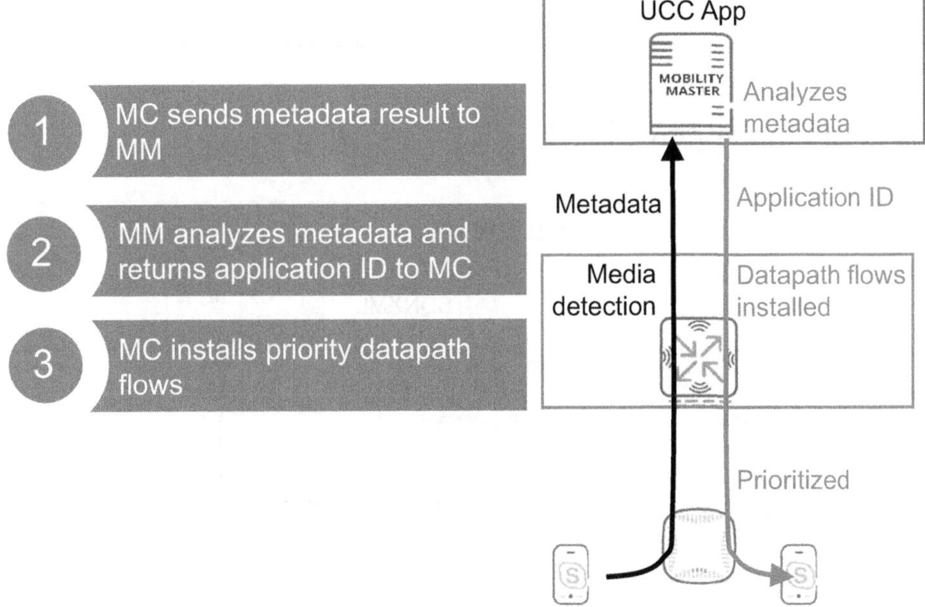

Figure 11-10 UCC heuristics mode

Heuristic mode deployments are more involved, but make for a more scalable solution for large deployments, with a lot of VoIP traffic. The heuristic algorithms automatically determine the traffic type, set appropriate markings, and open appropriate firewall ports.

Suppose that two users make a voice call:

- The MC's firewall permits this flow. This is based on Deep Packet Inspection (DPI) for either Session Traversal Utilities for NAT (STUN) or Real-time Transport Protocol (RTP) signatures in the flow's first packet.
- The heuristics algorithm runs on the MC's data path. It attempts to identify whether the flow is indeed RTP, by matching the pattern of the flow's subsequent packets. A maximum of nine packets adhering to the pattern are needed to confirm that the flow is RTP.

- Once the heuristics algorithm successfully identifies the flow as RTP, it sends a metadata packet to the MM's UCC App. This metadata enables the MM's UCC App to identify the application.
- Simultaneously, the post-classification stage is run in the MC data path for the first time. The heuristics algorithm returns an application ID, which helps determine any further actions needed for the flow.
- The MM's UCC App evaluates the metadata to identify the application.

Note

The DSCP value for downstream traffic (from MC to client) depends on UCC configuration.

UCC SDN API mode (SfB ONLY)

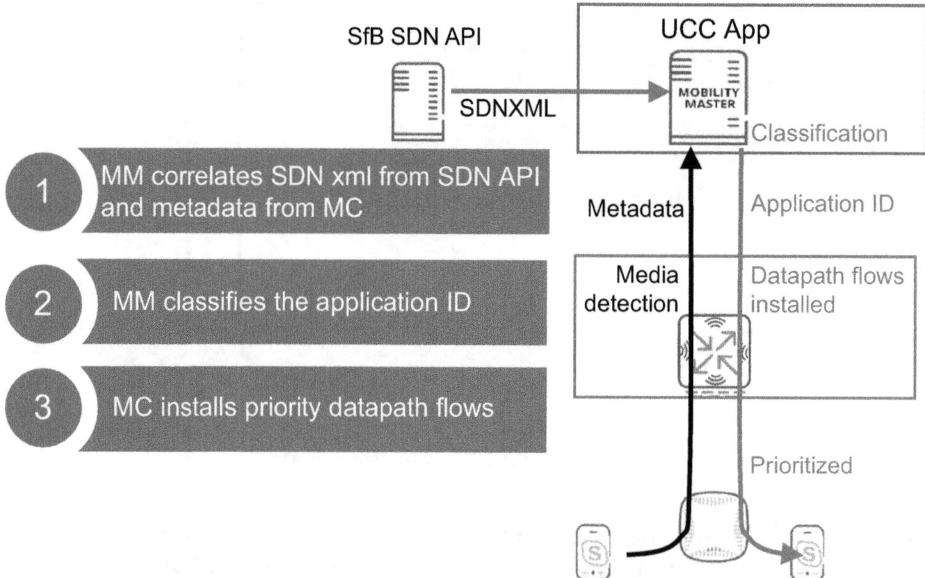

Figure 11-11 UCC SDN API mode (SfB ONLY)

Figure 11-11 provides a very high level overview of the SDN API deployment mode. Currently, this deployment mode only supports SfB deployments and requires that you add an SDN API service, running on a Microsoft server platform.

A media detection function is enabled by default in AOS8. Thus, any new RTP traffic based on video or audio calls are automatically allowed by the MC. The MC sends the media detection results (metadata) to the MM.

As of release AOS 8.0, the MM's UCC App receives XML message information from the SDN API. It also receives metadata from the MC, like heuristics mode. The MM correlates this info to confirm the application.

With SfB heuristics mode, only voice & video calls can be prioritized. Desktop sharing and file sharing sessions cannot be prioritized. To be prioritized, desktop sharing and file transfer sessions require Lync/SfB SDN API integration.

Please refer to the AOS user guide for more details about SDN API deployment.

QoS remarking example in UCC mode

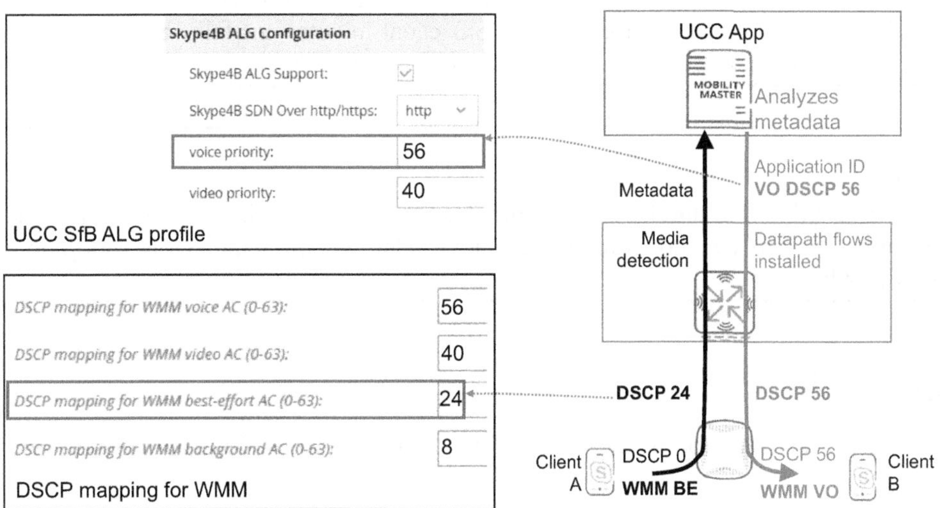

Figure 11-12 QoS remarking example in UCC mode

Here is a heuristics mode example (Figure 11-12). SDN mode is very similar.

Client A initiates a SfB voice call to Client B. Client A does not tag SfB voice traffic. The network is configured to detect SfB VO traffic using heuristics. By default, all the ALGs running on the UCC App on the MM undergo heuristics on the MC, whenever RTP traffic hits the MC.

1. In the upstream direction (client to MC), the AP looks at L2 Priority (WMM-AC as BE). It marks DSCP to 24, according to the DSCM-WMM mapping in the SSID profile.
2. The MC identifies the media flow. It sends flow metadata information to the MM's UCC App. This metadata packet information enables the MM's UCC App to identify the application.
3. The MM's UCC App evaluates the metadata information, to identify the application and prioritize SfB calls. It can, therefore, push appropriate DSCPs to MC.

4. The MC corrects the DSCP tag to 56 in the downstream direction (MC to client).
5. The UCC App also provides visibility for all voice calls made using the SfB ALG.
6. The UCC App dynamically opens the firewall for Voice and Video traffic, without the need for pre-configured exceptions.
7. The AP assigns WMM-AC as VO as per DSCP-WMM mapping in the MC.

Note

Session Traversal Utilities for NAT (STUN) is a standardized set of methods, including a network protocol. STUN is used to traverse Network Address Translation (NAT) gateways for real-time voice, video, messaging, and other interactive communications. For example, before media transmission, a Lync/SfB client initiates a STUN connectivity check. Sessions created by STUN are classified as RTP or non-RTP.

Note

Voice and Video priorities in SfB UCC profiles are not at the default setting of 46/34. This example uses 56/40. This example does not use the default DSCP-WMM-Mapping in the SSID profile.

Learning check

3. DSCP-WMM settings in an SSID profile will be overridden by UCC DSCP/WMM settings.
   a. True
   b. False
4. What QoS deployment modes are supported for SfB in AOS 8.1?
   a. End-to-end QoS mode
   b. WMM-only mode
   c. UCC SDN API mode
   d. UCC heuristics mode

UCC configuration, monitoring, and troubleshooting

UCC heuristics mode configuration—step 1

Step1: Enable OpenFlow controller on MM level (enabled by default)

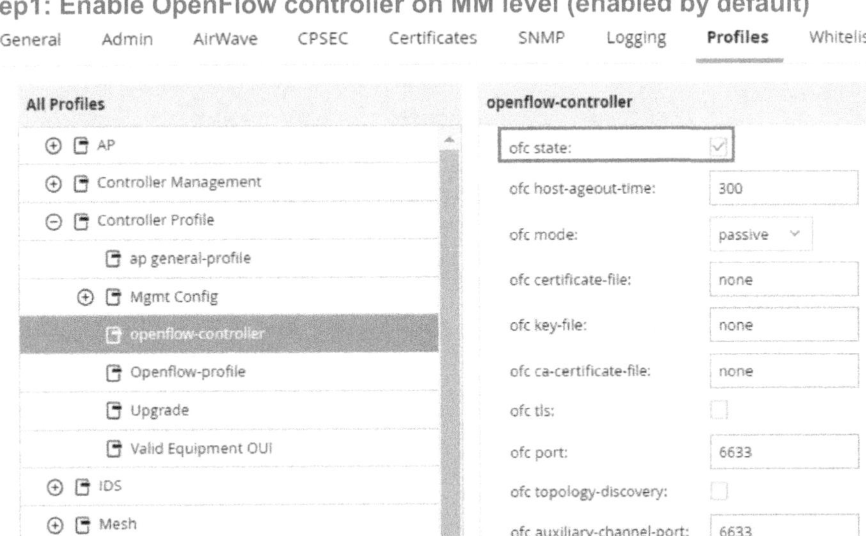

MM> Configuration > System >profile > Controller profile > OpenFlow-controller

Figure 11-13 UCC heuristics mode configuration—step 1

This and the next few pages explore configuring UCC in an AOS 8 MM-MC deployment model. The following are the pre-requisites for enabling UCC in AOS 8.0 in /MM-MC deployment model.

- Enable the OpenFlow controller on the MM, and the OpenFlow Profile in managed nodes.
- Bind user VLANs to the OpenFlow profile on managed nodes.
- Management server profile of type MM enables AMON feeds to be sent to the MM for various statistics.
- All the configurations specific to UCC should be done from the MM.

Figure 11-13 shows how to enable the OpenFlow controller on the MM. Navigate to **MM > Configuration > System > profile > Controller profile > OpenFlow-controller**. Then simply click the check box for "ofc state."

You also can configure with CLI on /MM:

```
(AOS_8.0) [/MM] (config) #OpenFlow-controller
(AOS_8.0) ^[/MM] (OpenFlow-controller) #OpenFlow-controller-enable
```

UCC heuristics mode configuration—step 2

Step2: Enable OpenFlow agent on Managed network level (enabled by default)

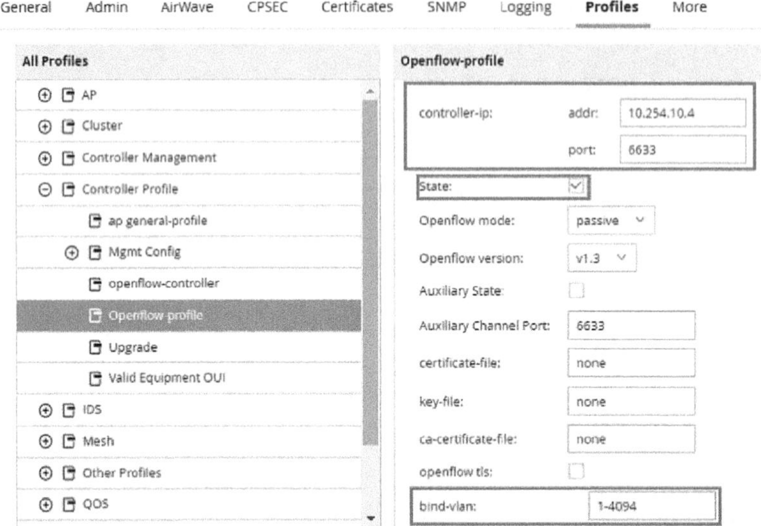

Managed Network> Configuration > System >profile > Controller profile > OpenFlow-profile

Figure 11-14 UCC heuristics mode configuration—step 2

Figure 11-14 shows how to enable the OpenFlow agent on MCs. Navigate as shown, and configure the OpenFlow profile. Specify the controller IP address and port, and enable it with the "State" checkbox. Then define which VLANs to bind to the profile. In this case, all VLANs are selected.

To do this OpenFlow configuration on each MC from the CLI:

```
(MC) ^[00:1a:1e:01:bd:b0](config) #OpenFlow-profile

(MC) ^[00:1a:1e:01:bd:b0](OpenFlow-profile) #controller-ip <master-ip> <port>

(MC) ^[00:1a:1e:01:bd:b0](OpenFlow-profile) #bind-vlan <list of user vlans>

(MC) ^[00:1a:1e:01:bd:b0](OpenFlow-profile) #OpenFlow-enable
```

UCC heuristics mode configuration—step 3

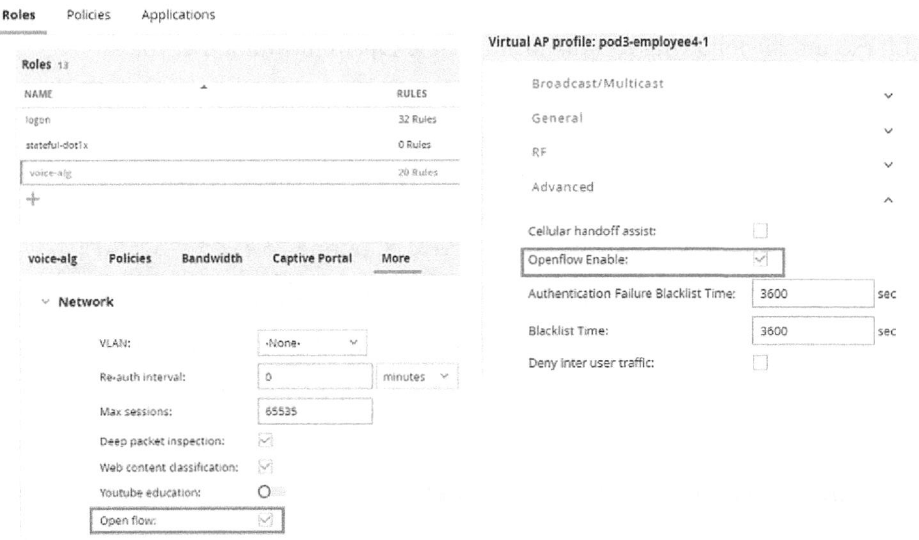

Figure 11-15 UCC heuristics mode configuration—step 3

In the WebUI, follow the procedure below to enable OpenFlow in the user-role and virtual AP using the WebUI (Figure 11-15):

1. In the Managed Network node hierarchy, navigate to **Configuration > Roles & Policies**.
2. In the Roles tab, select an existing role.
3. In the Roles > <custom-role> section, click Show Advanced View.
4. Under More, expand Network.
5. In the OpenFlow drop-down list, select Enabled.
6. Click Submit.
7. Navigate to **Configuration > System > Profiles**.
8. In All Profiles, expand **Wireless LAN > Virtual AP**. Select the default profile. (This procedure uses the default profile.)
9. In Virtual AP profile, expand Advanced.
10. Select the OpenFlow Enable check box.

11. Click Save.
12. Click Pending Changes.
13. In the Pending Changes window, select the check box and click Deploy changes.

In the CLI, execute the following commands to enable OpenFlow for a user role:

```
(host) [md] (config) #user-role <user-role>
(host) [md] (config-submode)#OpenFlow-enable
(host) [md] (config-submode)#write memory
Execute the following commands to enable OpenFlow for a VAP:
(host) [md] (config) #wlan virtual-ap <virtual-ap>
(host) [md] (Virtual AP profile "<virtual-ap>") #OpenFlow-enable
(host) [md] (Virtual AP profile "<virtual-ap>") #write memory
```

UCC heuristics mode configuration—step 4

The following shows an example user role, with ACLs applied, which is for Skype4B or Lync clients.

```
user-role  SfB-role
 access-list session dhcp-acl
 access-list session dns-acl
 access-list session tftp-acl
 access-list session skype4b-acl < permit TCP traffic for desktop sharing and file transfer >
 access-list session voip-applications-acl <Permit RTP/RTCP traffic>
```

It is mandatory to add the ACLs to permit specific application traffic. There must be an ACL rule present in the user-role to permit RTP/RTCP traffic. The following is a list of UCC applications that can be used to create application ACLs.

- alg-facetime
- alg-ftp
- alg-h323
- alg-jabber-audio
- alg-sip
- alg-sip-audio

- alg-sip-video
- alg-skype4b-app-sharing
- alg-skype4b-audio
- alg-skype4b-desktop-sharing
- alg-skype4b-file-transfer
- alg-skype4b-secure
- alg-skype4b-video
- alg-wifi-calling

UCC heuristics mode configuration—step 5

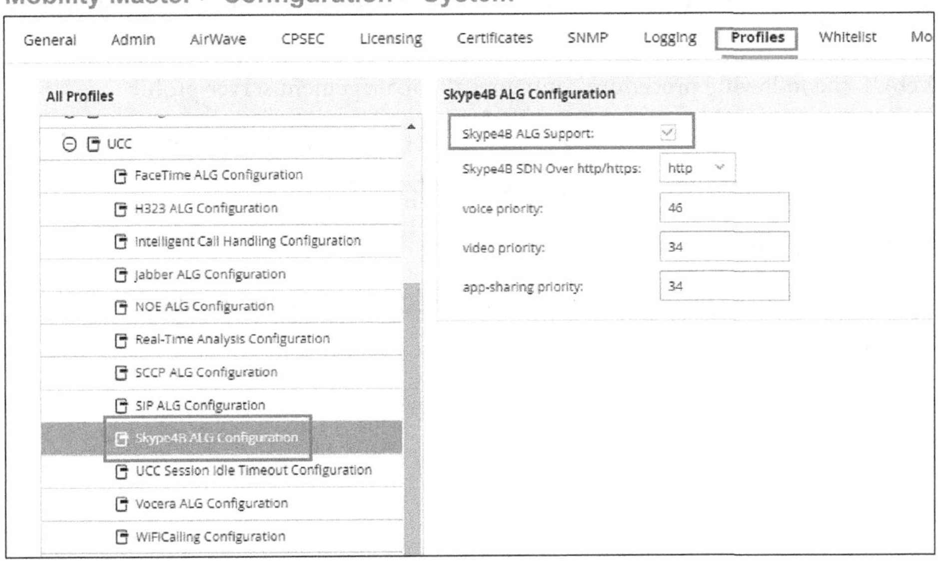

Figure 11-16 UCC heuristics mode configuration—step 5

The UCC ALGs must be configured from the MM node hierarchy of the MM (Figure 11-16). All the ALGs are enabled by default.

UCC heuristics mode configuration—step 6 (Optional)

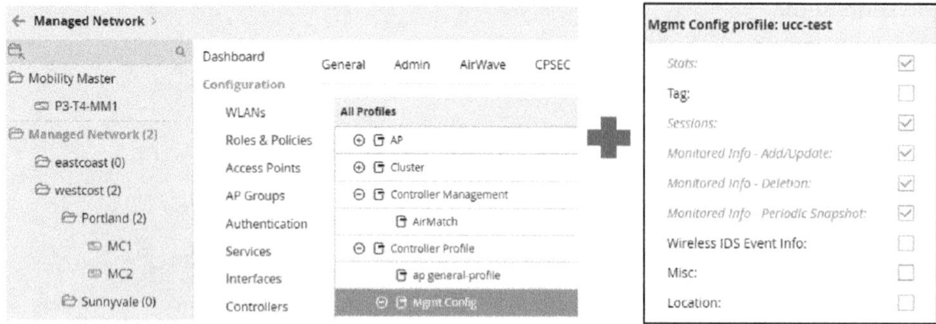

Figure 11-17 UCC heuristics mode configuration—step 6 (Optional)

You can configure the management server profile (Figure 11-17). This enables AMON feeds to be sent to the MM or MC for various statistics. You must configure this in the /md node hierarchy or the sub-nodes of MC.

In the WebUI, the following procedure configures the management server profile:

1. In the Managed Network node hierarchy, navigate to **Configuration > System > Profiles**.
2. In All Profiles, expand Controller Profile. Select Mgmt Config.
3. In Mgmt Config profile, click the + icon.
4. In the Profile name field, enter the name of the management server profile.
5. Select the following check boxes:
   - Stats
   - Sessions
   - Monitored Info—Add/Update
   - Monitored Info— Deletion
   - Monitored Info—Periodic Snapshot
6. Click Submit.
7. Navigate to Configuration > System > More.
8. Expand General. In MON Receivers, click the + icon.
9. In New MON Receiver, enter the following details:
   a. In the Server field, enter the Mobility Master or master controller IP address.
   b. In the Profile drop-down list, select the newly created management server profile.

10. Click Submit.
11. Click Pending Changes.
12. In the Pending Changes window, select the check box and click deploy changes.

In the CLI, the following commands configure management server profile:

```
(host)[md] (config) #mgmt-server profile <profile-name>
(host)^[md] (Mgmt Config profile "<profile-name>") #stats-enable
(host)^[md] (Mgmt Config profile "<profile-name>") #sessions-enable
(host)^[md] (Mgmt Config profile "<profile-name>") #monitored-info-enable
(host)^[md] (Mgmt Config profile "<profile-name>") #monitored-info-del-enable
(host)^[md] (Mgmt Config profile "<profile-name>") #monitored-info-snapshot-enable
(host)^[md] (Mgmt Config profile "<profile-name>") #!
(host)^[md] (config) #mgmt-server primary-server <MM-IP> profile <profile-name>
(host)^[md] (config) #write memory
```

UCC monitoring in global view

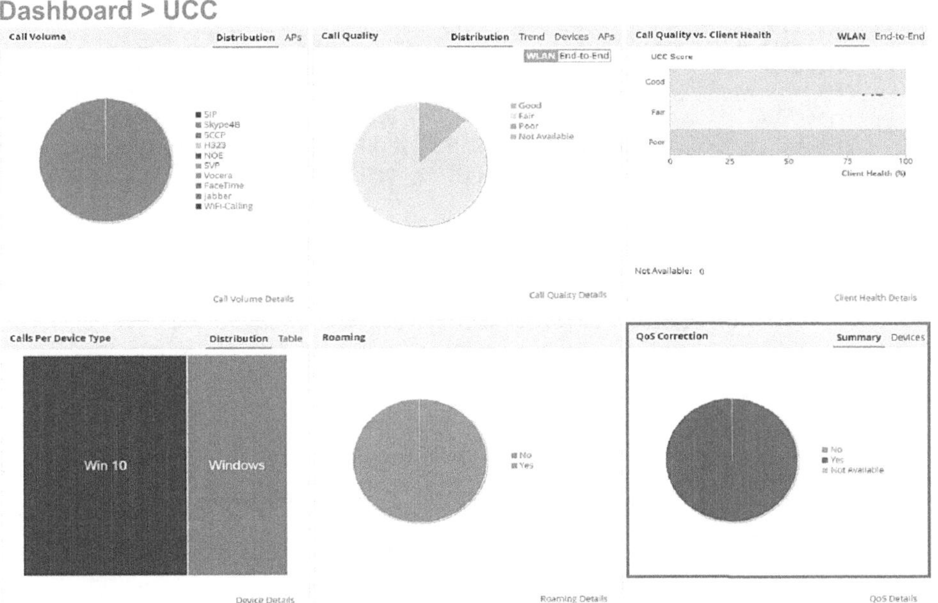

Figure 11-18 UCC monitoring in global view

The UCC Dashboard Aggregated Display shows an aggregated view of the UCC calls made in the Mobility Master (Figure 11-18). You can see a top-level view of the call quality assessment, and drill down into a specific view, based on the analysis required.

In the UCC global dashboard, you can see the QoS Correction status. In some cases, the DSCP value for client-transmitted RTP packets may differ from the corresponding priority value configured for the application. If so, the MM corrects the value, per the SSID profile definition. It then classifies the call as QoS corrected. This graph displays the number of UCC calls where this has occurred. The QoS correction is categorized as:

- No—No WMM-DSCP value correction
- Yes—WMM-DSCP value corrected by the MM
- Not Available—for WLAN calls lasting less than 60 seconds

Please refer to user guide for more detail parameter explanation.

UCC monitoring in global view—Wireshark example

Recall that clients may set DSCP values for RTP packets, prior to transmission. If this differs from the corresponding priority value configured for the application, the MM corrects the value as per the SSID profile definition. It then classifies the call as "QoS corrected."

Figures 11-19 and 11-20 show a UCC call packet capture, where the MM corrected the WMM-DSCP value.

Client→ Server (On client)

```
4324 28.155788   10.1.41.150        10.254.1.24       UDP      957 33707→57051 L
4325 28.155890   10.1.41.150        10.254.1.24       UDP      957 33707→57051 L

Frame 4324: 957 bytes on wire (7656 bits), 957 bytes captured (7656 bits) on int
Ethernet II, Src: AsustekC_08:47:8e (38:d5:47:08:47:8e), Dst: HewlettP_a2:ec:80
Internet Protocol Version 4, Src: 10.1.41.150, Dst: 10.254.1.24
  0100 .... = Version: 4
  .... 0101 = Header Length: 20 bytes (5)
v Differentiated Services Field: 0x00 (DSCP: CS0, ECN: Not-ECT)
    0000 00.. = Differentiated Services Codepoint: Default (0)
    .... ..00 = Explicit Congestion Notification: Not ECN-Capable Transport (0)
```

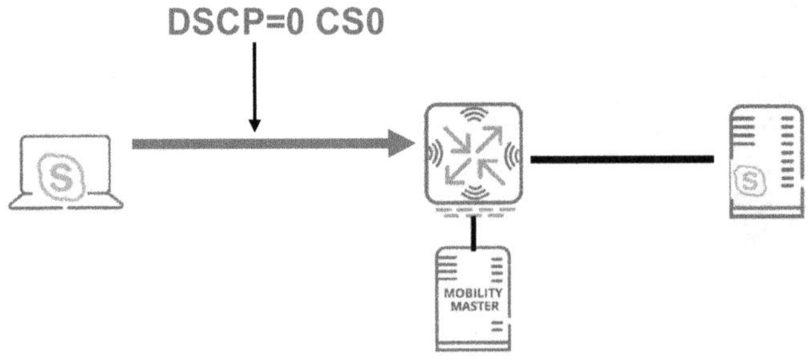

Figure 11-19 UCC monitoring in global view—Wireshark example

In Figure 11-19, the client's RTP packet's DSCP value is 0.

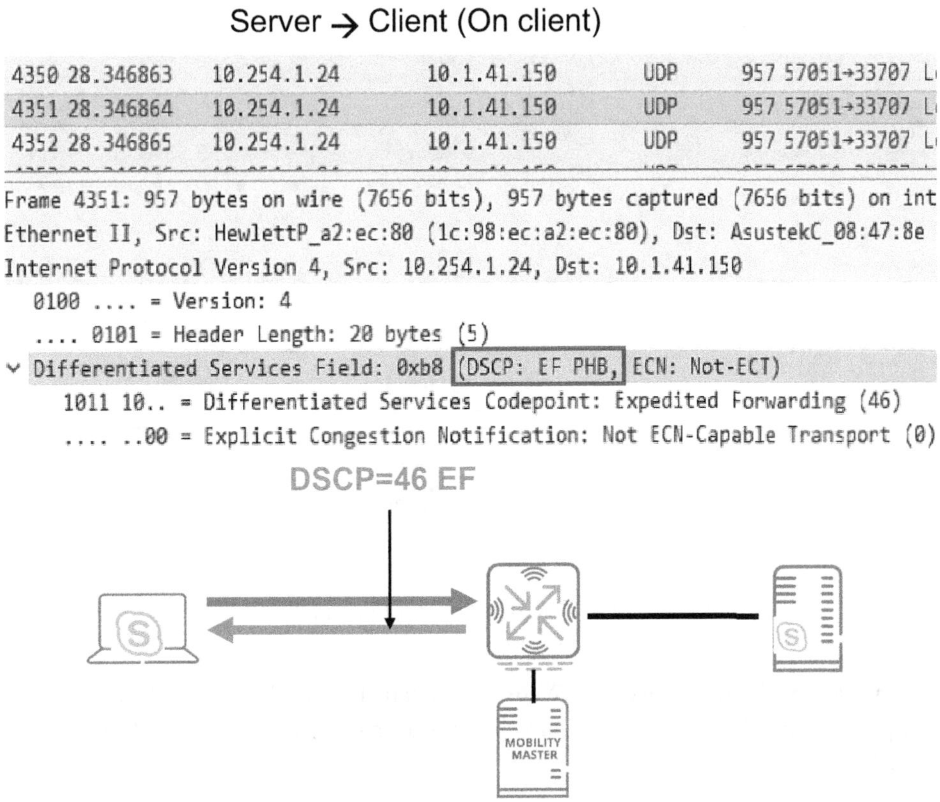

Server → Client (On client)

```
4350 28.346863    10.254.1.24    10.1.41.150    UDP    957 57051→33707 L
4351 28.346864    10.254.1.24    10.1.41.150    UDP    957 57051→33707 L
4352 28.346865    10.254.1.24    10.1.41.150    UDP    957 57051→33707 L

Frame 4351: 957 bytes on wire (7656 bits), 957 bytes captured (7656 bits) on int
Ethernet II, Src: HewlettP_a2:ec:80 (1c:98:ec:a2:ec:80), Dst: AsustekC_08:47:8e
Internet Protocol Version 4, Src: 10.254.1.24, Dst: 10.1.41.150
  0100 .... = Version: 4
  .... 0101 = Header Length: 20 bytes (5)
v Differentiated Services Field: 0xb8 (DSCP: EF PHB, ECN: Not-ECT)
    1011 10.. = Differentiated Services Codepoint: Expedited Forwarding (46)
    .... ..00 = Explicit Congestion Notification: Not ECN-Capable Transport (0)
```

DSCP=46 EF

MOBILITY MASTER

Figure 11-20 UCC monitoring in global view—Wireshark example

In Figure 11-20, UCC receives the client packet and "corrected" or remarked this to EF=46.

Remember, you can access the UCC global dashboard to see QoS "correction status" or remarking activity, as described on the previous page.

UCC monitoring in client view

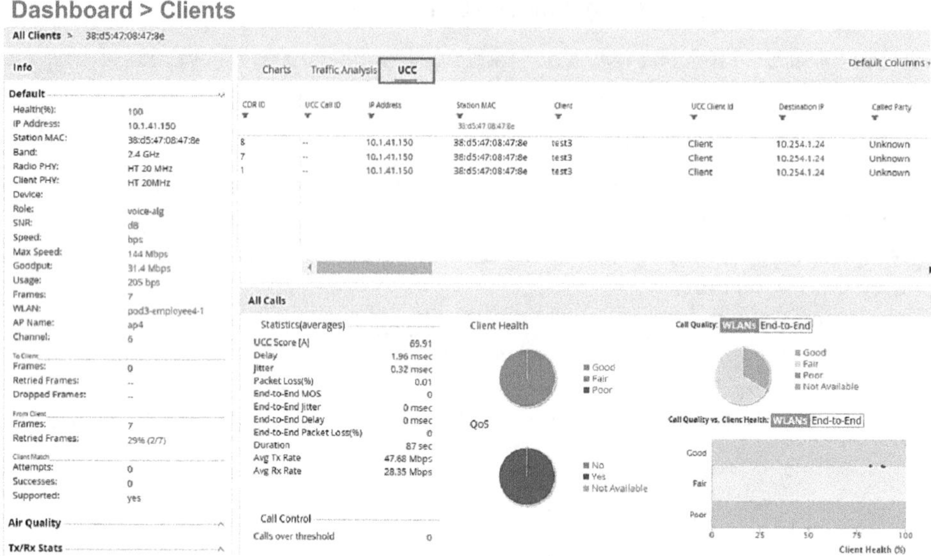

Figure 11-21 UCC monitoring in client view

On the **Dashboard > Clients** page of the WebUI, you can click on the client IP hyperlink to display the details page of the client. The UCC tab displays an aggregated list of UCC call data metrics (Figure 11-21).

UCC dashboard on AirWave Management Platform

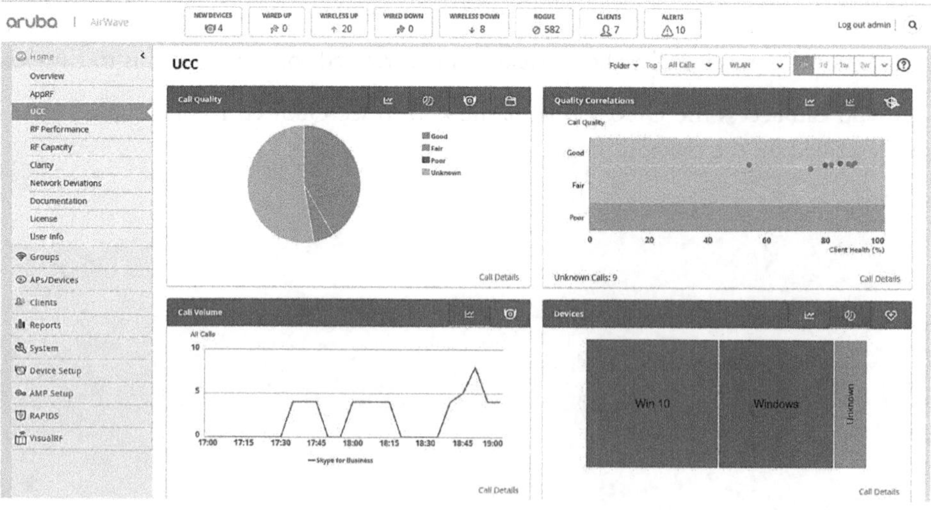

Figure 11-22 UCC dashboard on AirWave Management Platform

You can also monitor and diagnose UCC activity from the AirWave Management Platform (AMP) (Figure 11-22). There several advantages to using AMP for UCC monitoring, including the ability to store much longer communication history, and more granular call metrics.

UCC Dashboard on AirWave Management Platform (cont.)

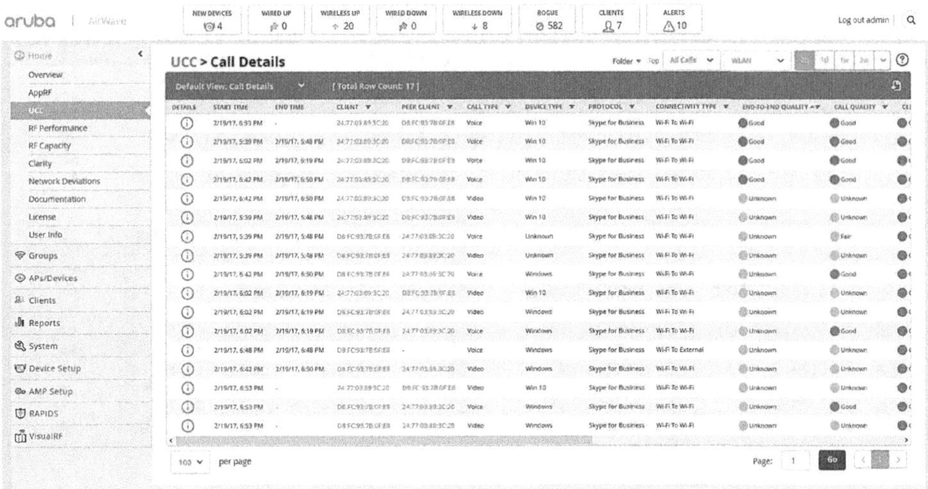

Figure 11-23 UCC Dashboard on AirWave Management Platform (cont.)

Figure 11-23 shows yet another nice feature of AMP—the ability to view detailed call history, along with call endpoint and quality information.

UCC troubleshooting—show ucc

```
(MM) [mynode] #show ucc client-info
Client Status:
--------------
Client IP     Client MAC          Client Name  ALG       Server(IP)  Registration State
---------     ----------          -----------  ---       ----------  ------------------
10.1.41.150   38:d5:47:08:47:8e   Client       Skype4B               REGISTERED

Call Status  AP Name  Flags  Device Type  Home_Agent    Foreign_Agent
-----------  -------  -----  -----------  ----------    -------------
In-Call      ap4             Win 10       10.1.40.100   NA
```

Figure 11-24 UCC troubleshooting—show ucc

The `show ucc client-info` command displays the UCC client status and CDR statistics, as shown in Figure 11-24.

```
(MM) [mynode] #show ucc call-info cdrs

Help: [C] - Metric calculated at the Controller
      [A] - Metric calculated at the AP
CDR:
----
CDR ID  UCC Call ID  Client IP     Client MAC         Client Name  ALG      Dir  Called to  Dur(sec)
------  -----------  ---------     ----------         -----------  ---      ---  ---------  --------
9       NA           10.1.41.150   38:d5:47:08:47:8e  Client       Skype4B  NA   NA         75
8       NA           10.1.41.150   38:d5:47:08:47:8e  Client       Skype4B  NA   NA         91
7       NA           10.1.41.150   38:d5:47:08:47:8e  Client       Skype4B  NA   NA         83
6       NA           10.1.41.151   38:d5:47:0d:10:f7  Client       Skype4B  NA   NA         86
5       NA           10.1.41.151   38:d5:47:0d:10:f7  Client       Skype4B  NA   NA         80
4       NA           10.1.41.151   38:d5:47:0d:10:f7  Client       Skype4B  NA   NA         78
3       NA           10.1.41.151   38:d5:47:0d:10:f7  Client       Skype4B  NA   NA         90
2       NA           10.1.41.151   38:d5:47:0d:10:f7  Client       Skype4B  NA   NA         93
1       NA           10.1.41.150   38:d5:47:08:47:8e  Client       Skype4B  NA   NA         87

Orig Time        Status  Reason      Call Type  Client Health  UCC Score[C]  UCC Score[A]  MOS
---------        ------  ------      ---------  -------------  ------------  ------------  ---
May 18 09:30:03  ACTIVE  NA          Voice      90             93.36/Good    71.03/Good    NA
May 16 16:44:37  SUCC    Terminated  Voice      88             84.65/Good    69.91/Fair    NA
May 16 16:42:54  SUCC    Terminated  Voice      89             84.67/Good    69.67/Fair    NA
May 16 10:15:38  SUCC    Terminated  Voice      86             80.83/Good    69.66/Fair    NA
May 16 10:04:00  SUCC    Terminated  Voice      97             84.38/Good    69.57/Fair    NA
May 16 07:40:34  SUCC    Terminated  Voice      89             84.67/Good    69.87/Fair    NA
May 16 07:29:58  SUCC    Terminated  Voice      90             93.36/Good    69.94/Fair    NA
May 16 07:26:43  SUCC    Terminated  Voice      89             93.36/Good    69.70/Fair    NA
May 16 07:22:17  SUCC    Terminated  Voice      82             93.36/Good    70.17/Good    NA
```

Figure 11-25 UCC troubleshooting—show ucc

The `show ucc call-info cdrs` command displays CDR statistics for UCC, as shown in Figure 11-25.

Please refer to the CLI Reference Guide for more command explanations.

UCC troubleshooting—show datapath

```
(MC1) #show datapath session table 10.1.41.150 | include 10.254.1.24

Datapath Session Table Entries
------------------------------

Flags: F - fast age, S - src NAT, N - dest NAT
       D - deny, R - redirect, Y - no syn
       H - high prio, P - set prio, T - set ToS
       C - client, M - mirror, V - VOIP
       Q - Real-Time Quality analysis
       u - Upstream Real-Time Quality analysis
       I - Deep inspect, U - Locally destined
       E - Media Deep Inspect, G - media signal
       r - Route Nexthop, h - High Value
       A - Application Firewall Inspect
       B - Permanent, O - Openflow
       L - Log

10.254.1.24   10.1.41.150  6   5061  49700  0/0  6  0   0  tunnel 15  88d2  305  224256  I
10.1.41.150   10.254.1.24  17  2349  50377  0/0  6  46  0  local      4     43   7926    FHPTCVBO
10.254.1.24   10.1.41.150  17  50377 2349   0/0  6  46  0  local      4     43   16186   FHPTCVBO
10.1.41.150   10.254.1.24  17  2348  50376  0/0  6  46  0  local      4     3    376     FHPTCIVBOu
10.1.41.150   10.254.1.24  6   49700 5061   0/0  6  0   0  tunnel 15  88d2  239  52546   CI
10.254.1.24   10.1.41.150  17  50376 2348   0/0  6  46  0  local      4     203  42556   FHPTCIVBOQu
```

Figure 11-26 UCC troubleshooting—show datapath

In this example, there is a "V" flag in the client communication session, which means the session is classified as VOIP (Figure 11-26).

Learning check

5. The Deep Packet Inspection option in global firewall settings must be enabled in Heuristics Mode configuration for all UCC applications.
    a. True
    b. False

12 Mesh

LEARNING OBJECTIVES

✓ This chapter focuses on the HPE Aruba mesh solution. You will learn the basics of mesh operation, including why, when, and where this solution is appropriate. You will learn what products support the feature, and how to deploy and configure those products in a best-practice mesh solution. Finally, you will discover various troubleshooting methods related to mesh networking.

Mesh introduction

Why do you need mesh?

The Aruba secure enterprise mesh solution is an effective way to expand network coverage for outdoor and indoor enterprise environments while minimizing the need for Ethernet cable runs. The mesh solution enables you to bridge multiple Ethernet LANs and/or to extend your wireless coverage. To maximize network resiliency, the mesh network automatically reconfigures around broken or blocked paths.

Additional features include:

- Self-healing for increased reliability and redundancy.
- Continued network operation, even with AP failures or lost connection.
- Centralized AP configuration and management.
- Local mesh APs provide encryption and traffic forwarding for mesh links.

Where do you need mesh?

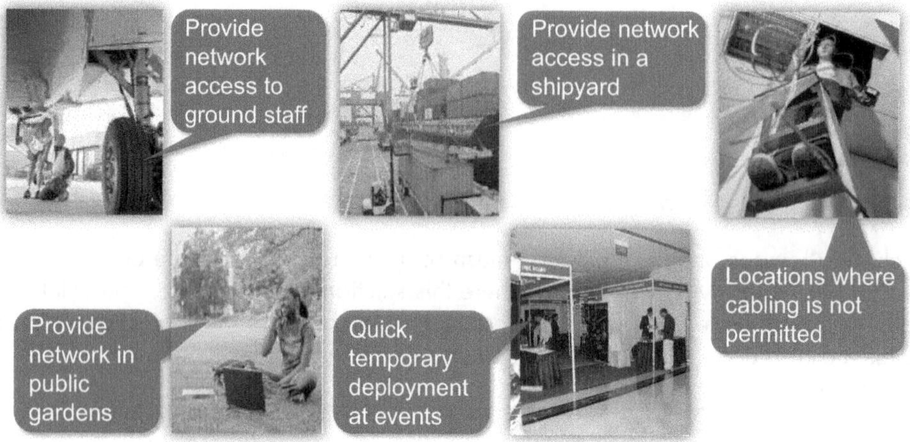

Figure 12-1 Where do you need mesh?

The Aruba OS controller-based mesh solution supports both indoor and outdoor mesh deployments (Figure 12-1). Regular, nonmesh APs typically accept end-user WLAN traffic and bridge it to a wired Ethernet link. Mesh networks allow some APs to form a backhaul link using their radio, instead of an Ethernet port. APs connect back to the Aruba controller by forming wireless mesh links with other APs.

You can deploy such an AP without an Ethernet connection. This is especially useful when it is not practical to run Ethernet cables. This is often outdoor areas to provide coverage for aircraft maintenance and ground staff personnel in a shipyard or in public parks and gardens.

Mesh basics

Mesh components

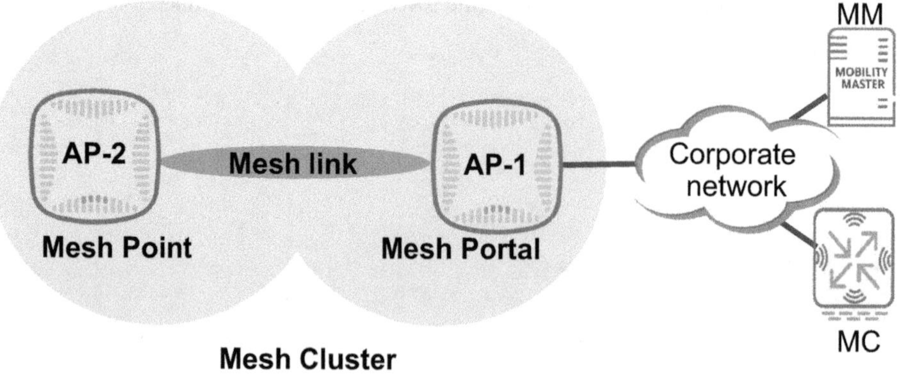

Figure 12-2 Mesh components

The Aruba mesh solution includes two modes of AP operation—Mesh Portal and Mesh Point.

The Mesh Portal (MPP) is the gateway between the wireless mesh network and the enterprise wired LAN. As shown in Figure 12-2, it has an Ethernet connection. You decide the best location for these APs[1] and configure them to perform the MP role.

The mesh portal broadcasts the configured mesh service set identifier (MSSID/mesh cluster name) and advertises the mesh network service to available mesh points.

Mesh Points (MP) provide traditional Aruba WLAN services such as client connectivity and Intrusion Detection System (IDS) services. Clients connect to MPs as normal, but MPs do not have an Ethernet connection. Therefore, user traffic is backhauled over a wireless mesh link to an MPP (Figure 12-2). The MPP then bridges this traffic onto the wired network.

Together, MPPs and MPs form a cluster. A mesh cluster is a logical set of mesh nodes. The cluster shares the common connection and security parameters required to create mesh links.

You can configure multiple mesh clusters on an Aruba Controller. You define which APs belong to the same cluster, and which devices are mesh portals and points. You can also see how mesh links are formed.

Note

[1]The decision as to where to locate MPPs is largely based on how feasible or costly it is to run Ethernet cable to a location and whether that location can also provide useful wireless backhaul connectivity. For example, in an outdoor mesh solution, you might be able to mount MPP APs just inside the building, where the APs are protected from the weather, and it is easy to run cable. Then you can mount external antennas on the outside of the building. Of course, you run these antenna cables through the building structure to connect them to the APs inside.

Usage of 5 GHz and 2.4 Hz bands

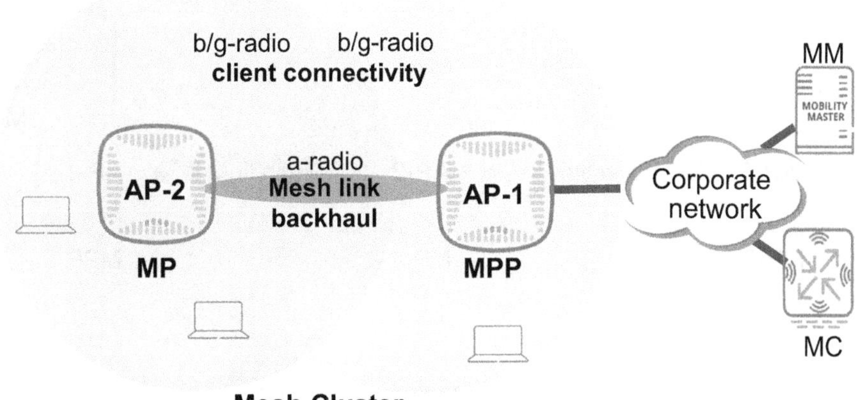

Figure 12-3 Usage of 5 GHz and 2.4 Hz bands

Figure 12-3 shows how mesh uses the 5 GHz (802.11a) and 2.4 GHz (802.11b/g) bands. Typically, the 5 GHz band is used for the mesh backhaul link, and the 2.4 GHz band serves wireless clients. This is because the 5 GHz band typically has less interference, making it more suitable for reliable backhaul service.

Note

WLAN client access may be provided on both the 2.4 GHz and 5 GHz bands simultaneously, even though the 5 GHz band is also being used for a backhaul connection. The radios are capable of simultaneously operating the mesh backhaul link and serving clients. However, this is not recommended, as this design reduces performance.

Controller and AP support

In AOS 8, all Aruba controllers support mesh. All APs based on 802.11n and 11ac (and many legacy APs) support mesh as well.

Keep in mind that mesh backhaul links are allowed between 802.11n and 802.11ac APs. However, the 802.11ac AP will fall back to 802.11n for mesh backhaul link compatibility.

Mesh details and best practices

Multi-hop mesh deployment

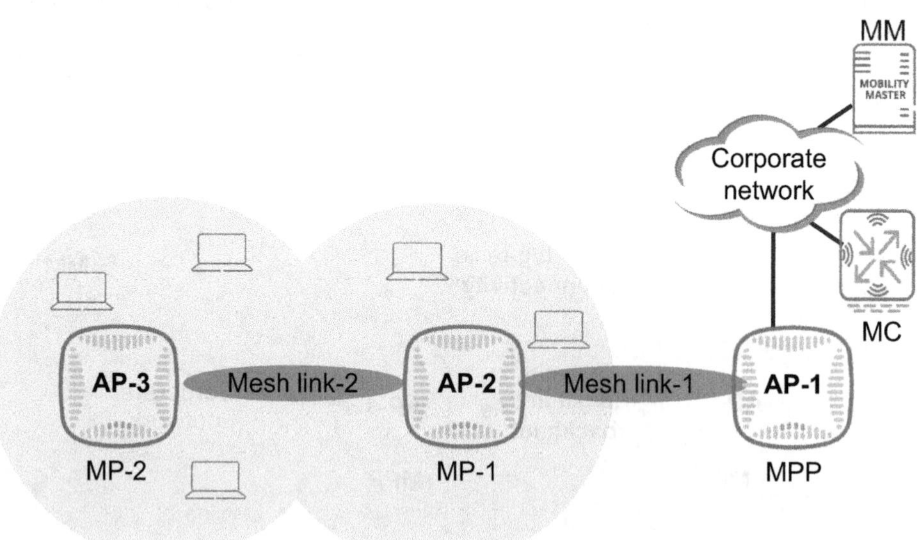

Figure 12-4 Multi-hop mesh deployment

Mesh deployments require at least one MPP, fulfilled by AP-1 in Figure 12-4. Other APs may be MPs or portals. When creating the initial mesh link, MPs consider their MSSID, as configured in their mesh cluster profile. They seek others advertising the same MSSID.

MPs scan the channels in its provisioned band of operation to identify a list of neighbors with a matching cluster profile. The MP then selects from the highest priority neighbors, based on the lowest expected path cost.

Mesh security and scalability

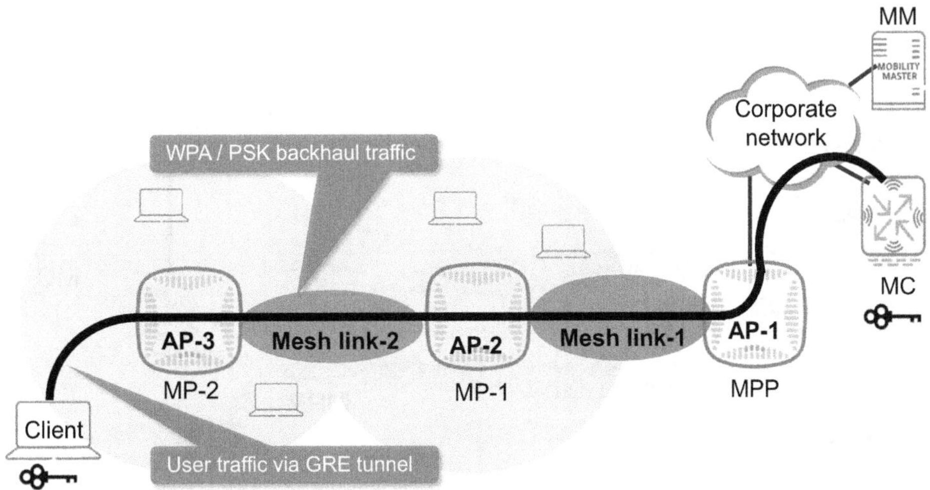

Figure 12-5 Mesh security and scalability

Figure 12-5 shows an example scenario with one MPP and two MPs, connected linearly. The 5 GHz backhaul link uses WPA2-PSK encryption, as configured in the mesh cluster profile. All WPA/WPA2 client traffic is encrypted at the client, then sent via mesh points/portals. The mesh points and mesh portals' GRE tunnel encapsulates this traffic and sends it back to the controller.

Control traffic between the APs and the controller is encrypted over the mesh backhaul link if you configure the link to use WPA2-PSK. This example has two hops between the edge MP-2 and the MPP.

Aruba supports up to 32 hops and 64 children. A "child" is a mesh AP that connects to a single mesh device. You should avoid approaching these limits due to performance concerns. With each hop, there is a multiplying effect on the reduction in bandwidth supported end-to-end. This is because client traffic on edge APs must traverse the entire mesh backhaul network.

Remember that 802.11 is a half-duplex medium, allowing only one device to transmit at a time, on any given channel. Therefore, a mesh AP sending traffic to another mesh AP cannot simultaneously send traffic to a third AP, and so forth. As best practice, try to limit the number of hops to two or three, if at all possible. Instead, try to add more MPPs and clusters. Also, try to limit the number of children to two or three.

Mesh channel selection

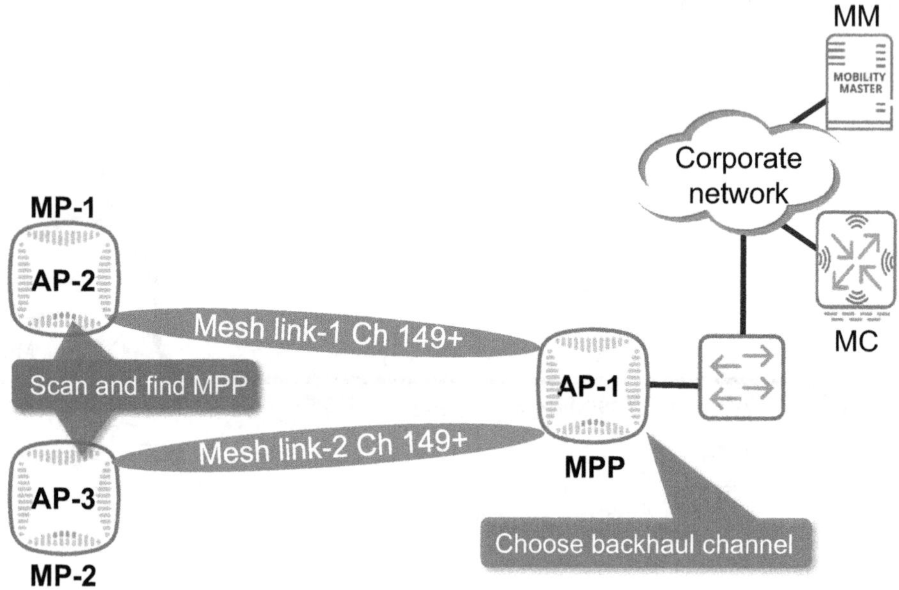

Figure 12-6 Mesh channel selection

The MPP uses AirMatch to find the best channel for backhaul links (Figure 12-6). All MPs connected to the same MPP must use the same backhaul channel. The MPP scans and chooses the channel, then advertises its MSSID on that channel.

MPs scan and find the MSSID that they should connect to, according to their AP group's mesh cluster profile. The MP connects to the MPP via the established backhaul link. Thus, all MPs find the MPP's backhaul MSSID and communicate on the same channel.

In deployments with unhealthy RF environments, frequent backhaul channel changes are worse than moving to a channel with less interference. In this case, let AirMatch find a channel with the least interference for the backhaul link, then statically set this channel in the AP group's dot11 radio profile.

Of course, the disadvantage of this technique is that your network will not be able to adapt to any new interference on that channel. The healthier your RF environment, the more you might avoid static channel configuration.

Mesh deployment models

In a thin AP wireless backhaul deployment, mesh provides services and security to remote wireless clients. All control and user traffic to the MC is sent over a wireless backhaul mesh link. This is the solution you have been learning about so far in this chapter. You are providing typical WLAN coverage for clients while minimizing the need for Ethernet cable drops.

The remaining deployments described offer a different solution—they allow you to extend your existing wired network or connect two separate wired networks. These solutions provide a wireless bridge between Ethernet LAN segments.

You can use these deployments to bridge Ethernet LANs between floors, office buildings, campuses, factories, warehouses, and other environments where you do not have access to physical ports or cable to extend the wired network.

Thin AP services with wireless backhaul deployment

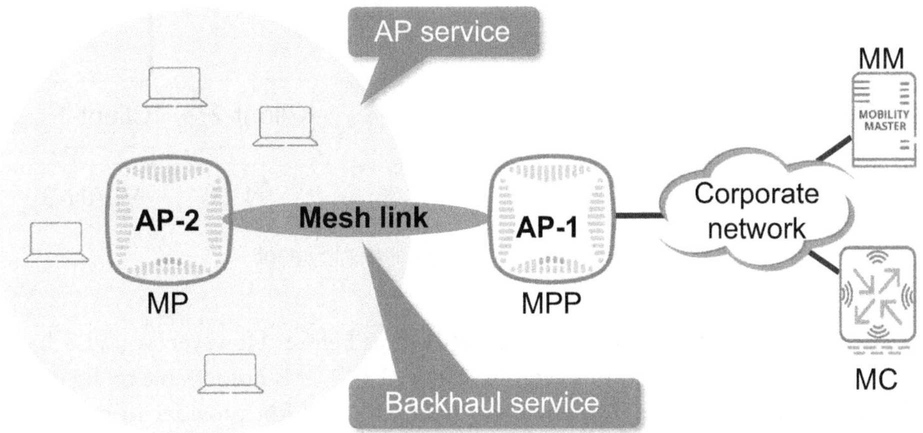

Figure 12-7 Thin AP services with wireless backhaul deployment

In this scenario, you need to expand wireless coverage for a single wired infrastructure. Figure 12-7 shows a single corporate network, perhaps inside a single building. However, there is a large parking area outside of this building, which you would like to blanket with WLAN service. In this scenario, it is not feasible to dig up the parking lot and run Ethernet cables.

This calls for thin AP services with a wireless backhaul. The MP provides network access for wireless clients and establishes a link to the MPP, which uses its wired interface to connect to the controller. Again, this is providing typical WLAN service for clients, while minimizing the need for Ethernet cable drops.

As is typical, the 2.4 GHz radio is used for end-user connectivity, while the 5 GHz radio provides backhaul services.

Point-to-point deployment

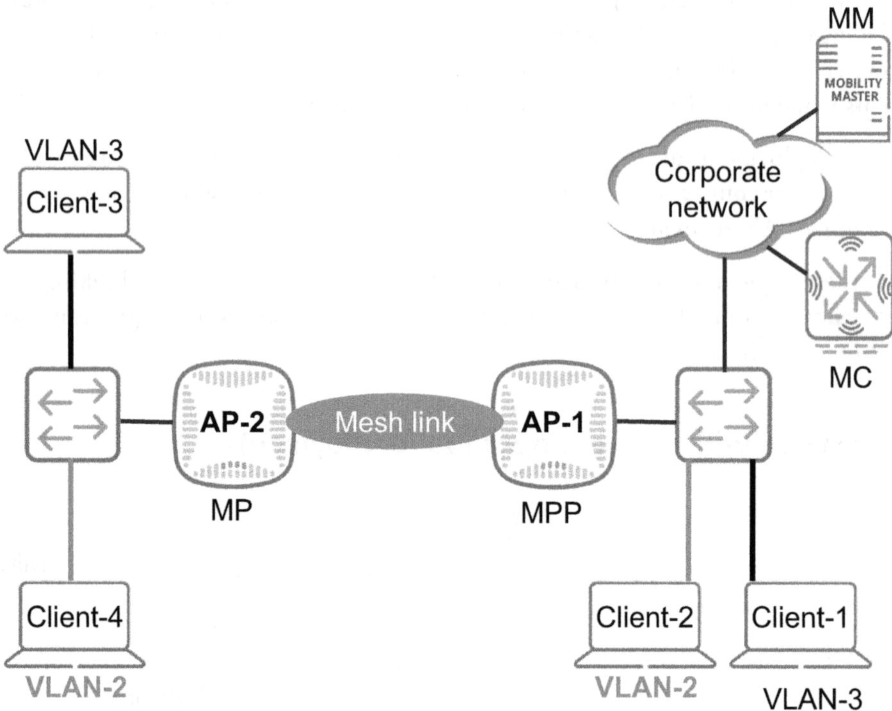

Figure 12-8 Point-to-point deployment

In this scenario, you have the same corporate network as before. However, you also have another building, across a two-lane road in your campus (Figure 12-8). It is not feasible to dig up the road to run an Ethernet or a Fiber cable. You could contract with a WAN provider to connect these two offices, but that creates a recurring expense. Plus, the two offices are very close together.

This is a perfect scenario for an HPE Aruba point-to-point mesh solution. You will connect these two separate wired networks with a wireless bridge connection. This connection carries both client services traffic and mesh-backhaul traffic between the MPP and the MP.

Thus, the two offices are connected with only a small initial cost, and no recurring costs.

Point-to-multipoint deployment

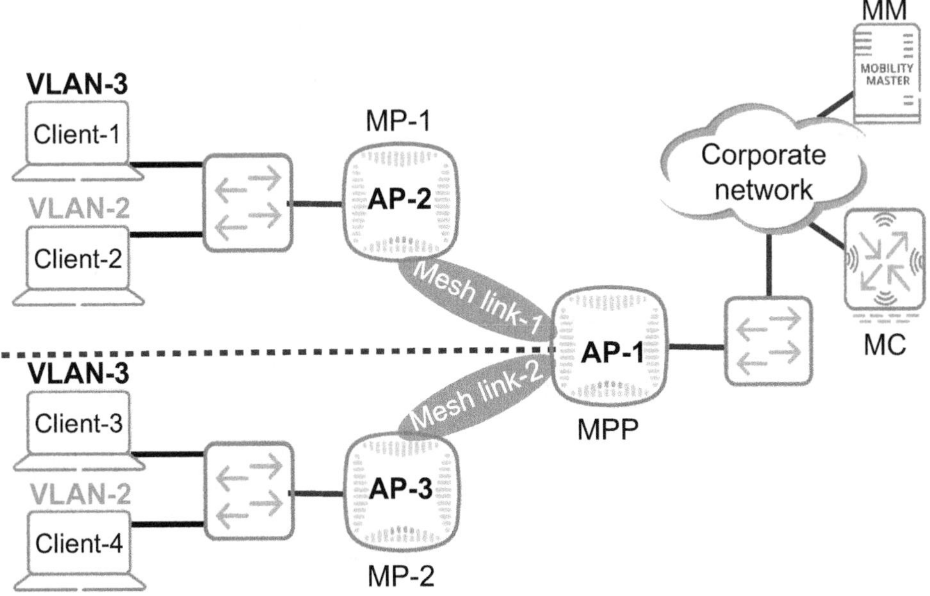

Figure 12-9 Point-to-multipoint deployment

This scenario is very much like the point-to-point scenario, only there is more than one office to connect (Figure 12-9). Of course, a point-to-multipoint deployment provides a great connectivity solution.

Each small office has a MP that connects to the MPP, like the previous point-to-point scenario. Thus, each small office has connectivity back to the corporate network.

Learning check

1. Which of the following radios is used for backhaul (mesh link) communication?
   a. Only a radio
   b. Only g radio
   c. a or g radio
2. Traffic through mesh link (backhaul) can also be encrypted.
   a. True
   b. False

Single cluster with multiple portals

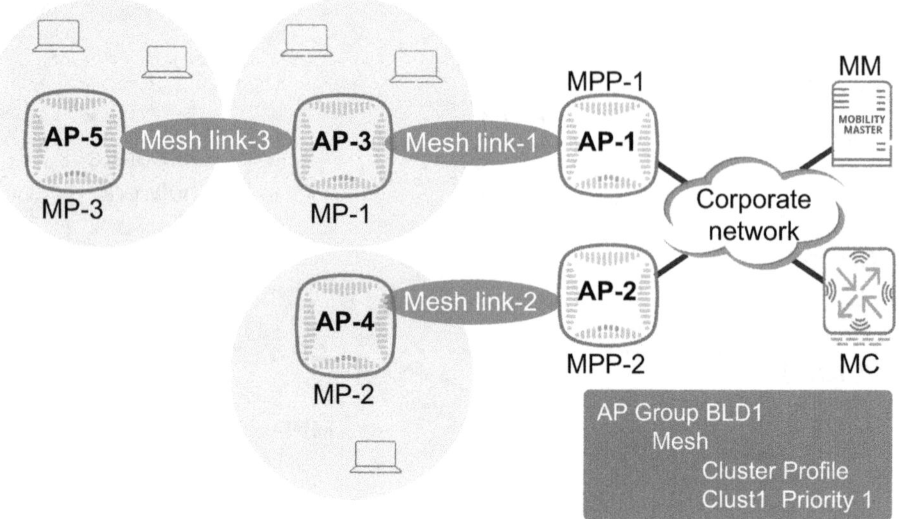

Figure 12-10 Single cluster with multiple portals

Figure 12-10 shows that you decided to leverage multiple MPPs. This splits the load between the two backhaul 5 GHz channels, which reduces bandwidth utilization for each mesh link. You have created a more scalable solution.

Multiple clusters and cluster priority

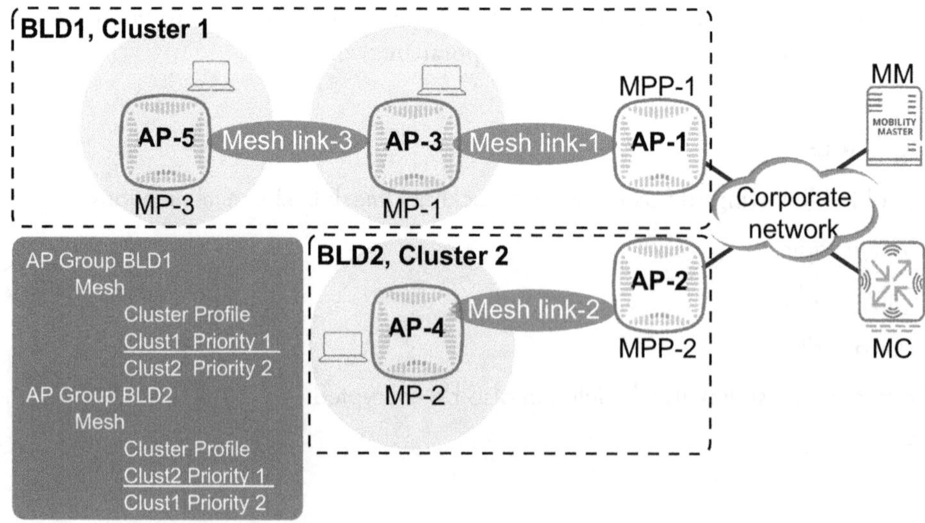

Figure 12-11 Multiple clusters and cluster priority

In the previous scenario, you added another MPP to an existing cluster. This splits the load between the two MPPs—a nice improvement.

Another tactic is to configure a second cluster (Clust2), perhaps supporting the APs in Building 2; so you provision Building 2 APs to a separate AP group (Figure 12-11).

You can see how performance improves in this situation, as with the previous scenario. It can also improve redundancy by assigning cluster priority levels. The APs in group BLD1 will prefer connectivity to cluster 1, since it has a lower priority. Should this connection fail, they will connect to cluster 2. APs in group BLD2 connect to cluster 2, since its priority is set to a lower numerical value. They can use Cluster 1 as a backup. You may also reduce the hop count for MPs.

You will learn more about cluster redundancy in the pages that follow.

Mesh cluster redundancy—introduction

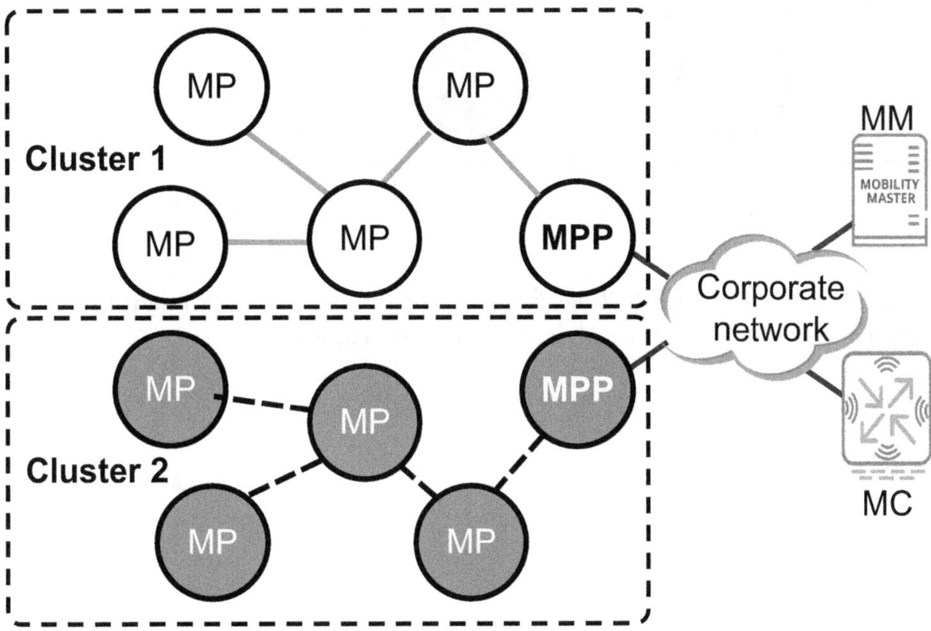

Figure 12-12 Mesh cluster redundancy—introduction

Figure 12-12 shows a deployment with two clusters. Each cluster has a single MPP and four MPs. Currently, all devices are operational.

Mesh cluster redundancy—failure condition

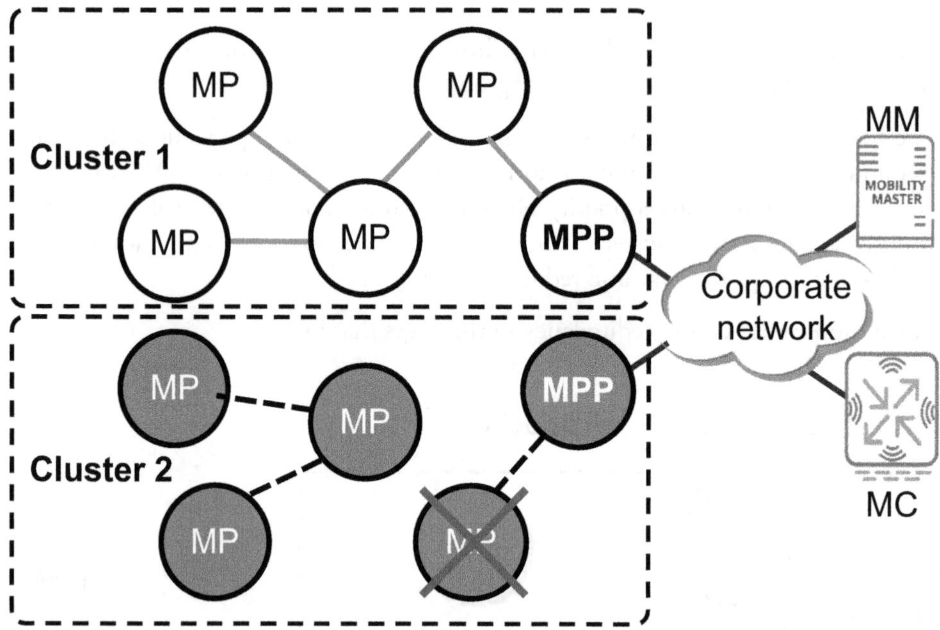

Figure 12-13 Mesh cluster redundancy—failure condition

In Figure 12-13, one MP in cluster 2 has failed, so the downstream MPs might lose connectivity. They are too far from their current cluster's MPP to form a connection.

Mesh cluster redundancy—failover

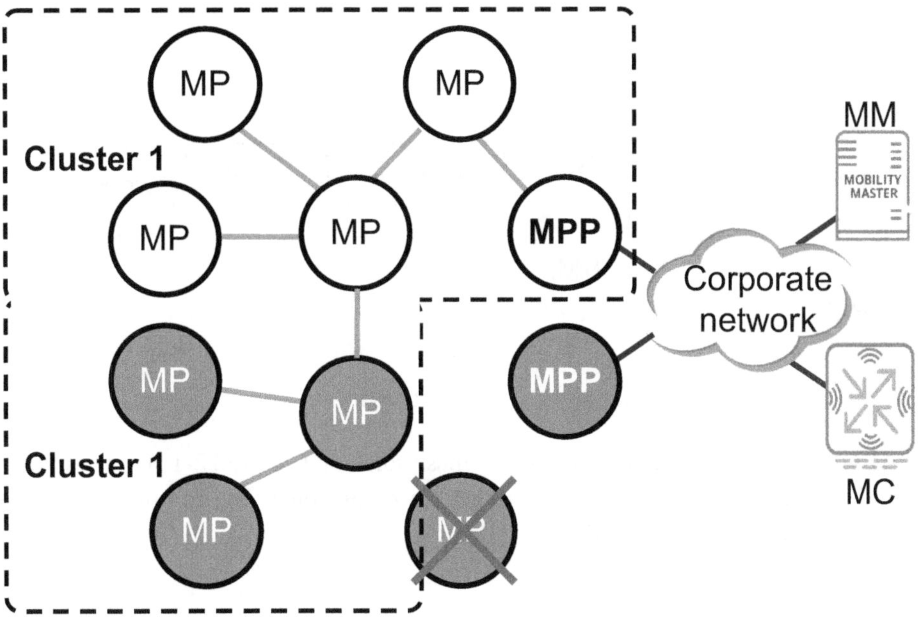

Figure 12-14 Mesh cluster redundancy—failover

However, you have wisely configured cluster redundancy. One MP in cluster 2 is close to a MP in cluster 1—close enough to connect. This MP forms a connection and the remaining, functional MPs join cluster 1 (Figure 12-14).

Remote mesh portal

Remote Mesh Portals (RMP) provide mesh services at a branch office. You can configure a single AP that acts as both a RAP and a MPP. In other words, it not only opens an IPsec tunnel back to the controller as a RAP but also advertises the MSSID on the backhaul radio. Thus, it acts as an MPP, as shown in Figure 12-15 below. You configure other mesh nodes in the branch office as MPs. These other APs need not be configured as RAPs because they act as Campus AP MPs.

RMP components

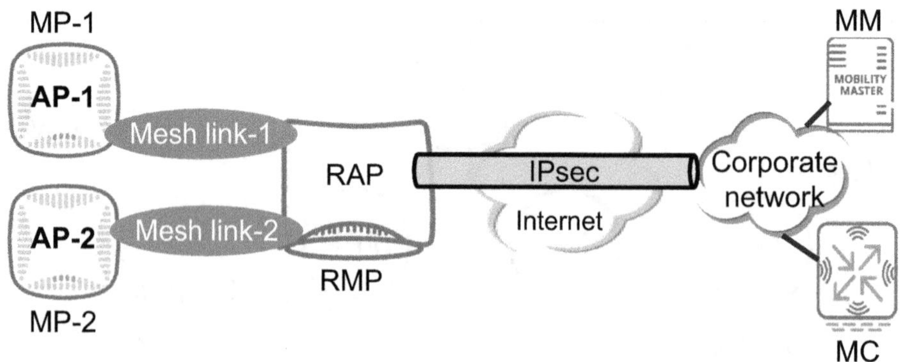

Figure 12-15 RMP components

The RMP mesh network operates like the campus mesh solution (Figure 12-15). The only difference is that the traffic is sent via IPsec tunnel back to the Aruba controller. The components are the same, except for the configuration of the RMP.

Configuring a mesh network

Configuration—mesh cluster profile

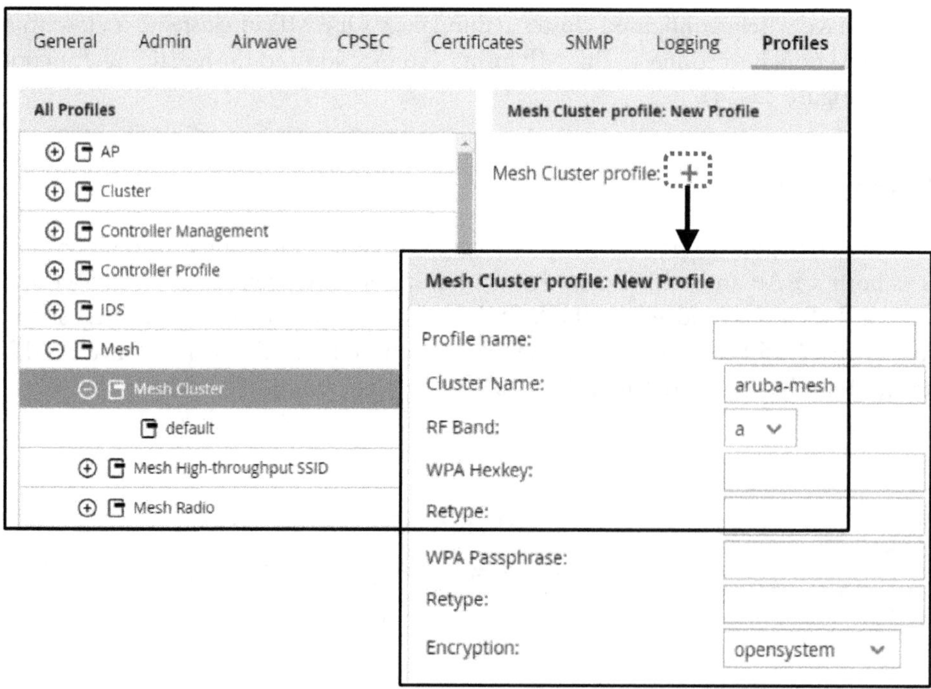

Figure 12-16 Configuration—mesh cluster profile

Figure 12-16 shows how to configure a mesh cluster profile via the WebUI.

1. In the Managed Network node hierarchy, navigate to **Configuration** > **System** > **Profiles**.
2. Expand the Mesh tab, open the Mesh Cluster profile, and click on +.
3. Enter a name for the new profile.
4. Configure the mesh cluster settings (Cluster name, RF band, Encryption key).

Configuration—mesh radio profile

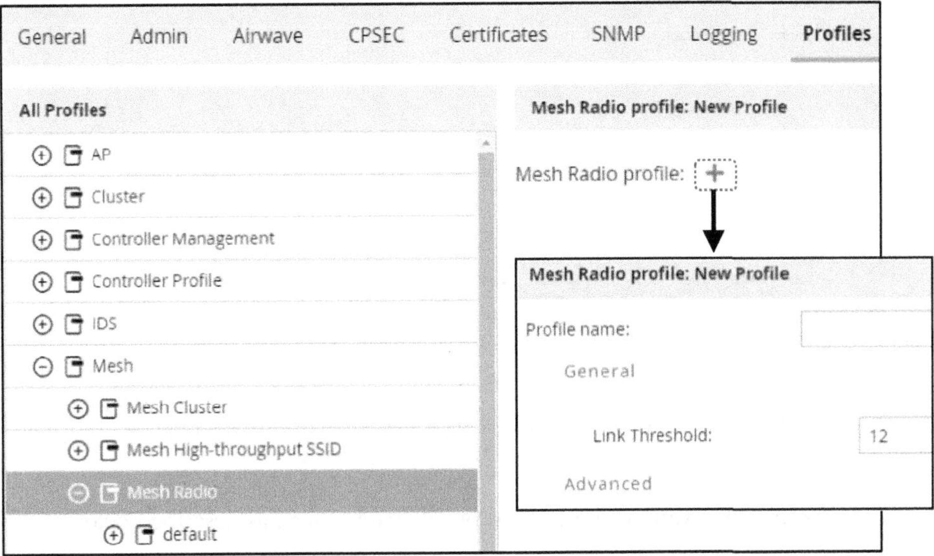

Figure 12-17 Configuration—mesh radio profile

Now you need to configure a mesh radio profile, as described below (Figure 12-17):

1. In the Managed Network node hierarchy, navigate to the **Configuration** > **System** > **Profile**.
2. Expand the Mesh tab, then open the Mesh Radio profile.
3. Click the + icon and configure your desired mesh radio settings.

Note

The procedure to create a new mesh profile varies slightly from the procedure to edit an existing profile.

Configuration—advanced mesh radio profile

Advanced

802.11a Transmit Rates:	6	9	12	18
	24	36	48	54
802.11g Transmit Rates:	1	2	5	6
	9	11	12	18
	24	36	48	54

Allowed VLANs on mesh link:	1-4094
BC/MC Rate Optimization:	☑
Heartbeat threshold:	10
Maximum Children:	64
Maximum Hop Count:	8
Mesh Private Vlan:	0
Metric algorithm:	distributed-tree-rssi
Rate Optimization for delivering EAPOL frames and mesh echoes:	☐
Reselection mode:	startup-subthreshold
Retry Limit:	8
RTS Threshold:	2333 byt

Figure 12-18 Configuration—advanced mesh radio profile

Figure 12-18 shows several advanced mesh radio profile parameters, as described below:

802.11a transmit rates—Indicates the transmit rates for the 802.11a radio. The AP attempts to use the highest transmission rate to establish a mesh link. If a rate is unavailable, the AP goes through the list and uses the next highest rate.

802.11g transmit rates—Indicates the transmit rates for the 802.11g radio. The AP attempts to use the highest transmission rate to establish a mesh link. If a rate is unavailable, the AP goes through the list and uses the next highest rate.

Allowed VLANs on mesh link—List the VLAN ID numbers of VLANs allowed on the mesh link.

BC/MC rate optimization—Broadcast/Multicast Rate Optimization dynamically selects the rate for sending broadcast/multicast frames on any BSS. This feature determines the optimal rate for sending broadcast and multicast frames based on the lowest of the unicast rates across all associated clients.

Heartbeat threshold—Indicates the maximum number of heartbeat messages that can be lost between neighboring mesh nodes. The default: 10 missed heartbeats. Range is 1–255.

Maximum children—Indicates the maximum number of children a mesh node can accept. Default: 64 children. Range: 1–64.

Maximum hop count—Indicates the maximum hop count from the MPP. Default: 8 hops. Range: 1–32.

Mesh private VLAN—A VLAN ID for control traffic between an RMP and mesh nodes. This VLAN ID must not be used for user traffic. Range: 0–4094. Default: 0 (disabled).

Metric algorithm—This parameter specifies the algorithm used by a mesh node to select its parent. Use this setting to optimize operation of the link metric algorithm. Available options are the following:

- **best-link-rssi**—Selects the parent with the strongest RSSI, regardless of the number of children a potential parent has.
- **distributed-tree-rssi**—Selects the parent based on link-RSSI and node cost based on the number of children. This option evenly distributes the MPs over high-quality uplinks. Low-quality uplinks are selected as a last resort. Default: distributed-tree-rssi. This is recommended.

Reselection mode—Used to optimize operation of the link metric algorithm. Available options are

- reselect-anytime
- reselect-never
- startup-subthreshold
- subthreshold-only

Retry limit—Indicates the number of times a mesh node can re-send a packet. Default: 4 times. Range: 1–15

RTS threshold—Defines the packet size sent by mesh nodes. Mesh nodes transmitting frames larger than this threshold must issue request to send (RTS) and wait for other mesh nodes to respond with clear to send (CTS) to begin transmission. This helps prevent mid-air collisions. Default: 2333 bytes. Range: 256–2346.

Best practices

For maximum mesh link performance, do not support client access VAPs on backhaul radios. In other words, use the 2.4 GHz radio for client access, and use the 5 GHz radio exclusively for backhaul access.

APs that form a mesh link should see each other with an RSSI of between –50 and –65 dBm. If mesh-linked APs are farther apart, or there is high interference and noise, drop to HT40 or even HT20 to stabilize the link.

Also, disabling ARM, Scanning, WIDS, and similar features can help stabilize mesh links.

Learning check

3. A single cluster can have more than one Mesh-portal.

   a. True

   b. False

4. Which of the following SSIDs is used by the mesh-point to discover the neighbor in the same cluster?

   a. ESSID

   b. BSSID

   c. MSSID

13 Administration

LEARNING OBJECTIVES

✓ This chapter covers various administration concepts and configurations. You will learn how to create and manage various types of management and guest-provisioning accounts. You will learn how to set RADIUS and TACACS servers to authenticate these accounts.

✓ Then you will explore how to disable console access on managed devices and how to enable remote Telnet and SSH access. The chapter ends with a discussion of configuring seamless logon.

Management accounts and password esetting

Management user account roles

Aruba supports the following types of management user account roles, as described below.

- **Root**—permits access to all management functions (commands and operations) on the managed device. This is considered the "super user."
- **Guest-provisioning**—permits the configuration of guest users in the managed device's internal database only. This user only has access via the WebUI to create guest accounts; there is no CLI access.
- **Network-operations**—Allows you to generate reports, view clients and blacklisted clients, view inventory, and similar monitoring functions. You can monitor WLANs, ports, and packet captures. You have access to the CLI, but are limited to monitoring-related commands.
- **Read-only**—permits access to CLI show commands or WebUI monitoring pages only.
- **Location-api-mgmt**—permits access to location API information and the CLI. However, you cannot use any CLI commands. This role does not permit access to the WebUI.
- **Nbapi-mgmt**—permits configuring a North Bound Application Programming Interface (NBAPI) management role. NBAPIs allow third-party applications to gain visibility into the Aruba network.
- **AP-provisioning**—permits access only to AP provisioning commands and no access to other configuration commands on the MM.

Creating admin user accounts

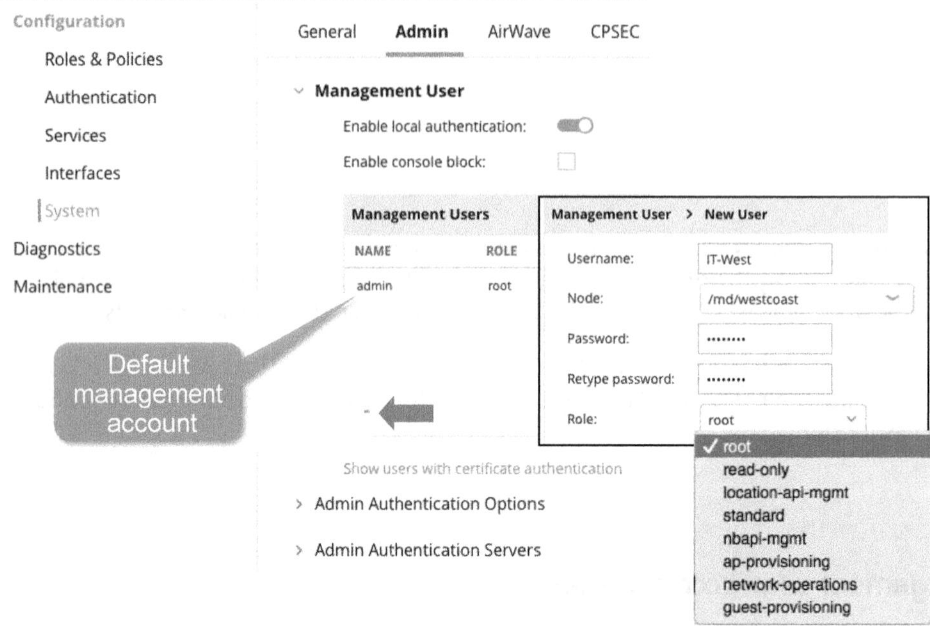

Figure 13-1 Creating Admin User accounts

The default root account is a user named Admin. To create other accounts, navigate as shown in Figure 13-1, to **Configuration > System > Admin**. Then click the + symbol and enter the credentials and role.

Guest provisioning

Guest-provisioning account

Guest-provisioning features allow IT staff to delegate guest management tasks to less technically oriented, more customer-facing staff members.

For example, a receptionist can use this account to create guest accounts. He or she logs into the controller, creates a guest user account, and perhaps prints a badge label for the newly created guest user.

All other GUI functions are hidden from the guest-provisioning user.

Guest-provisioning users can be authorized via internal database or external RADIUS or LDAP server. But remember, the guest accounts created by the receptionist will exist only in the controller's internal database. The guest-provisioning user can guest user's time limits, bandwidth, and other details related to guest accounts.

Guest-provisioning user tasks

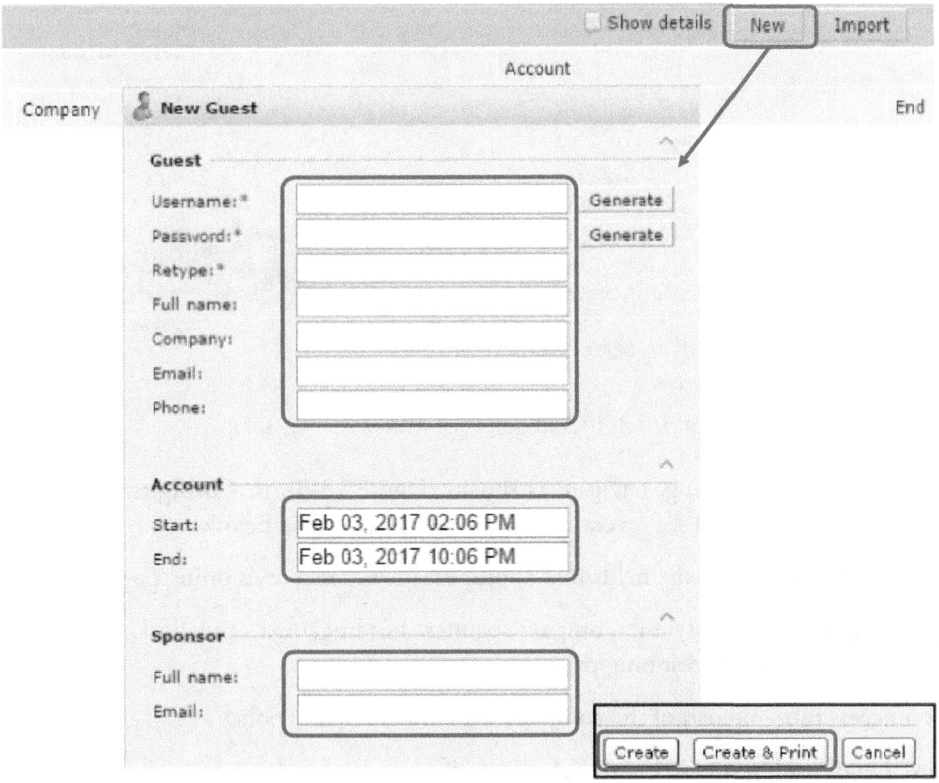

Figure 13-2 Guest-provisioning user tasks

To create guest accounts, the guest-provisioning user enters information on the guest-provisioning page. Tasks include creating, editing, manually sending email, enabling, printing, disabling, and deleting guest accounts.

To create a new guest account, the guest provisioning user clicks New to display the New guest window (Figure 13-2). They enter information into the fields shown, then click **Create**, or **Create & Print**.

To see details about an existing user account, highlight an existing account and select the "Show Details" check box. The "Show Details" popup will display.

You can import multiple guest entries into the database from a CSV file. This enables you to efficiently create multiple guest entries at once.

Configure guest-provisioning setup

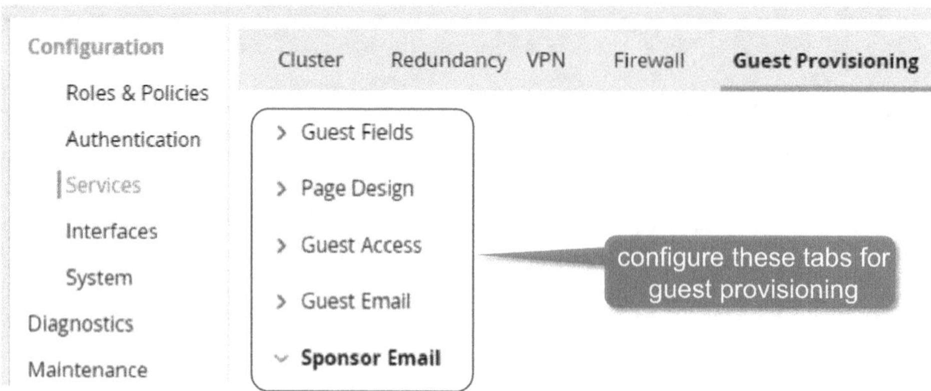

Figure 13-3 Configure guest-provisioning setup

To configure guest provisioning, navigate as shown (Figure 13-3), to **Configuration > Services > Guest Provisioning**. You will see several tabs available, as described below.

- **Guest Fields tab**—select the fields that appear on the Guest Provisioning page.
- **Page Design tab**—specify the company banner, heading, text, and background colors that appear on the Guest Provisioning page.
- **Guest access tab**—upload of the company logo and company policy text.
- **Guest Email and Sponsor Email Tabs**—specify an email to be sent to the guest, sponsor, or both. Email messages can be sent automatically at account creation time. They can also be sent manually by the administrator from the guest provisioning page.

Configure guest fields

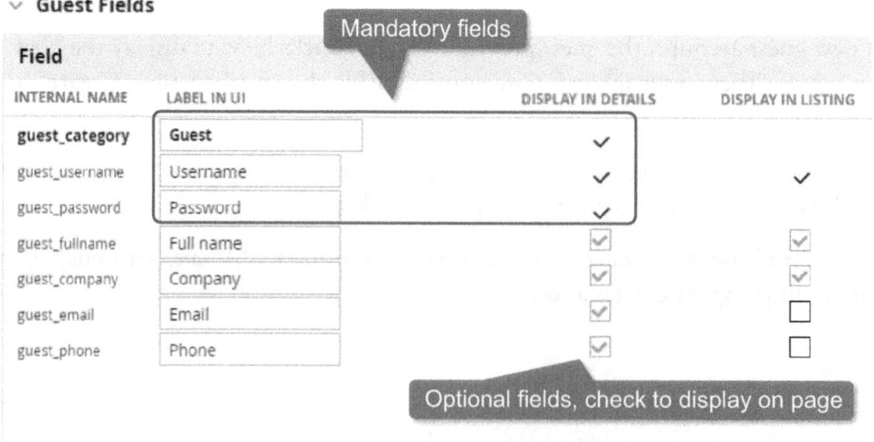

Figure 13-4 Configure guest fields

To configure guest fields in the managed device node hierarchy, navigate to **Configuration > Services > Guest Provisioning**. Click on the "Guest Field" tab. This section contains the following columns (Figure 13-4):

- **Internal Name**—The unique identifier that is mapped to the label in the UI.
- **Label in UI**—A customizable string that displays in both the main listing pane and details sheet on the guest-provisioning page.
- **Display in Details**—Fields with selectable check boxes appear in the Show Details popup-window.
- **Display in Listing**—Fields with selectable check boxes appear as columns in the management user summary page.

Select the box next to each field that you want to appear on the guest-provisioning page. Alternatively, you can customize the label that displays in the UI.

While you are designing the look and feel of the guest-provisioning page, you can see what it looks like. Simply click "Preview Current Settings" in the guest access section.

Configuring page design

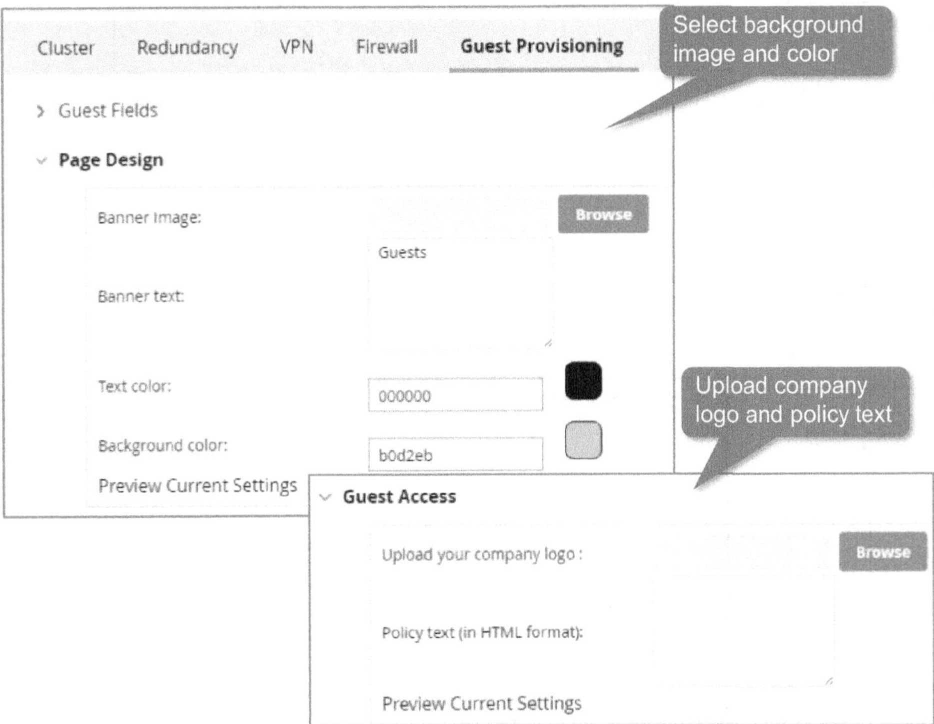

Figure 13-5 Configuring page design

The Page Design section lets you specify the company banner, heading, text, and background colors that appear on the guest-provisioning page.

In the Managed Device node hierarchy, navigate to **Configuration > Services > Guest Provisioning**, and click on the "Page Design section" tab (Figure 13-5).

Here you can customize and review the following options:

- **Banner Image**—Enter the filename that contains the company banner, or click Browse to search for the filename.
- **Banner Text**—Enter the label for the guest.
- **Text Color**—Enter the hex value for the color of the text.
- **Background Color**—Enter the hex value for the color of the background.

Select the "guest Access" tab to upload the company logo and text for the policy.

While you are designing the look and feel of the guest-provisioning page, you can see what it looks like. Simply click "Preview Current Settings" in the guest access section.

Configuring email messages

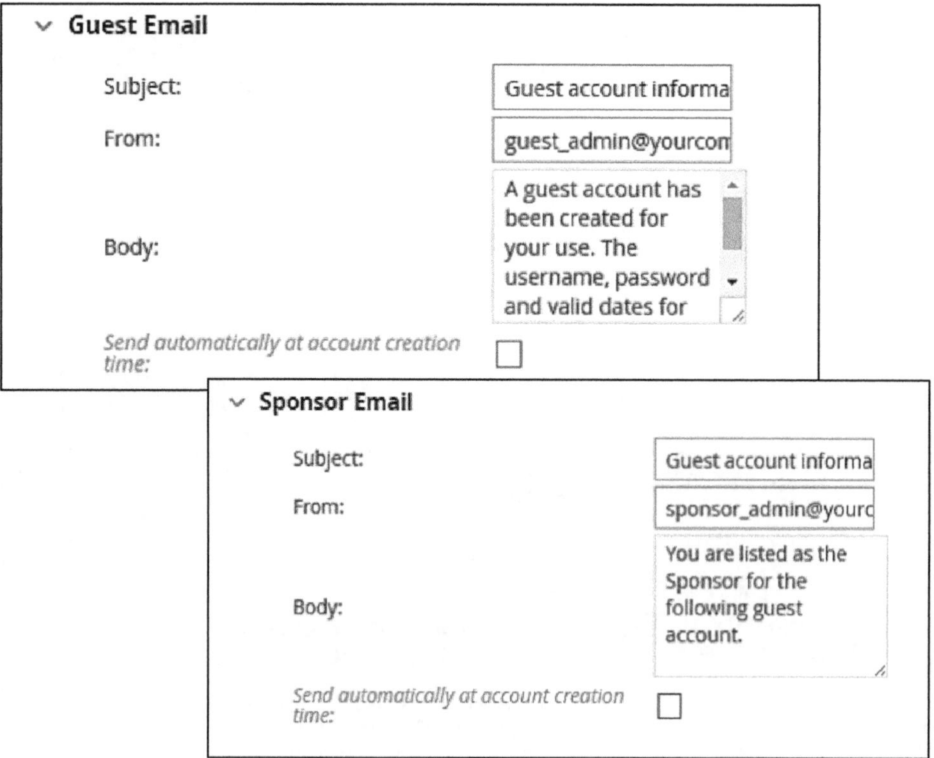

Figure 13-6 Configuring email messages

In the managed device node hierarchy, navigate to **Configuration > Services > Guest Provisioning**, then click on the "guest email" (or sponsor email) tab (Figure 13-6).

You can specify an email to be sent to the guest, sponsor, or both. Email messages can be sent automatically at account creation time or sent manually by the network administrator. They can also be sent through the guest-provisioning user from the guest-provisioning page at any time.

You can also choose to select the "Send automatically at account creation time" check box when you want an email message to be sent to the guest and/or sponsor, alerting them that a guest account has just been created.

Configuring a guest-provisioning user

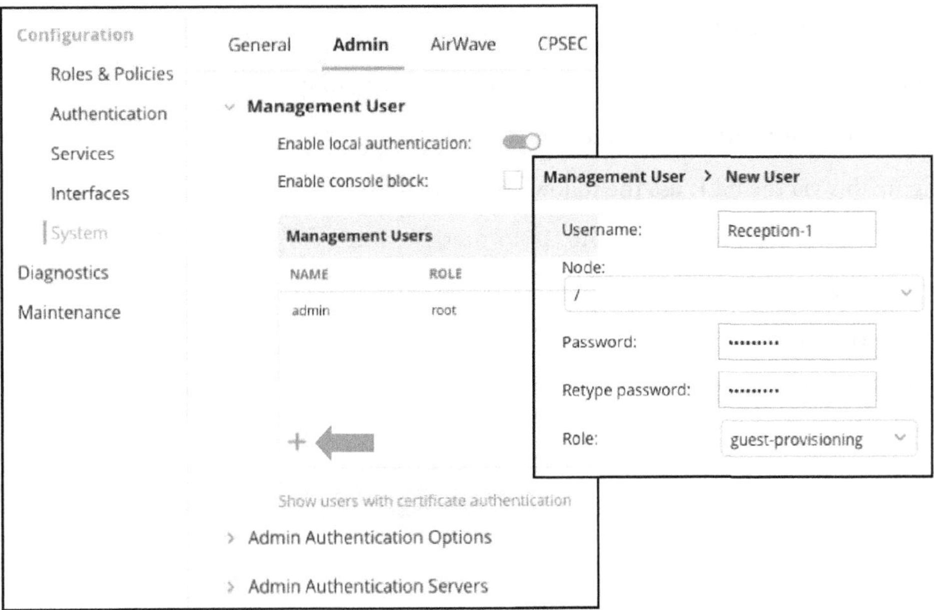

Figure 13-7 Configuring a guest-provisioning user

In the Managed Device node hierarchy, navigate to **Configuration > System > Admin**. Then click the + symbol to create a new guest-provisioning user (Figure 13-7).

The guest-provisioning user has access to the Guest Provisioning Page (GPP) to create guest accounts. The guest-provisioning user is usually a person at the front desk who greets guests and creates guest accounts.

From the CLI, you can use the following syntax:

```
(host) (config)# mgmt-user <username> guest-provisioning
```

Learning check

1. An admin user with guest-provisioning role can also manage the configuration of the controller.
   a. True
   b. False

Management authentication with RADIUS and TACACS

Using RADIUS for admin authentication

The following summarizes the steps to leverage a RADIUS server for administrator authentication:

1. Configure the RADIUS server IP
2. Map the authentication server (RADIUS) to the server-group
3. Set the Admin authentication options

To configure this via the CLI, use the following commands:

```
aaa authentication-server RADIUS <name> host <ipaddr>

aaa server-group <name>

auth-server <name>

aaa authentication mgmt

default-role root

enable

server-group <name>
```

Setting admin authentication options

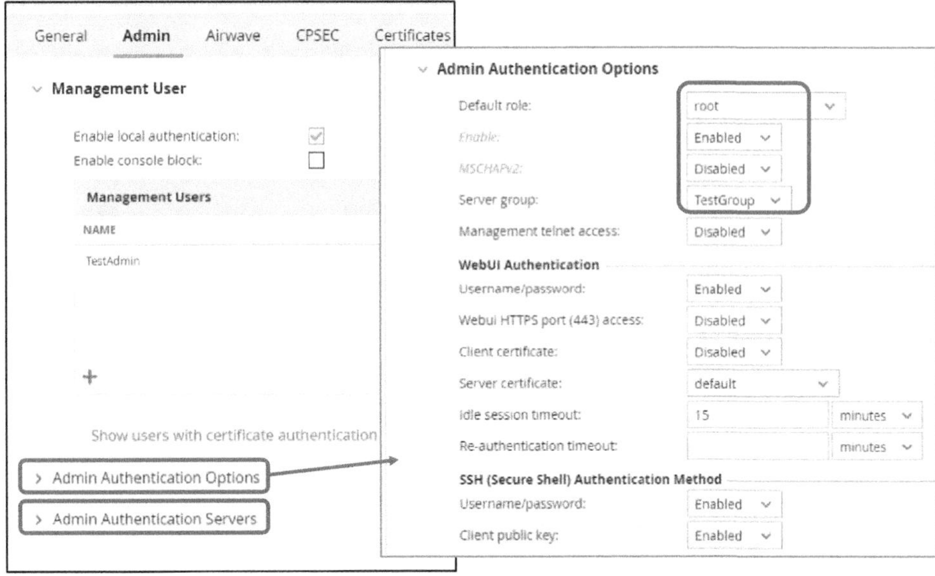

Figure 13-8 Setting admin authentication options

To configure administrator authentication options, navigate to **Configuration > System > Admin**. Then expand Admin Authentication Options (Figure 13-8).

1. Set the default role as root.
2. Set Enable as enabled.
3. Set the server group.

Other settings are optional.

Note

You should ensure that a valid RADIUS server is mapped to the selected authentication server group. To do this click on "Admin Authentication Servers." You will see a list of authentication servers to work with.

Configuring a TACACS server

The following summarizes the steps to configure a TACACS server:

1. Configure the TACACS server IP address and secret key.
2. Map the TACACS authentication server to the server-group.
3. Set the Admin authentication options.

A CLI-based configuration is shown below.

```
aaa authentication-server tacacs <name>
  host <ipaddr>
  key <psk>
  Enable
aaa server-group <name>
  auth-server <name>
aaa authentication mgmt
  default-role root
  enable
  server-group <name>
```

Seamless logon (remote telnet and SSH)

The Seamless Logon feature enables you to log in from the MM to a managed controller without entering a password.

The user can remotely login from the MM to any managed controller and execute show and configuration commands.

To login to a managed device use the following CLI syntax:

```
(host) [mynode] #logon 10.10.10.101
```

Console access control and remote telnet and SSH

Disabling console access

As of Aruba OS 6.5.0.0, you can disable the console login using the command - `mgmt-user console-block`. This enables you to lock down all console ports. This includes micro USB and mini USB ports on the managed device.

This also insures that no Secure Shell (SSH) access is allowed at the remote branch office. The SSH is only allowed from the headquarters through the IPsec tunnel.

Example—disable the console:

```
(host) [MyNode] (config) #mgmt-user console-block
```

Re-enable the console:

```
(host) [MyNode] (config) #no mgmt-user console-block
```

Resetting admin or enable password

```
User: password
Password: forgetme!

(Data-Zone1) [mynode] #configure t
(Data-Zone1) [mynode] (config) #mgmt-user admin root
Password:******
Re-Type Password:******
(Data-Zone1) ^[mynode] (config) #exit
(Data-Zone1) ^[mynode] #exit

User:
```

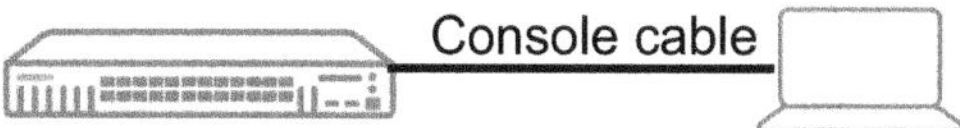

Figure 13-9 Resetting admin or enable password

Use the following procedure if the administrator user account password is lost or forgotten (Figure 13-9):

1. From the console, login to the managed device, using the username "password" and the password "forgetme!"
2. Enter enable mode by typing in **enable**, followed by the password **enable**.
3. To configure the administrator user account, enter **mgmt-user admin root**, enter a new password for this account, and retype the same password to confirm.

Note

This procedure also resets the enable mode password to enable. If you have defined a management user password policy, make sure that the new password conforms to this policy.

Learning check

2. Which of the following credentials are used to access the controller, for resetting the admin password?
    a. User = admin, Password = allowme!
    b. User = admin, Password = forgetme!
    c. User = password, Password = allowme!
    d. User = password, Password = forgetme!
3. You can disable/enable console access to a Managed Device.
    a. True
    b. False

14 Operations

LEARNING OBJECTIVES

- ✓ This chapter is focused on network operations. You will learn how to load new controller images, centralize image upgrades, and use the AP image preload option to minimize downtime.
- ✓ This is followed by a discussion of using the cluster image upgrade manager, which handles in-service upgrades for controllers and APs.
- ✓ Then you will explore controller auto rollback, disaster recovery, and using the bulk edit option to ease configuration efforts.
- ✓ Then you will learn how to work with Loadable Service Modules (LSM), and how to generate tar logs, tech-support, and crash dump files.

Upgrading images

Loading a new image

You can upgrade individual controllers from the LCD panel, or via the WebUI or CLI. You can also have centralized image upgrades on the Mobility Master (MM), which has multi-image support. These options are explained in the pages that follow.

Load image to MM via LCD

Some controllers are equipped with an LCD panel, which displays a variety of information about controller status. It also provides a menu of basic operations, such as initial setup, reboot, maintenance, and more.

Use the maintenance menu option for basic controller operations, such as uploading an image or rebooting a system.

Use the steps below to upgrade your image or to upload a saved configuration by using a USB drive and LCD commands:

1. Copy a new controller image to your USB drive, into a directory named/Arubaimage.
2. Insert the USB drive into the controller's USB slot. Wait 30 seconds for the controller to mount the USB device.

3. Navigate to Upgrade Image in the LCD maintenance menu. Select a partition, confirm the upgrade, and then wait for the controller to copy the image from USB to system partition.
4. Reboot the system, either from the LCD menu (Maintenance > System reboot) or from the CLI.

Load image to MM via WebUI or CLI

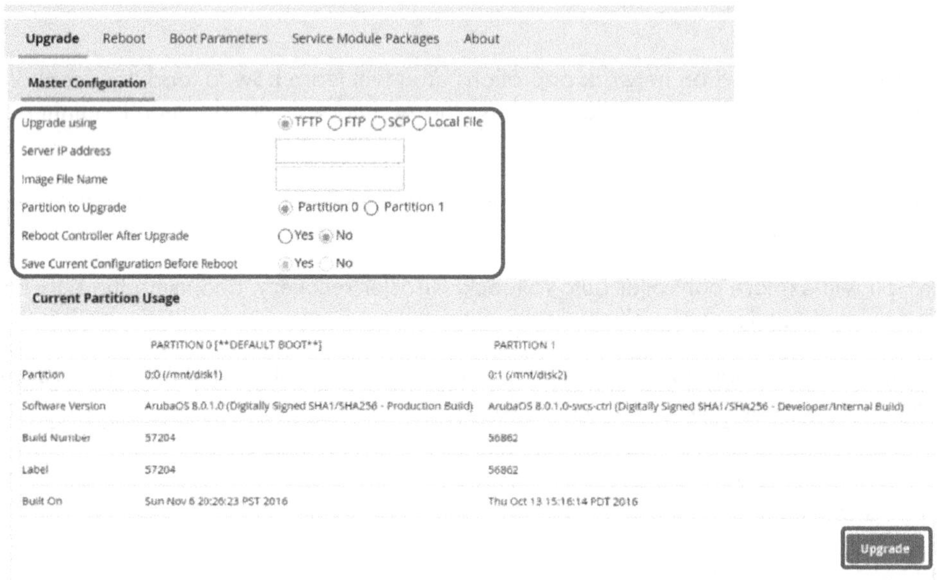

Figure 14-1 Load image to MM via WebUI or CLI

You can download an ArubaOS image file onto an MM from a TFTP, FTP, or SCP server (Figure 14-1). In addition, the WebUI allows you to upload an ArubaOS image file from the browser on your local PC. Follow the steps below.

1. On the MM, navigate to **Maintenance** > **Software Management** > **Upgrade** > **Master Configuration**.
2. Select TFTP, FTP, SCP, or upload Local File.
3. Enter or select the appropriate values for the file transfer method.
4. Select the system partition to which the image file is copied.
5. Specify whether the managed device is to be rebooted after the image file is transferred and whether the current configuration is saved before the managed device is rebooted.
6. Click Upgrade.

In the CLI, you can use the following commands:

```
copy tftp: <tftphost> <filename> system: partition [0|1]}

copy ftp: <ftphost> <user> <filename> system: partition {0|1}

copy scp: <scphost> <username> <filename> system: partition [0|1]
```

Load image to MC via WebUI or CLI

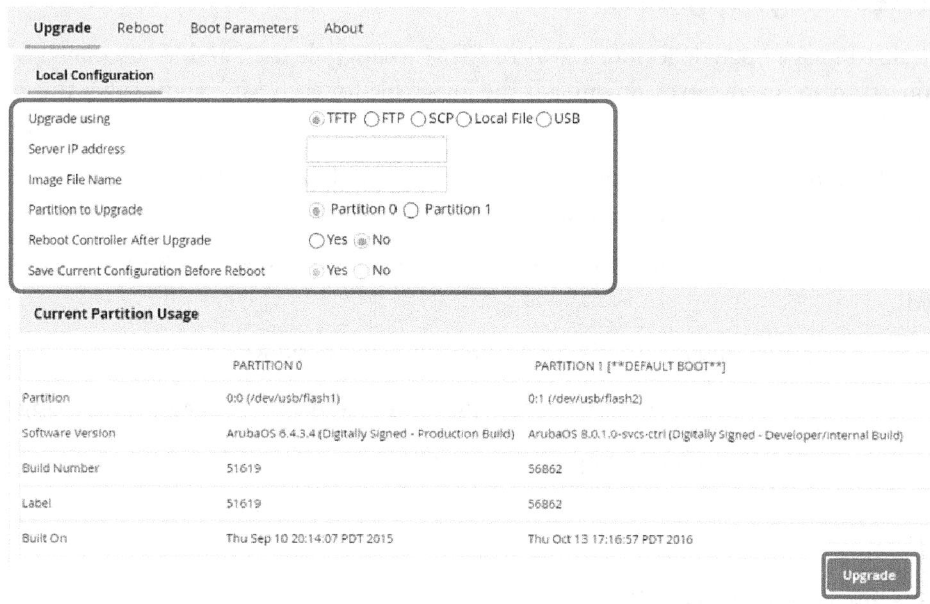

Figure 14-2 Load image to MC via WebUI or CLI

You can download an ArubaOS image file onto an MC from a TFTP, an FTP, or a SCP server (Figure 14-2). In addition, the WebUI allows you to upload an ArubaOS image file from the browser on your local PC. Follow the steps below.

1. On the MM, navigate to **Maintenance > Software Management > Upgrade > Local Configuration**.
2. Select TFTP, FTP, SCP, or upload Local File.
3. Enter or select the appropriate values for the file transfer method.
4. Select the system partition to which the image file is copied.
5. Specify whether the managed device is to be rebooted after the image file is transferred, and whether the current configuration is saved before the managed device is rebooted.
6. Click **Upgrade**.

In the CLI, you can use the following commands:

```
copy tftp: <tftphost> <filename> system: partition [0|1]}

copy ftp: <ftphost> <user> <filename> system: partition {0|1}

copy scp: <scphost> <username> <filename> system: partition [0|1]
```

Centralized upgrade

Centralized image upgrades

The centralized image upgrade feature allows the MM to upgrade itself and its associated MCs. The MM connects to an image server, downloads the image file for each MC, and verifies the validity of the image files.

After the MM verifies image file validity, the MC connects to the image server, downloads the appropriate image file, and upgrades to the downloaded image file.

This feature can only be configured on an MM and supports up to one hundred simultaneous downloads.

To configure this feature in the MM's WebUI, use the following steps:

1. In the MM node hierarchy, navigate to **Maintenance > Software Management > Upgrade**.
2. Under Master Configuration, configure the parameters.
3. Click Upgrade.

Creating an upgrade profile

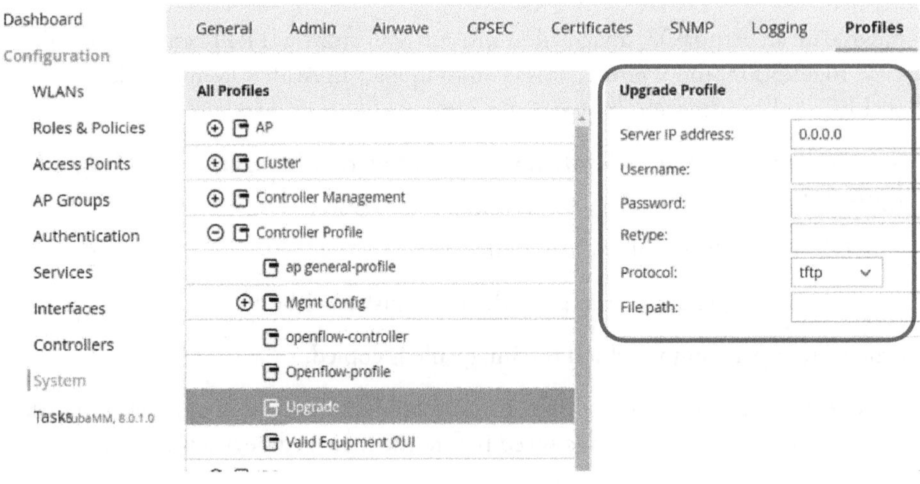

Figure 14-3 Creating an upgrade profile

To facilitate centralized upgrades, you can create upgrade profiles (Figure 14-3). Follow the steps below.

1. In the required managed device node hierarchy, navigate to **Configuration > System > Profiles**.
2. Under All Profiles, select **Controller Profile > Upgrade**.
3. Under Upgrade Profile, configure the parameters.
4. Click Submit.
5. Click Pending Changes.
6. In the Pending Changes window, select the required check box and click Deploy changes.

Upgrading an MC

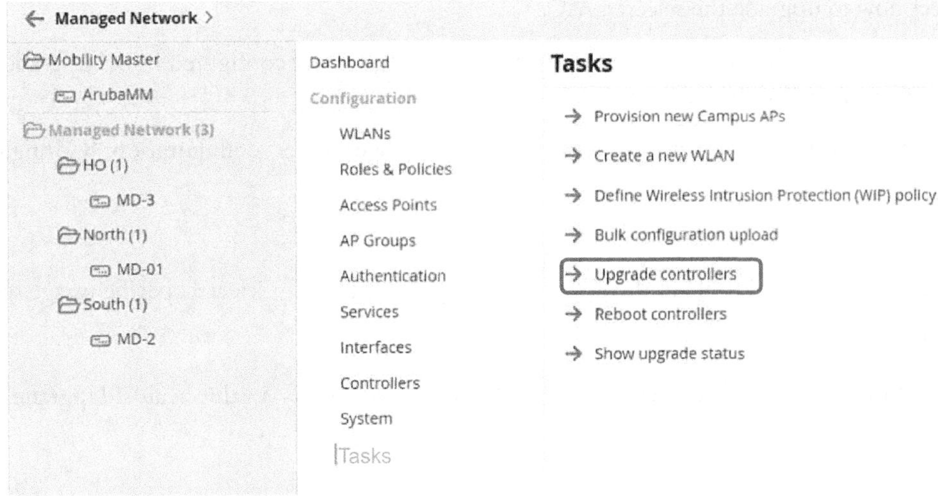

Figure 14-4 Upgrading an MC

Figures 14-4 and 14-5 show how to upgrade an MC image, as described below.

1. In the required MC hierarchy, navigate to **Configuration > Tasks** (Figure 14-4).
2. Under Tasks, click Upgrade controllers (Figure 14-4).

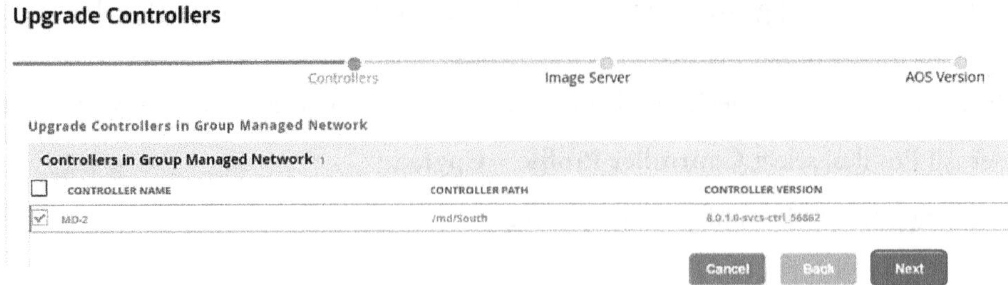

Figure 14-5 Upgrading an MC

3. Under Controllers in Group /md/managed device, select the managed devices to upgrade (Figure 14-5).
4. Click Next (Figure 14-5).
5. Select how to upgrade the selected MC.
    a. Upgrade profile in group hierarchy—uses the image server configured in the upgrade profile of the managed device.
    b. Specified image server—uses the specified image server configuration. Configure the parameters.
6. Click Next.
7. Select Use Upgrade Profile in the group hierarchy (or optionally select a specific image server).
8. Click Next.
9. Select how to upgrade the selected managed devices and specify a value against Upgrade to:
    a. version
    b. file
    c. force-version
    d. force-file
10. Select the Auto-reboot check box to reboot the selected managed devices after the upgrade.
11. Select the partition on the selected managed devices to upgrade against Partition.
    a. Auto—upgrades the default boot partition on the selected managed devices.
    b. Partition 0—upgrades partition 0 on the selected managed devices.
    c. Partition 1—upgrades partition 1 on the selected managed devices.
12. Click Finish.

Upgrading an MC (cont.)

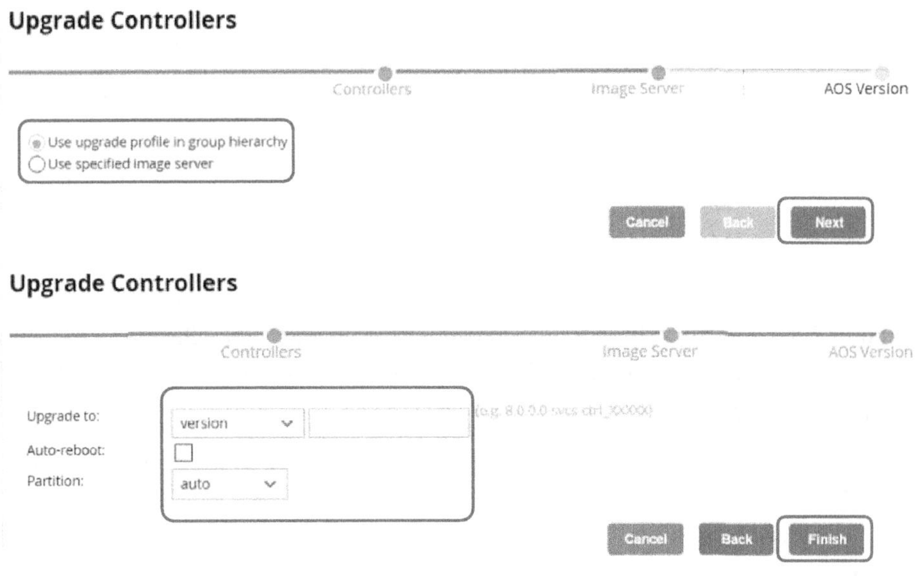

Figure 14-6 Upgrading an MC (cont.)

13. Select Use Upgrade Profile in the group hierarchy (or select a specific image server; Figure 14-6).
14. Click Next.
15. Select how to upgrade the selected managed devices and specify a value against Upgrade to:
    a. version
    b. file
    c. force-version
    d. force-file
16. Click the Auto-reboot check box to reboot the selected managed devices after the upgrade.
17. Select the partition on the selected managed devices to upgrade against Partition.
    a. Auto—Upgrades the default boot partition on the selected managed devices.
    b. Partition 0—upgrades Partition 0 on the selected managed devices.
    c. Partition 1—upgrades Partition 1 on the selected managed devices.
18. Click Finish.

Multi-image version upgrades

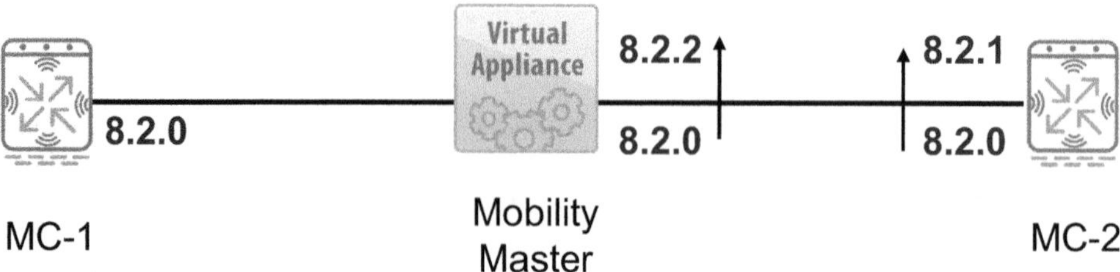

Figure 14-7 Multi-image version upgrades

The MM and its MCs can run different AOS versions. This gives you the flexibility to upgrade controllers to different versions, at different times. For AOS8.x centralized image upgrade, you can specify the upgrade image version for managed devices.

Figure 14-7 shows an example where an MM is upgraded from 8.2.0 to 8.2.2, and MC-2 is upgraded from 8.2.0 to 8.2.1.

Learning check

1. Which of the following folder names is used to keep the image file in a USB drive?
    a. Aruba/arubaimage
    b. /Arubaimage
    c. Aruba/image
    d. /image
2. Which of the following methods/protocols can be used for uploading images?
    a. FTP, TFTP, and SCP
    b. Only FTP and TFTP
    c. FTP, TFTP, and Local File
    d. FTP, TFTP, SCP, and Local file

AP image preload

AP preload overview

The AP image preload feature minimizes the downtime required for a managed device upgrade. An MC's associated APs can download new images before the MC starts running the new version. APs continue normal operations while they are downloading their new software version. When the download completes, the AP informs the MC that it has either successfully downloaded the image or failed.

The next four figures detail this process. As you read along, pay attention to the image versions for the MC on the left and the AP on the right. This is what changes as you follow the scenario.

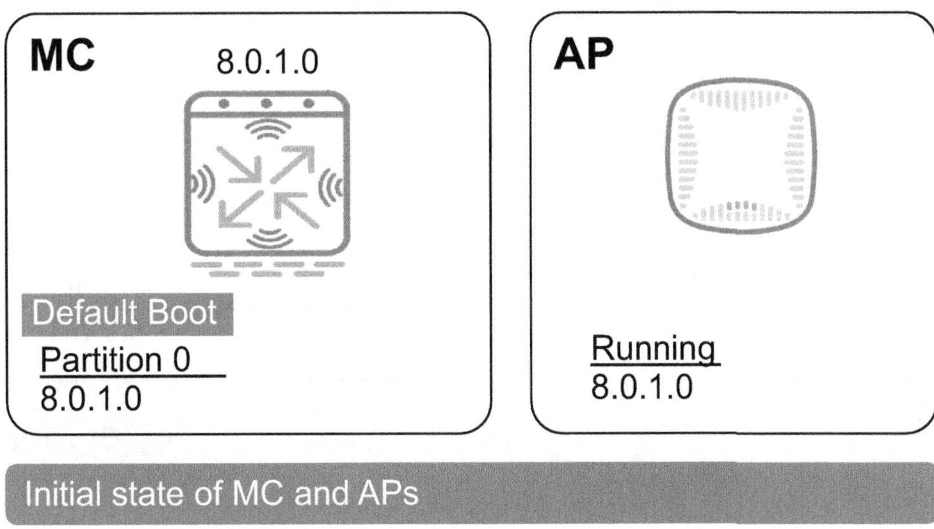

Figure 14-8 Initial State

In Figure 14-8, there is a single image on Partition 0. You have not begun the AP preload process yet. The MC runs version 8.0.1.0, and so does the AP.

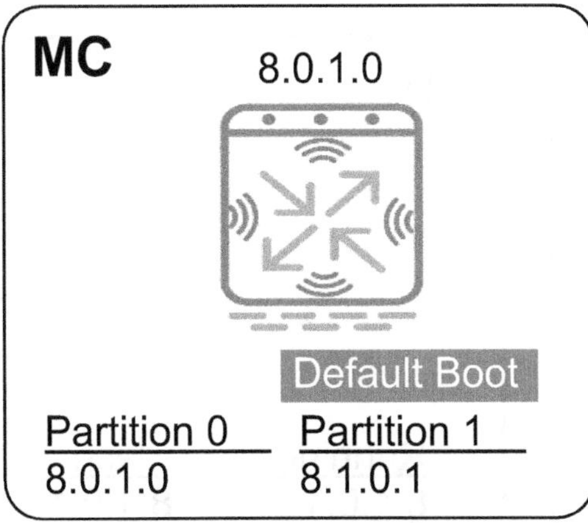

1. Download new image to MC

Figure 14-9 Download new image to MC

In Figure 14-9, you start by downloading a new image to the MC. This is placed in the assigned partition, and becomes the default boot partition. Of course, the AP is still running version 8.0.1.0, as this remains the only version stored locally on the AP.

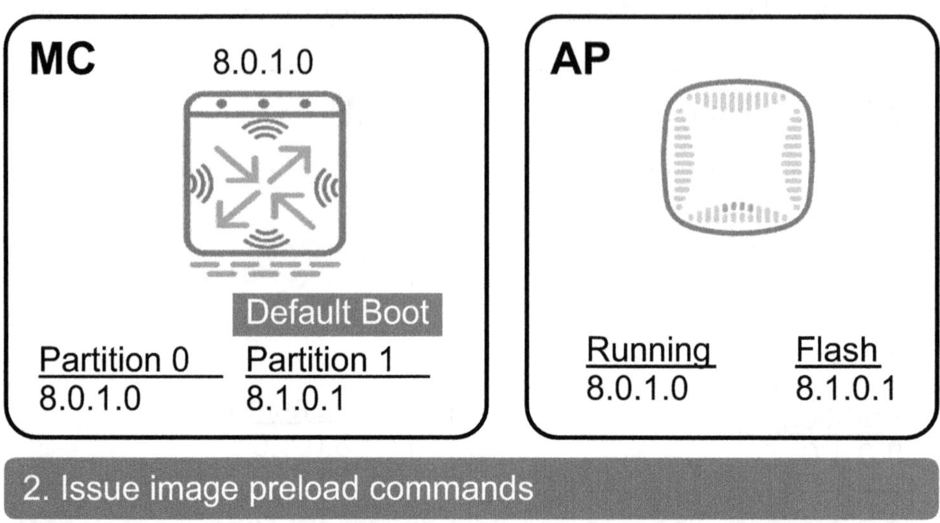

Figure 14-10 Issue preload commands

From the CLI you issue the preload commands `ap image-preload add` and `ap image-preload activate`. You will learn more details about these commands soon. As shown in Figure 14-10, this loads the boot image into AP flash. Notice that AP flash now contains the 8.1.0.1 image. However, the AP continues to provide client services using the original image.

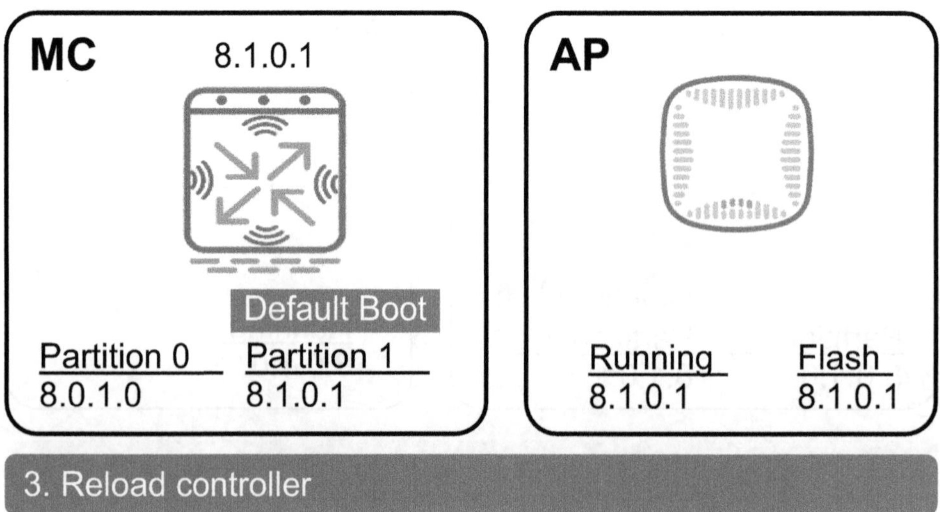

Figure 14-11 Reload the controller

Finally, you reload the controller. The AP also reloads, booting directly with the new image. Figure 14-11 shows this condition, after the reboot, with both devices running the new image version.

If you had not done the AP preload operation, the MC would boot with its new image, and the APs would of course reboot with their old image. When the APs connect to the MC, they would download the new image at that time, then reboot again, finally operating on the correct version.

As you can see, the AP preload feature drastically reduces down time due to image upgrades.

AP image preloading

You can allow every AP on a managed device to preload a new software version. Also, you can create a custom list of AP groups or individual APs that can use this feature.

To configure the AP image preload feature using the CLI, enter the following commands in enable mode:

```
ap image-preload

activate <all-aps / specific-aps >
```

Optional parameters:

```
[partition <part-num>]

[max-downloads <max-downloads>]
```

Other Options

```
add { ap-group <ap-group> / ap-name <ap-name>}

cancel

clear-all

delete {ap-group <ap-group> / ap-name <ap-name>}
```

You can monitor the current preload status of APs using the image preload feature. Use the following command:

```
show ap imagepreload status summary
```

You can also see a more detailed information with the following command:

```
#show ap image-preload status all
....
AP Image Preload AP Status
--------------------------
AP Name AP Group AP IP       AP Type Preload State Start Time End Time Failure Count  Failure Reason
------- -------- -----       ------- ------------- ---------- -------- -------------  -------- ------
AP1     APgroup1 192.168.3.2 225     Preloading    2017-06-19 07:42:01 0
AP2     APgroup1 192.168.3.3 225     Preloading    2017-06-19 07:42:01 0
AP3     APgroup1 192.168.3.4 225     Preloading    2017-06-19 07:42:01 0
```

AP image

Before you reload the MC, ensure that all the APs have been preloaded. To do this, issue the command `show ap image-preload status list`. Focus on the "Preload State" column in the output below. Notice that all APs are indeed in the preloaded state.

```
(P3T5-MC-J) [mynode] # show ap image-preload status list
AP Image Preload AP Status
--------------------------
AP    AP        AP           AP    Preload                                                 Failure Reason
Name  Group     IP           Type  State      Start Time           End Time              Count   Count
----- --------  -----        ----- ---------- ----------           ---------             -----   -----
AP1   APgroup1  192. 168.3.2 225   Preloaded  2017-06-19 07:42:01  2017-06-19 07:44:26  0       0
AP2   APgroup1  192.168.3.3  225   Preloaded  2017-06-19 07:42:01  2017-06-19 07:44:26  0       0
AP3   APgroup1  192.168.3.4  225   Preloaded  2017-06-19 07:42:01  2017-06-19 07:44:26  0       0
```

To verify what has been reloaded issue the command `show ap image version ap-name (name)`. In the following example, you can see the running image 8.0.1.0 and the flash image 8.1.0.1.

```
(P3T5-MC-J) [mynode] # show ap image version ap-name AP1

AP          Running Image Version String   Flash (Production) Image Version
String      Flash (Provisioning/Backup) Image Version String    Matches Num
Matches  Num Mismatches  Bad Checksums  Bad Provisioning Checksums  Image
Load Status

--------  ----------  ---------  ----------  -----------  -----------

192.168.3.2    8.0.1.0(p4build@lemnos)#57204  SMP  Sun  Nov  6  18:32:36
8.1.0.1(p4build@pr-hpn-build05)#59688

SMP Thu May 18 17:10:46 UTC 2017  6.5.1.0-4.3.1.2(p4build@samos)#58595
SMP Thu Mar 2 04:02:25 PST 2017

Yes      1           0           0           0                      Done
```

Now you simply need to reload the MC.

Cluster upgrade

Cluster AOS upgrade

You just learned how the AP Preload feature can minimize downtime during upgrades. Even so, there is still some downtime.

In-service controller and APs in a cluster provide for *zero* downtime and minimal RF impact. It avoids manual intervention during upgrades.

The seamless image upgrade feature allows managed devices and APs in a cluster to automatically upgrade the software from ArubaOS 8.1.x versions to higher ArubaOS versions. Thus, you can benefit from some of the newer features or bug fixes in later versions, without having to manually upgrade each controller in the cluster.

Managed Devices in a cluster can be seamlessly upgraded by specifying the new image file and a target partition.

Basic requirements for In-service upgrade

There are three basic requirements for in-service upgrade.

- The cluster has redundancy enabled.
- In-service upgrade is only feasible with RF redundancy.
- The cluster should be L2-connected.

The first requirement listed above is fairly self-explanatory—you must enable redundancy.

The second requirement means that RF coverage during an upgrade depends on the relative positioning of APs. If APs are not placed to provide for RF redundancy, then the seamless image upgrade is not feasible. So, if your APs are spread far apart, AirMatch may have tuned AP power at or near maximum values, just to get 10% to 20% coverage overlap between adjacent APs.

This is not good. While some APs are rebooting during the upgrade process, other APs will not be able to “fill in the gaps” to service clients.

On the other hand, suppose your APs are spaced a bit closer together. When one AP reboots during an upgrade, surrounding APs will be able to fill the hole in RF coverage and service clients in that area.

The final requirement is that all cluster members be L2-connected. In other words, they must all be on the same broadcast domain—the same VLAN.

Cluster RF coverage

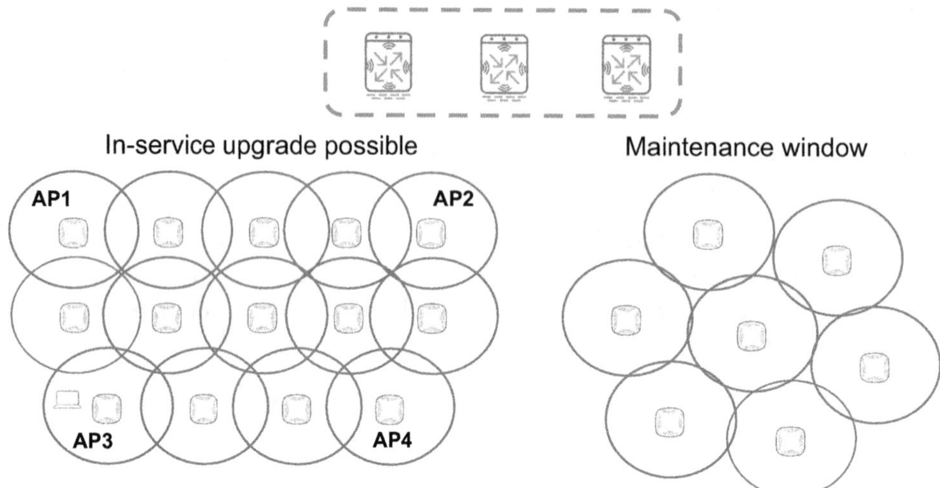

Figure 14-12 Cluster RF coverage

In-service upgrade requires good RF coverage with ample overlap. In Figure 14-12, the example on the left shows that the APs are spaced close enough to have ample overlap. This is especially true for APs near the middle of the coverage area. They are completely, or at least nearly surrounded by three or more APs. As they reboot, their clients will likely be serviced by other APs.

But what about APs 1 through 4, in the corner of the building? When these APs reboot, the other APs may not be able to provide coverage for all clients.

This issue is even more pronounced in the right-hand example in Figure 14-12. In this scenario, the APs have less coverage overlap, and there is only one AP that is completely surrounded by other APs.

For these reasons, it is best to plan a maintenance window for a cluster upgrade.

How it works

The following provides an overview of the cluster upgrade process. This process is detailed in the pages that follow.

- Cluster manager and AirMatch communicate
- Partitioning APs for RF coverage redundancy based on 5 GHz channel
- Target MC assignment for each AP partition

- Cluster update manager triggers all MCs to copy the image sequentially
- MC upgrades and APs failover to S-AAC
- AP image preload and terminate on target MC
- Cluster update manager restarts MC's one by one
- Load Balance if needed

Cluster upgrade

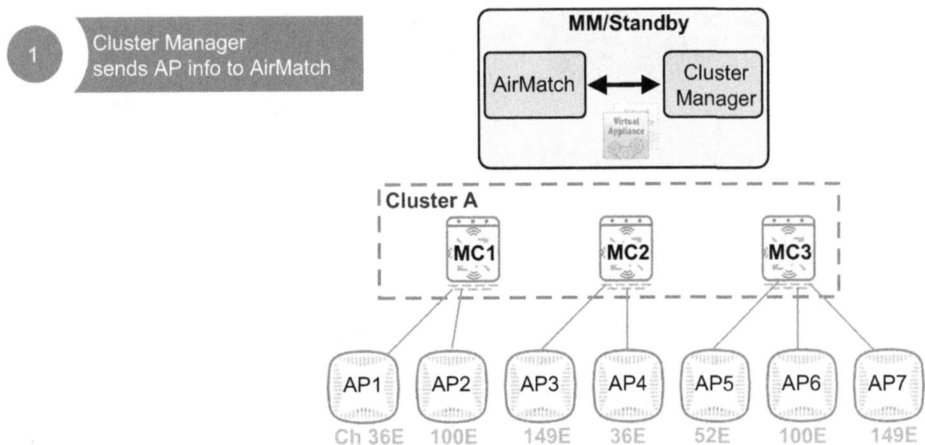

Figure 14-13 Cluster upgrade

A new process in the MM orchestrates all aspects of the upgrade. It is called the cluster upgrade manager. It maintains the context of APs and controllers in the cluster. It learns about APs in the cluster through internal processes, from the APs' respective AACs.

The information maintained includes each AP's Ethernet MAC address, cluster membership, and AAC IP address. This information is fed to AirMatch.

Figure 14-13 shows a deployment with redundant MMs, three MCs, and several APs. You see two software processes running in the MM—AirMatch and Cluster Manager. These processes collaborate to maximize in-service upgrade success.

AP partitions

You have learned that AirMatch is used to optimize RF coverage patterns. It assigns unique RF channels to physically adjacent APs and optimizes the RF coverage overlap between them. In other words, APs set to the same channel will not be physically adjacent. This is especially true for the 5 GHz band, which has several nonoverlapping channels.

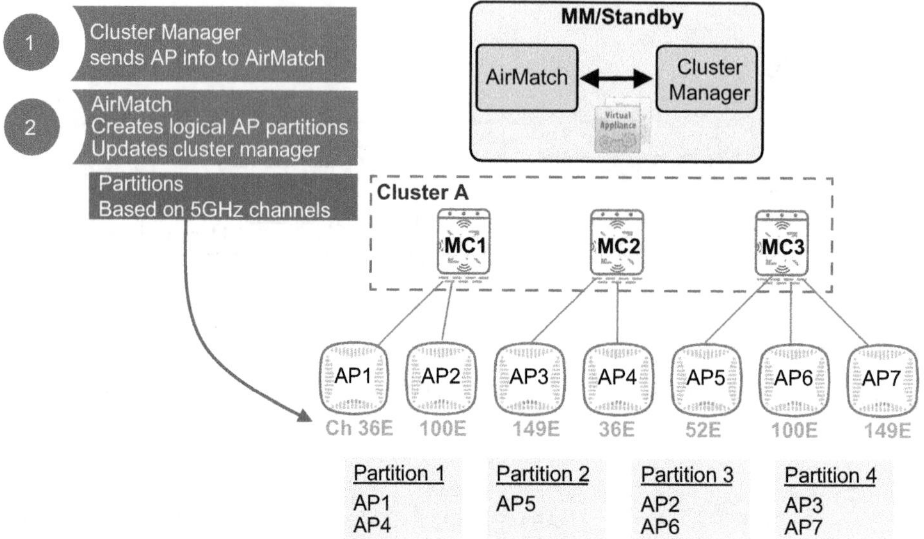

Figure 14-14 AP partitions

AirMatch partitions APs into groups, based on their assigned 5 GHz channel. In Figure 14-14, AP1 and AP4 are both on channel 36, and so are assigned to the same partition—Partition 1 in this example. AP5 is on channel 52 and is assigned to Partition 2. APs 2 and 6 are both on channel 100 and are assigned to Partition 3. Similarly, AP3 and AP7 are in Partition 4.

This sets up the solution for successful in-service upgrades. If all APs in a given partition reboot simultaneously, the surrounding APs (in other partitions) will provide the necessary RF coverage. Of course, this assumes a very healthy RF coverage pattern, with ample overlap, as previously described.

After partitioning, AirMatch communicates the partitions to the cluster upgrade manager.

Assign target MC

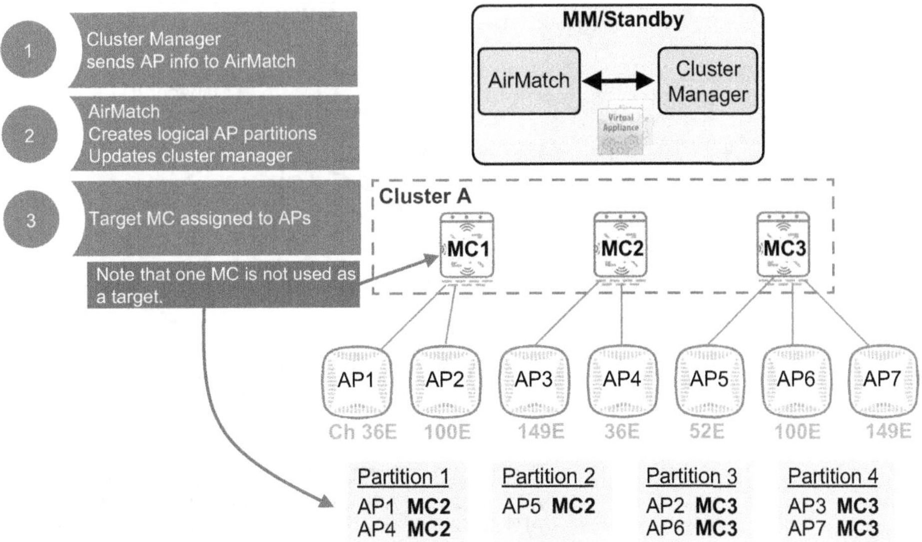

Figure 14-15 Assign target MC

Cluster upgrade manager assigns a target controller for each AP partition (Figure 14-15). It tries to load balance the assignment as much as possible, assigning APs to N-1 controllers in an N node cluster. All APs in Partitions 1 and 2 are assigned to target MC2. APs in Partitions 3 and 4 are assigned to target MC3. Notice that this target MC assignment is purely for in-service upgrade purposes.

This does not affect the AP's Active and Standby AP Anchor Controller (A-AAC, S-AAC). In Figure 14-15, you can see that AP1 and 2 are still controlled by MC1, their A-AAC. AP3 and 4 are controlled by MC2, and so forth.

One controller intentionally has no target assignments. This will be the last controller to reboot/upgrade. In the scenario shown in Figure 14-15, this is MC1. Since there will be no APs on this controller, you can reboot MC1 without special consideration. You will see this as you continue exploring the scenario.

MCs download new OS

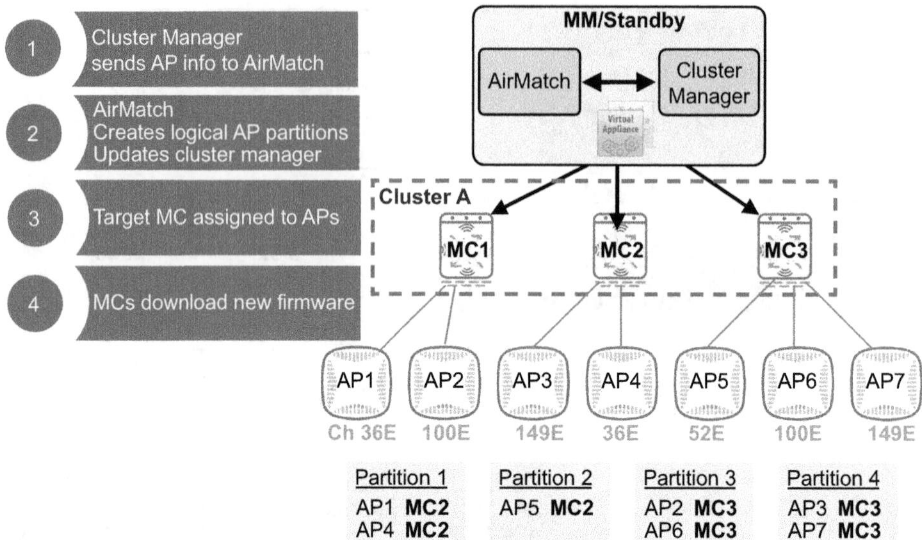

Figure 14-16 MCs download new OS

After AP partitions are assigned a target MC, the cluster update manager triggers all MCs to copy the image, sequentially. This is indicated by the arrows in Figure 14-16, emanating from the MM to each MC. The centralized image update manager handles this process.

Upgrade MC AOS

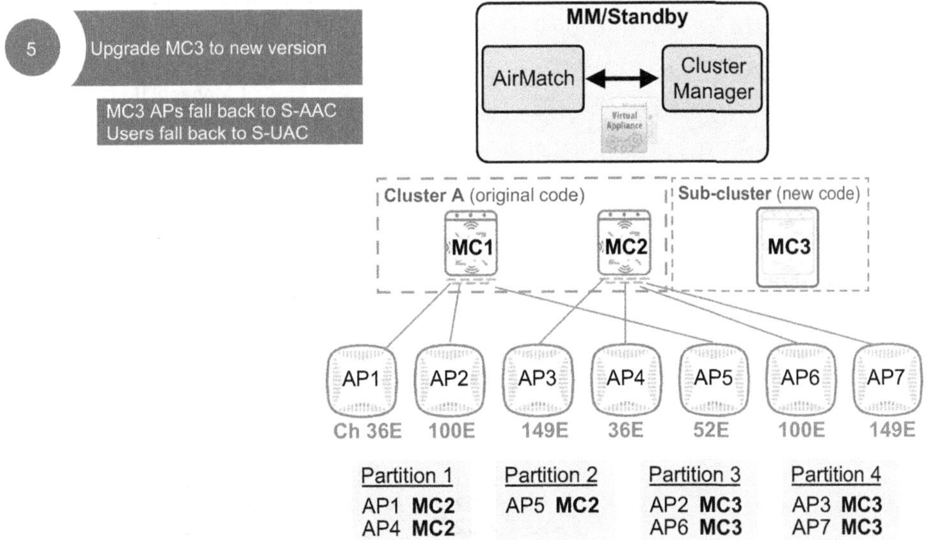

Figure 14-17 Upgrade MC AOS

The MCs are still running the current version of AOS but have copied the new version of code to local storage. The upgrade manager selects one MC to upgrade—MC3 in this example. This MC reboots.

All of MC3's APs failover to their S-AAC, as normal. Recall from the previous figures that MC3 was the A-AAC for APs 5, 6, and 7. Figure 14-17 shows that these APs have failed over to their S-AAC.

Meanwhile, clients on those APs failover to their Standby User Anchor Controller (S-UAC). There is no disruption of service. All APs continue operating, controlled by either MC-1 or MC-2.

The rebooted MC3 comes back up with its newer version of code. No APs are yet associated to this MC. Since it has a different code version, it is not yet a part of the cluster. MC3 is in a "sub-cluster," by itself.

MC and AP upgrade

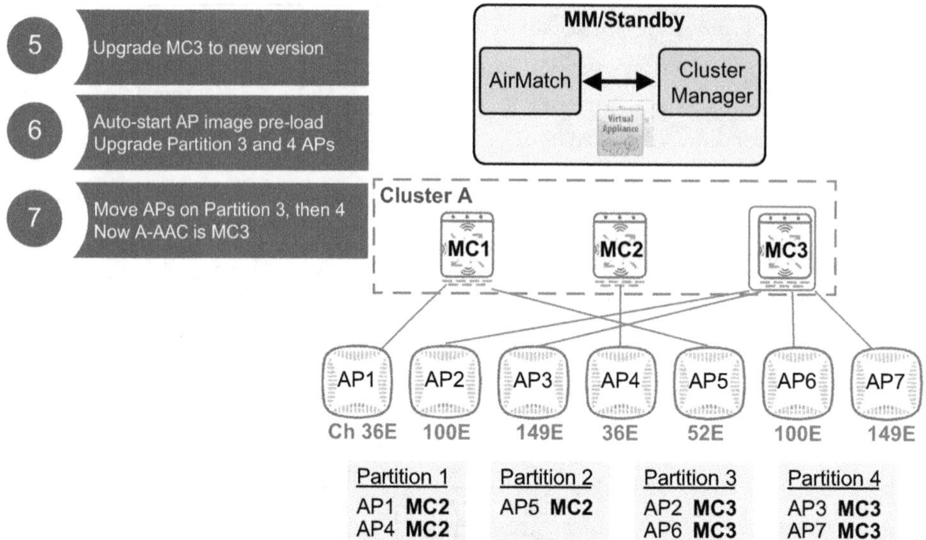

Figure 14-18 MC and AP upgrade

The cluster image manager triggers APs to preload the new image. This minimizes AP downtime. In Figure 14-18, APs in Partitions 3 and 4 are assigned to target MC3. Once all these APs are preloaded, they are moved to MC3, one partition at a time.

During the short time when Partition 3 APs reboot, surrounding APs provide uninterrupted coverage. After they boot with new code, these APs become functional on their target—MC3. Then Partition 4 APs reboot, and come back up on MC3.

Now that these APs are running their new code, their target MC (MC3) becomes their new A-AAC.

Cluster upgrades

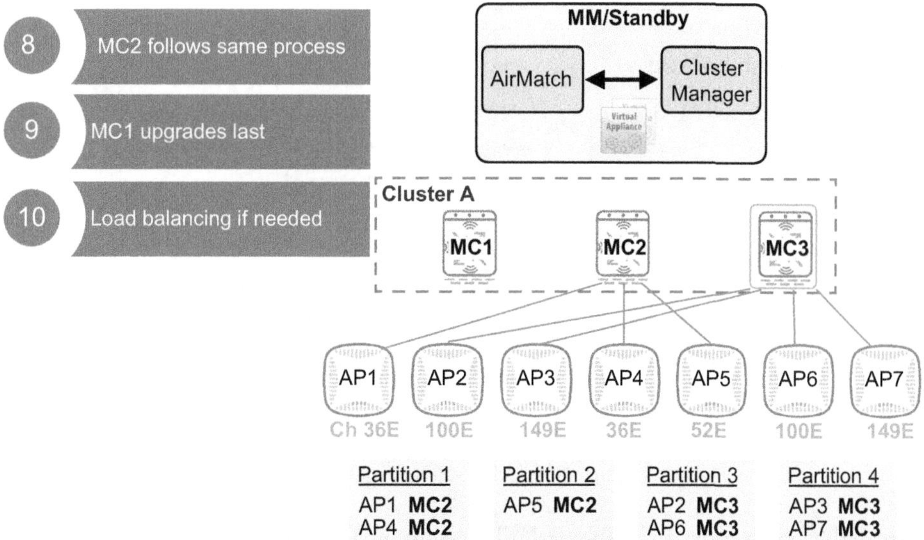

Figure 14-19 Cluster upgrades

The process repeats for MC2. It upgrades, and all APs in its assigned partitions reboot, upgrade their AOS, and end up on MC2 as their A-AAC.

Now all APs are on MC2 and MC3. MC1 is not a designated target, and so is controlling no APs. Thus, you now can upgrade MC1.

After the upgrade, APs may not be equally distributed among MCs. In this case, load balancing automatically mitigates the issue. Figure 14-19 shows the scenario after MC1 has been upgraded, but prior to load balancing.

Learning check

3. Which statement is true about the AP image preload feature?
   a. AP gets image and reboots along with the controller.
   b. AP gets image after the controller is upgraded and rebooted.
   c. AP gets image after the controller is upgraded and reboots along with the controller.
   d. AP gets image along with the controller but reboots after the controller.

Managing configuration files and bulk edits

Managing configuration files

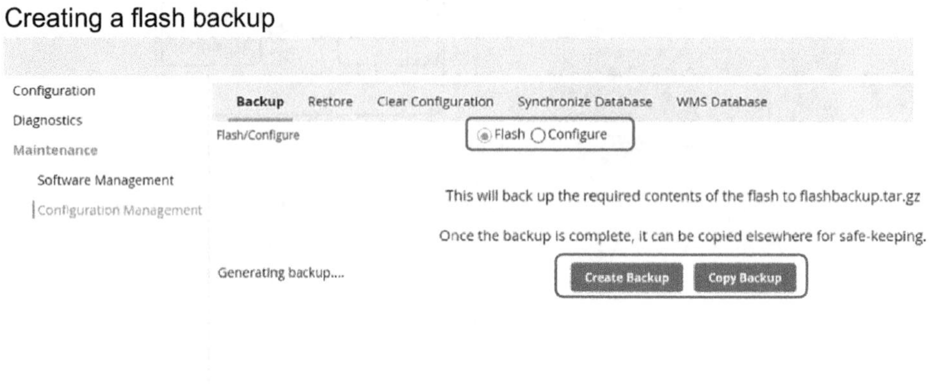

Figure 14-20 Creating Flash Backup

You can store the entire contents of the flash file system on a managed device, in a compressed archive file. You can then copy the archive file to an external server for backup purposes. If necessary, you can restore the backup file from the server to the flash file system. To create a backup of flash, perform the following steps (Figure 14-20):

1. In the Managed Device node hierarchy, navigate to **Maintenance > Configuration Management > Backup**.
2. Click Create Backup to back up the contents of the flash system to the flashbackup.tar.gz file.
3. Click Copy Backup to enter the Copy Files page where you can select the destination server for the file.
4. Click Apply.

To backup Flash file system in the CLI, use the following commands:

```
backup flash

copy flash: flashbackup.tar.gz tftp: <tftphost> <destfilename>

copy flash: flashbackup.tar.gz scp: <scphost> <username> <destfilename>
```

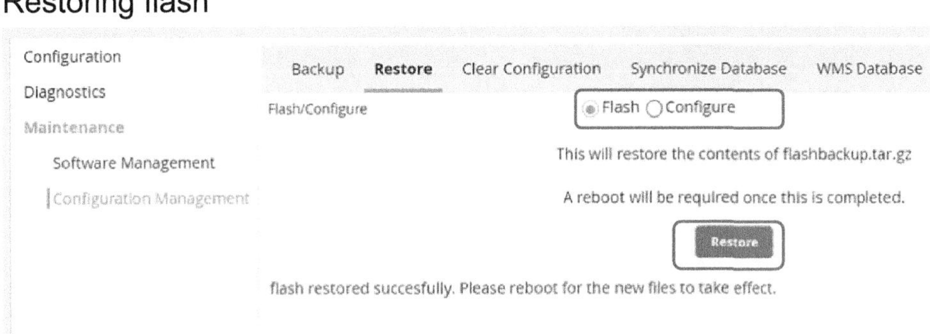

Figure 14-21 Restoring Flash

To restore the Flash file system in the WebUI, perform the following steps (Figure 14-21):

1. In the Managed Device node hierarchy, navigate to **Maintenance > Configuration Management > Restore**.
2. Click Restore to restore the flashbackup.tar.gz file to the flash file system.

To restore the Flash file system in the CLI, use the following commands:

```
copy tftp: <tftphost> <srcfilename> flash: flashbackup.tar.gz

copy scp: <scphost> <username> <srcfilename> flash: flashbackup.tar.gz

restore flash
```

Bulk edit

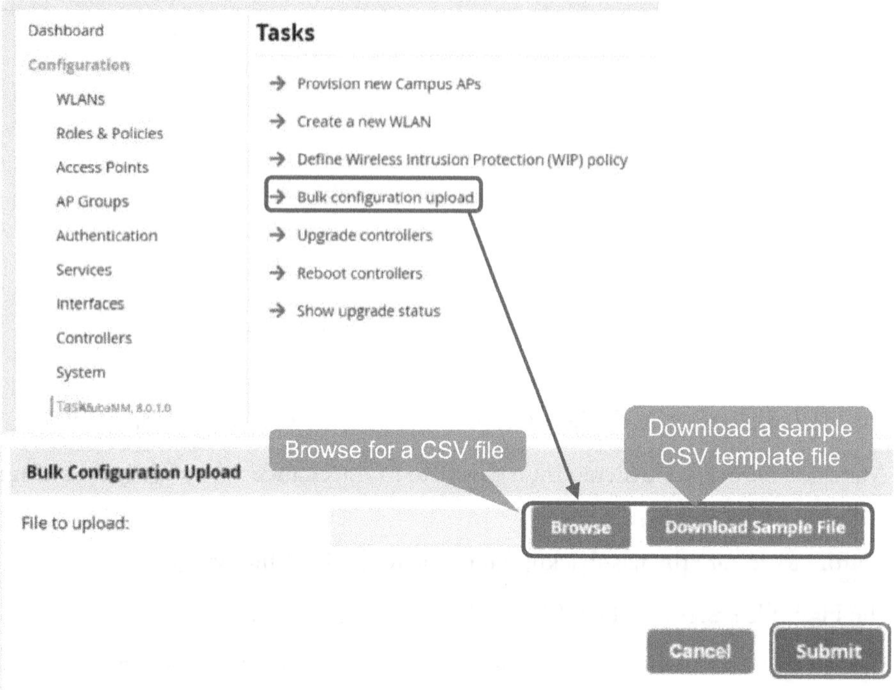

Figure 14-22 Bulk edit

The Bulk Edit feature enables you to do a bulk configuration in the MM (Figure 14-22). This option helps reduce the time required to perform configuration tasks.

To enable the Bulk Edit Feature:

1. In the Managed Network node hierarchy, navigate to **Configuration > Tasks > Bulk configuration upload**.
2. Click Download Sample File.
3. Enter values in the fields provided in the template.
4. Save the file.
5. Select Browse and navigate to the path where the template is stored.
6. Click Submit.
7. Click Pending Changes.
8. In the Pending Changes window, select the check box and click Deploy Changes.

Serviceability

Auto roll-back

Certain configurations can affect MM-MC connectivity. Some examples include the following:

- Uplink port shut down
- Partially configured uplink VLAN
- Limiting bandwidth contract policy
- Bad ACL

Even if you discover the error, the bad configuration may have already caused connectivity loss, preventing you from pushing the correct configuration to the MC.

To address this, the MM supports an auto-rollback mechanism, which is enabled by default. This reverts the managed device to the last known good configuration, prior to the management connectivity loss. The Config ID is used for the roll back.

The MM also indicates if a device has recovered from a bad configuration. To see this, use the command `show switches`. If the rollback configuration successfully recovered the device, the output shows the managed device state as CONFIG ROLLBACK.

When the user fixes the bad configuration on the MM, the managed device recovers automatically, and the state changes to "UPDATE SUCCESSFUL."

Disaster recovery

Occasionally, auto roll-back from a bad configuration fails, and MM-MC connectivity remains disrupted. In this case, you can enable Disaster Recovery mode on the MC using the command `disaster-recovery on`. You have full control of the /mm node, so you can make local modifications on each MC to restore MM-MC connectivity.

Disaster Recovery mode grants users access to the /mm node through the managed devices, while blocking any further configuration syncs from the MM.

After connectivity is restored and verified, you must exit the Disaster Recovery mode. Syntax examples are shown below.

```
(host) [mynode] #disaster-recovery on

(DR-Mode) [mynode] #disaster-recovery off
```

Loadable Service Modules (LSM)

LSMs allow you to dynamically upgrade or downgrade individual AOS features, without requiring an entire system reboot. The following service modules are LSM-capable, and the default service packages are bundled with the ArubaOS image:

- **AirGroup**—Enable Bonjour® services like Apple® AirPrint and AirPlay from mobile devices in an efficient manner.
- **AppRF**—Deep packet inspection (DPI) of local traffic. Detects over 1500 applications on the network.
- **ARM CM**—Automatic AP channel and power selection.
- **AirMatch**—Next-generation automatic AP channel and power selection, as of AOS 8.0.
- **NBAPI**—North Bound API enables third-party systems to gain visibility into the Aruba deployment.
- **UCM**—Unified Communications Manager enhances management of mobile devices that use voice, video, and collaboration applications.
- **WebCC**—Web Content Classification enables URL filtering, IP reputation, and geolocation filtering.
- **WMS**—The WLAN Management System monitors wireless traffic to detect and classify anomalous devices.

Every service module has a corresponding service package, which can be downloaded from the Aruba support site and installed on MM.

Downloading a service package

Upgrade Reboot Boot Parameters **Service Module Packages** About

Service Module Packages

TYPE	NAME	AOS VERSION	BUILD #	STATUS
AirGroup	default_airgroup_pkg	ArubaOS_MM_8.0.1.0	57204	Active
airmatch	default_airmatch_pkg	ArubaOS_MM_8.0.1.0	57204	Active
AppRF	default_appRF_pkg	ArubaOS_MM_8.0.1.0	57204	Active
ARM CM	default_arm_cm_pkg	ArubaOS_MM_8.0.1.0	57204	Active
NB API Helper	default_nbapi_helper_pkg	ArubaOS_MM_8.0.1.0	57204	Active
UCM	default_ucm_pkg	ArubaOS_MM_8.0.1.0	57204	Active

Load New Package

Access method: TFTP FTP SCP Local file
Host IP address:
Image file name:
Destination file name:

Cancel Submit

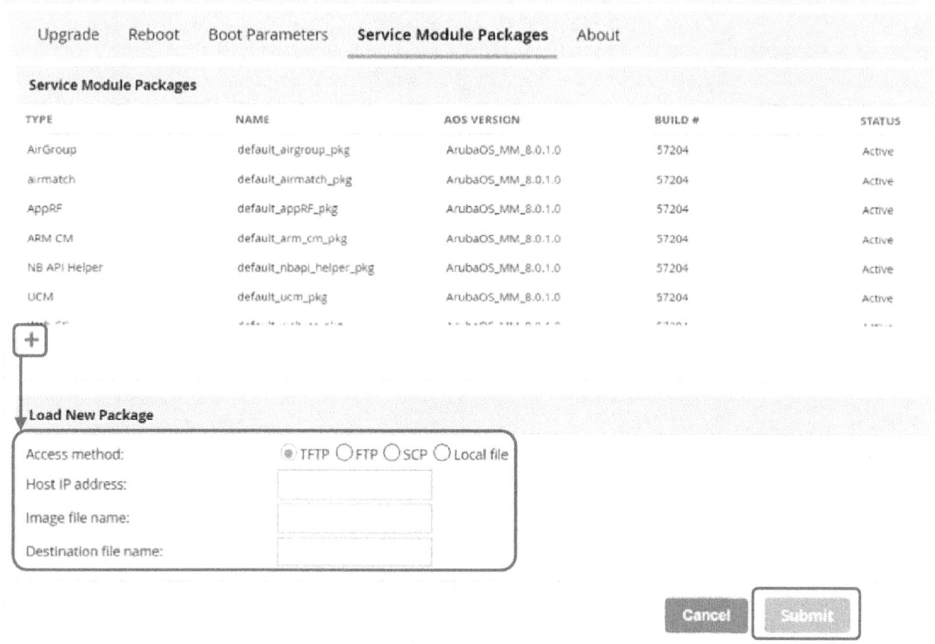

Figure 14-23 Downloading a service package

Figure 14-23 shows how to download an LSM service package, as described below.

1. Obtain the required service package from the Aruba support site.
2. In the MM node-hierarchy, navigate to **Maintenance > Software Management > Service Module Packages.**
3. Click the + icon at the bottom of the Service Module Packages table to add a new service package.
4. Under Load New Package, select the Access method used to fetch the package.
5. Click Submit to validate the package.

An example filename, for the AirMatch and AppRF features are shown below.

- ArubaOS_MM_8.0.1.0-svcs-ctrl_**airmatch**_56862
- ArubaOS_MM_8.0.1.0-svcs-ctrl_**appRF**_56862

Activating and removing service packages

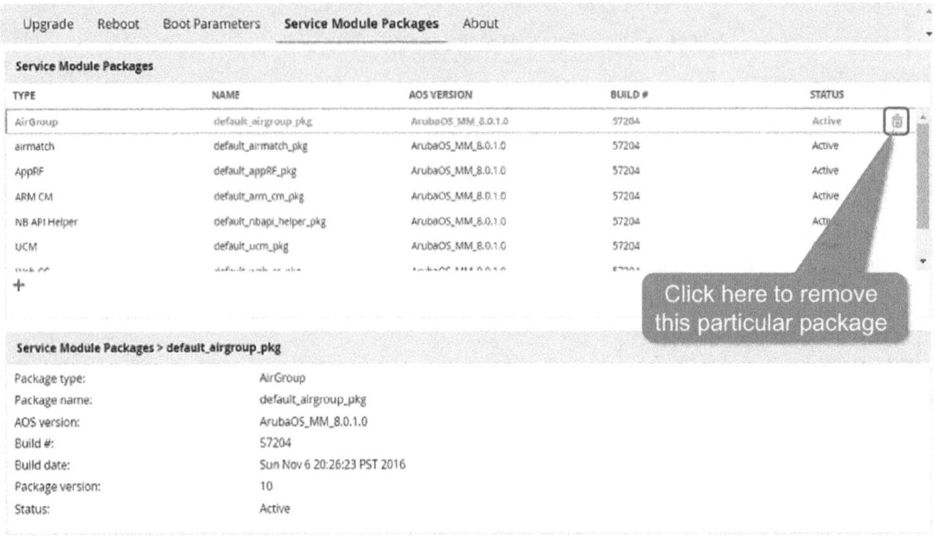

Figure 14-24 Activating and removing service packages

Figure 14-24 shows how to manage service packages, as described below.

1. In the MM node hierarchy, navigate to **Maintenance > Software Management > Service Module Packages.**
2. Select the new package from the Service Module Packages table. The **Service Module Packages > [name]** window appears at the bottom of the work screen.
3. Set the Status to Active to activate the new service package.
4. Click Submit.

To do this at the CLI, use the following commands:

```
(host) [mynode] #upgrade-pkg activate <packagename>
```

To remove a Service Package:

1. Navigate as above, to **Maintenance > Software Management > Service Module Packages.**
2. Select a package from the Service Module Packages table. The trash icon for the highlighted package appears.

3. Click the trash icon. When the package delete window opens, click Delete.
4. Click Submit.

To do this at the CLI:

```
(host) [mynode] #upgrade-pkg remove <packagename>
```

Downloadable Regulatory Table (DRT) and technical support

Downloadable Regulatory Table (DRT)

The DRT feature allows you to update country domain options without upgrading the ArubaOS software version. A separate file, called the Regulatory-Cert, contains AP regulatory information. This will be released periodically on the HPE Aruba customer support site. The Regulatory-Cert file can then be uploaded to a controller and pushed to APs.

The Regulatory-Cert includes the following information for each AP:

- All countries supported in the current release of ArubaOS (not just United States, but the rest of world or any subset of countries)
- Allowed channels for each country
- Max EIRP for each channel and each country in the allowed list. The max values are specified for each PHY type at which the AP is allowed to transmit on.

The classified PHY-types are

- 802.11 OFDM rates (802.11a/g mode)
- 802.11b rates (CCK rates)
- 802.11n HT20 and 802.11ac VHT20 rates (MCS0-7)
- 802.11n HT20 and 802.11ac VHT40(MCS0-7)
- 802.11ac VHT80 rates
- DFS functionality for each channel and each country in the allowed list

Copy the regulatory-cert file

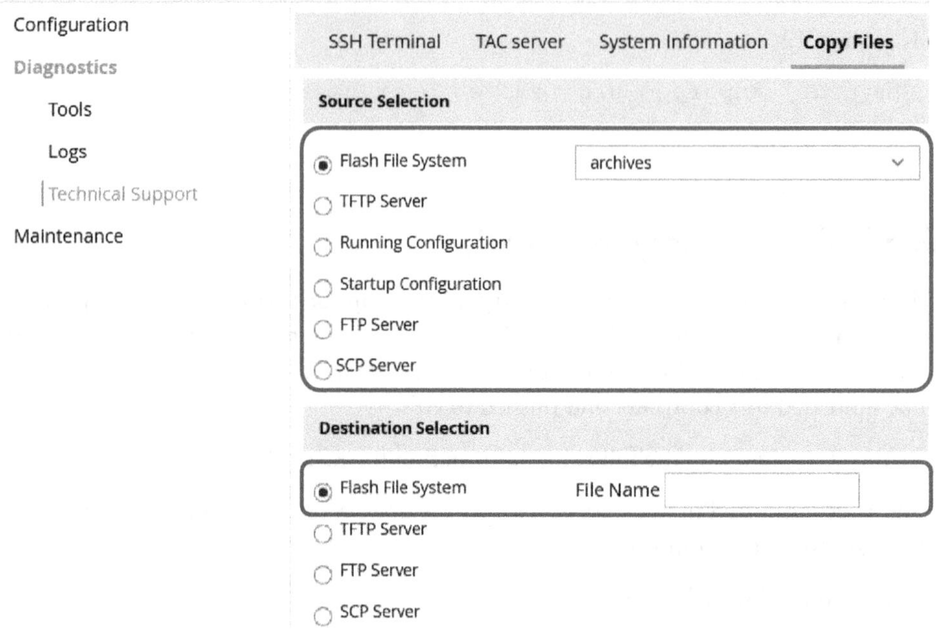

Figure 14-25 Copy the regulatory-cert file

Figure 14-25 shows how to copy the regulatory-cert file. Use the following procedure.

1. Navigate to **Diagnostics > Technical Support > Copy Files**.
2. Select the source where the file exists.
3. The controller WebUI automatically selects Flash File System under the Destination Selection menu.
4. Click Apply.

To do this via CLI, use one of the following copy commands to download the DRT file to the controller:

```
copy scp: <scphost> <username> <filename> flash: <destfilename>

copy tftp: <tftphost> <filename> flash: <destfilename>

copy usb: partition <partition-number> <filename> flash:  <destfilename>
```

Activate the regulatory-cert

```
(ArubaMM-Lab) [mynode] #dir

-rw-r--r--    1 root     root          387 Mar 25 01:02 AUDITTRAIL-HISTORY.log
-rw-r--r--    1 root     root          213 Mar 25 01:02 AUDITTRAIL-LOGIN_OUT-HI
-rw-r--r--    1 root     root          144 Apr 14 17:59 blimits
-rw-r--r--    1 root     root           40 Apr 12 09:47 bmap
-rw-r--r--    1 root     root        13156 Mar 24 17:21 default.cfg
drwxr-xr-x    4 root     root         4096 Mar 25 00:20 fieldCerts
-rw-r--r--    1 root     root        62714 Mar 29 22:26 flashbackup.tar.gz
drwxr-xr-x    2 root     root         4096 Mar 25 00:19 full
-rw-r--r--    1 root     root           18 Mar 25 01:04 mac_addr.cfg
-rw-r--r--    1 root     root          179 Mar 30 12:43 rbcm.json
-rw-r--r--    1 root     root       136405 Apr 14 18:00 reg-data-1.0_59118.dat
-rw-r--r--    1 root     root           15 Mar 30 13:33 rules-f.custom
-rw-r--r--    1 root     root         4884 Mar 30 13:33 rules.custom
-rw-r--r--    1 root     root          179 Mar 30 13:02 rules.default1
-rw-r--r--    1 root     root         4884 Mar 30 13:32 rules.default5
-rw-r--r--    1 root     root          180 Mar 30 13:28 rules.default7
drwxr-xr-x    2 root     root         4096 Mar 24 17:23 upgrade-2017-03-24_17-2
-rw-r--r--    1 root     root            5 Mar 25 01:01 vclock.time
-rw-r--r--    1 root     root          179 Mar 30 12:56 vj-rbcm.rules

(ArubaMM-Lab) [mynode] #ap regulatory activate reg-data-1.0_59118.dat
(ArubaMM-Lab) [mynode] #show ap regulatory

Regulatory Version     :1.0_59118
```

Regulatory data file in Flash

Verify regulatory version
Use to activate

Figure 14-26 Activate the regulatory-cert

Once the DRT file has been added to the controller, the new regulatory information must be activated and pushed to the APs (Figure 14-26). To do this from the CLI, use the following command:

```
ap regulatory activate <filename>
```

To return to the factory default regulatory-cert, use the following command:

```
ap regulatory reset
```

There are several commands available to verify DRT status.

```
show ap regulatory

show ap allowed-channels country-code <country-code> ap-type <ap-type>

show ap allowed-max-eirp ap-name <ap-name> country-code <country-code>

show ap debug received-reg-table ap-name <ap-name>
```

Technical support

You might have a network emergency and decide to reboot the controller before you call Aruba Technical Assistant Center (TAC). You may do this as a quick troubleshooting step to see if the issue gets resolved after rebooting the controller. Before you reboot, you can also generate the following files for TAC analysis.

- Tar logs
- Tech support file
- Crash dump

Capture this information before the reboot, because all the logs and the audit trail information on the controller are lost when the controller is rebooted. These logs help TAC to better understand your issues. In certain cases, TAC may be able to identify the root cause on the issues reported.

Generating tar logs

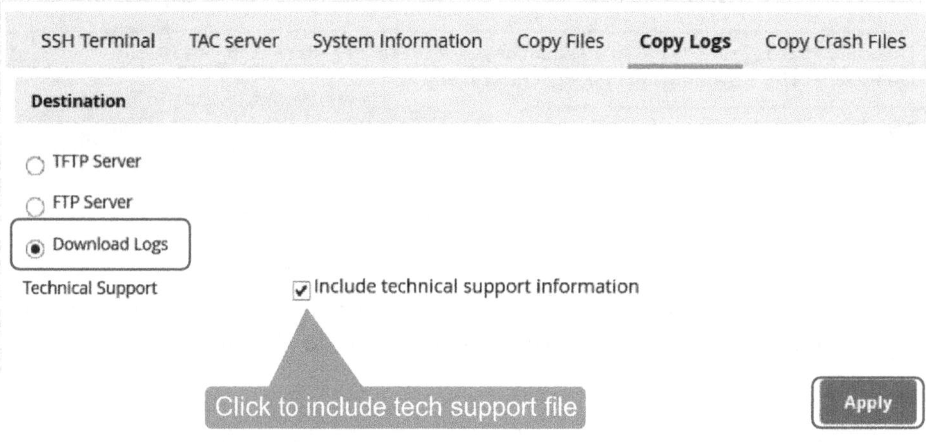

Figure 14-27 Generating tar logs

Use the following procedure to generate a tar log from the WebUI (Figure 14-27):

1. In the Managed Network node hierarchy (or web access to a particular controller), navigate to **Diagnostics > Technical Support > Open Copy Logs.**
2. Select Download Logs option and click Apply.

The above steps will generate a file in flash named "logs.tar." This can be downloaded into the local drive.

Note

Select the "Include technical support information" option if you want to include tech support information in the Tar logs file.

To do this procedure at the CLI:

```
(ArubaMM) [mynode] #tar logs [tech-support]
```

Generating a tech support file

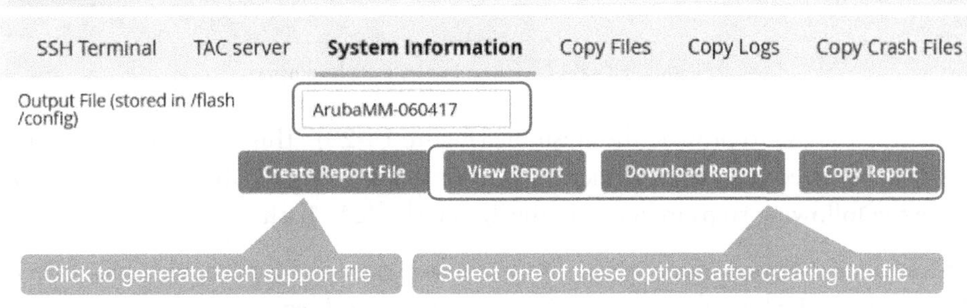

Figure 14-28 Generating a tech support file

To generate a tech support file, perform the following (Figure 14-28)

1. In the Managed Network node hierarchy (or web access on a particular controller), navigate to **Diagnostics > Technical Support > Open System Information.**
2. Enter a name for the output File.
3. Click on "Create Report File."
4. You can view, download, or copy the report of the tech-support file.

Generating a crash dump

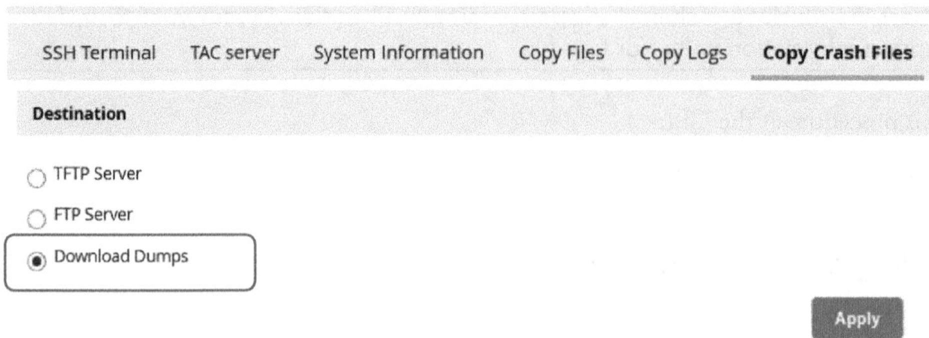

Figure 14-29 Generating a crash dump

Usually TAC will ask you to provide the crash file (Figure 14-29). This helps to understand the technical issues that occurred before the device crashed or malfunctioned. If there is crash information available, use the following steps to generate the Tar crash file in flash.

1. In the Managed Network node hierarchy (or on web access of a particular controller), navigate to **Diagnostics > Technical Support > Open Copy crash files.**
2. Select the Download Dumps option (you can also select the FTP/TFTP option to copy the file).
3. Click Apply.

A crash.tar file will be created in the flash and the same file will be downloaded into the local system drive.

To do this on the CLI:

```
(ArubaMM) [mynode] #tar crash
```

 **Note**

The crash file s generated if the crash info (crash dump) is available in the controller. Use the command `show switchinfo` to determine if crash information is available.

Learning check

4. What is the primary use for disaster mode?
   a. To recover the controller when it is crashed.
   b. To recover the controller when it loses its configuration.
   c. To configure the MC when it loses connection with the MM.
   d. To configure the MC when it loses its configuration.

15 AirGroup

LEARNING OBJECTIVES

- ✓ This chapter is focused on the HPE Aruba AirGroup feature, which accommodates Apple Bonjour and various Digital Living Network Alliance (DLNA) applications.
- ✓ You will learn about the AirGroup solution, along with configuration, and integration with ClearPass. You will also learn about monitoring and troubleshooting this feature.

AirGroup introduction

AirGroup is an HPE Aruba feature that leverages zero configuration networking to enable Bonjour® services like Apple® AirPrint and AirPlay from mobile devices in an efficient manner. Bonjour, the trade name for the zero configuration implementation introduced by Apple, is the most common example.

AirGroup also supports DLNA for Windows and Android devices. Read on to learn more about Bonjour and DLNA, and how the AirGroup feature enhances performance for these protocols.

Bonjour and DLNA

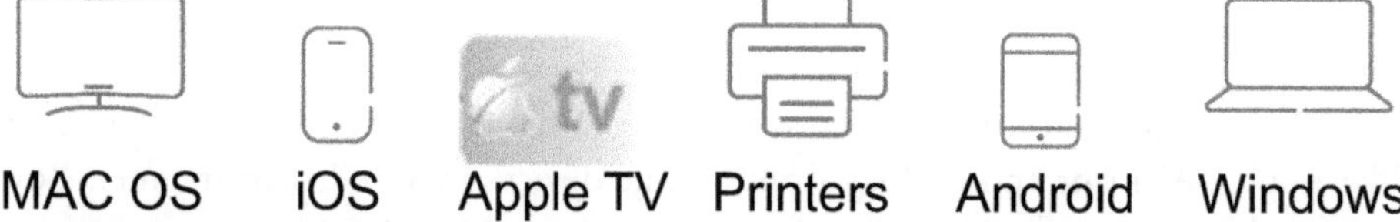
Bonjour protocol suite
• Link-local addressing and naming
• Name-to-address translation
• Locate devices via mDNS
• **Multicast on a single VLAN**
tv
MAC OS
iOS
Apple TV
Printers
Android
Windows
Digital Living Network Alliance
• Share media among Windows and Android Devices
• Derived from Universal Plug and Play (UPnP)
• Uses Simple Service Discovery Protocol (SSDP)
• UDP-based multicast

Figure 15-1 Bonjour and DLNA

Bonjour

Zero configuration networking is an Apple® technology that enables service discovery, address assignment, and name resolution for various devices. This includes desktop computers, mobile devices, and network services. It was designed for flat, single-subnet IP networks.

The suite of protocols introduced by Apple® for zero configuration networking are referred to as Bonjour®. This protocol suite is supported by most devices in the Apple product line. It can be installed on Microsoft Windows® and is supported by most printers (Figure 15-1).

The Bonjour protocol consists of addressing, link-local addressing for devices, naming for name-to-address translation, and discovery to find services and devices. Bonjour is often used in home networks to allow Windows and Apple devices to share printers.

Bonjour locates devices such as printers, computers, and their offered services using multicast Domain Name System (mDNS). Bonjour uses link-scoped multicast addresses so that each query or advertisement is limited to a single VLAN or broadcast domain.

An mDNS query is sent out for a given service type and domain, and any matching services reply with their names. The result is a list of available services to choose from. Each host listens on the mDNS port, 5353, and resolves requests to its IP address. Bonjour is supported by most of the Apple product lines including the Mac OS X® operating system, iPhone®, iPod®, iPad®, Apple TV®, and AirPort Express®. Bonjour is also included within popular software programs such as Apple iTunes®, Safari, and iPhoto®. Bonjour can be installed on computers running Microsoft Windows® and is supported by most new network-capable printers.

To summarize, Bonjour provides a very user-friendly way for nontechnical people to share devices and services. However, discovery is only possible within a single subnet, this limits flexibility. Also, the use of multicast packets adds overhead. This can reduce scalability and performance—especially for wireless networks.

Digital Living Network Alliance (DLNA)

A Digital Living Network Alliance (DLNA) network is a standard that is derived from Universal Plug and Play (UPnP). DLNA uses Simple Service Discovery Protocol (SSDP) for service discovery (Figure 15-1). This protocol provides the ability to share digital media between multimedia devices like Windows and Android. It sends UDP-based multicast packets on address 239.255.255.250

The Aruba AirGroup solution

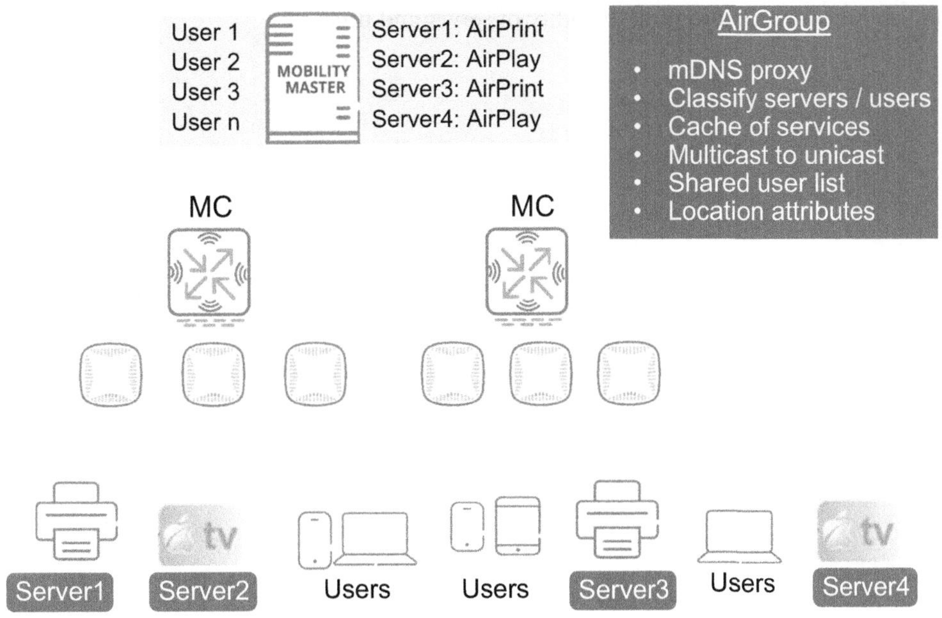

Figure 15-2 The Aruba AirGroup solution

The AirGroup feature enhances performance and flexibility for WLANs that support Bonjour and DLNA-based services (Figure 15-2).

- Performance—The controller acts as an mDNS proxy. It sends unicast responses to mDNS queries to reduce the overhead caused by multicast traffic.
- Flexibility—Controllers ensure cross-VLAN visibility of mDNS devices and services. They terminate all mDNS queries and responses from clients and classify all mDNS devices as either servers or users. Controllers can also allow or block mDNS services based on user roles, or for all users.

AirGroup is location-aware. It matches the user devices to their closest Wi-Fi-based mDNS servers. This requires ClearPass. AirGroup also supports IPv6 mDNS devices and responds to IPv6 mDNS queries.

AirGroup servers and users are all mDNS devices. Servers advertise at least one Bonjour service. Users only query for those Bonjour services.

The MM maintains a cache table of mDNS records for all mDNS service advertisements that it sees. Cache records are maintained only for services/VLANs that are allowed by AirGroup.

The controller receives an mDNS query and consults the mDNS cache table. It sends a unicast response to the client, for all matching records found in the table. By default, all AirGroup servers are visible to all AirGroup users.

You can apply various access control policies to control the visibility of AirGroup servers and services. You can use a "disallowed role" option to restrict visibility for a particular AirGroup service to a set of user roles.

The MM can process 400 mpps (multicast packets per second). In many environments, this is more than enough. However, in very large deployments, this traffic should be measured.

Location attributes are used to limit visibility of server and users.

Configuration

Enable AirGroup protocols

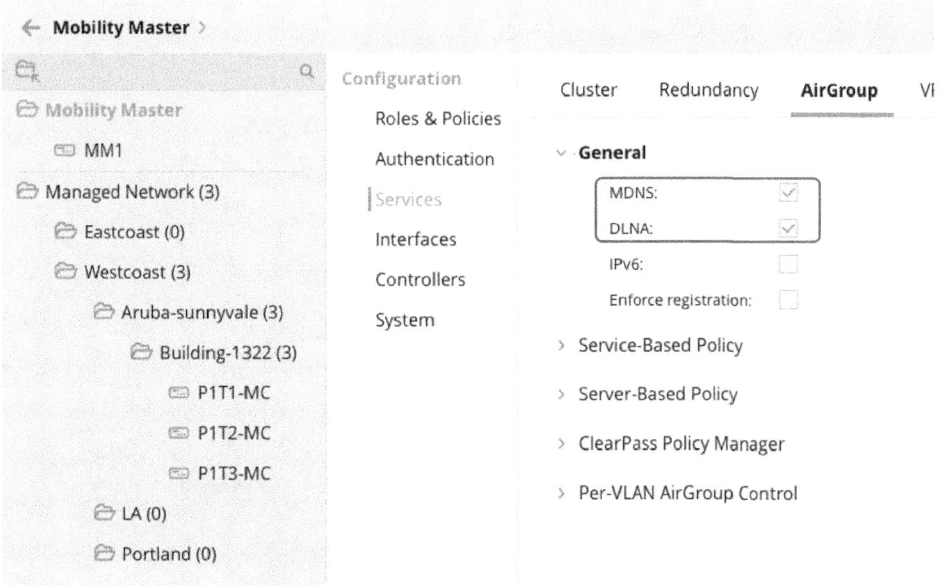

Figure 15-3 Enable AirGroup protocols

You must be in the Mobility Master level of hierarchy to enable AirGroup. As shown in Figure 15-3, you can enable mDNS, which supports zero configuration networking to Apple devices and services.

You can also enable DLNA SSDP for service discovery on the network. DLNA enables digital media sharing between multimedia devices, like Windows and Android.

Enable AirGroup services

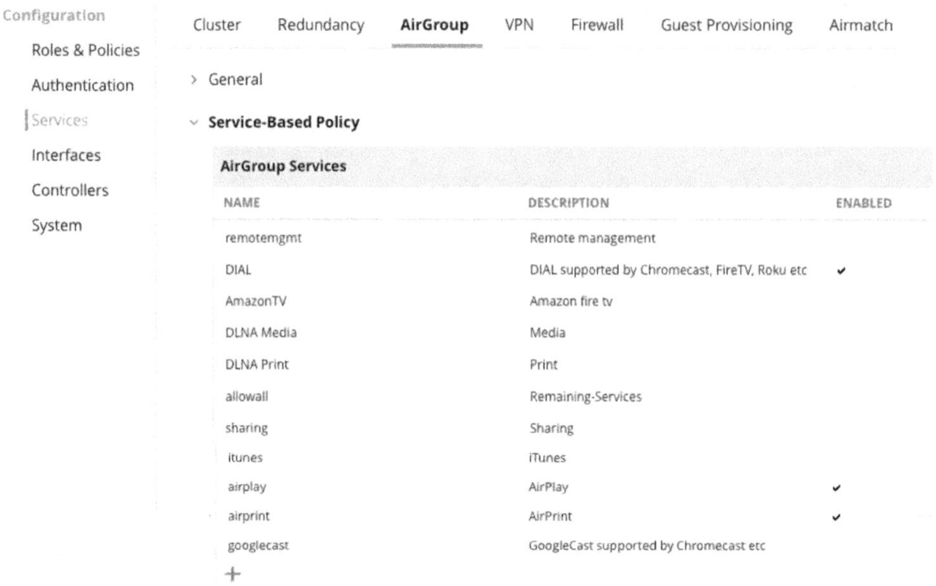

Figure 15-4 Enable AirGroup services

You can enable or disable individual AirGroup services. Just navigate to **Configuration > Services > AirGroup** (Figure 15-14). Select **Allow All** to enable every service. Or you enable any of the preconfigured services listed below.

- **AirPlay**—Allows wireless streaming of music, video, and slide shows from an iOS device to the Apple TV and other devices that support AirPlay.
- **AirPrint** —Print from an iPad, iPhone, or iPod Touch directly to any AirPrint compatible printer.
- **DIAL**—Allows Wi-Fi-enabled streaming devices such as Google Chromecast, Roku, Amazon FireTV, and more to advertise the Discovery and Launch (DIAL) protocol. This allows clients to search for an available device on a wireless network.
- **DLNA Media**—Applications such as Windows Media Player use this service to browse and play media content on a remote device.
- **DLNA Print**—Used by printers that support DLNA.
- **GoogleCast**—Google Chromecast uses this service to stream video and music content from a smart phone to a TV screen using a wireless network.

- **iTunes**— Used by iTunes Wi-Fi sync and iTunes home-sharing applications across all Apple devices.
- **RemoteMgmt**—Use this service for remote login, remote management, and FTP utilities on Apple devices.
- **Sharing**—Applications, such as disk sharing and file sharing, use this service's ID on one or more Apple devices.

Service-based policies

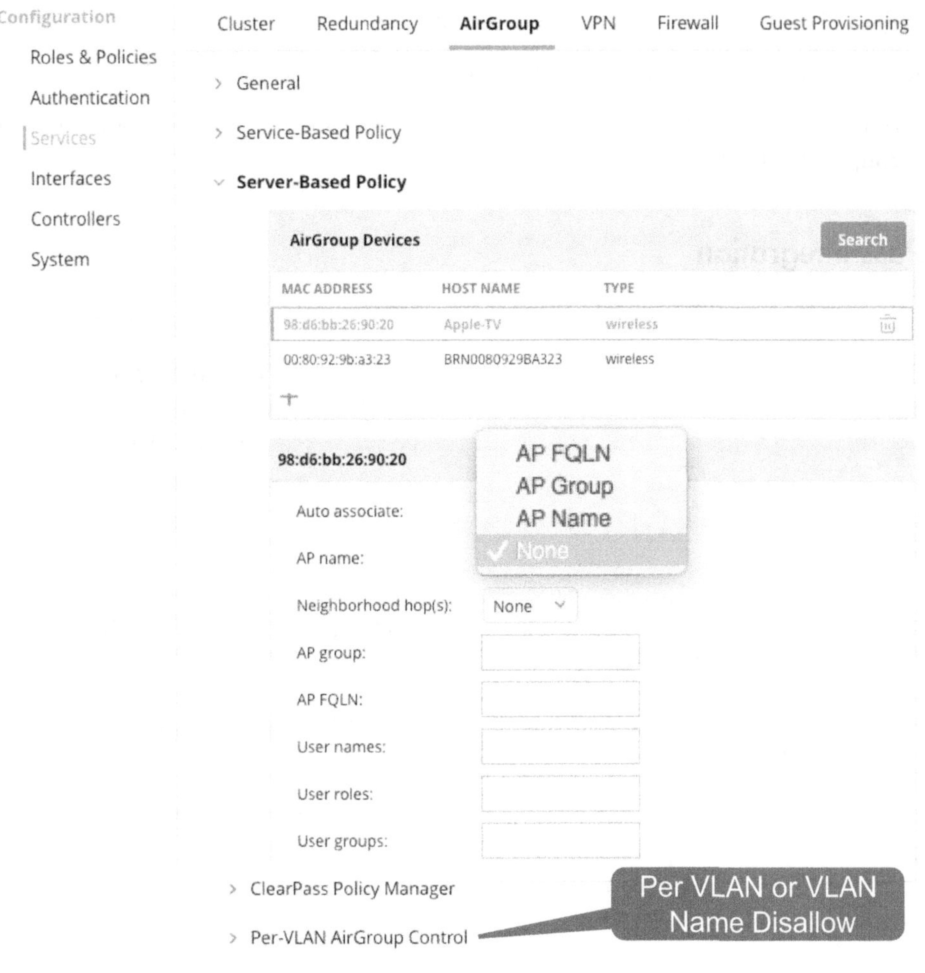

Figure 15-5 Service-based policies

You can configure location-based policy limits based on AP names, AP groups, and AP Fully Qualified Location Names (FQLN). This minimizes AirGroup server visibility to AirGroup users. To do this, navigate to **Configuration > Services > AirGroup** (Figure 15-5). Configure the appropriate location attributes, as described below.

- **AP-Group**—All users connected to APs in this AP-group can access the shared device.
- **AP FQLN**—All users connected to APs on the same floor or a floor above or below the shared device can access the AP.
- **AP-Name**—All users connected to the same AP or those that hop RF neighbors can access the shared device.
- **Role-based**—Limit server and users to a specific role.
- **Hops**—Define an area in the AP neighborhood, up to X hops from this AP.
- **VLAN Disallow**—Disallowed VLAN IDs can be configured at the AirGroup service level and AirGroup global level.

ClearPass integration

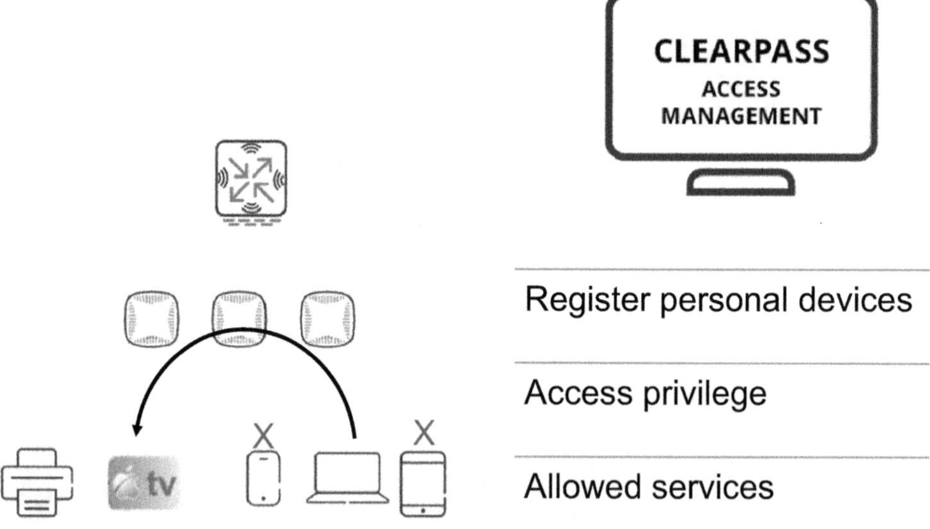

Figure 15-6 ClearPass integration

ClearPass adds additional capabilities to the AirGroup solution (Figure 15-6). It allows registration portals, so that users can register their personal and shared devices (Apple TVs, printers, and so forth). You can also register shared devices such as conference room Apple TVs and printers. A registered personal device is visible to the device owner or to others with whom the device owner has shared.

ClearPass can define "personal AirGroups." This is a list of users among which devices can be shared. The ClearPass Policy Manager (CPPM) allows you to apply more granular access control policies to AirGroup servers—shared user lists, shared role lists, and location policies.

Visibility of a shared device depends on the various sharing attributes, as listed above. CPPM helps provide a filtered mDNS response to users and reduce noise. This is recommended for large deployments.

Dashboard

AirGroup summary

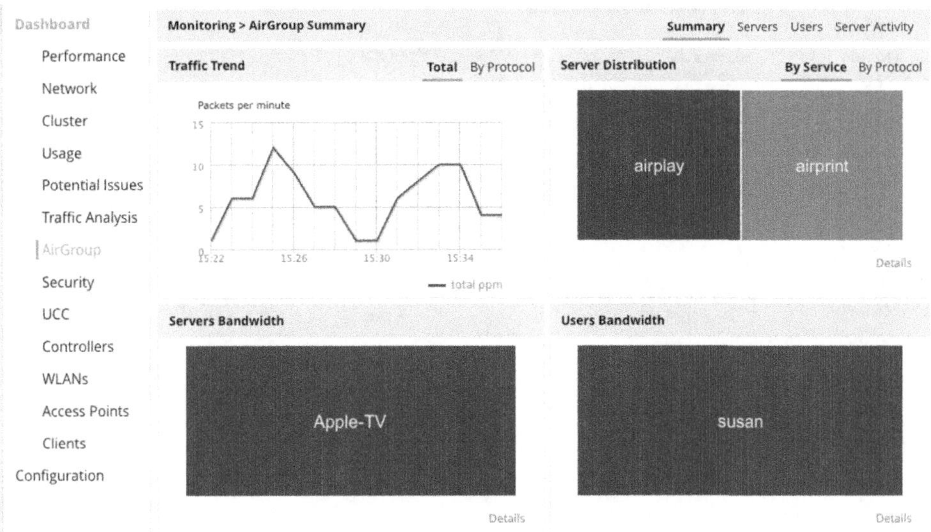

Figure 15-7 AirGroup summary

AirGroup devices generate query and response packets to discover and publish services. AirGroup performance is directly dependent on the number of packets a server or an user generates. Under a heavy load, CPU utilization-based rate limiting/throttling may drop queries and responses.

The trend chart provides packet-per-minute trending over the last 15 minutes (Figure 15-7). This chart helps you to visualize the network's AirGroup control traffic. This trend chart is also displayed per protocol (mDNS/DLNA).

The server distribution chart shows service-based distribution of AirGroup servers. This includes both custom and default services. Click on any service to see the server page, filtered by the selected service. Server-to-user data traffic is displayed. This can help you to determine which server's aggregated active sessions have been consuming maximum data. The chart shows the top 20 highest utilized servers at that instant. These sessions are exported to the dashboard every 2 minutes. When a session ends, it might not be deleted from view for up to 2 minutes.

Large deployments often support many advertised Bonjour services, which can consume significant system resources. In this scenario, you should enable the AirPlay and AirPrint services, disable the allowall service, and then block all other Bonjour services.

AirGroup servers

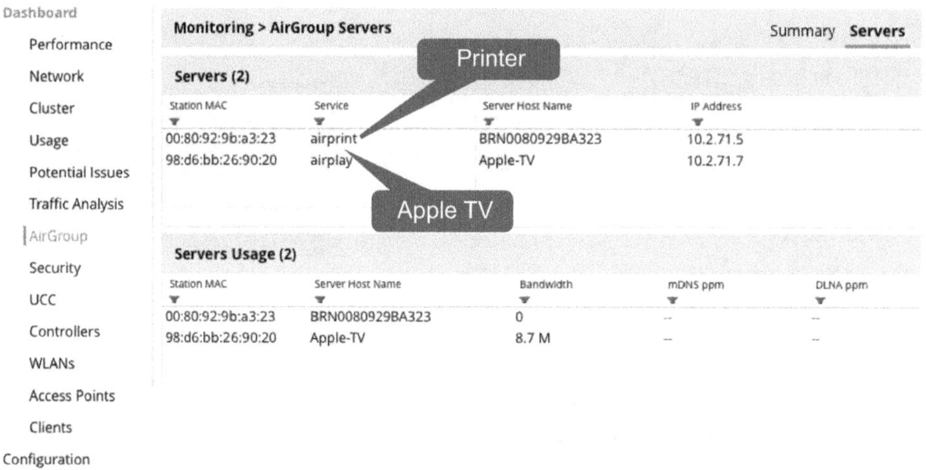

Figure 15-8 AirGroup servers

AirGroup servers and users generate two types of traffic—control and data.

Control traffic is in the form of queries and responses, used to publish and discover services. All the control traffic is consumed by AirGroup. In Figure 15-8, you can see that two AirGroup servers have been discovered, and the services they support are listed.

Once the user discovers a service and wants to use the service, data traffic between server and user is established. This data traffic is comprised of UDP and TCP sessions.

AirGroup users

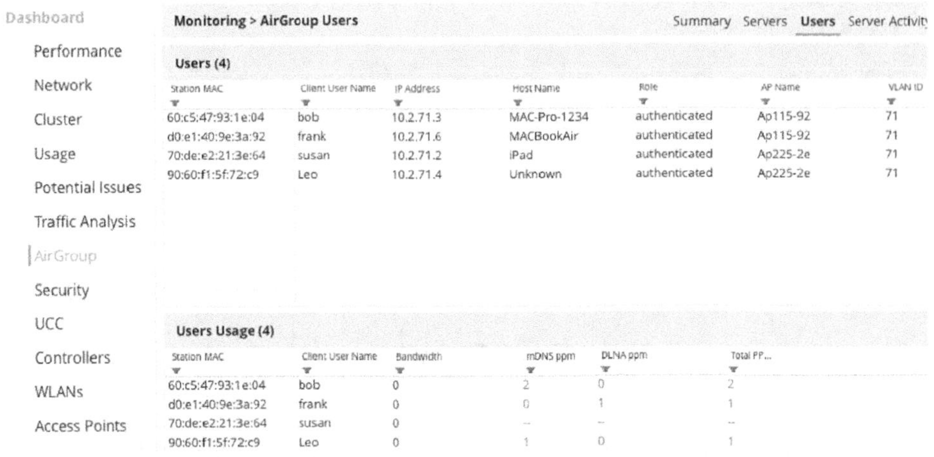

Monitoring > AirGroup Users

Users (4)

Station MAC	Client User Name	IP Address	Host Name	Role	AP Name	VLAN ID
60:c5:47:93:1e:04	bob	10.2.71.3	MAC-Pro-1234	authenticated	Ap115-92	71
d0:e1:40:9e:3a:92	frank	10.2.71.6	MACBookAir	authenticated	Ap115-92	71
70:de:e2:21:3e:64	susan	10.2.71.2	iPad	authenticated	Ap225-2e	71
90:60:f1:5f:72:c9	Leo	10.2.71.4	Unknown	authenticated	Ap225-2e	71

Users Usage (4)

Station MAC	Client User Name	Bandwidth	mDNS ppm	DLNA ppm	Total PP...
60:c5:47:93:1e:04	bob	0	2	0	2
d0:e1:40:9e:3a:92	frank	0	0	1	1
70:de:e2:21:3e:64	susan	0	--	--	--
90:60:f1:5f:72:c9	Leo	0	1	0	1

Figure 15-9 AirGroup users

The User tab provides user lists and utilization details (Figure 15-9). The top half list of all AirGroup users and their properties such as VLAN, role, AP Name, Group, and more.

The bottom of the report provides the user usage. This includes both control and data traffic trends, per user. Control traffic is shown as a trend chart. This pops up when you click on any data for a user.

Data traffic shows the total bandwidth consumed by the user and total number of servers used by the assessed user.

Server Activity tab

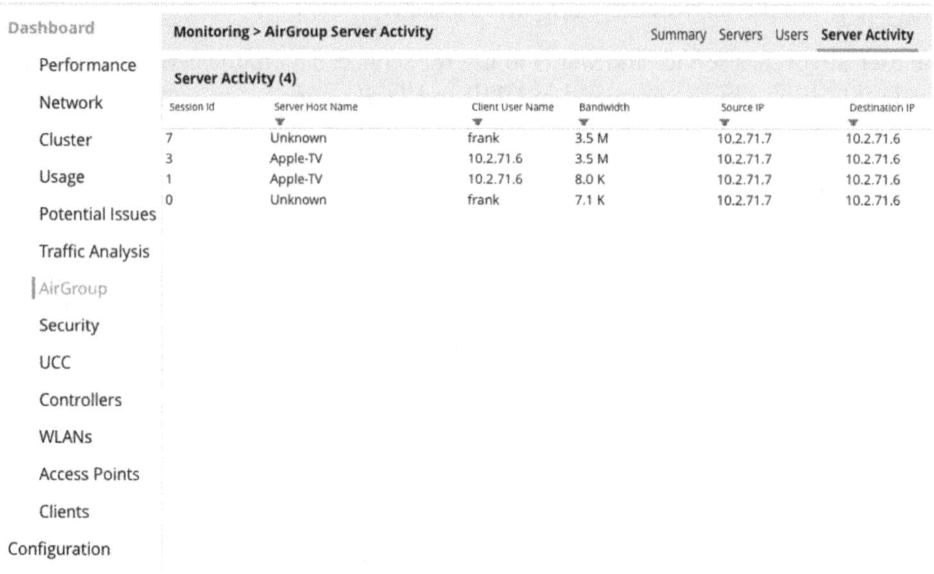

Dashboard
Performance
Network
Cluster
Usage
Potential Issues
Traffic Analysis
AirGroup
Security
UCC
Controllers
WLANs
Access Points
Clients
Configuration

Monitoring > AirGroup Server Activity Summary Servers Users **Server Activity**

Server Activity (4)

Session Id	Server Host Name	Client User Name	Bandwidth	Source IP	Destination IP
7	Unknown	frank	3.5 M	10.2.71.7	10.2.71.6
3	Apple-TV	10.2.71.6	3.5 M	10.2.71.7	10.2.71.6
1	Apple-TV	10.2.71.6	8.0 K	10.2.71.7	10.2.71.6
0	Unknown	frank	7.1 K	10.2.71.7	10.2.71.6

Figure 15-10 Server Activity tab

The Server Activity tab lists server and user data traffic details (Figure 15-10). This includes the source IP as the server IP, destination IP as the client IP, and bandwidth. This helps you to identify which server was used by which user and vice versa.

The "Servers by Bandwidth" chart does not show any server that uses peer-to-peer for media. Since the controller never sees those sessions, you will not see those statistics.

Services like remote management and file transfer between users require the user to announce these services. When these services are enabled, one or both users are marked as an AirGroup server. Any session between these two users (remote management, file transfer, and so forth) may result in one user being marked as the server and other as the user. To be consistent, the lower IP address will be marked as the server and higher IP address as the user. This is only applicable if AirGroup is used for discovery, and these services are enabled.

Troubleshooting

Servers and users

You can view servers and users from the CLI.

The command `show airgroup servers` reveals what type of service the servers are advertising and what protocol is being used. In the following example, this is mDNS.

```
(MM1) [mynode] #show airgroup servers
AirGroup Servers
----------------
MAC                IP          Type  Host Name         Service   VLAN  Wired/Wireless  Role           AP-Name
---                --          ----  ---------         -------   ----  --------------  -------------  -----
98:d6:bb:26:90:20  10.2.71.7   mDNS  Apple-TV          AirPlay   71    wireless        authenticated  Ap225-2e
00:80:92:9b:a3:23  10.2.71.5   mDNS  BRN0080929BA323   AirPrint  71    wireless        authenticated  Ap115-98
Num Servers: 2.
```

The following output from the command `show airgroup users` shows that the users can support both mDNS and DLNA.

```
(MM1) [mynode] #show airgroup users
AirGroup Users
--------------
MAC                IP          Type       Host Name     VLAN  Wired/Wireless  RoleGroup      Username  AP-Name
---                --          ----       ---------     ----  --------------  ---------      --------  ------
d0:e1:40:9e:3a:92  10.2.71.6   mDNS,DLNA  MACBookAir    71    wireless        authenticated  frank     Ap115-98
60:c5:47:93:1e:04  10.2.71.3   mDNS,DLNA  MAC-Pro-1234  71    wireless        authenticated  bob       Ap115-98
Num Users: 2.
```

Monitoring servers and users

You can monitor servers and users from the CLI.

The command `show mon-serv-lic-table airgroup` reveals the status and counters for monitored servers. In the following example, three controllers are shown, with their server count and number of users.

```
(MM1) [mynode] #show mon-serv-lc-table airgroup
MON_SERV AirGroup Table
------------------------
LC IP        Servers Users Server Usage User Usage Server Ip Entries User Ip Entries Ag sessions
-----        ------- ----- ------------ ---------- ----------------- --------------- -----------
10.2.70.101  1       2     1            2          0                 0               2
10.2.60.100  0       0     0            0          0                 0               0
10.2.70.102  1       0     1            0          1                 0               2
Total        2       2     2            2          1                 0               4
(MM1) [mynode] #
```

16 Tunneled Node

LEARNING OBJECTIVES

✓ In this chapter, you will learn about wired security risks and how to mitigate them using the Tunneled Node feature.

✓ This includes both port-based and user-based Tunneled Node operation, configuration, and monitoring.

Wired security risks

Wired access security risks

Corporate network

Wired Security
- Open
- MAC Auth
- 802.1X

Wireless Security
- 802.1X
- MAC Auth
- Captive portal
- Firewall

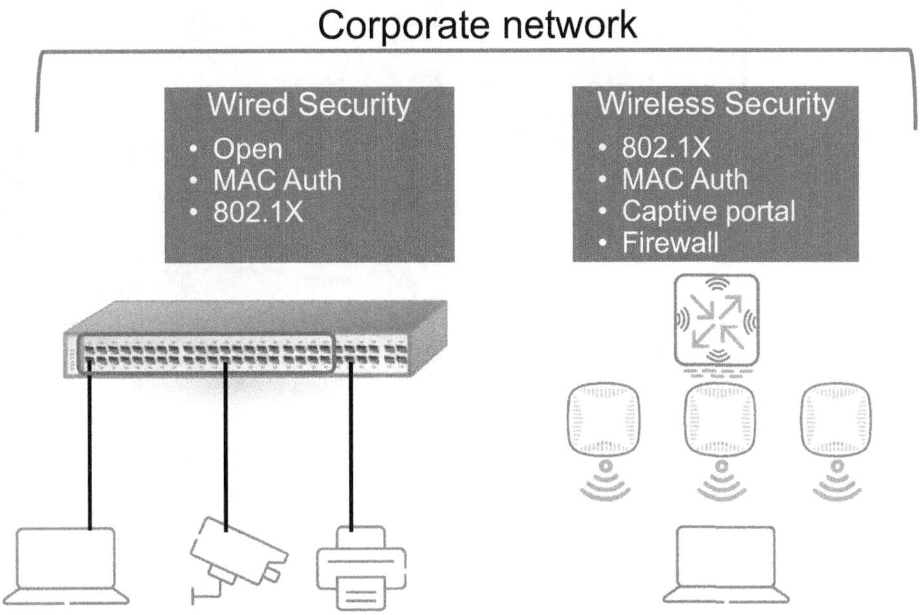

Figure 16-1 Wired access security risks

Most enterprise-class wireless networks are very secure. Aruba's Wi-Fi solution supports strong wireless authentication, encryption, hashing, and firewalling services for all WLAN traffic. A centralized firewall feature ensures consistent security (Figure 16-1).

However, wired networks may not be so secure. They often rely on low-level security features, if any. The few security features that may be in use are often inadequate. For example, end-user IP addresses can be easily discovered. Many solutions are deployed on backend servers, instead of at the access level.

Implementing wired-side 802.1X security provides very strong security. However, many wired devices lack 802.1X support. The best you can do on these devices may be open or MAC-based authentication, leaving security holes in the corporate network.

Firewalling all the various wired ports in the network is also very inconsistent. HPE Aruba deployments offer a superior solution.

Unified policy enforcement for wired and wireless clients

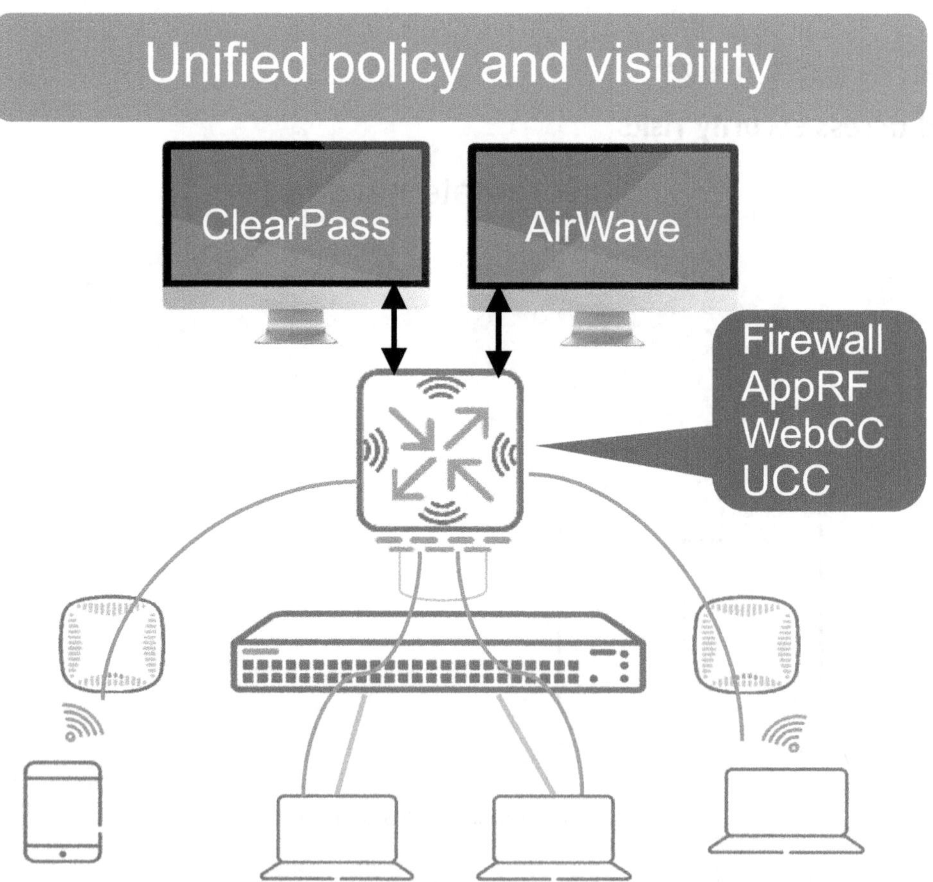

Figure 16-2 Unified policy enforcement for wired and wireless clients

In a traditional campus mobility solution, wireless client traffic is tunneled between AP and controller (Figure 16-2). However, wired traffic is typically not managed and often traverses the wired network unencrypted. If desired, you can enable the per-port tunneled node feature on ArubaOS-based switches. Thus, switch-connected wired users are encapsulated like controller-connected wireless users.

With the tunneled node feature, you can configure per-port tunnels between the access switch and the campus controller. Individual switch ports can be configured as desired. Then the switch creates a single tunnel to the controller. However, the controller perceives each tunneled node port as a separate tunnel. This provides more granular visibility and control.

Tunneled node

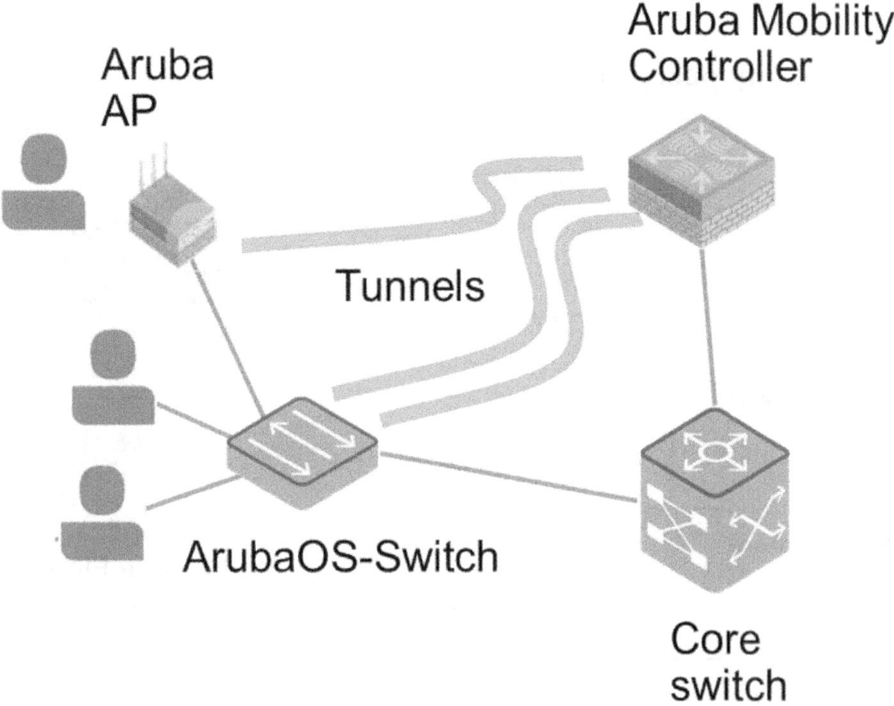

Figure 16-3 Tunneled node

In most networks, wireless and wired networks operate as separate architectures, with different authentication methods and security policies. Tunneled node gives you a consistent architecture with centralized wired and wireless policy enforcement. Tunneled node offers:

- Two forms of configuration—port-based or role-based (also called user-based).
- All switch traffic can be sent to the controller for consistent firewall, fingerprint, and packet inspection services.
- All traffic from the switches are GRE-tunneled to the controller.
- A backup controller can provide redundancy. Controller clusters can also terminate Aruba Switch tunnels.
- Only newer switches like the 2930 or those listed in the slide support user-tunneled node.
  - Port-based tunnels can be supported on slightly older switches, as shown in Figure 16-3. Full support on 5400R/v3, 3810, and 2930F/M. Port-based support on 2540/2560/2620
- User-tunneled node is supported as of AOS 8.1.

Centralized security policy and authentication

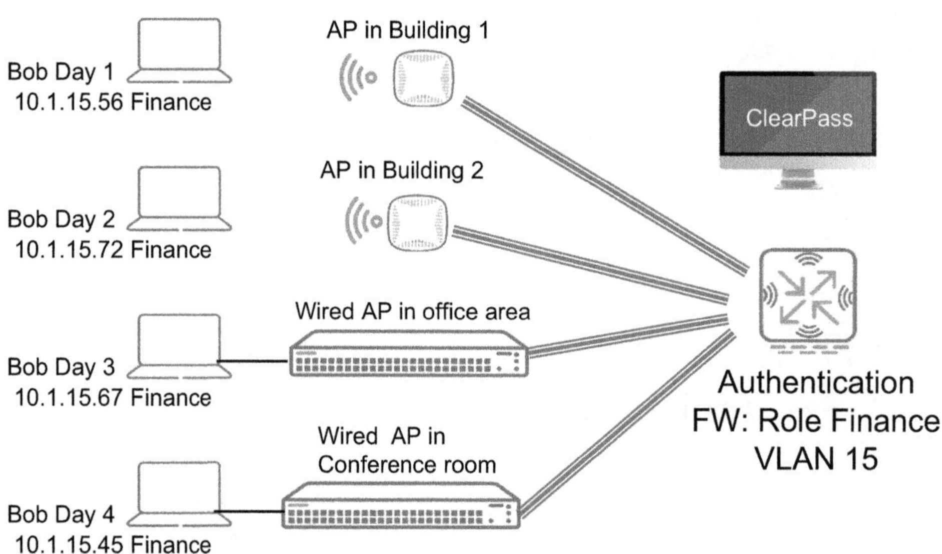

Figure 16-4 Centralized security policy and authentication

Figure 16-4 shows the advantages of a centralized security policy. In this scenario, user Bob moves around over the course of a four-day period. Here's what happens.

1. Bob associates to an AP in Building 1 and authenticates. He is assigned to the Finance role, and placed in VLAN 15.
2. The next day, Bob associates to an AP in Building 2. As before, he is assigned to the Finance role, and placed in VLAN 15.
3. On the third day, Bob returns to his desk and connects to a wired switch. Guess what? Bob is assigned to the Finance role and placed in VLAN 15.
4. On day four, Bob has a meeting and so connects to a wired switch in the conference room. You guessed it! Bob is assigned to the Finance role and placed in VLAN 15.

In this four-day scenario, Bob was assigned a different IP address in the same VLAN, but this is not relevant to your centralized policy. Wherever and however users connect, they retain the same security policies and can be placed in the same VLAN as needed.

Port-based tunneled node

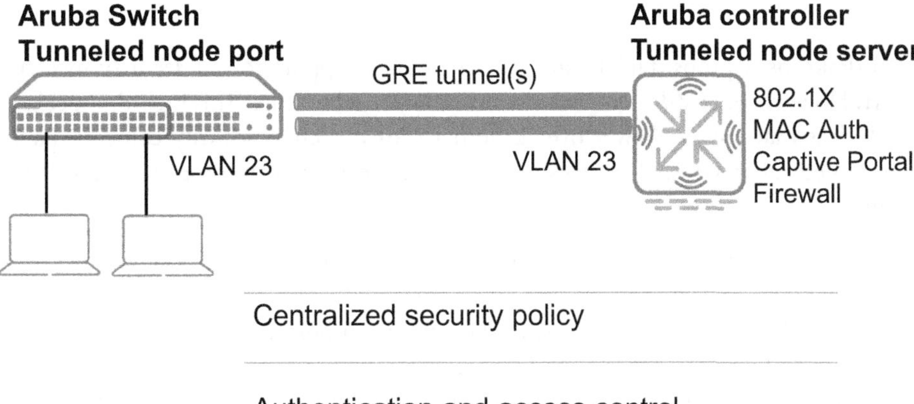

Figure 16-5 Tunneled node

Tunneled node can form GRE tunnels between Aruba switches and controllers (Figure 16-5). The switch is referred to as a tunneled node port, and the controller is called the tunneled node server.

These tunnels allow controllers to provide centralized security policy, authentication, and access control. Every functional tunneled port creates a GRE tunnel to the controller. User traffic is forwarded to the controller for processing. However, the Aruba switch continues to locally forward traffic for nontunneled node ports.

User-based tunnel node

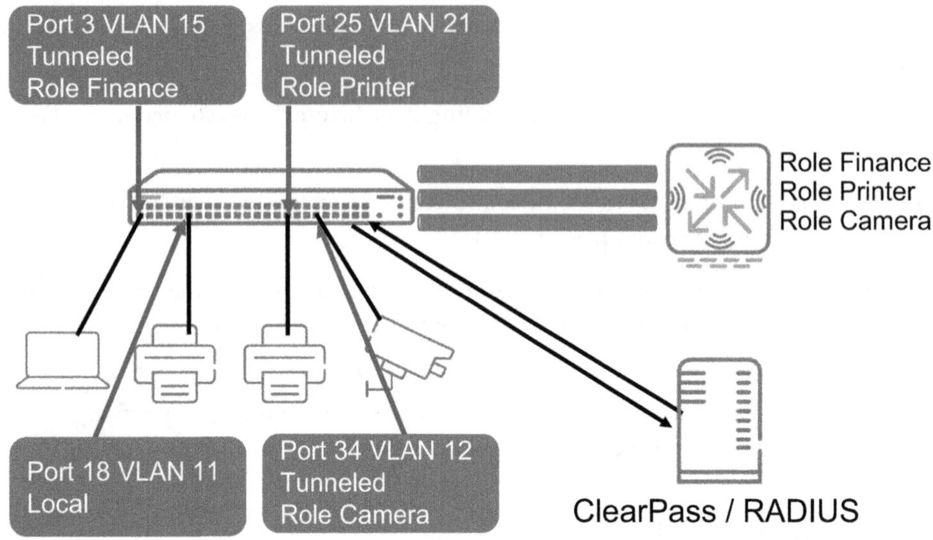

Figure 16-6 User-based tunnel node

All modern desktops, laptops, tablets, and smart phones support robust security mechanisms like 802.1X/EAP. However, many devices lack these security mechanisms. This includes specialty devices, and some devices that rely on Power over Ethernet (PoE), such as security cameras, payment card readers, and medical devices. This lack of endpoint security can pose a serious risk to your infrastructure.

Figure 16-6 shows how per-user tunneled node can authenticate these devices using ClearPass and tunnel the client traffic. The devices connected to ports 3, 25, and 34 are tunneled to the controller with appropriate VLANs and roles assigned. The printer on port 18 is not tunneled. Perhaps it has adequate security and needs to act as a local printer for certain devices. This enables you to centralize firewall and secure policy services at the Aruba mobility controller. You can continue to use these devices without compromising network security.

ClearPass profiles each device, deems appropriate endpoints as "acceptable," and sends accept messages to the controller. The messages include tunnel information, assigned VLAN, and secondary role. ClearPass can also indicate if a device should remain local. These devices are simply forwarded by the switch, as normal, and do not use the tunneled node feature.

Per port versus per user tunneled node

Table 16-1 compares port-based and role-based tunneled node.

Table 16-1 Per port vs per user tunneled node

Port-Based Tunnel	Role-Based Tunnel
Tunneled interface traffic forwarded to controller.	Switch decides based on user role: redirect to MC or local traffic.
Controller does user authentication. Controller decides user role for wired users.	Switch does user authentication. Switch sends user role information to controller.
Wired users map to wired authentication. AAA profile configured on controller.	Wired users map to default-tunneled-user AAA profile.
Supported in standalone MC, NO cluster support.	Supported in standalone MC and MC cluster.
No VMC support.	No VMC support.
Model—2920, 3800, 3810, 5400R, 2930M, 2930F.	Model—2930F, 2930M, 5400R, 3810.
Version—xx_16_02_xx.	Version—xx_16_04_xx.

If you configure port-based tunnel on a port, all of its traffic is always tunneled to the MC. Configuring ports for role-based tunneling increases feature flexibility. The tunnel forms based on a connected user's role. Table 16-1 also highlights differences in how users are authenticated, and how the feature is supported. Notice that only role-based tunnels support cluster connectivity.

The role-based variant is also called Per User Tunneled Node (PUTN). This feature allows you to redirect specific, wired-user traffic from the switches to the controller. This enables the following features:

- Deep Packet Inspection (DPI) and firewall functionality
- Application visibility
- Bandwidth control

PUTN is supported as of Aruba OS 8.1 on controllers and on Aruba switch OS version 16-04. It works with most topologies including standalone, cluster, and MD controllers. However, there is currently no VMC support.

You can combine this feature with a cluster for added scalability, performance, reliability, redundancy, and load-balancing.

Presently a switch can either support Per Port Tunneled Node (PPTN) or PUTN, and the switch can only connect to one controller or one cluster.

License requirements

The Aruba switch does not require any licenses, but will consume MM Licenses just like an AP. Every switch or switch stack will consume one MM license as well as one AP, PEF, and RFP license.

With a standalone MC, the switch will consume one AP, PEF, and RFP license.

Learning check

1. The HPE Aruba switch runs OS 16.04. User-based tunneled node is supported in which of the following cases?
   a. MM—MC architecture
   b. Cluster
   c. Standalone MC
   d. VMC

Per port tunnel

Per-port mode

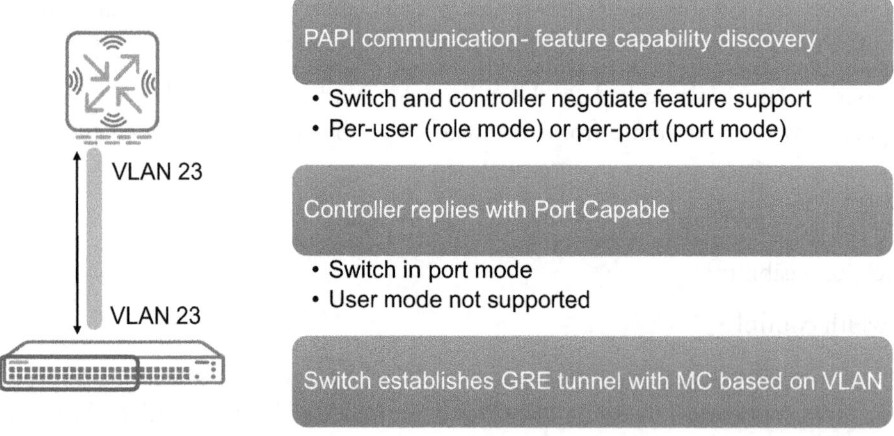

Figure 16-7 Per-port mode

The Aruba switch and controller negotiate feature support (per-user or per-port) using capability discovery (Figure 16-7). To do this, the switch sends a Protocol Application Programming Interface (PAPI) message to the controller. If the controller firmware is AOS 8.1 and above, it responds with a special message. This tells the switch that the controller is capable of per-user and per-port tunneling. The Aruba switch works in per-user or per-port mode, but not both.

In this scenario, the port is configured as an access port on VLAN 23. Therefore, the switch sets up a GRE tunnel to the controller for VLAN 23. You must also setup VLAN 23 on the controller.

Tunneled node authentication

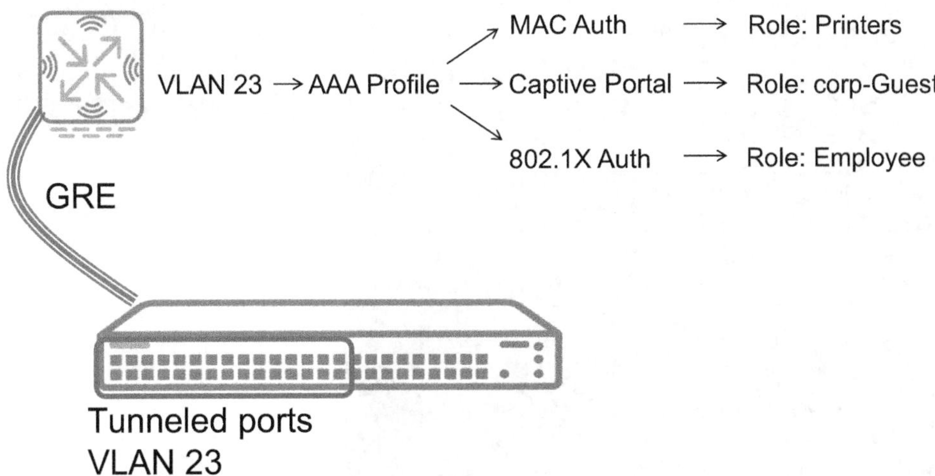

Figure 16-8 Tunneled node authentication

The tunnel is built when the interface state transitions to "up" (Figure 16-8). The tunnel is torn down when the tunneled node interface is disconnected, or if the heartbeat keep-alive message is not heard during the retry period. The default interval is 60 seconds with three retries.

Tunneled node clients can be controller-authenticated, using either 802.1X, Captive Portal, or MAC authentication. Controller authentication configuration for wired tunneled node clients is like that for wireless clients. All tunneled-node traffic is treated as untrusted by the controller.

In the example shown in Figure 16-8, if a wired device is in the MAC database, it falls into the printer role. If not, then authentication fail through allows the next authentication method to take place. If the device initiates a successful 802.1X exchange, the employee role is assigned. If the device did not initiate 802.1X messages, but sent a DHCP request, the corp-guest role is assigned. In this case, the user must authenticate to a captive portal page.

Note

Per-port tunneled node is not supported on port channels—ports configured to use the Link Aggregations Control Protocol (LACP).

Tunneled node switch configuration

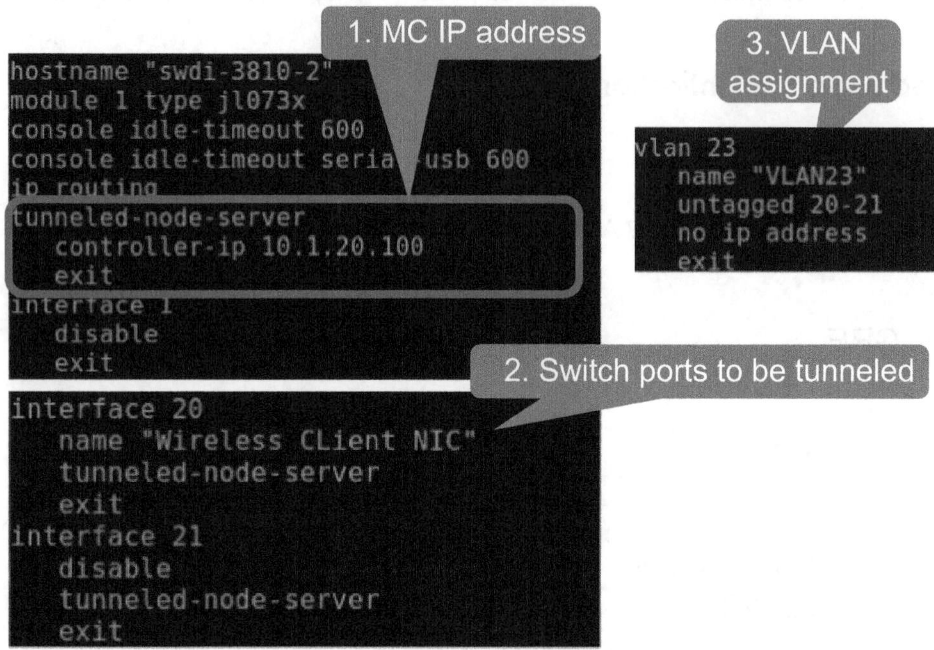

Figure 16-9 Tunneled node switch configuration

Figure 16-9 summarizes tunneled node switch configuration. To start, configure the tunnel node server's IP address. This is the terminating MC's IP address. Then you enable the feature on each desired interface. Finally, assign the ports to the correct VLAN. This should match the controller's VLAN configuration.

At this point, the feature is applied to any device that connects to switch port 20 or 21. This traffic is tunneled to the controller, where authentication and other security services are performed.

Tunneled node MC configuration

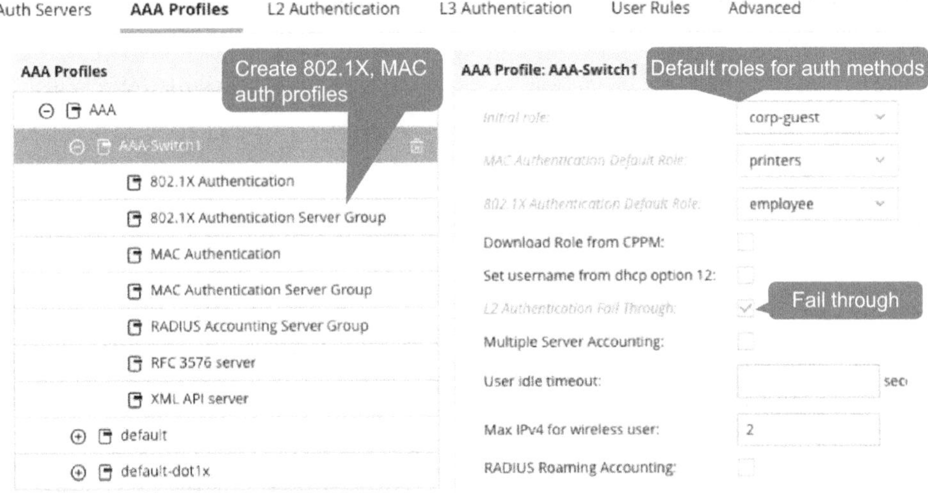

Figure 16-10 Tunneled node MC configuration

Figure 16-10 summarizes how to configure the MC for tunneled node. Start by creating an AAA profile, with the appropriate authentication methods, such as 802.1X or MAC authentication. Then specify the default roles for each authentication method.

If a user device connects on a tunneled node switch port, MAC authentication will occur first. If the MAC address is not in the list, MAC authentication fails. But in this case, you enabled L2 authentication fail through, and the user device supports 802.1X. Therefore, 802.1X authentication is used.

A device that lacks 802.1X support will simply initiate a DHCP request. If this is the case, the device will fall into the corp-guest role. The user gets an IP address, opens a browser, and is redirected to a captive portal page.

 **Note**

For a complete solution, you must configure 802.1X, MAC, and captive portal authentication. Since you have learned how to do that in previous lessons, this will not be covered here.

Monitor users

The following output shows how to monitor users with the command `show user-table`.

```
controller1) #show user-table

IP              MAC                Name              Role      Age(d:h:m)   Auth
 VPN link   AP name    Roaming  Essid/Bssid/Phy            Profile    Forward mode  Type
----------     ------------       ------            ----      ----------   ----

172.16.12.254  00:80:77:a9:7e:4e  00:80:77:a9:7e:4e  Printers  00:00:10     MAC
 tunnel 9   Wired    10.1.20.100/0b:86:6a:57:40  AAA-switch  tunnel
192.168.1.250  00:1a:6b:66:08:60  MarkC              guest     00:00:00     Web
 tunnel 13  Wired    10.1.20.100/0b:86:6a:57:40  AAA-switch  tunnel         Win XP
10.1.11.101    3c:07:54:20:da:60  Bill               employee  00:00:10     802.1x-Wired
 tunnel 11  Wired    10.1.20.100/0b:86:6a:57:40  AAA-switch  tunnel         OS X
10.1.11.103    00:11:25:d7:07:8f  AlfredoB           employee  00:00:16     802.1x-Wired
 tunnel 10  Wired    10.1.20.100/0b:86:6a:57:40 AAA-switch  tunnel          Win 7
```

You can see that all users are connected to the same switch, at 10.1.20.100. However, each user has been authenticated differently.

- User 172.16.12.254 was MAC authenticated. This device is a printer and assigned the Printer's role.
- User 192.168.1.250 authenticated via Captive Portal. This device is a Windows XP laptop, assigned the guest role.
- User 10.1.11.101 authenticated with 802.1X. This is a MAC OSX laptop, assigned the employee role.
- User 10.1.11.103 authenticated with 802.1X. This is a Windows 7 device, assigned the employee role.

Also, notice that each authentication method has placed the devices in different subnets.

Per-user tunnel

Per-user mode

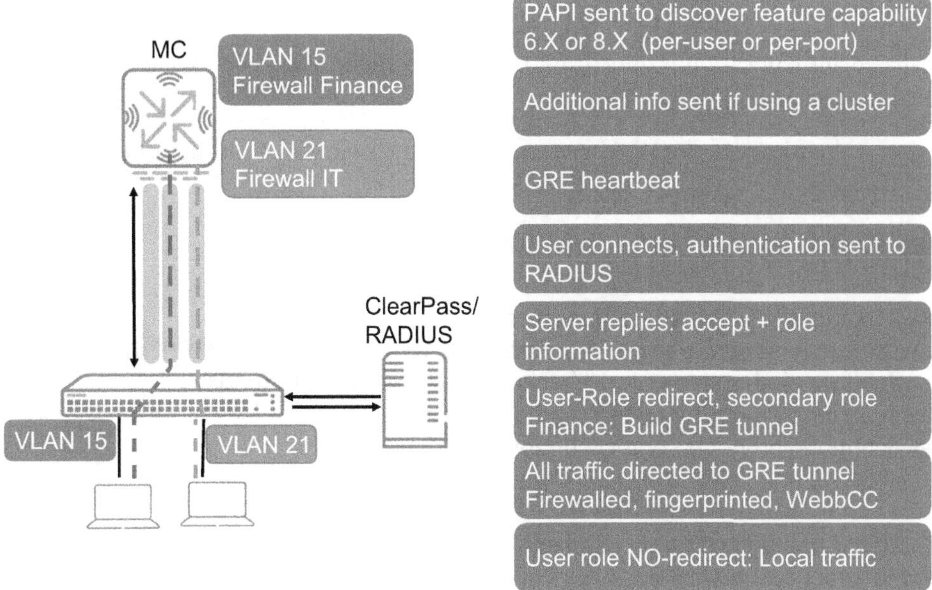

Figure 16-11 Per-user mode

The Aruba switch and controller negotiate feature support (per-user or per-port) using capability discovery (Figure 16-11). To do this, the switch sends a PAPI message to the controller. If the controller firmware is AOS 8.1 and above, it responds with a special message. This tells the switch that the controller is capable of per-user and per-port tunneling. The Aruba switch works in per-user or per-port mode, but not both. This process is detailed below.

1. Switch and controller negotiate feature support.
2. Additional information is sent if in cluster mode.
3. The switch establishes heartbeat with the controller. **Warning!** The switch reboots when role-based tunneled node is configured.
4. The client connects to the secured switch port.
5. The switch and RADIUS server authenticate the client via 802.1X or MAC authentication.
6. RADIUS replies with access-accept, authorizes the client, and sends role information.
7. If the user-role is mapped with a redirect attribute and secondary role, the switch establishes the user GRE tunnel. A message is sent to the MC. This contains the user MAC, GRE key (port index), user-role, VLAN, and tagged/untagged information.

8. A user entry is created with the secondary role on the controller.
9. All configured policies are applied to the user. This includes DPI, firewall, and WebCC.

A new process that has been introduced on the controller for PUTN is "tnld_node_mgr." The main differences between port and user-based tunneled node are as follows:

- User-based authentication is done from the Aruba switch, while port-based authentication happens at the controller.
- For user authentication, the VLAN exists on both the switch and on the controller.

Per-user switch tunnel configuration

```
switch(config)# tunneled-node-server
switch(tunneled-node-server)# controller-ip 10.1.20.100
switch(tunneled-node-server)# backup-controller-ip 10.1.20.101
switch(tunneled-node-server)# mode role-based
switch(tunneled-node-server)# enable

(config)# aaa authorization user-role name tunnel-employee
switch(user-role)# vlan-id 23
switch(user-role)# tunneled-node-server-redirect secondary-role employee
switch(user-role)#exit
```

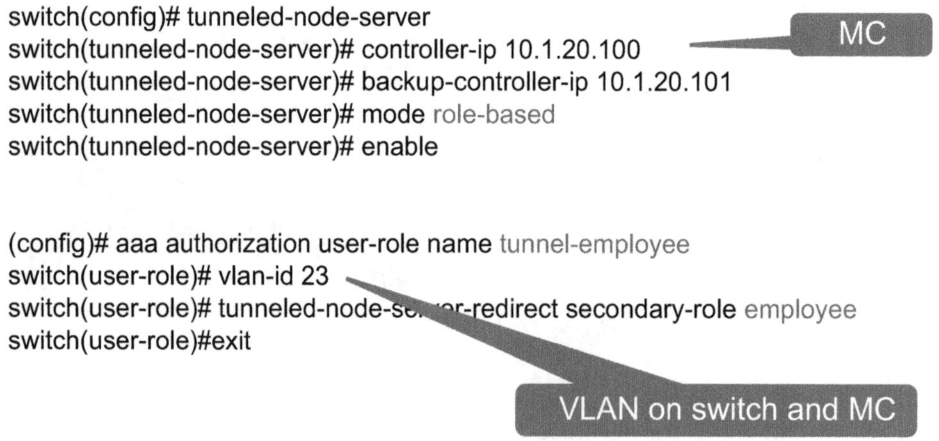

Figure 16-12 Per-user switch tunnel configuration

Figure 16-12 summarizes per-user tunnel node switch configuration. To start, configure the tunnel node server's IP address. This is the terminating MC's IP address, or the cluster VIP. A backup MC can also be configured. Set the mode to role-based.

Configure the AAA authorization user-role name. During authentication, ClearPass returns an HPE-User-Role, with the value of this AAA name. This role places the user in VLAN 23. However, ClearPass could specify a VLAN, and redirect the traffic to the MC, in a GRE tunnel.

On the MC, the user will be placed in the employee firewall role.

802.1X and MAC authentication

```
Radius setup
# radius server 10.254.1.23
# radius-server key "aruba"
# aaa authorization user-role enable
# aaa port-access eap-radius

MAC Auth
# aaa port-access  mac-based <port #>
# aaa port-access  mac-based <port #> addr-limit <1-256>

802.1X Auth
# aaa port-access authenticator  <port #>
# aaa port-access authenticator active
```

Figure 16-13 802.1X and MAC authentication

MAC and 802.1X authentication requires a RADIUS server. Figure 16-13 shows how to configure the switch with the appropriate RADIUS server IP address and shared key.

You also configure the ports that require 802.1X and/or MAC authentication.

By default, a controller supports the PUTN feature, so no further configuration is required. The PUTN VLAN and user role must be configured on the controller.

Configure ClearPass for wired 802.1X

Summary | Service | Authentication | Roles | Enforcement

Name:	Switch-tunnel-Port-Service
Description:	802.1X Wired Access Service
Type:	802.1X Wired
Status:	Enabled
Monitor Mode:	☐ Enable to monitor network access without enforcement
More Options:	☐ Authorization ☐ Posture Compliance ☐ Audit End-hosts ☐ Profile Endpoints ☐ Accounting Proxy

Service Rule

Matches ○ ANY or ◉ ALL of the following conditions:

	Type	Name	Operator	Value
1.	Radius:IETF	NAS-Port-Type	EQUALS	Ethernet (15)
2.	Radius:IETF	Service-Type	BELONGS_TO	Login-User (1), Framed-User (2), Authenticate-Only (8)
3.	Click to add...			

Figure 16-14 Configure ClearPass for wired 802.1X

You can configure ClearPass to support wired 802.1X authentication, as shown in Figure 16-14. You can also set up a MAC authentication service, which is not shown here. Detailed ClearPass configuration is beyond the scope of this book.

ClearPass enforcement profile

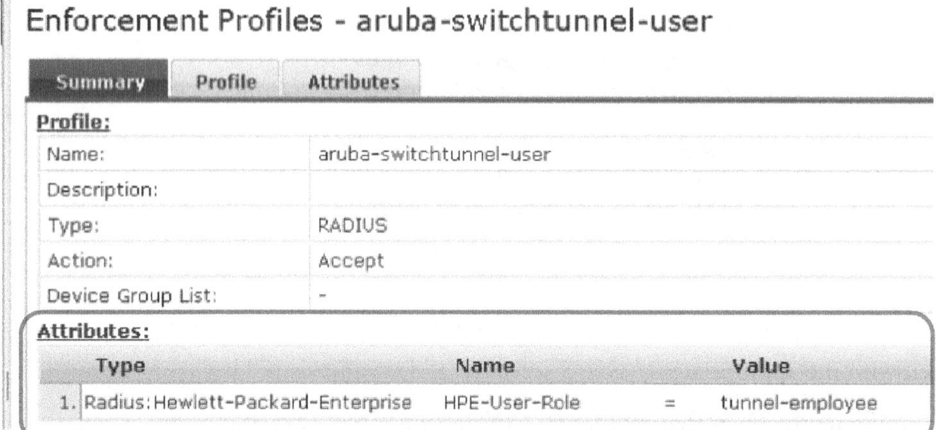

Figure 16-15 ClearPass enforcement profile

Figure 16-15 shows a ClearPass enforcement profile. In this example, if authentication is successful and the user is accepted, the attribute **HPE-User-Role** returns the value **tunnel-employee**.

This value matches an AAA authorization user role name on the switch. The AAA service redirects the user over a GRE tunnel to the MC. It also specifies a secondary role that the controller will use. This is a firewall role on the MC.

Learning check

2. When connecting to a switch in user-based mode, how are devices authenticated?

   a. A GRE tunnel is built to the controller, then the controller sends all authentication frames to ClearPass.

   b. Before the GRE tunnel is built to the controller, the controller sends all authentication frames to ClearPass.

   c. Before the GRE tunnel is built to the controller, the switch sends all authentication frames to ClearPass.

   d. A GRE tunnel is built to the controller, then the switch sends all authentication frames to ClearPass.

Monitoring and troubleshooting

The following shows use of the **show tunneled-node-server state** Aruba switch command:

```
swdi-3810-02# show tunneled-node-server state

Local Master Server (LMS) State

LMS Type      IP Address      State        Capability Role

Primary   :   10.1.20.100     Complete     Per User   Operational Primary

Switch Anchor Controller (SAC) State

               IP Address       Mac Address              State

SAC          : 10.1.20.100      000b86-b6b007            Registered

Standby-SAC : 10.1.20.101       000b86-b6b177            Registered

User Anchor Controller (UAC) : 10.1.20.100

User                Port       VLAN       State        Bucket ID

643150-a153c3       22         21         Registered   49

User Anchor Controller (UAC) : 10.1.20.101

User                Port       VLAN       State        Bucket ID

005056-9fead9       20         21         Registered   172
```

The command `show tunneled-node-server state` displays the MC and backup MC, along with state information for each. The Registered state indicates successful registration with the MC. You can also see that the tunnels are terminating on a cluster. The users were distributed among the two MCs in the cluster.

Monitoring and troubleshooting (cont.)

The command `show port-access clients` reveals switch ports that are tunneling to the MC. You also see each user's assigned role. In this following example, the user role was derived from ClearPass.

```
Aruba-3810M(config)$ show port-access clients

 Port Access Client Status

  Port  Client Name   MAC Address       IP Address      User Role          Type   VLAN
  ----- ------------- ----------------- --------------- -----------        -----  ----
  17    000000001002  000000-001002     n/a             tunneled-printer   MAC     100
  19    test1         005056-9fead9     10.1.23.182     tunneled-employee  8021X   23
  22    test2         643150-a153c3     n/a             denyall            8021X   20
```

The command also shows the authentication method used by the device. Note that user test2 is receiving a deny all. You will need to troubleshoot in ClearPass to solve this problem.

Aruba switch logs

Looking at logs is always a good idea. The following shows an example of the **show log –r** command. Note the –r option is to reverse the order and place the most recent logs at the top. This can be more efficient than paging through large amounts of log activity to find what you need.

```
(config)#    show logs -r

I 05/20/17 13:44:26 00076 ports: port 22 is now on-line
I 05/20/17 13:44:24 00435 ports: port 22 is Blocked by STP
W 05/20/17 13:44:24 05204 dca: Failed to apply user role  to 8021X client
              643150A153C3 on port 22: user role is invalid.
I 05/20/17 13:42:31 00435 ports: port 22 is Blocked by AAA
I 05/20/17 13:42:26 00077 ports: port 22 is now off-line
I 05/20/17 13:42:06 00435 ports: port 22 is Blocked by AAA
```

These logs reveal several problems. First, note that the port is blocked by AAA. To add insult to injury the port is also blocked by STP.

Monitoring and troubleshooting (cont.)

The command `show tunneled-node-users` displays each device tunneled to the MC, along with the assigned secondary role. The secondary role maps to a firewall role in the MC.

```
Aruba-3810M(config)$ show tunneled-node-users all

PORT    MAC-ADDRESS     TUNNEL-STATUS   SECONDARY-USERROLE   FAILURE-REASON
2/17    000000-001002   UP              printer
2/19    005056-9fead9   UP              employee
```

The command `show tunneled-node-server state` reveals device states, along with assigned VLAN. The bucket ID relates back to a cluster of MCs. This maps the user to a specific MC in the cluster.

```
Aruba-3810M(config)$ show tunneled-node-server state
 Local Master Server (LMS) State
 LMS Type    IP Address      State        Capability Role
 Primary   : 10.10.10.145    Complete     Per User   Operational Primary
```

```
User Anchor Controller (UAC) : 10.1.20.100
 User              Port       VLAN       State       Bucket ID
 000000-001002     2/17       100        Registered  18
 005056-9fead9     2/19       23         Registered  13
```

MC tunneled node

Now we have moved from the switch CLI to the MC. The following shows use of the command `show tunneled-node-mgr tunneled-nodes`.

```
(MC1) #show tunneled-node-mgr tunneled-nodes

Tunneled Node Table Entries

---------------------------

Flags: A - Active  Switch Anchor Controller(A-SAC),

       S - Standby Switch Anchor Controller(S-SAC),

       U - Active  User   Anchor Controller(A-UAC),

       X - Standby User   Anchor Controller(S-UAC),

Tunneled Node Mac  IP Address Key    Tunnel Index  SAC IP Addr  S-SAC IP Addr  A-Users S-Users Flags

-----------------  ---------- -----  ------------  -----------  -------------  ------- ------- ----

9C:DC:71:A4:77:00  10.1.20.5  57069  tunnel 17     10.1.20.100     --              0       0      A
```

This command displays the tunneled node configuration details and the state of the tunneled node. You see all tunneled nodes in the database.

You see the switch MAC and IP addresses, the tunnel ID, and the terminating MC IP address. The flag column indicates that this entry is an A-SAC.

MC tunnel

The following shows output from the command `show datapath tunnel`.

```
(MC1) #show datapath tunnel

Datapath Tunnel Table Entries

-----------------------------

Flags:    E - Ether encap,  I - Wi-Fi encap,  R - Wired tunnel,  F - IP fragment OK

          W - WEP,  K - TKIP,  A - AESCCM,  G - AESGCM,  M - no mcast src filtering

          S - Single encrypt,  U - Untagged,  X - Tunneled node,  1(cert-id) - 802.1X Term-PEAP

          2(cert-id) - 802.1X Term-TLS,  T - Trusted,  L - No looping, d - Drop Bcast/Unknown Mcast,

          D - Decrypt tunnel,  a - Reduce ARP packets in the air, e - EAPOL only

          C - Prohibit new calls, P - Permanent, m - Convert multicast

          n - Convert RAs to unicast(VLAN Pooling/L3 Mobility enabled), s - Split tunnel
```

```
        V - enforce user vlan(open clients only), x - Striping IP, z - Datazone
        H - Standby (HA-Lite), u - Cluster UAC tunnel, b - Active AAC tunnel, t - Cluster s-AAC tunnel
        c - IP Compression, g - PAN GlobalProtect Tunnel, w - Tunneled Node Heartbeat
Source        Destination  Prt Type MTU   VLAN  Acls       BSSID              Decaps  Encaps  Heartbeats  Flags
------        -----------  --------------  ---  ---------- -----------------  ------  ------- ---------   -----
17 10.1.20.100 10.1.20.5    47 deed 1500    0    0 0 0 0 0  9C:DC:71:A4:77:00   69       0        65918   TESw
```

You see the various tunnels created. This output reveals a tunnel that uses protocol 47—a GRE tunnel. This originated from the switch to the MC.

MC tunneled user

To see tunneled users on the MC, use the command `show user`. This command displays all wireless and wired users.

The following example shows one user, which was tunneled from switch to MC. The user has IP address 192.168.20.96, in VLAN 30. You also see that this user is "Wired," so you know this is a switch-connected user, as opposed to a wireless user.

```
(MC1) #show user

Users

-----

IP               MAC          Name      Role  Age(d:h:m)  Auth  VPN link  AP name      Roaming
Essid/Bssid/Phy    Profile                  Forward mode  Type  Host Name  User Type

----------                            ------------       ------    ----

192.30.30.96  00:11:50:e7:ac:ac  untaggedvlan30  00:00:00    tunnel 17  Wired
TUNNELED_NODE_ESSID/70:10:6f:86:bc:00/-  default-tunneled-user  tunnel TUNNELED USER
```

Learning check

3. What MC configuration is needed for user-tunneled mode?
   a. Firewall roles
   b. AAA profile
   c. VLANs
   d. Install tunneled node license

17 Introduction to AirWave

LEARNING OBJECTIVES

✓ This chapter is focused on the AirWave Management System (AWMS). You will get an introduction to this platform, with a focus on groups and folders. You will also learn how to add devices to AWMS.

Introduction to AirWave

AirWave features

HPE Aruba AirWave is a centralized visibility and management platform for multivendor access networks. You can proactively monitor the health and performance of all things connected—both wired and wireless.

AirWave provides an intuitive, centralized interface for real-time monitoring, proactive alerts, historical reporting, and efficient troubleshooting. Dedicated dashboard views reveal issues with RF coverage, Unified Communications and Collaboration (UCC), application performance, and network health.

You can deploy AirWave as software running on a Virtual Machine (VM), or as a combined hardware/software appliance.

HPE Aruba AirWave provides the following features:

- Monitor and troubleshoot network devices and end users, both wired and wireless.
- AirWave Rogue Access Point Intrusion Detection System (RAPIDS) works with RFProtect Wireless Intrusion Protection (wIPS) to mitigate issues with rogue APs, rogue clients, and other security events. This is active for both wireless and wired networks, with data and events correlated between the two.
- RAPIDS collect data on the network and classifies devices. It determines whether devices are authorized or rogue. Configurable rules enable you to customize this classification system to your needs.
- You can configure how triggers will generate alerts, based on your specific needs.
- There are 22 types of predefined reports. However, you can also customize reports as desired.

- The network health features offer many graphs for deep, granular visibility into network performance, capacity, deviation, and UCC.
- AppRF provides deep visibility into common applications and web traffic to ensure that mission-critical applications get priority, to prevent employee use of risky sites, and to gauge usage patterns.
- The Clarity add-on module proactively analyzes user quality of experience, with great granularity. You can see time and response failures for device-to-AP connections, RADIUS authentication delays, DHCP assignments, and DNS resolution times.
- AirWave can be used to configure IAPs and switches. This is very useful when you have a large amount of IAP clusters or switches.
- VisualRF location and mapping provides insight into RF coverage patterns and health, along with the underlying wired topology. You get a clear, accurate picture of who is connected, where they are, and what level of performance they experience. This can reduce the time required to isolate issues to a specific client, floor plan, or location.

The AirWave platform

The AirWave Management Platform (AMP) engine provides the following features:

- Monitoring and managing services for wireless and wired devices. This includes Mobility Masters (MMs), Mobility Controllers (MCs), VM-based MCs (VMCs), APs, switches, routers, and third-party devices
- Network health
- Visual RF—heat maps, building walls, client tracking, and AP location
- RAPIDS—detects wired and wireless rogue APs and detects wireless IDS events
- Reports and Alerts

Additional AirWave Servers:

- Aruba Glass monitors and manages multiple AMPs for system-wide reports and searching.
- Failover provides redundancy in a single-server AMP installation

Note

Glass and failover are configured using the same standard AMP installation. However, to use these additional server types, a different license is required.

AirWave architecture

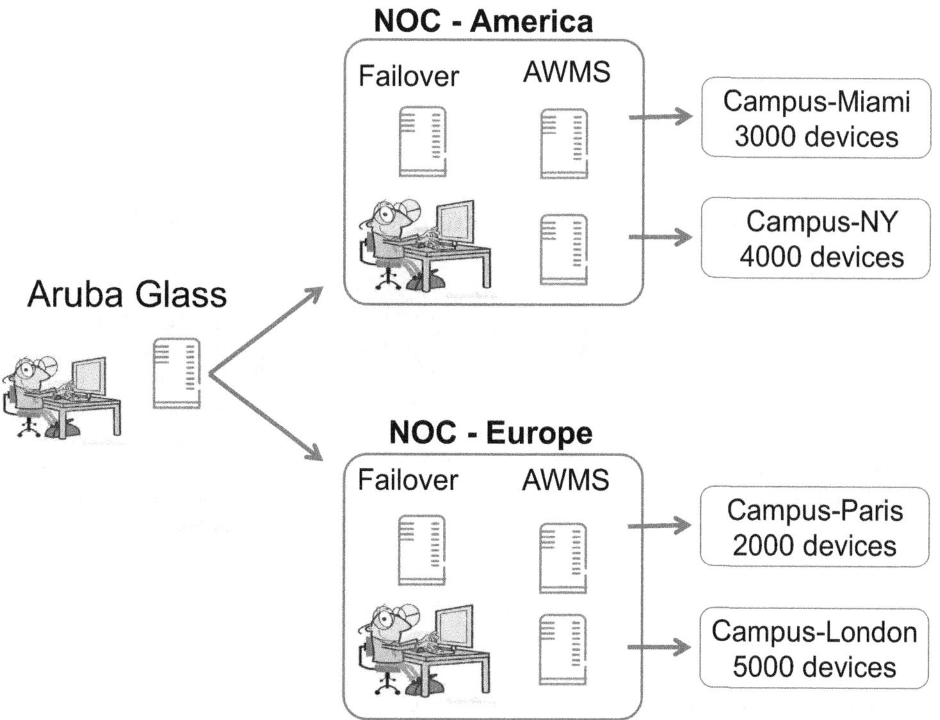

Figure 17-1 AirWave architecture

Figure 17-1 illustrates AWMS architecture. You see a Network Operations Center (NOC) in North America, with an AMP for Miami, an AMP for New York, and a failover AMP for redundancy. The NOC in Europe also has three AMP servers. The information from these multiple AMPs can be aggregated into a single management interface with Aruba Glass.

The AWMS monitors and manages wired/wireless networks to which it has routable access. The AMP can manage up to 5000 devices, depending on the hardware platform. Anything beyond 5000 devices requires another AMP server.

AWMS provides failover capability for high availability environments. AirWave also integrates with other network management platforms, such as HPE IMC, HPE ProCurve manager, Netcool, and OMNIbus.

Monitor and manage device communication

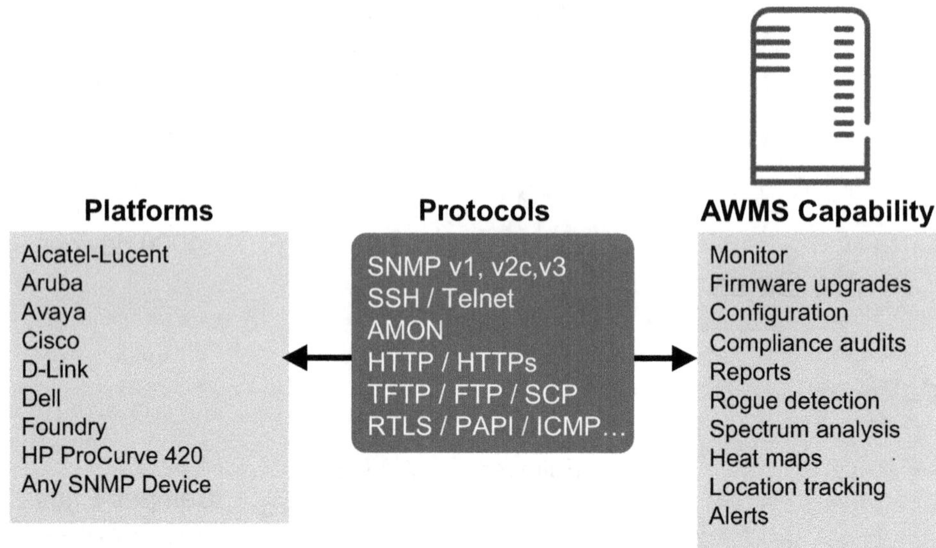

Figure 17-2 Monitor and manage device communication

AWMS can manage most leading brands and models of wireless infrastructure (Figure 17-2). There is also a universal device support that enables basic monitoring of many of the less commonly used devices. This means that AWMS gets basic monitoring information from any device—switches, routers, APs, and more, whether they are supported or not.

You can optionally configure device Simple Network Management Protocol (SNMP) credentials. If you do not, AWMS will provide Internet Control Message Protocol (ICMP) monitoring of universal devices. This allows you to monitor key elements of the wired network infrastructure, including upstream switches, RADIUS servers, and other devices. The following list shows the ports and protocols used by AWMS, depending on which device or device type is being monitored.

- 21 TCP FTP Firmware distribution > APs or controllers
- 22 TCP SSH Configure devices > APs or controllers
- 22 TCP SSH Configure AMP from CLI < laptop or workstation
- 22 TCP VTUN Support connection (optional) > AirWave support home office
- 22 TCP SCP Transfer configuration files or FW < APs or controllers

- 23 TCP Telnet Configure devices > APs or controllers
- 23 TCP VTUN Support connection (Optional) > AirWave support home office
- 25 TCP SMTP Support email (optional) > AirWave support email server
- 49 UDP TACACS AMP Administrative Authentication > Cisco TACACS+
- 53 UDP DNS lookup from AMP > DNS Server
- 69 UDP TFTP Transfer configuration files or FW < APs or controllers
- 80 TCP HTTP Configure devices—Legacy APs
- 80 TCP VTUN Support connection (optional)—AirWave support home office
- 161 UDP SNMP Get and set operations—APs or controllers
- 162 UDP SNMP Traps from devices—APs or controllers
- 162 UDP SNMP Traps from AMP—NMS
- 443 TCP HTTPS Web management—laptop or workstation
- 443 TCP HTTPS WLSE polling—WLSE
- 443 TCP VTUN Support connection (optional) > AirWave support home office
- 1701 TCP HTTPS AP and rogue discovery—WLSE
- 1741 TCP HTTP WLSE polling—WLSE
- 1812 UDP RADIUS authenticates and authorizes AMP administrative users on a RADIUS server.
- 1813 UDP RADIUS accounting
- 2002 TCP HTTPS Retrieve client authentication info—ACS
- 5050 UDP RTLS Real Time Location Feed—Aruba thin APs
- 8211 UDP PAPI Real Time Feed—WLAN switches
- 8211 UDP PAPI AMON
- ICMP Ping Probe—APs or controllers

AirWave monitoring

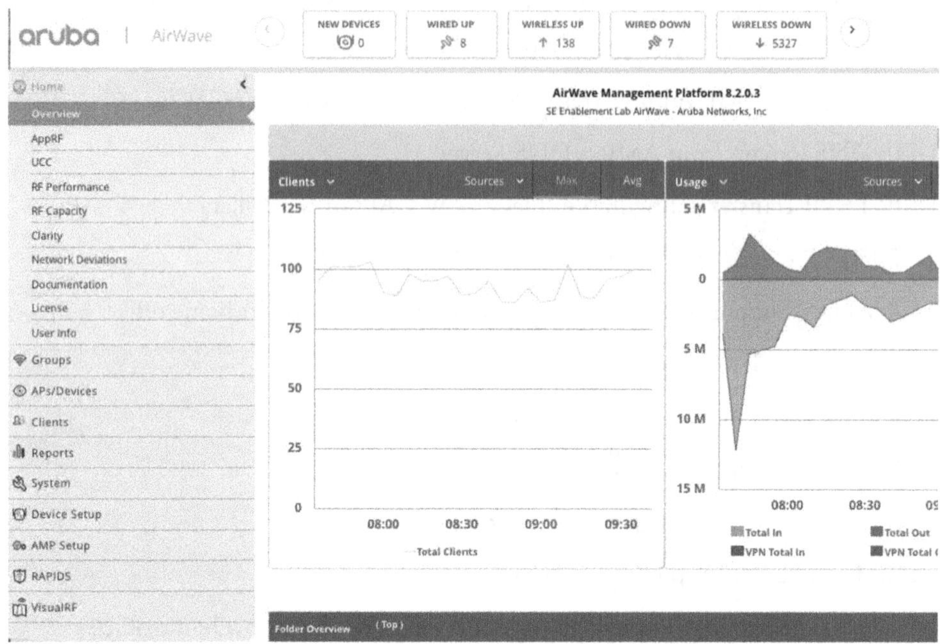

Figure 17-3 AirWave monitoring

The **Home > Overview** and the **Home > License** pages condense a large amount of information about AMPs. You can view the health and usage of your network, select common links and shortcuts, and view system information.

The illustration in Figure 17-3 shows conditions that are not normal. There are higher levels of down or misconfigured devices than would not be tolerated in a production environment.

Main toolbar

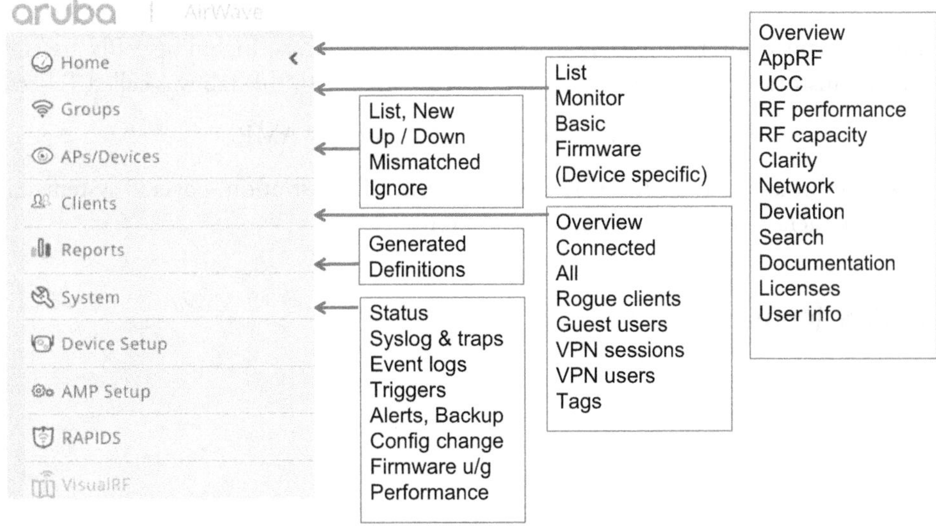

Figure 17-4 Main toolbar

Each selection in the main tool bar has a set of submenus (Figure 17-4). These may vary by the type of devices being monitored and are described below.

- **Home**—Basic AirWave information. This includes system name, host name, IP address, current time, running time, and software version. It also provides a central point for network status information and monitoring tools—graphical displays for network activity—and links frequently used tools.
- **Groups**—Information about logical device groups, used for efficient monitoring and configuration.

 **Note**

Some subtabs do not appear for all groups. They are visible based on the device type field. The **Groups > Basic** subtab is the first page to appear when adding or editing groups.

 **Note**

When individual device configurations are specified, device-level settings override the group-level settings to which a device belongs.

- **APs/Devices**—Detailed information about authorized APs and controllers, including all configuration and current monitoring data. These pages interact with several additional other pages in AirWave.
- **Clients**— Detailed information about client devices and users, including VPN users. You see current and historically associated clients. Prior to version 7.4, this tab was called "Users."
- **Reports**—Lists all standard and custom reports generated by AMP.
- **System**—Information about AirWave operation and administration—overall system status, job scheduler, triggers/alerts, administration, and more.

Main toolbar (cont.)

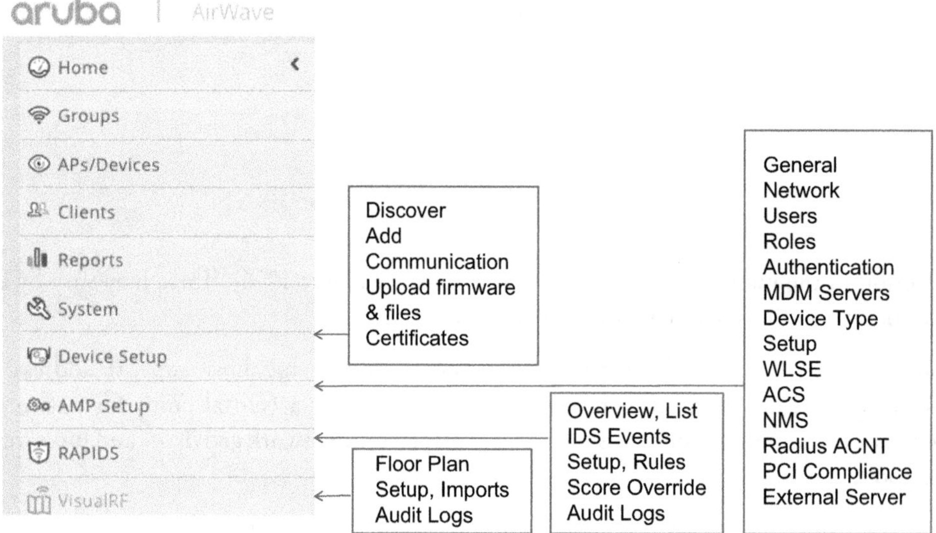

Figure 17-5 Main toolbar (cont.)

Other selections in the main toolbar (Figure 17-5) are described below.

- **Device Setup**—Add, configure, and monitor devices. Set AP discovery parameters, manage firmware, define VLANs, and more.
- **AMP Setup**—Information about the AirWave configuration itself and its network connectivity. This page contains several AMP processes, configurations, and tools.

- **RAPIDS**—Information about rogue APs. This includes methods of discovery and lists of discovered and possible rogues. The RAPIDS page may not be visible, depending on your configured role in AMP.
- **VisualRF**—Graphical access to floor plans, client location, and RF visualization for floors, buildings and campuses.

Folders and groups

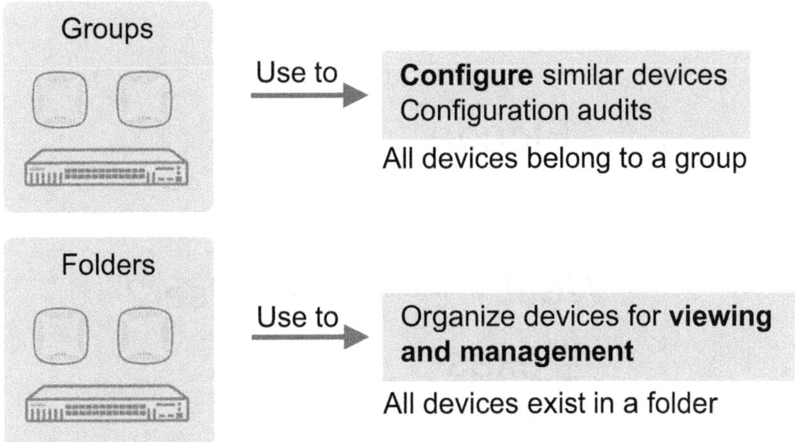

Figure 17-6 Folders and groups

AWMS allows you to efficiently manage settings at a group level. However, you still have the granularity to manage individual devices.

A group is a subset of the devices. A group could consist of a single device, or hundreds of devices (Figure 17-6). You create groups for devices that share common configuration settings. All devices belong to a group.

Folders logically organize devices, irrespective of their configuration groups. This enables you to quickly view basic device statistics. You must use folders if you want to limit what APs and devices AWMS users can see.

Manage devices in folders

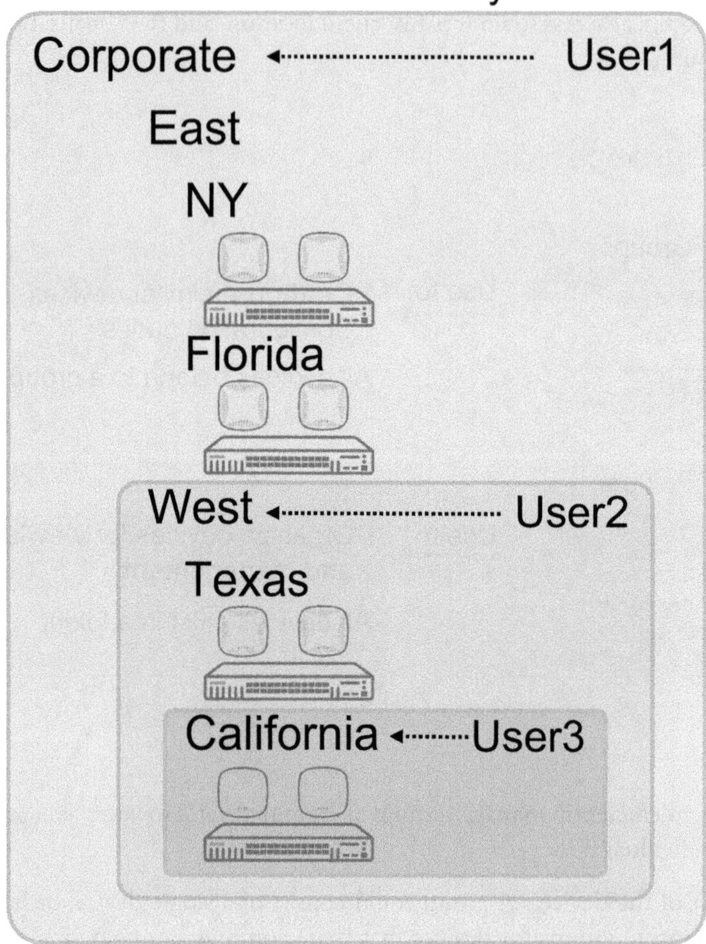

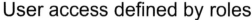

Figure 17-7 Manage devices in folders

You use folders to limit AMP users to specific APs and devices. You create folders in a standard hierarchical tree structure (Figure 17-7). In the figure, folder Corporate has two sub-folders—East and West. Each of these subfolders contains two subfolders. These state-named folders contain actual devices—APs and controllers. Folder views are persistent in AMP.

In this example, User1 has access to folder Corporate, and so can view all hierarchy below that level. User2 can only view devices in the West folder (and its subfolders), and so lacks access to East or Corporate. User3 is limited to the California folder and will only see devices contained therein.

Each user's capability to view and manage devices is based on their assigned role. Suppose User1 selects the East Coast folder. She clicks the "down" link at the top of the page, to view a device that is down in that folder. To every down device, she can click "Expand Folders to show all devices." Thus, she sees all devices that satisfy the page criteria, in this case devices that are down. You also see an additional column that lists the device's containing folder.

Adding a new folder

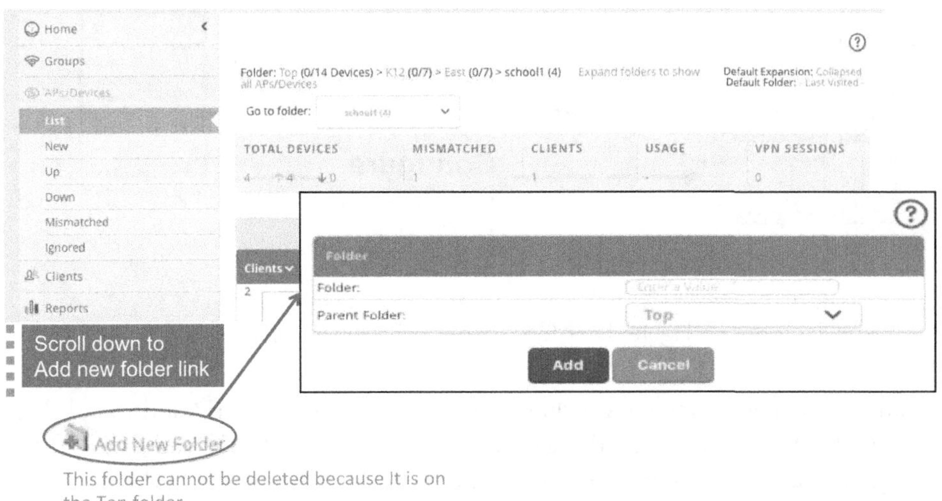

Figure 17-8 Adding a new folder

The "Add New Folder" icon is under the APs/Devices UP, Down, and Mismatched table. The devices on this page include List, Up, Down, and Mismatched fields. These devices are arranged in groups called folders.

Click this icon to return to the **APs/Devices> List** page, to add a new folder (Figure 17-8).

You can add a new folder in any of these locations:

- APs/Devices > List
- APs/Devices > Up
- APs/Devices > Down
- APs/Devices > Mismatched

Only empty folders can be deleted.

Configure devices in groups

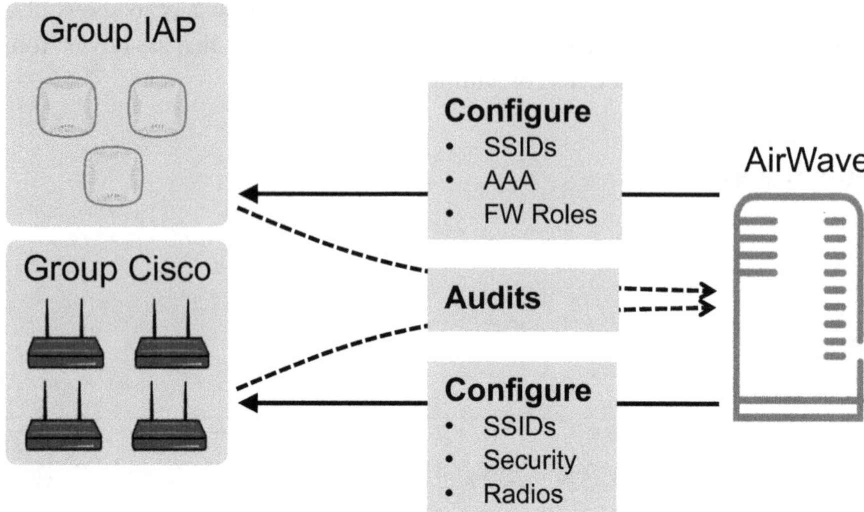

Figure 17-9 Configure devices in groups

Typical group configuration variables include basic settings, such as SSID and the SNMP polling interval (Figure 17-9). It includes security settings such as VLANs, 802.1X, and ACLs. There are also radio settings, such as data rates, fragmentation threshold, RTS threshold, DTIM, and preamble.

The configurations that you apply to a group are automatically assigned to member devices. Such changes must be applied with every device in "managed mode." Manage mode is when AirWave is in full control of the configuration for a device. This is for IAPs but NOT done for controllers, as of AOS 8.0.

Group definition

Enterprise APs, controllers, routers, and switches have hundreds of settings. These settings must be precisely configured or performance and network security may suffer.

Configuring individual devices is time-consuming and error prone. AWMS addresses this challenge by automating device configuration and compliance auditing. This relies on device groups.

Remember, you group devices that share common configuration settings. Other settings are still managed at an individual device level.

You often create groups based on geographical location, usage or security policies, function, or device type.

These ideas are summarized in Table 17.1.

Table 17.1 Group function and definition

Group function	Group-level configuration	All devices in a group share a basic configuration
	Variables	Specific settings at an individual device level
	Devices	IAPs, routers and switches have hundreds of variable settings
	Compliance audits	Verifying compliance
Group definition	Common configuration	Devices that share certain common configuration settings
	Based on	Geography
		Usage or security policies
		Function
		Type of devices

New groups

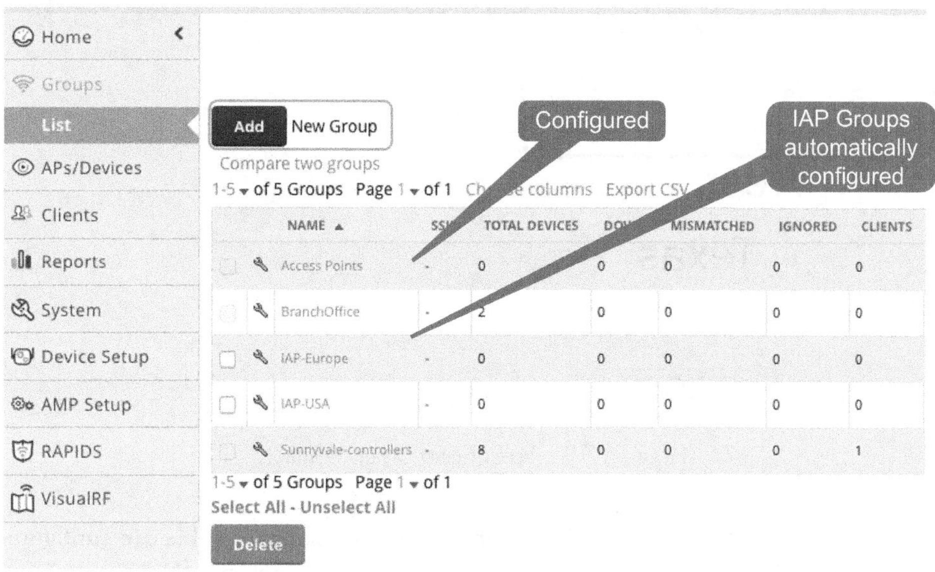

Figure 17-10 New groups

The **Add Group** option launches a page for you to add a new group. Groups are automatically added when IAPs join the AirWave server (Figure 17-10).

You add groups to MMs only for auditing purposes.

Folder and group conflicts

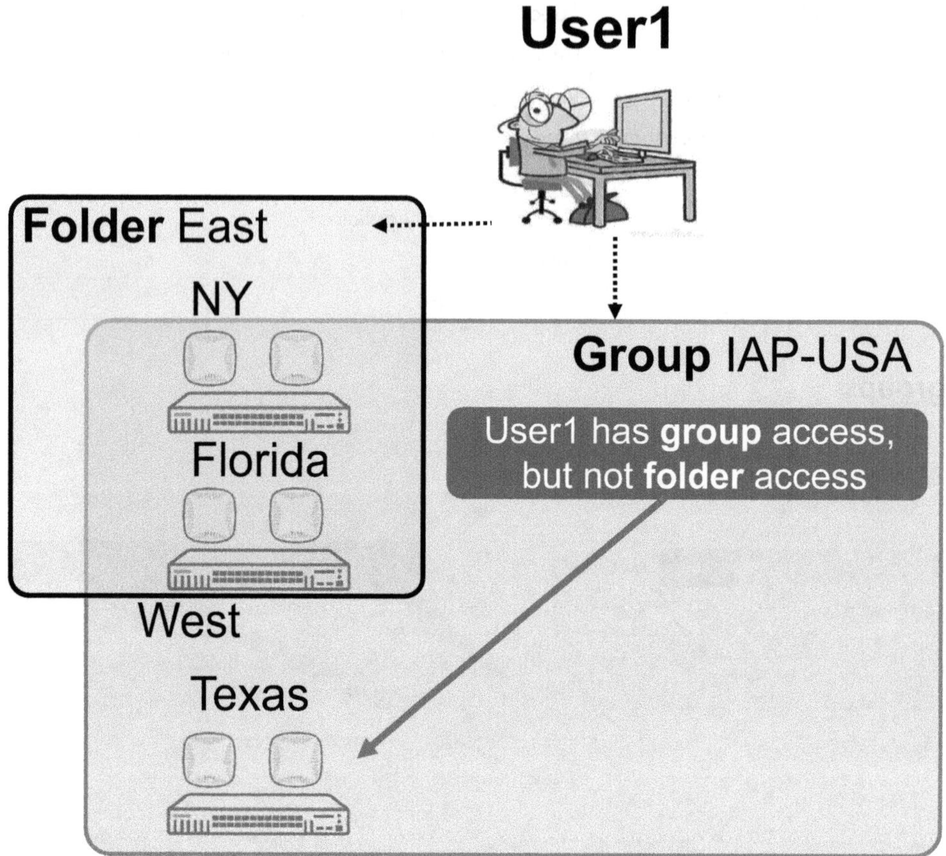

Figure 17-11 Folder and group conflicts

Figure 17-11 shows a conflict with User1's folder and group assignments. He can configure devices in group IAP-USA, which includes all devices shown in the figure. However, User1 only has access to devices in folder East, which does not include Texas.

In such a case, User1 will receive error messages when attempting to push down a configuration to group IAP-USA. You must ensure that this does not occur. Users must have the required authority to perform their job tasks.

Learning check

1. What is the top folder?
   a. Above
   b. Top
   c. Summit
   d. AP group

Device credentials

Default device credentials

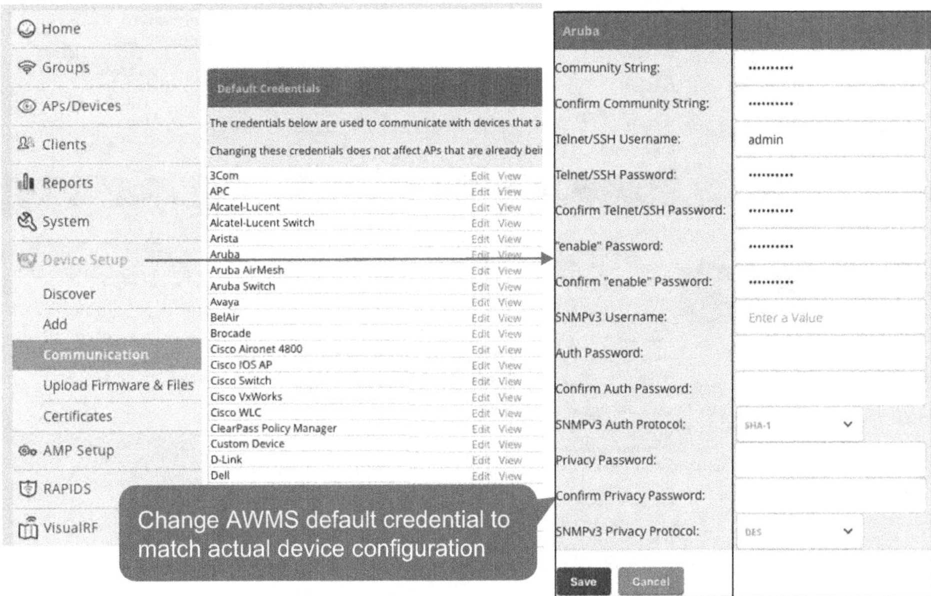

Figure 17-12 Default device credentials

Device credentials are used to discover devices, to perform SNMP get and set commands, and to retrieve or send device changes (Figure 17-12). Key aspects of credentials are described below.

- Device credentials can be set in several places and each has a specific use in AWMS.
- Default credentials are set by vendor device type. They are applied when new devices from a specified vendor are added into AWMS.

- Scan credentials are only used to discover devices. When newly discovered devices are added into AWMS, the default credentials are applied to the device, not the scan credentials.
- SNMP may be sufficient to monitor devices, but may not be enough to do firmware upgrades or send commands. Therefore, user Telnet and/or SSH credentials may also be required.

Default credentials are applied to devices after they are found during a scan. The default credentials are applied to the device when it is added to the system. If the device's actual credentials do not match these defaults, errors occur. You should change the AWMS default credentials prior to scanning for devices, to prevent this error.

Specific device credentials

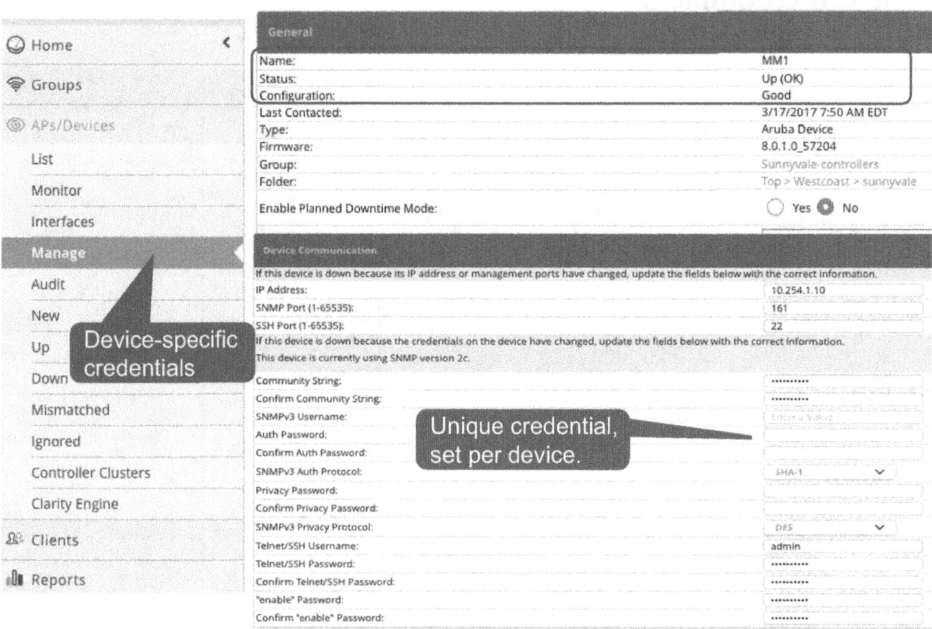

Figure 17-13 Specific device credentials

Once devices are added, any communication errors can be corrected. Simply modify the device-specific credential in the APs/devices manage page (Figure 17-13). Multiple devices can also be selected from the AP/Device list page. You can modify credentials by clicking the "Update" button to update the credentials AMP uses to communicate with these devices.

Adding devices

Methods to add devices to AWMS

You can manually add a device to AWMS by entering its IP address and credentials. This is commonly used for switches, routers, and other network devices. You can also create a Comma Separated Value (CSV) file to facilitate a mass import of devices.

All devices reporting to an MM or an MC are automatically discovered; the subnets are scanned with credentials. The Activate cloud service will direct IAPs to the AirWave server.

When a monitored device knows of other devices, then AirWave will place them as newly discovered devices.

Manually adding a device

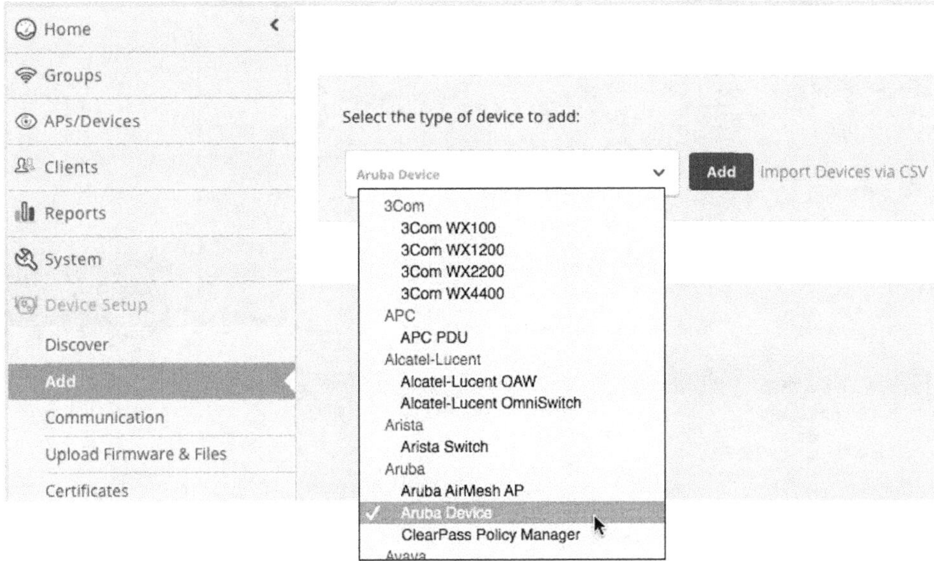

Figure 17-14 Manually adding a device

Manually added devices are automatically added to a group and a folder, and placed in monitor or managed mode, per your configuration.

If the AirWave group has no configuration, you can update the group setting. The member device with the best or most complete configuration should be selected to populate group settings.

Devices can be manually added on the device setup as follows (Figure 17-14):

- Navigate to the **Device Setup > Add** tab
- Select the type of device
- Enter the IP address and credentials
- Specify the group and folder
- Select monitor or managed mode
- Apply changes

Manually adding device credentials

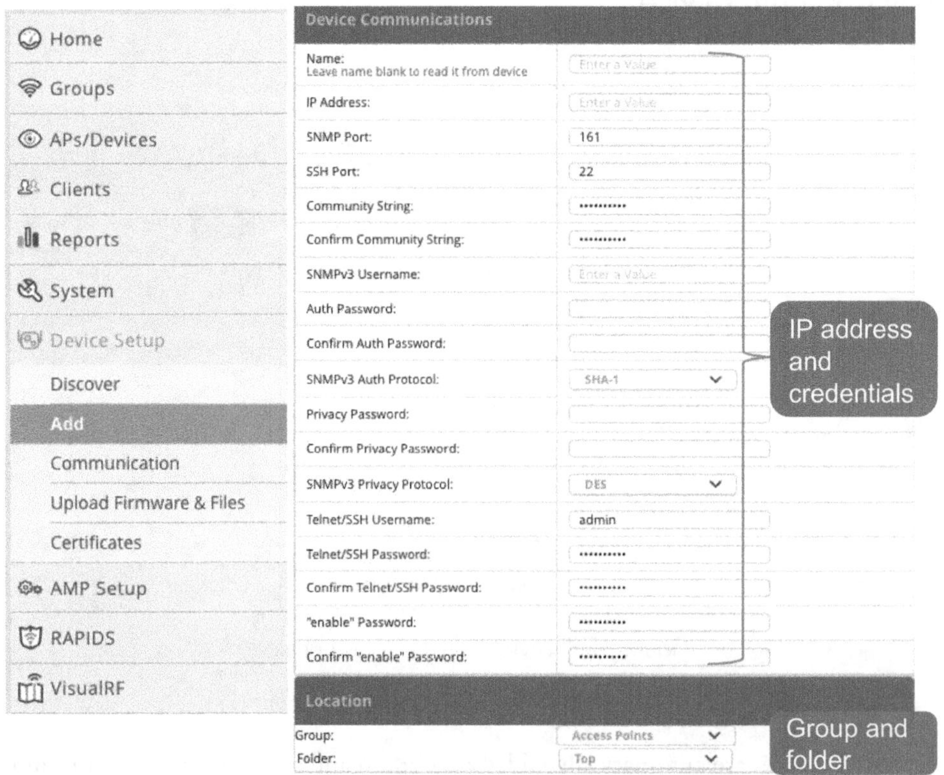

Figure 17-15 Manually adding device credentials

Devices can be manually added on the **Device Setup > Add** tab, as previously described.

You select the device type, enter the IP address and credentials, and specify the group and folder (Figure 17-15).

You can add the device in monitored or managed mode. Always start with monitor, then apply the changes.

Adding in devices is made easier, since automatic discovery will assist you. For example, if you add an MM, all its "child" MCs are automatically discovered.

Importing devices via CSV

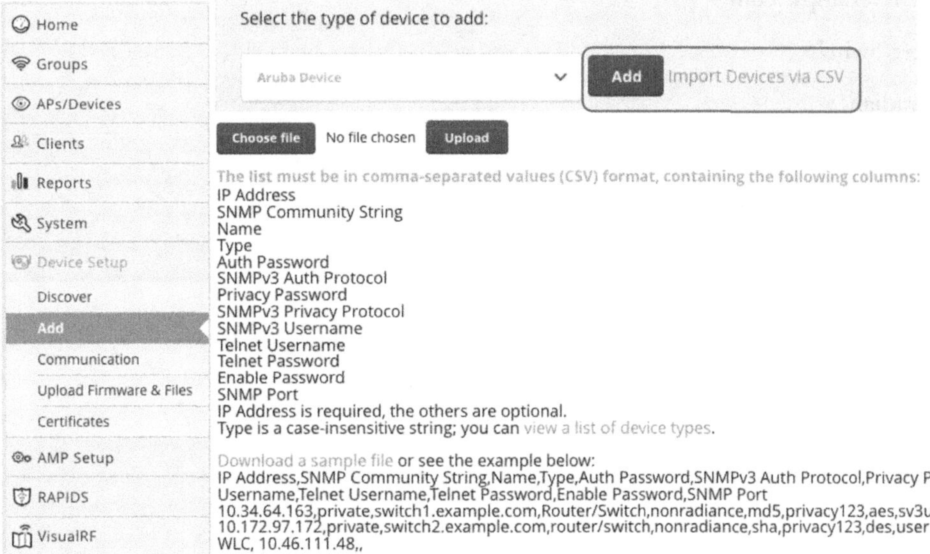

Figure 17-16 Importing devices via CSV

You can create a .csv file to perform a mass import of devices. The file lists each device to be imported. At minimum, an IP Address is required. Other fields are optional. The device "Type" field is not case sensitive. To use the file, navigate to **Device Setup >Add**. Click Import Devices via CSV, click browse to locate the CSV file, and then click upload.

Figure 17-16 shows a sample file, where each field to be imported is in a specific order. Fields are separated by commas. These fields are listed below.

- IP Address
- SNMP Community String
- Name
- Type
- Auth Password
- SNMPv3 Auth Protocol
- Privacy Password

- SNMPv3 Privacy ProtocolSNMPv3 Username
- Telnet Username
- Telnet Password
- Enable Password
- SNMP Port 10.34.64.16, private
- Switch1.example.com
- Router/Switch
- Nonradiance
- Md5
- Privacy123
- Aes
- Sv3user
- Telnetuser
- Telnetpwd
- Enable,161 10.172.97.172
- Private
- Switch2.example.com
- Router/switch, nonradiance
- Sha,privacy123,des,user 10.70.36.172
- Public
- Cisco-WLC-4012-3
- Cisco 4000 WLC, 10.46.111.48.

Learning check

2. When adding a device what information do you need?
    a. IP address of device
    b. SNMP community
    c. MAC address
    d. User id/Password

Dynamic installation

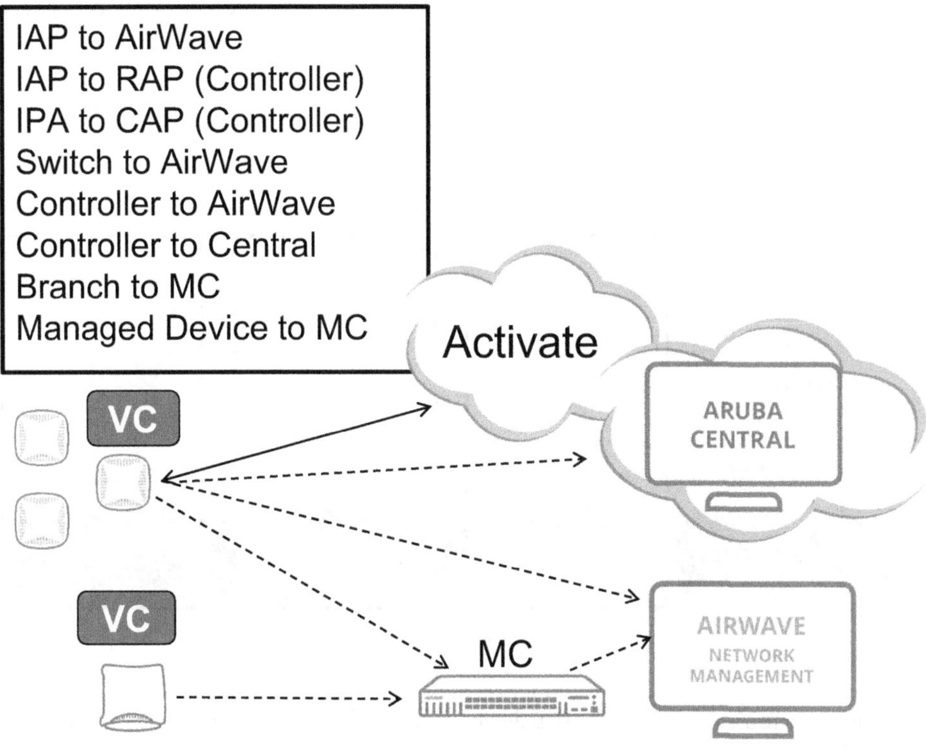

Figure 17-17 Dynamic installation

If an IAP has access to the Internet, it will communicate with the cloud-based Activate server. If Activate has a configuration for this IAP, the IAP receives this configuration. As shown in Figure 17-17, there are a few ways that an IAP can communicate with the Activate server:

- **IAP to AirWave**—Communication starts between the IAP Virtual Controller (VC) and an AirWave server.
- **IAP to RAP**—Mostly used by RAPs (Rap3, RAP 109, and Rap 155) to convert themselves from IAPs to RAPs. The Activate process sends the controller's IP and AP group to the RAP. A home user need only connect the RAP to their network (with Internet access). The RAP is automatically configured with proper SSIDs, authentications, and encryption.
- **IAP to CAP**—Allows you to reconfigure your IAP as a campus AP and direct it to the controller's IP address, and to join the appropriate AP group.
- **IAP to Central**—Starts communication between the IAP VC and Aruba Central, which is a cloud-based management system for smaller deployments.

Why might you use Aruba Central instead of AirWave? There are many variables involved in choosing a management system. If pricing is your main concern, then a good dividing line is around 500 monitored devices. Anything over 500 monitored devices will require AirWave. For less than that, it may be reasonable to use Central.

Automatic discovery

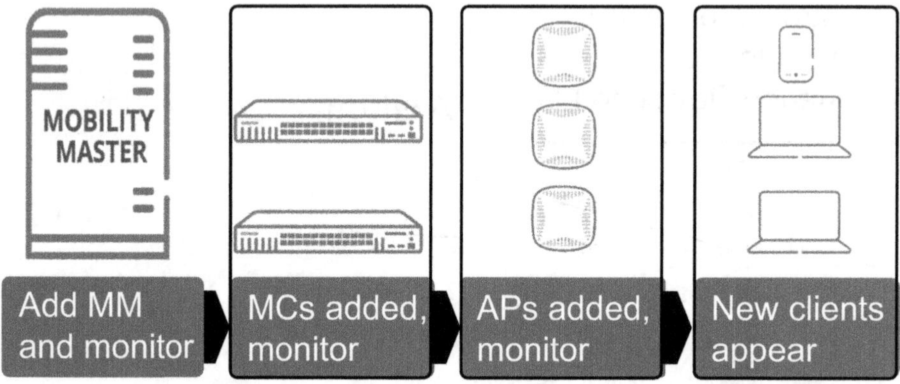

Figure 17-18 Automatic discovery

Adding a device to monitor will cause that device to list other known devices and display them as NEW devices. You can choose to monitor these new devices or ignore them.

As shown in Figure 17-18, suppose you add an MM and start monitoring it. Its MCs are automatically discovered and added as new devices. You decide to start monitoring the MCs, and its APs appear as new devices. Once APs are added, you begin to monitor them, and the AP clients appear. Note you do not need to add clients, since they are not network devices.

This is also true of switches and routers. Once you monitor a switch or a router, AirWave will know of any other switch or router that your own device can see. This is due to LLDP discovery between those devices. In the case of IAPs, once you add in the VC, all the IAPs in the cluster are automatically added in.

Adding new devices

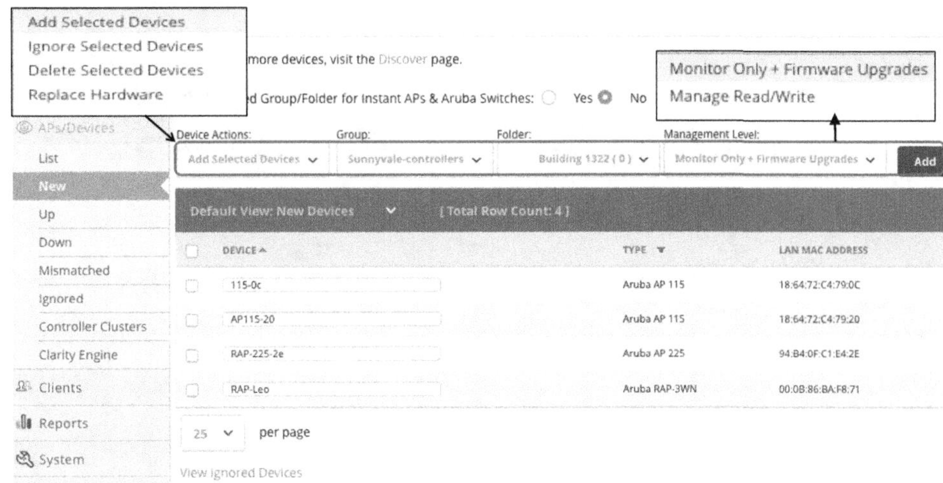

Figure 17-19 Adding new devices

All discovered devices are not automatically added into AirWave. After they have been discovered, you decide whether you want to monitor them. If you do decide to monitor the device, then it will cost you one license. You decide how much control AirWave should have over the device.

As shown in Figure 17-19, you select the check box next to the device name and then choose Add Selected devices. Then choose a group and folder. Finally, select a management level.

If you choose “Manage Read/Write,” then AirWave both monitors and configures the device.

Warning! Manage Read/Write configures the device based on the group settings. This could overwrite an existing device configuration!

Another option is to choose Monitor Only mode so that AirWave will make no configuration changes to the device. It only performs monitoring functions.

When the device is added to AWMS on this page, it takes on the default credential for the vendor type. Essentially, the default credentials are copied into the device specific settings. It is best practice to define the default credentials prior to adding the device to AWMS.

Moving device folder and/or group

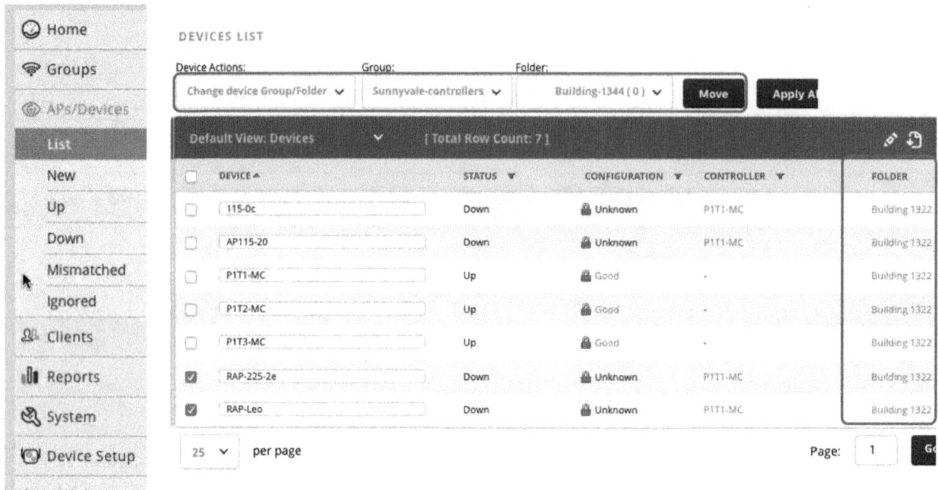

Figure 17-20 Moving device folder and/or group

Over time, you may decide to move a device to a different folder or group. To do this navigate, to **APs/Devices > List**. You can see the containing folder for each device, in the far-right column, as shown in Figure 17-20.

In the list, select the devices for which action should be taken. In Figure 17-20, two RAPs have been selected. Then select the appropriate action, as shown near the top of Figure 17-20. In this example, the action is "Change device Group/Folder."

Then the appropriate group and folder are selected.

Changing a device group or folder

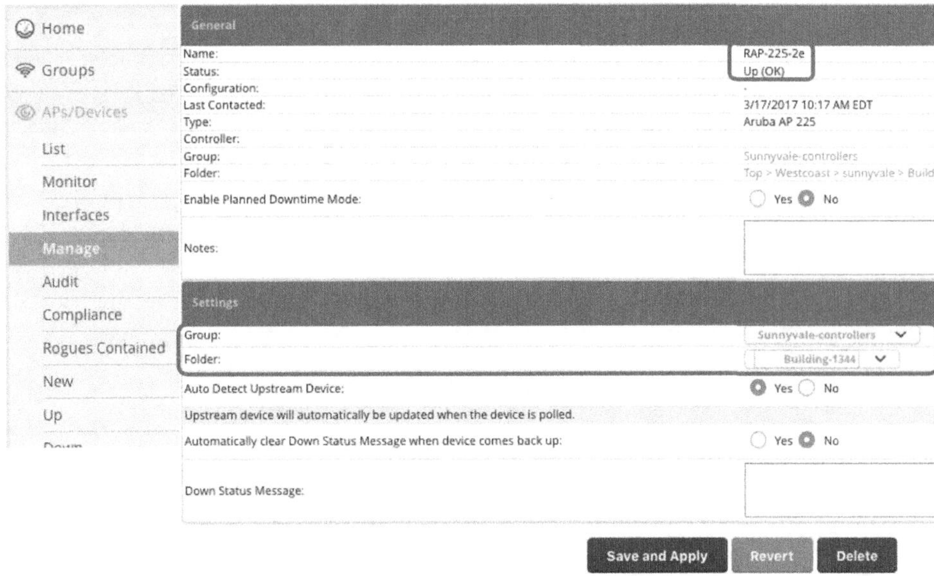

Figure 17-21 Changing a device group or folder

Another method to change device folder or group is shown in Figure 17-21. Navigate to **APs/Devices > Manage**, and select a specific device. You see that the status of the device shown is "Up (OK)."

Move down to the Settings section to modify the group and/or folder. Then click **Save and Apply**.

Learning check

3. What is the best way to add all devices in an Aruba network?
   a. Add MM then wait
   b. Add MM and MC and APs
   c. ZTP
   d. Discovery

18 AirWave Network Health

LEARNING OBJECTIVES

- ✓ In this chapter, you will learn how to use HPE Aruba AirWave to assess network health and resolve network issues. This begins with a discussion of the AirWave diagnostics page, which includes indicators for client, network, AP, controller, and switch.
- ✓ Then you will explore network performance tabs and learn how to identify the source of network issues and how to resolve them. This includes a discussion of best practice guidelines.
- ✓ You will understand how to collect information from AirWave using reports, the client detail tab, alerts section, and monitoring pages. You will learn how to collect information from the controller. To do this, you can send CLI commands and retrieve output, and you can perform spectrum analysis.
- ✓ You will learn how to modify various aspects of your deployment. This includes controller ARM and AirMatch settings, the switching infrastructure, and AP layout.
- ✓ The chapter ends with an exploration of AirWave performance graphs and the Clarity module.

Home tab

Figure 18-1 Home tab

AirWave's Home tab provides the most frequent starting point for monitoring network status and establishing primary AMP functions.

The Overview page condenses a large amount of information about your AMP (Figure 18-1). You can view the health and usage of your network and use shortcuts to view system information.

The client chart is a graphical summary of the number of users on the network during a period of time. The time frame can be adjusted. Select "Show All" to display a list of data series that this graph can display, such as the user count by SSID. The usage adjustable chart displays bandwidth data over time. The status pie chart shows the percentage of all devices that are up and down on the network. The configuration pie chart displays all known device configuration statuses on the network.

Network RF performance—Client overview

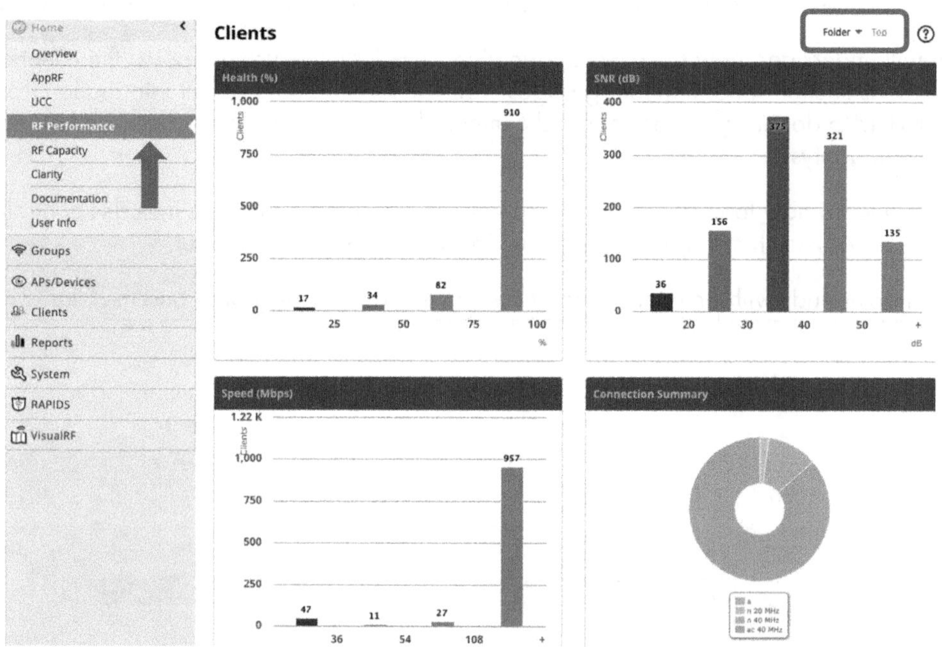

Figure 18-2 Network RF performance—Client overview

Figure 18-2 shows the RF performance dashboard for clients. You can filter by folder to analyze problem clients in different areas of our network.

The SNR graph represents signal strength as compared to noise. Remember that a low SNR may also affect user data rates. It is a good idea to correlate the speed graph with SNR information, to build a more holistic view of RF health. Assess the areas that have an unusually large number of clients with slow data rates and low SNR. Have APs been spaced too far apart in these areas? Have new walls or other obstructions been added to these areas? Perhaps somebody has manually adjusted power settings to overly low values.

The Health graphs compare actual AP-to-client transmission time to the ideal transmission time, expressed as a percentage. This reflects the overall RF health of a client.

The client health metric is a normalization of client quality based on capabilities. So green, orange, and red colors in the chart represent associated client health as good, questionable, and bad, respectively. This is calculated as a ratio between the ideal airtime versus actual airtime available for a given client. It is measured for every packet sent to the client, and the information is updated on the controller every minute.

Speed and goodput graphs are only populated for monitored Aruba devices since this requires Aruba's AMON data collection. To enable this, access the controller CLI and enter the following commands:

```
configure terminal
mgmt-server type amp primary-server <AMP IP> profile default-amp
write mem
```

Thus, the controller can send AMON messages to the AirWave system.

Network RF performance—Client detail

Least Healthy Clients

CLIENT	HEALTH (%) ▲
Ray Emery	8
Martin Gerber	9
Leo Bird	9
Michael Wall	15
Ivan Sukova	16

Lowest SNR Clients

CLIENT	SNR (DB) ▲
George Contimous	6
Bryan Lavender	7
Gordon Bell	8
Marie Laventeur	8
John Smith	9

Lowest Speed Clients

CLIENT	SPEED (MBPS) ▲
Brian Furgeson	6
Lauren Adams	6
Wei Tang	6
Bill Baker	6
John Henry	7

Connection Summary

CLIENTS ▲	2.4 GHZ	5 GHZ
a	-	1
ac 40 MHz	-	904
n 20 MHz	19	2
n 40 MHz	0	121
Total	**19**	**1028**

Figure 18-3 Network RF performance—Client detail

The bottom of the Clients page lists users with the lowest health, speed, and SNR (Figure 18-3). You also get a connection summary with users in the different bands.

Click on a client name to see client diagnostics, as covered in the Chapter 19, "Client Troubleshooting."

RF capacity

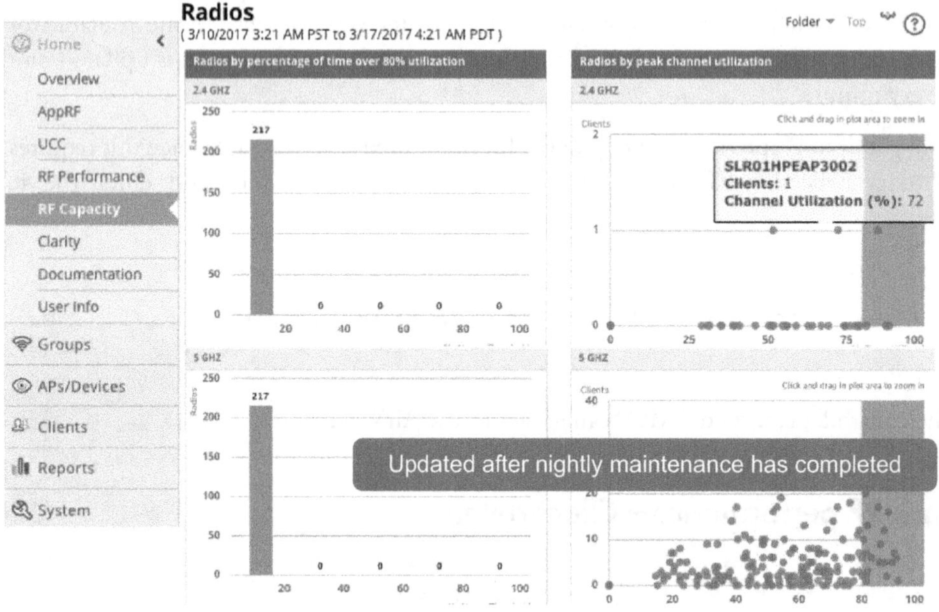

Figure 18-4 RF capacity

The RF capacity page summarizes client and channel information for the previous week's traffic (Figure 18-4). This page is updated after nightly maintenance has completed. The process determines maximum client count and channel utilization for each radio.

This page includes two sets of graphs. The top tables show the total number of clients that have connected over the last week, for both 2.4 GHz and 5 GHz. It also shows the percentage of these that were above the usage threshold.

The client graphs show the number of clients that were connected during low and high channel utilization.

Note

The time when there is no association to an AP is not included in any of these calculations.

RF capacity detail

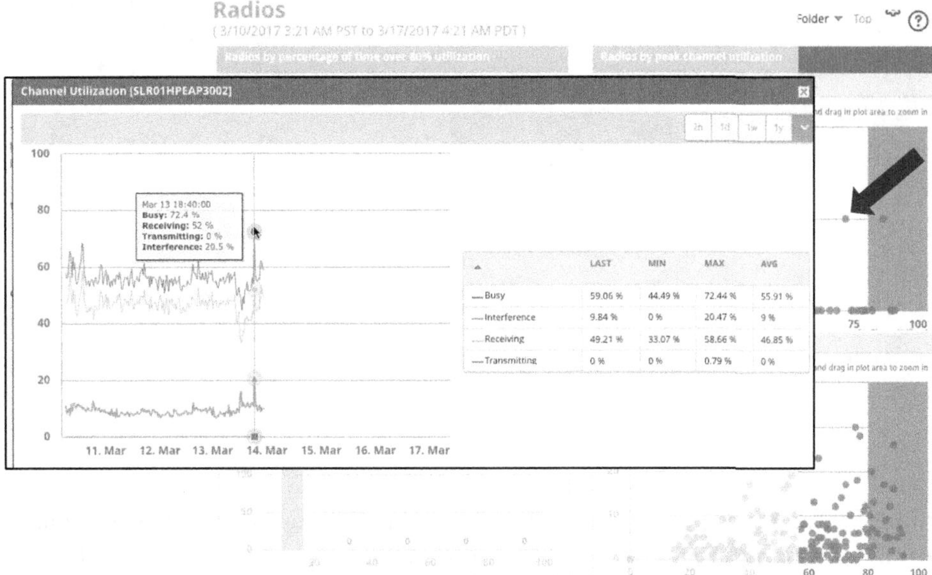

Figure 18-5 RF capacity detail

You can click on a bar in the upper graphs to see a detailed list of the devices that connected in the week before the RF Capacity page was run. This popup includes additional drill downs to the device, the controller, and the folder.

You can select plot points in the lower graph to view detailed channel utilization information for the selected plot point (Figure 18-5).

Network deviation

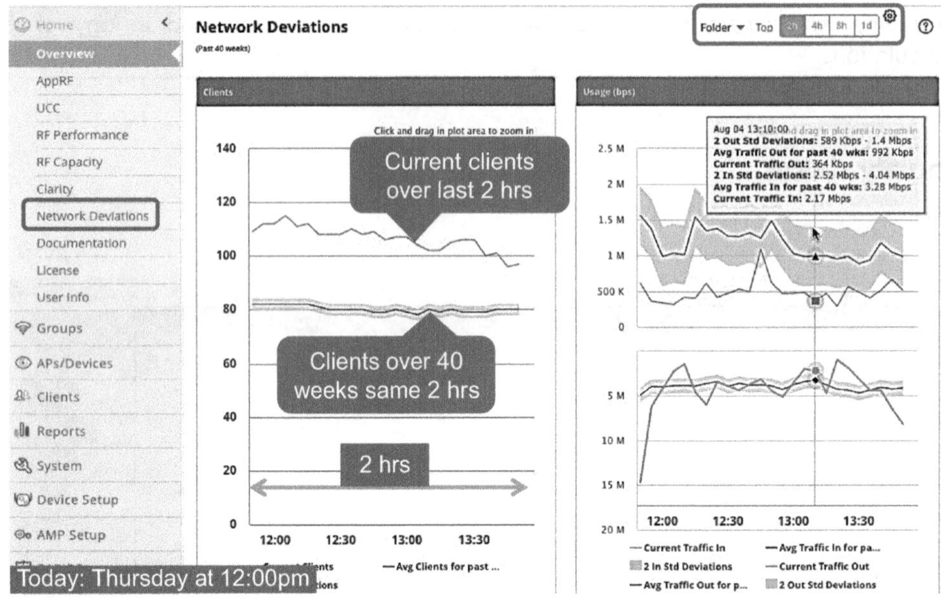

Figure 18-6 Network deviation

The Network Deviations page tracks network client and usage information, drawing your attention to unusual usage patterns (Figure 18-6). For example, these graphs can show you if heavy network traffic is occurring during off hours. They can be used to detect the times of day when your network traffic peaks.

By default, you see the previous two hours of client and usage information in five-minute intervals. This is for the current day of the week, averaged out over the last 40 weeks. The shaded area indicates the standard deviation, which defaults to 1.

Say you launch this page at 9:00 a.m. on Friday. A two-hour graph shows the current and average number of connected clients and usage between 7:00 a.m. and 9:00 a.m., on all Fridays over the last 40 weeks. You see plot points showing the number of clients per five-minute interval.

You can also select and drag a set of plot points to zoom in and view a more precise time range. Click the Reset zoom button to return to the specified time range. You can change the time range of the graphs to four hours, eight hours, or one day—just use the time range options in the upper-right corner of the page. AMP will remember this new setting the next time the page is launched.

The first time this page is launched, the graphs show information for all devices in the "Top" folder. To specify a different folder, simply select one from the folder drop down in the upper-right corner, and then refresh the page.

AppRF

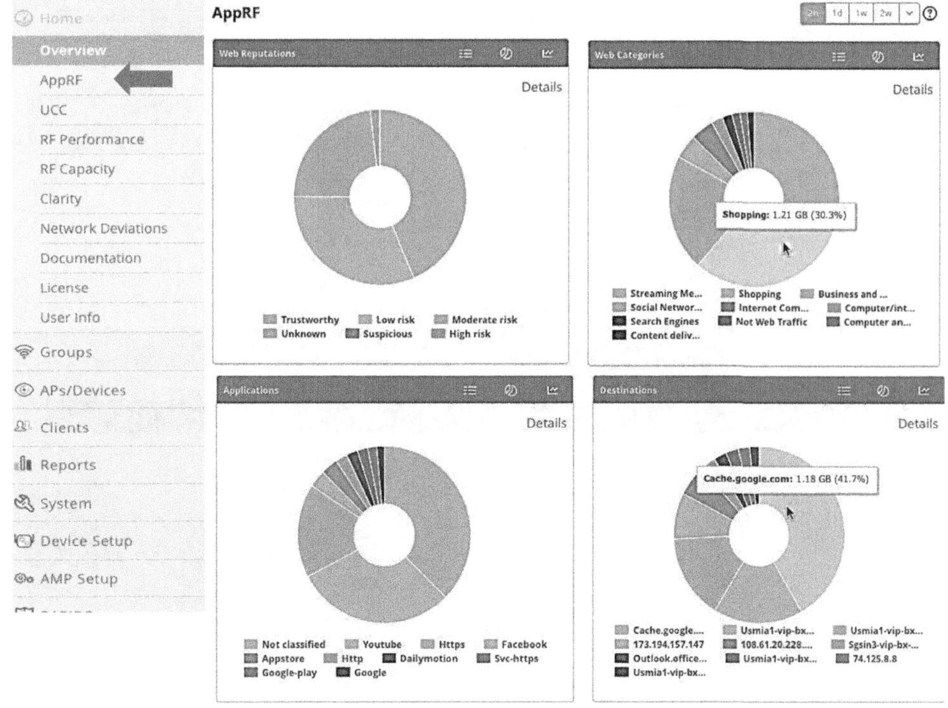

Figure 18-7 AppRF

AppRF pages display mobile app usage and performance (Figure 18-7). This page mimics the AppRF/Firewall dashboard page on the controller. It provides eight charts to easily view trending information. It breaks down the information in pie charts labeled “Web Reputations,” “Web Categories,” “Applications,” “Destinations,” and “Applications for a Selected Folder.” AirWave can provide up to two weeks of network data for multiple controllers.

AppRF (cont.)

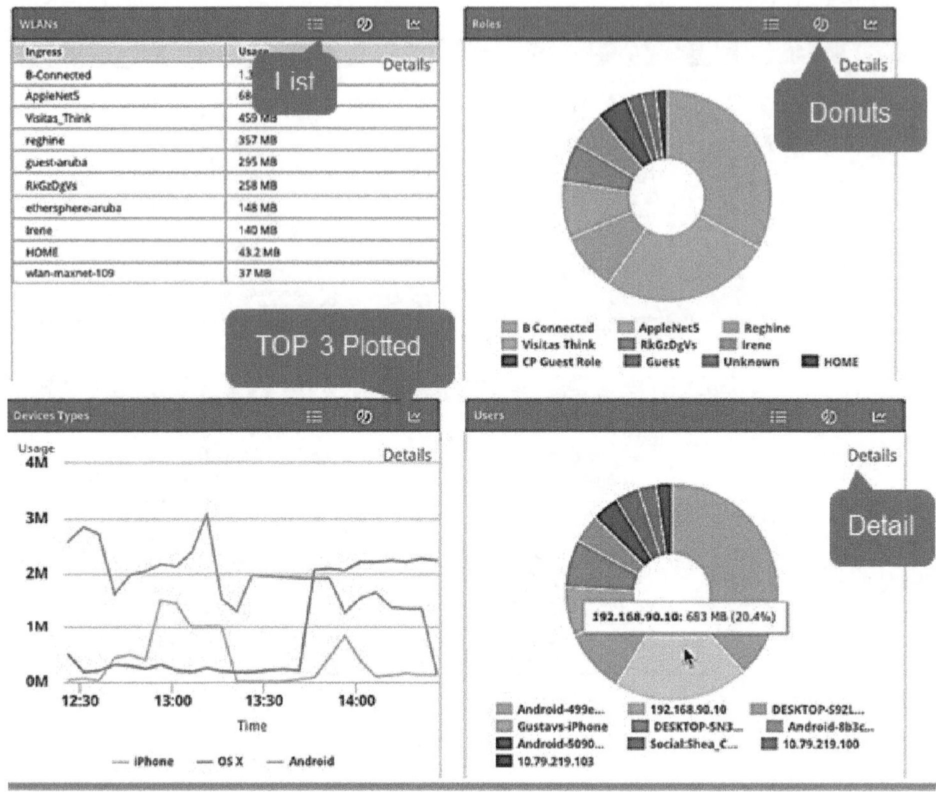

Figure 18-8 AppRF (cont.)

The bottom AppRF graphs show WLAN and Firewall usage, as well as device types and users (Figure 18-8). You can click on the list, click the donuts, or even plot the top three, for various types of graphs. Click on "Details" to see more information, as shown in Figure 18-9 below.

AppRF application detail

AppRF › Application

Detail

Application	Bytes	Packets	Web Rep...	Web Cate...	Destinati...	User Role	Devices	User Na...	Device M...	WLANs
Not classified	1.12 GB	0	6	33	1548	14	11	47	44	14
youtube	911 MB	16 K	3	5	54	7	5	12	12	6
https	874 MB	180 K	6	32	439	17	14	54	52	13
dailymotion	178 MB	0	2	2	7	1	1	1	1	1
facebook	165 MB	27.2 K	3	6	61	10	5	26	25	7
dns	71.8 MB	417 K	1	2	21	18	13	73	56	16

Users on Facebook

AppRF › Application (facebook) › User

Detail

User Name	Bytes	Packets	Web Reput...	Web Categ...	Destination	User Role	Devices	Device Mac	WLANs
Mickey	64.5 MB	0	3	2	15	1	1	1	1
	39.3 MB	0	2	1	10	1	1	1	1
Goofy	15.3 MB	0	3	2	8	1	1	1	1
	7.09 MB	0	2	1	6	1	1	1	1

Figure 18-9 AppRF application detail

You can drill down to view more specific information based on the application, destination, device, WLAN, user, and role. Figure 18-9 shows AppRF applications. Then you can click on, say Facebook, to see all the users using that application.

This data can be used to troubleshoot application performance in real time, to set WLAN policies, and to plan for future network enhancements.

AppRF application detail—Devices

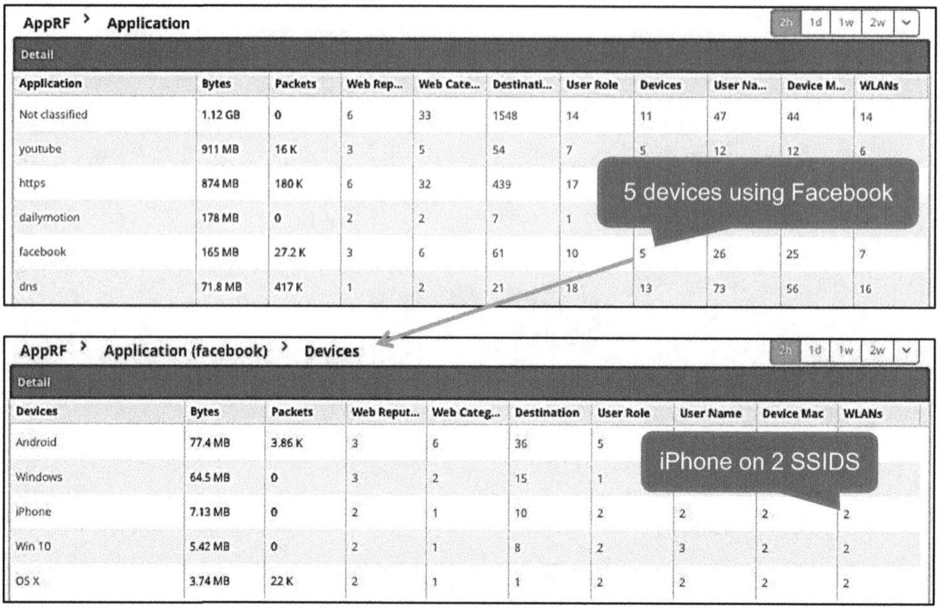

AppRF › Application

2h 1d 1w 2w

Detail

Application	Bytes	Packets	Web Rep...	Web Cate...	Destinati...	User Role	Devices	User Na...	Device M...	WLANs
Not classified	1.12 GB	0	6	33	1548	14	11	47	44	14
youtube	911 MB	16 K	3	5	54	7	5	12	12	6
https	874 MB	180 K	6	32	439	17				
dailymotion	178 MB	0	2	2	7	1				
facebook	165 MB	27.2 K	3	6	61	10	5	26	25	7
dns	71.8 MB	417 K	1	2	21	18	13	73	56	16

5 devices using Facebook

AppRF › Application (facebook) › Devices

2h 1d 1w 2w

Detail

Devices	Bytes	Packets	Web Reput...	Web Categ...	Destination	User Role	User Name	Device Mac	WLANs
Android	77.4 MB	3.86 K	3	6	36	5			
Windows	64.5 MB	0	3	2	15	1			
iPhone	7.13 MB	0	2	1	10	2	2	2	2
Win 10	5.42 MB	0	2	1	8	2	3	2	2
OS X	3.74 MB	22 K	2	1	1	2	2	2	2

iPhone on 2 SSIDS

Figure 18-10 AppRF application detail—Devices

You can look at apps in many ways. Figure 18-10 shows that five types of devices are using Facebook. You can click on any of the numbers to get a list.

In this scenario, you clicked on the number five—the number of devices using Facebook. A new window opens showing you more detail on those five devices.

Learning check

1. Where can an administrator go to see a graphical view of the types of traffic?
   a. Network deviation
   b. AppRF
   c. Clarity Live
   d. Folders and Groups

Client overview

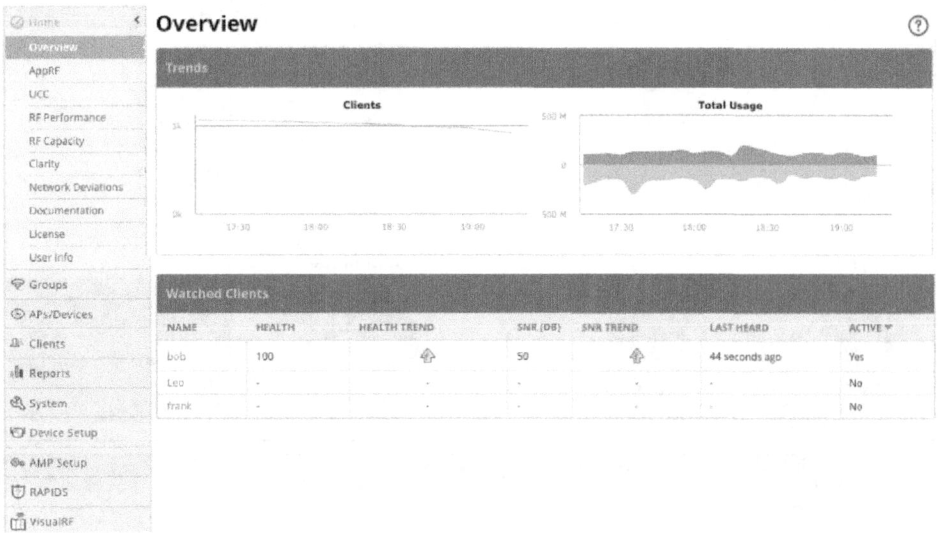

Figure 18-11 Client overview

The **Clients > Overview** page provides a graphical summary of all clients, including client and network usage trends (Figure 18-11).

Below the trends is a list of watched clients. If any clients are configured to be watched, then a watched client's table will also appear on this page. These are clients who were put on a watch list for some issue.

Client overview (cont.)

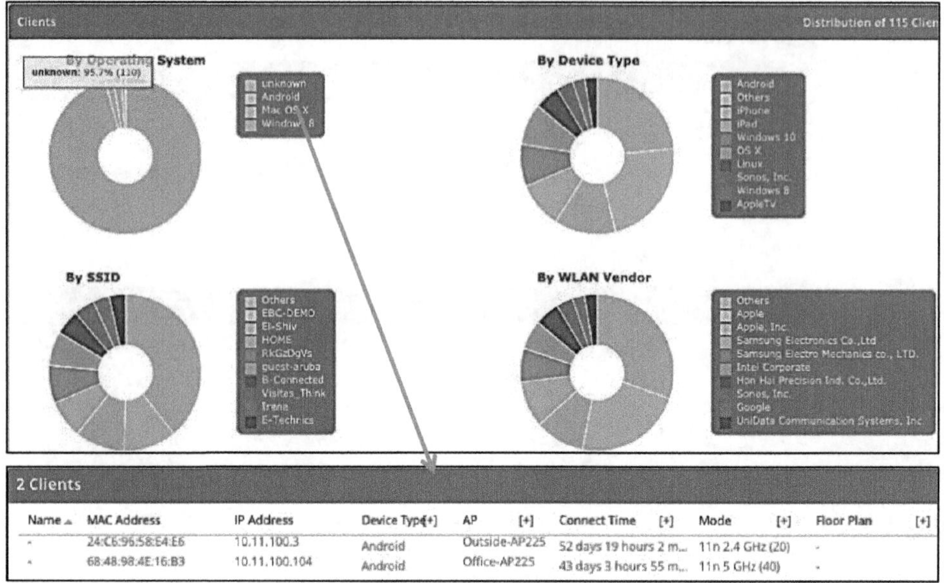

Figure 18-12 Client overview (cont.)

Look a little further down on the client overview page to see pie charts. These have a distribution breakdown by OS, vendor, device type, and SSID (Figure 18-12). You can click on either chart to open a pop-up. From this pop-up, you can change the time range to one day, five days, a month, or a year. You can also click on a specific entry such as Apple and get a pop-up chart showing all Apple products.

UCC—voice

Figure 18-13 UCC—voice

Figure 18-13 shows an aggregated view of the Unified Communication and Collaboration (UCC) calls made in the network. This page mimics the UCC dashboard page on the controller. It displays trending information for UCC call volume, quality, and clients. You can see a top-level view of the call quality assessment, and drill down further into a specific view, based on the analysis required.

Call quality is encapsulated into an Aruba-proprietary metric called the UCC score. The UCC score for voice and video calls is measured by considering delay, jitter, and packet loss.

AirWave obtains these metrics from RTCP messages sent from the client, if it can send them. For audio calls, the metrics come from values calculated by the Aruba AP that inspects RTP flows.

Select a call to see its detail. In addition to call quality and client health, you get details about jitter, delay, and packet loss. This is not shown, but the graph shows call quality and client health mapped over time. A red icon shows the point at which the client roamed during the call.

 **Note**

RTCP stands for RTP Control Protocol. RTP stands for Real-time Transport Protocol.

Clarity

Network issues

The following list summarizes some common network issues that you might encounter. These are issues that can be much easier to solve with AirWave's Clarity module. Without this feature, you may struggle a bit more to resolve issues like those described below.

- **The client cannot connect**—APs reject client connection requests. This could be because the AP is overutilized, has reached its maximum association limit, or some other issue. The time it takes to associate can help to resolve this problem, as it is tracked over time.
- **Helpdesk gets a report of the Wireless that does not work**—This could be a DHCP scope issue. The DHCP server has run out of leases so the client cannot get on the network.
- **RADIUS server load issues**—A report states that one server goes unusably slow, and most requests fall to second server. This masked the problem.
- **NAS issue**—You have four RADIUS servers for load balancing, but all are not being used. This could be because the controller was not added as a NAS on Server-3. You cannot see the problem since clients connected and did not report issues.
- **Network Admins see "RADIUS Auth is Slow"**—However, they cannot determine if it is a network or a client issue. They cannot tell if it is changing over time or if there are any device-specific problems.
- **MacBooks started taking 20 seconds to accept the server cert**—This caused network connection issues and reports of broken wireless.

Controller in line

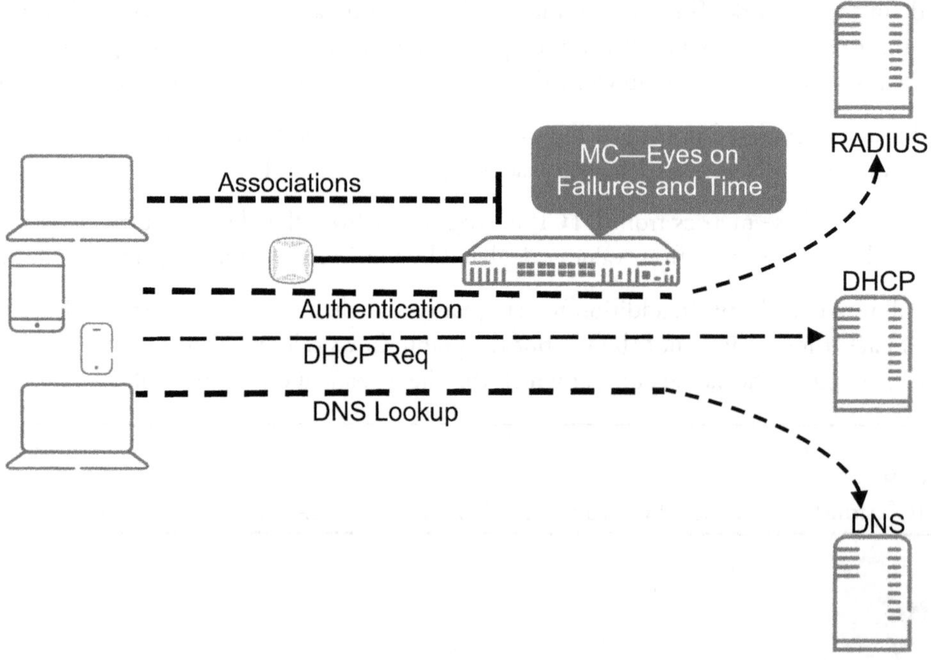

Figure 18-14 Controller in line

When the controller is in tunnel mode, it sees all client requests, and tracks of response times and servers responding (Figure 18-14). Metrics are tracked for association times, DHCP and DNS response times, and RADIUS authentication times.

These metrics are all linked to the servers that fulfill these requests. Thus, you can more easily identify client issues related to DHCP, DNS, and RADIUS problems.

Clarity Live failures

Figure 18-15 Clarity Live failures

Figure 18-15 shows a particular day, when there were zero association failures out of 93. However, five out of seven authentication attempts failed. This is a rather high 71% failure rate, which is why it is shown in red. There have been 0 DHCP failures out of 29, while DNS failures are at 69% with 23,400 failures out of 33,000 attempts.

Analyze these numbers. Since there were only seven total authentication attempts, you do not have a large enough sample to really decide about network health. This could simply be one improperly configured client, who finally entered a correct PSK, for example.

However, the DNS failures are statistically relevant, and are cause for alarm. You should explore this issue in more detail.

Clarity Live failures (cont.)

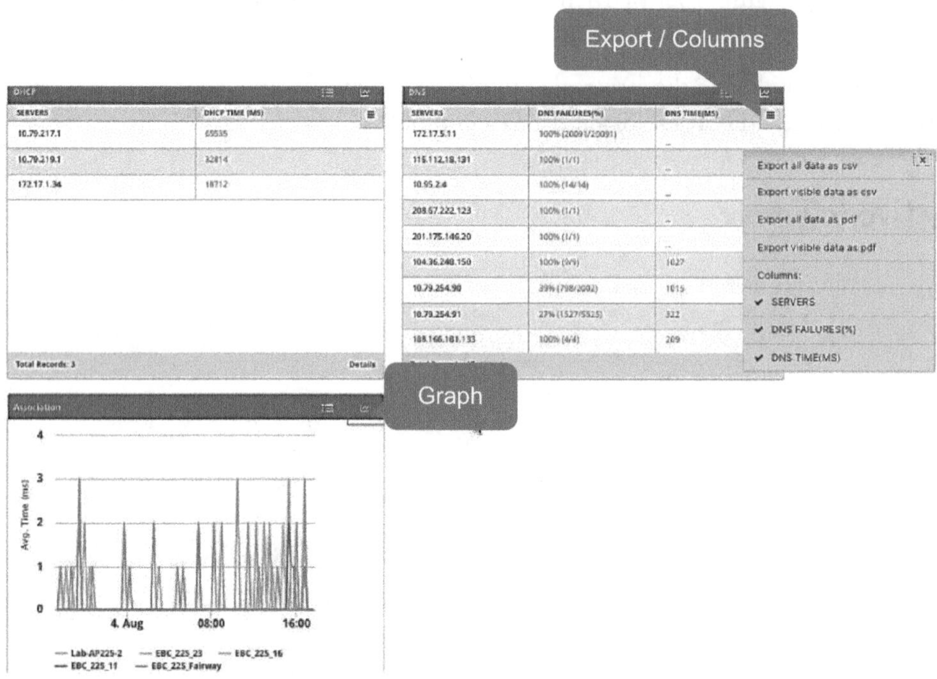

Figure 18-16 Clarity Live failures (cont.)

Three more displays show you DHCP times, DNS failures and times, and association failures and times (Figure 18-16). These charts can also be listed as graphs, but only the top three will be displayed. All this information can also be exported in a CSV or a PDF format.

Clarity time

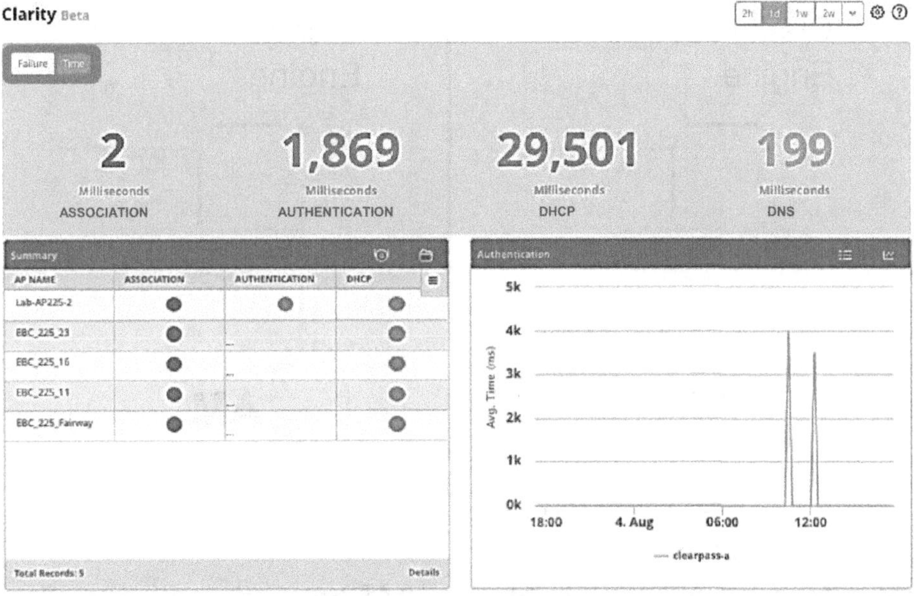

Figure 18-17 Clarity time

Figure 18-17 shows response times, as opposed to failures. Network association times are averaging two milliseconds. This seems quite healthy.

However, authentication is taking an average of 1.8 seconds. This is too high, and so is displayed in red. DHCP is taking an average of 29 seconds! Ouch!! Of course, this is also displayed in red. DNS requests take 199 milliseconds to fulfill, on average. Based on this information, the Wi-Fi network appears to be working well, but the backend servers (and/or connecting infrastructure) are not.

Clarity synthetic

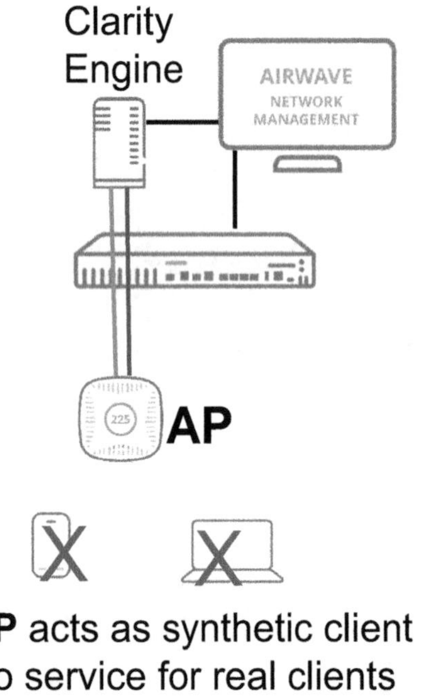

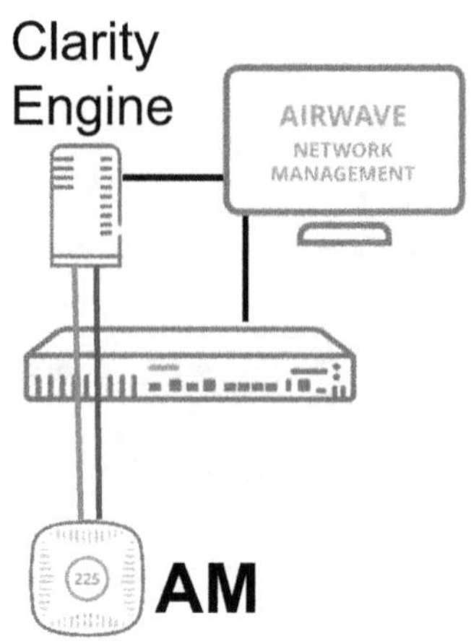

Figure 18-18 Clarity synthetic

You can simulate traffic on your network and analyze the results by converting an AP into a so-called "synthetic client." There are two choices for generating client traffic (Figure 18-18).

First, a normal AP can be converted into a synthetic client. This AP will no longer offer services to real clients.

Second, you can convert an Air Monitor (AM) into a synthetic client in hybrid mode. The AM acts as a synthetic client while continuing to perform AM functions.

Either way, you can simulate network traffic such as WPA, DHCP, ICMP, WebServer, DNS, Query, Traceroute, iPerf-UDP and TCP, Convert AP, Hybrid AM, and AS-100 sensor.

Scheduled or on demand tests measure network health during "off hours." This also provides for on-demand troubleshooting.

Proactive alerts help you to see trends and built-in Key Performance Indicators (KPI) to track the health of the network.

A new dashboard for Clarity Synthetic provides the ability to correlate synthetic results with other network data on AirWave.

You can also use the Northbound API (NBAPI) to export test results to third-party collectors.

Clarity mobile app

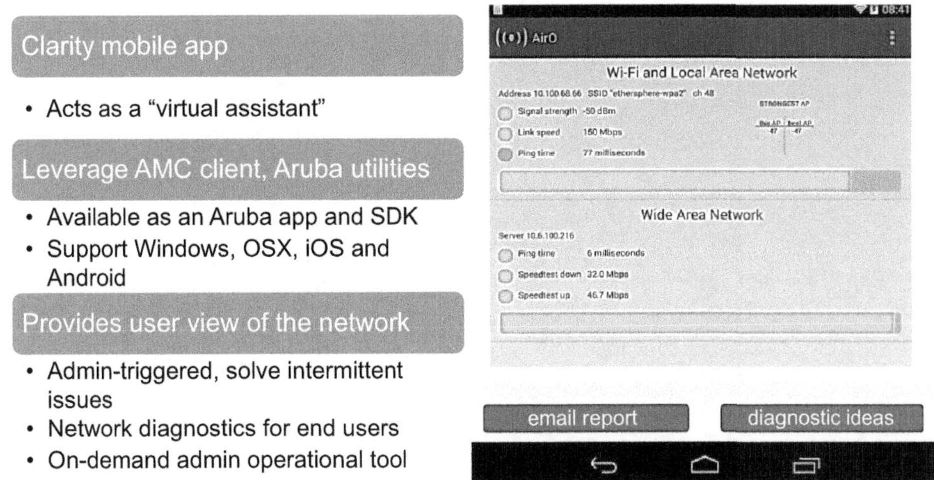

Figure 18-19 Clarity mobile app

The Clarity mobile app offers the following features for users (Figure 18-19):

- Inform the user about connection health.
- Tips on how to improve network performance/auto-remediation.
- The ability to report problems.

The app offers the following benefits for administrators:

- Continuous near real-time performance of the network from the user perspective.
- The ability to run subsets of synthetic tests.
- Alerts and trouble tickets for performance issues with diagnostics.
- Historical data, trends, and comparisons on AirWave.
- Use the AirWave Management Client (AMC) to aggregate client information.

Learning check

2. What are the two types of Clarity?
   a. Live
   b. Answers
   c. Synthetic
   d. Abstract

19 AirWave Troubleshooting Clients and Wireless Networks

LEARNING OBJECTIVES

- ✓ You will learn about using AirWave to troubleshoot client issues in this chapter. This includes how to find specific clients easily, resolve association, authentication, and RF-related client issues.
- ✓ Some client issues are AP-related, so you will learn about AP diagnostics, and move upstream through the network and to the controller. You will learn to gather pertinent information from both the controllers and from AirWave.
- ✓ The chapter ends with discussions about spectrum analysis and general problem resolution tips.

Find clients

Client issues

When a client calls with an issue, you should start by finding the client in the system. Ask the client for some basic information to facilitate this search. At a minimum, you should get their name and login ID. Depending on the situation and how evolved your internal systems are, you may then be able to determine the client's IP and MAC addresses from their name, or you can walk them through giving you this information.

Searching for users

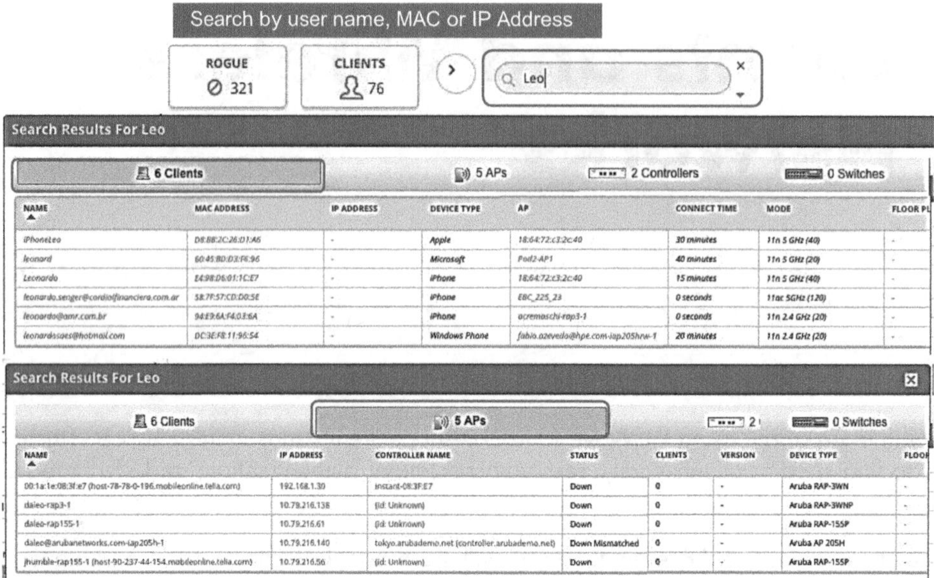

Figure 19-1 Searching for users

Suppose that a user named Leo calls the help desk with an issue. To find this user, you enter the user's name, Leo, in to the AirWave search bar (Figure 19-1). This search feature is found right on the home screen.

All device names containing the entered string are displayed. At the top, there are six matching clients, five matching APs, and two matching controllers. The client list shows each user's name, device type, and connected AP. You can use this information to determine the target user.

Items displayed in an italic font represent clients that are not currently connected. Items shown with a regular, nonitalic font are currently connected clients. You can click on the name, MAC address, or AP link for that user. Depending on the client's connectivity status, and on which link you click, you will be directed to the client detail page, or the diagnostic page, as described below.

Associated client status

Figure 19-2 Associated client status

Clients that are associated to an AP are shown in a regular, nonitalic font. If you click on such a user's MAC address, you will go directly to a diagnostics tab (Figure 19-2).

Unassociated client status

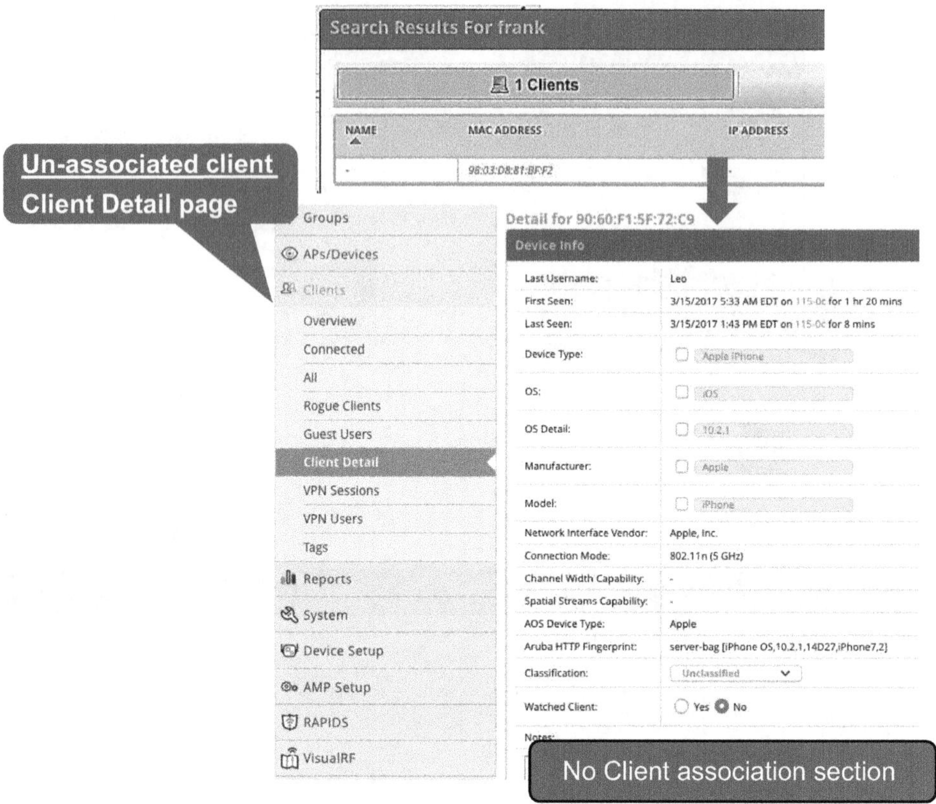

Figure 19-3 Unassociated client status

Clients that are not associated to an AP are shown in an italic font (Figure 19-3). If you click on the name or the MAC address, you go to the client detail page. This is because the diagnostics tab is only relevant for clients that are currently connected.

Unassociated client

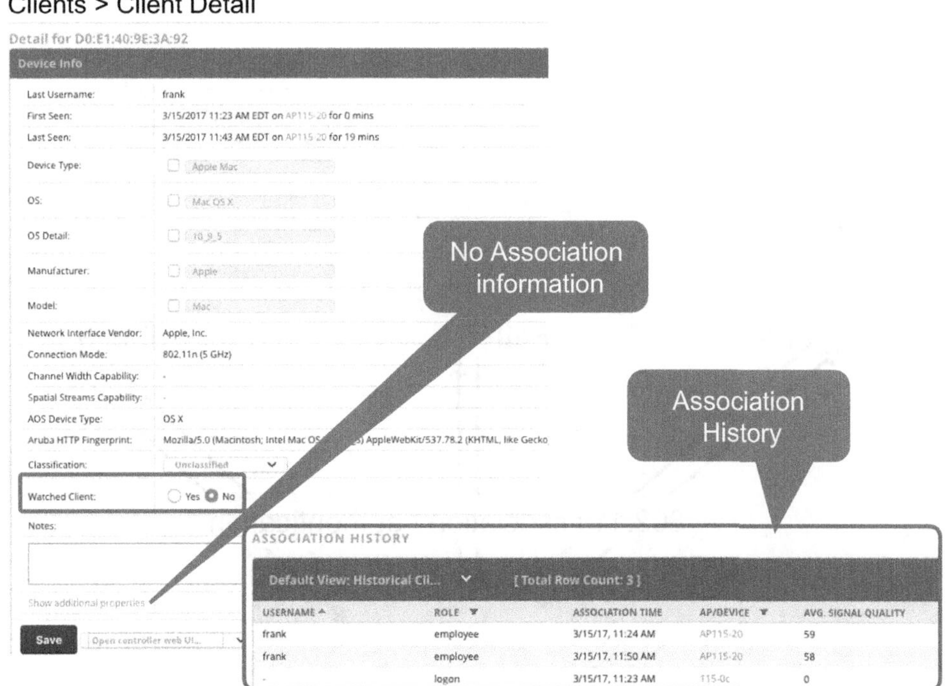

Figure 19-4 Unassociated client

You know that clicking on an unassociated client link takes you to its details page. Alternatively, you can navigate to this page as shown in Figure 19-4. If desired, you can put this client on a watched list, so it displays in the client overview page. You will learn more about this later in this book.

More pertinent to this scenario, you see past association details of a client, which is tracked in the Association History section of this page. These are the APs that the client has attempted to associate with. You can use this information to diagnose client connectivity issues.

Client trying to associate

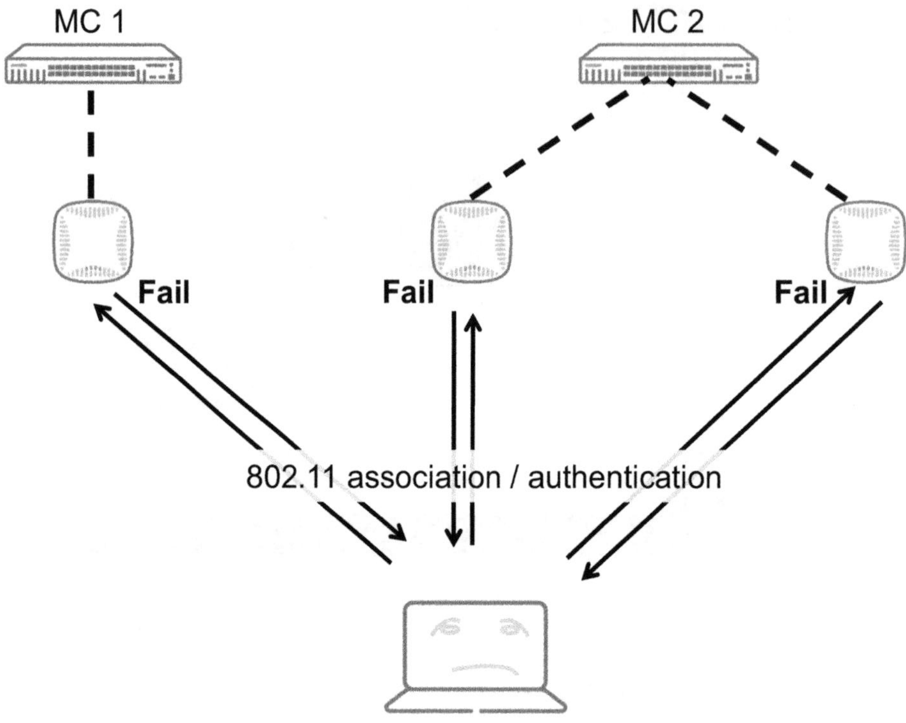

Figure 19-5 Client trying to associate

Clients do not typically attempt to associate to just a single AP. Remember, when the client sends the initial probe request frame, all APs within range respond with a probe reply. The client chooses one of those APs to associate with. If the association attempt fails on one AP, it typically tries other APs in the area.

In the example shown in Figure 19-5, the device attempted to associate with three different APs. Each attempt resulted in failure. If you look closely, you may detect a slightly sad, dejected look about this poor laptop. Perhaps we can help!

Client associating—MC and AP

APs/Devices > Monitor

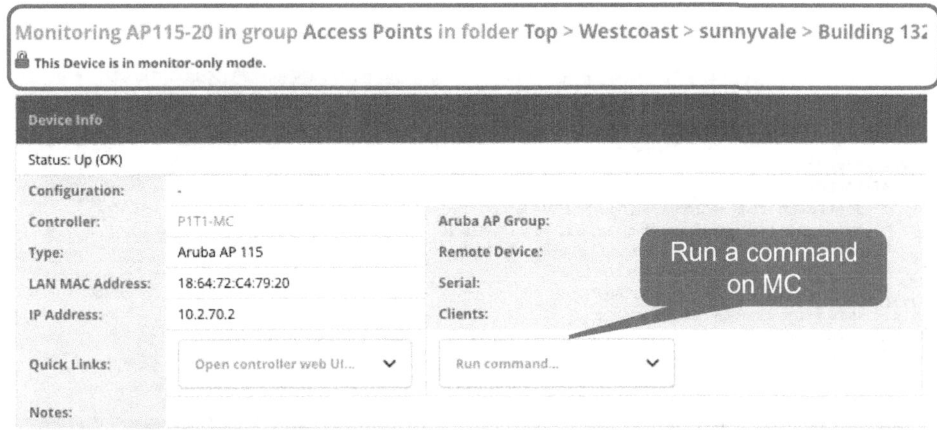

Radios

INDEX ▲	NAME	MAC ADDRESS	CLIENTS	USAGE (KBPS)	CHANNEL	TX POWER	CHANNEL WIDTH	ROLE	SSID
1	802.11bgn	18:64:72:C7:92:00	0	0.00	1	6 dBm	20 MHz	Access	emplo
2	802.11an	18:64:72:C7:92:10	0	0.00	161	12 dBm	Below 40 MHz	Access	emplo

Figure 19-6 Client associating—MC and AP

You learned how to determine the APs to which associations are attempted by looking at client association history on the details page. In our scenario, you saw that the client was primarily trying to associate to AP115-20. This is the AP you want to focus on.

Navigate to **APs/Devices > Monitor** and select the Run Command drop-down menu—a list of CLI commands (Figure 19-6).

Client associating—controller AP

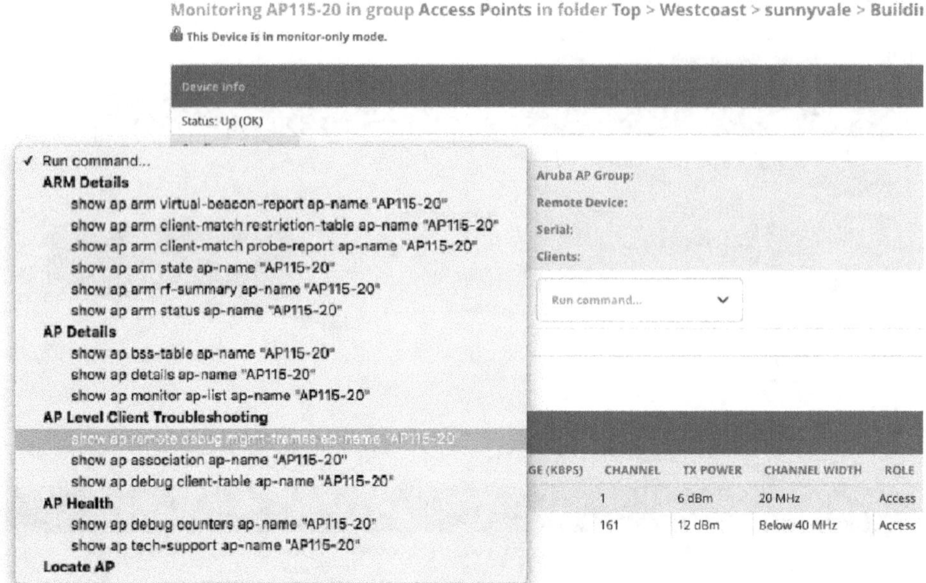

Figure 19-7 Client associating—controller AP

In this scenario, you want to see AP management frames, both inbound and outbound. Select the command `show ap remote debug mgmt-frames ap-name <ap-name>` (Figure 19-7).

Without AirWave, you would need to logon to the Aruba controller, know what APs are near the client, and determine which one to focus on. In this scenario, you used AirWave to do this more efficiently.

The following output shows three successful user associations. However, the AP then deauthenticates the client, for various reasons.

Note

In the output shown below, the first three bytes of each MAC address have been deleted. This improves legibility of the output.

```
Controller1# show ap remote debug mgmt-frames ap-name <ap> | include
< client mac >
```

Client 1:

```
Timestamp          stype        SA          DA          BSS         signal  Misc
Mar  1 05:57:24   deauth       5a:3e:10    70:3c:66    5a:3e:10    15      STA has left
                                                                             and is deauth
Mar  1 05:53:24   assoc-resp   5a:3e:10    70:3c:66    5a:3e:10    15      Success
Mar  1 05:53:24   assoc-req    70:3c:66    5a:3e:10    5a:3e:10    51      -
Mar  1 05:53:24   auth         5a:3e:10    70:3c:66    5a:3e:10    15      Success
Mar  1 05:53:24   auth         70:3c:66    5a:3e:10    5a:3e:10    60      -
```

Client 1 has just been deauthenticated. This could be a simple misconfiguration on the user's part.

Client 2:

```
Mar 3 06:54:48   deauth       20:30:68   01:49:69   20:30:68    15  - (internal only)
Mar 3 06:54:16   assoc-resp   20:30:68   01:49:69   d20:30:68   15 Capability
                                                                    requested by STA
                                                                    unsupported by AP
Mar  3  06:54:16  assoc-req  01:49:69  20:30:68  20:30:68  62      -
Mar  3  06:54:16   auth       20:30:68  01:49:69  20:30:68  15  Success (seq num 2876)
Mar  3  06:54:16  auth       01:49:69  20:30:68  20:30:68  44      -
```

Client 2 shows the AP is not supported in the association request parameters. This is most likely another issue of misconfiguration.

Client 3:

```
Mar  3 05:35:49  deauth       20:30:60  01:49:69  20:30:60  15  Response to EAP
                                                                  Challenge Failed
Mar  3 05:35:19  assoc-resp   20:30:60  01:49:69  20:30:60  15  Success
Mar  3 05:35:19  assoc-req    01:49:69  20:30:60  20:30:60  63     -
Mar  3 05:35:19  auth         20:30:60  01:49:69  20:30:60  15  Success
Mar  3 05:35:19  auth         01:49:69  20:30:60  20:30:60  12
```

Client 3 is failing authentication. This appears to be an issue related to 802.1X/EAP authentication.

Client 4:

```
No association frames
```

Client 4 is not even trying to associate to any AP. This is a client issue.

Client associating—IAP

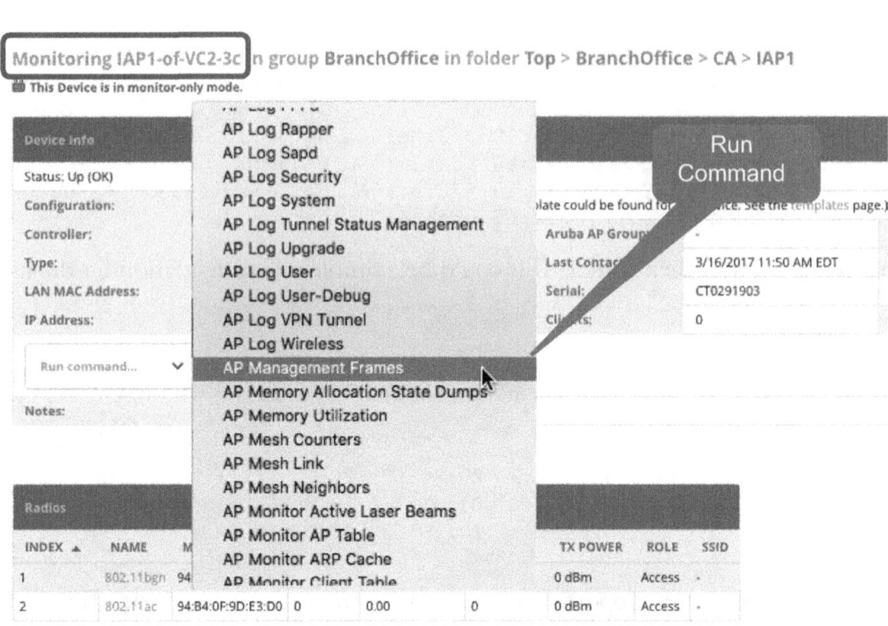

Figure 19-8 Client associating—IAP

This scenario relates to client associations with an IAP. To troubleshoot, select the IAP and run the command `AP Management Frames`. (Figure 19-8)

802.11 and 802.1X negotiation—IAP

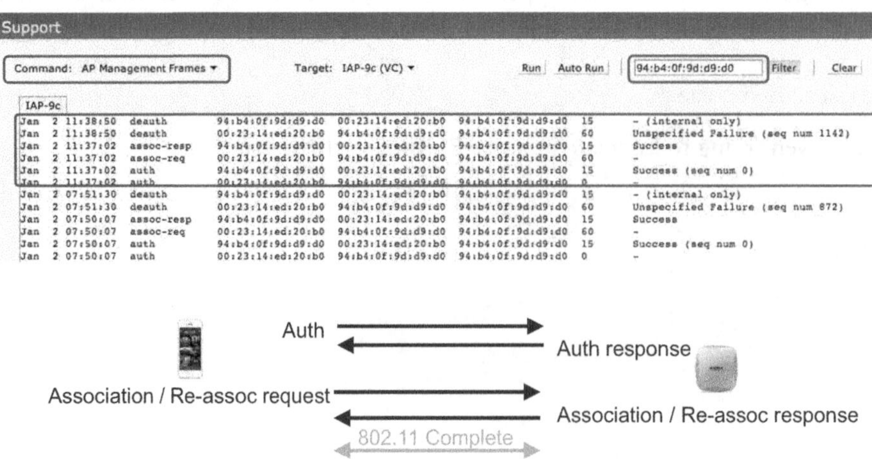

Figure 19-9 802.11 and 802.1X negotiation—IAP

The command `AP Management Frames` shows 802.11 and 802.1X messages, between IAP and client (Figure 19-9). This is very useful in troubleshooting client issues.

Learning check

1. A user cannot associate what could be the cause?
   a. Wi-Fi is off on the device
   b. Wrong Wi-Fi settings
   c. Bad user ID and Password
   d. AP has reached the user limits
2. During the 802.11 association process, what comes after the authentication frames?
   a. Deauthentication frame
   b. Association frames
   c. 802.11 complete frame
   d. 802.1X authentication frames

Associated client

Associated client diagnostics

Figure 19-10 Associated client diagnostics

Each section of the **Clients > Diagnostics** page helps you to evaluate possible user issues (Figure 19-10). This includes the current association, usage, SNR value, health, steer events, and more.

Client diagnostic graphs

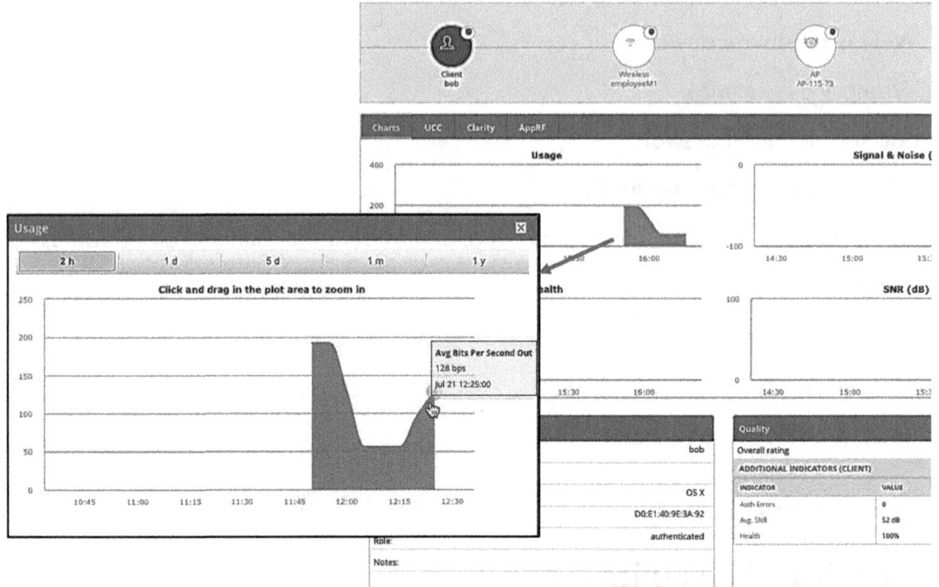

Figure 19-11 Client diagnostic graphs

Click on any of the graphs to get a pop-up on that specific graph (Figure 19-11). This example shows the usage graph for a client named Bob. Click the tabs across the top to display the last two hours, one day, five days, one month, or one year of information.

Associated client thresholds

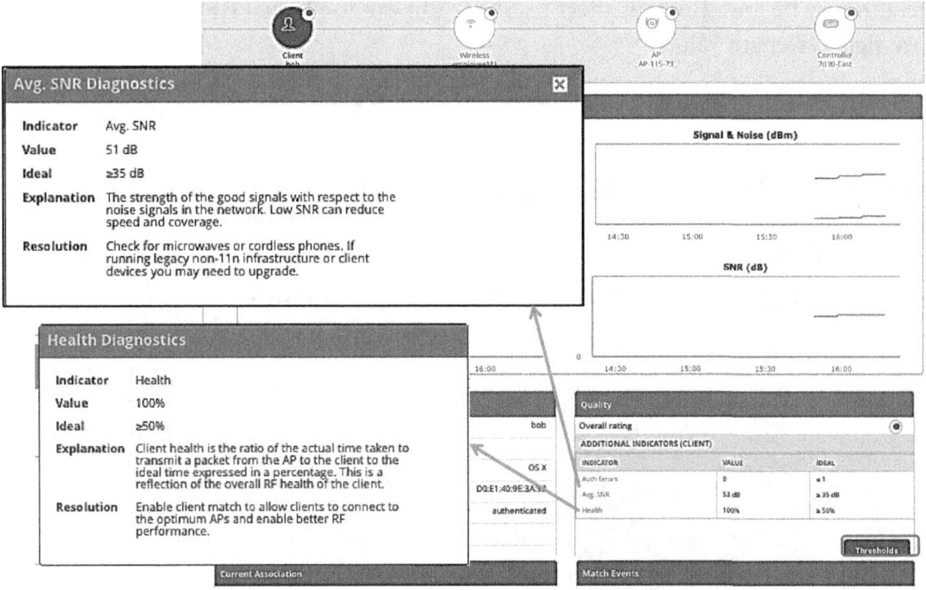

Figure 19-12 Associated client thresholds

There are thresholds for client SNR value and health values. This can alert you when RF health falls below acceptable limits (Figure 19-12).

You can configure Good and Fair threshold values for APs, clients, controllers, networks, and switches. Just click on the Thresholds button in the right panel. The values that fall below Fair are automatically considered as poor.

Understanding SNR

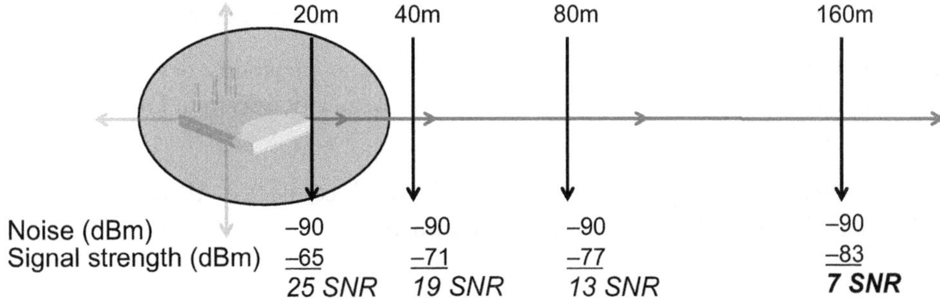

Figure 19-13 Understanding SNR

As the client moves further away from the AP, its signal strength drops (Figure 19-13). A client might be physically located close to an AP, but due to RF attenuation from surrounding materials, its actual signal strength may be low. This will affect its SNR. You can use Visual RF for client location history to compare signal strength values.

An SNR of 25 or higher is very good. An SNR of 19 is not great, but usable. An SNR of 11 is bad.

Low average SNR—further analysis

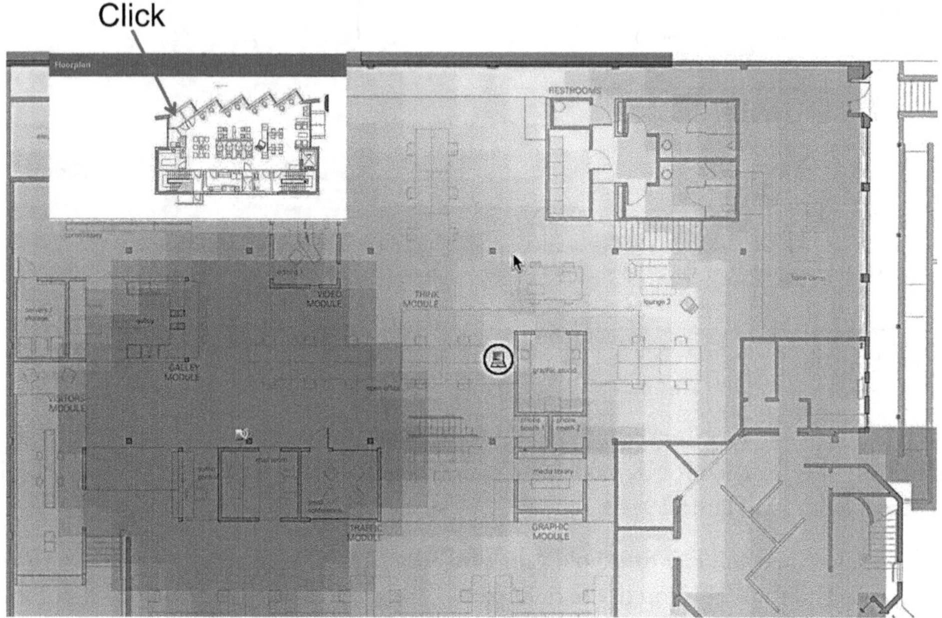

Figure 19-14 Low average SNR—further analysis

You may suspect that poor RF signal quality is the source of user issues. With the user on the phone, here is a simple test to determine if client-to-AP distance is a contributing factor.

Navigate to the **Clients > Diagnostics** page for the client, as previously described. Figure 19-14 shows the floor plan that appears in the left pane's Current Association section. Double-click the floor plan to open the pop-up, and click the heat map tab.

Using the map, determine the physical location of the user's connected AP. Ask the user to move closer to the AP and report whether performance improves.

Low average SNR—further analysis (cont.)

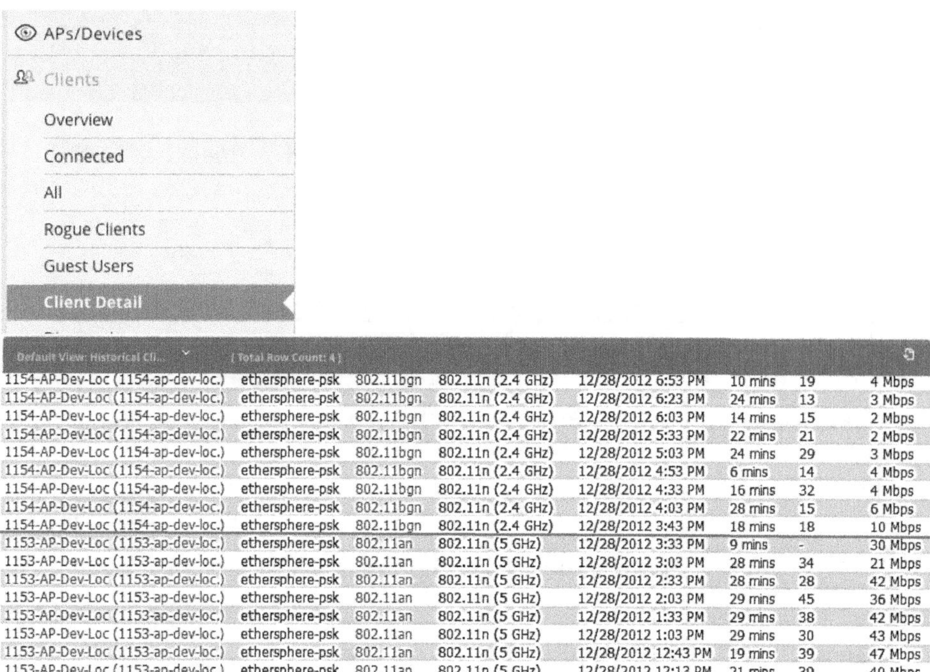

1154-AP-Dev-Loc (1154-ap-dev-loc.)	ethersphere-psk	802.11bgn	802.11n (2.4 GHz)	12/28/2012 6:53 PM	10 mins	19	4 Mbps
1154-AP-Dev-Loc (1154-ap-dev-loc.)	ethersphere-psk	802.11bgn	802.11n (2.4 GHz)	12/28/2012 6:23 PM	24 mins	13	3 Mbps
1154-AP-Dev-Loc (1154-ap-dev-loc.)	ethersphere-psk	802.11bgn	802.11n (2.4 GHz)	12/28/2012 6:03 PM	14 mins	15	2 Mbps
1154-AP-Dev-Loc (1154-ap-dev-loc.)	ethersphere-psk	802.11bgn	802.11n (2.4 GHz)	12/28/2012 5:33 PM	22 mins	21	2 Mbps
1154-AP-Dev-Loc (1154-ap-dev-loc.)	ethersphere-psk	802.11bgn	802.11n (2.4 GHz)	12/28/2012 5:03 PM	24 mins	29	3 Mbps
1154-AP-Dev-Loc (1154-ap-dev-loc.)	ethersphere-psk	802.11bgn	802.11n (2.4 GHz)	12/28/2012 4:53 PM	6 mins	14	4 Mbps
1154-AP-Dev-Loc (1154-ap-dev-loc.)	ethersphere-psk	802.11bgn	802.11n (2.4 GHz)	12/28/2012 4:33 PM	16 mins	32	4 Mbps
1154-AP-Dev-Loc (1154-ap-dev-loc.)	ethersphere-psk	802.11bgn	802.11n (2.4 GHz)	12/28/2012 4:03 PM	28 mins	15	6 Mbps
1154-AP-Dev-Loc (1154-ap-dev-loc.)	ethersphere-psk	802.11bgn	802.11n (2.4 GHz)	12/28/2012 3:43 PM	18 mins	18	10 Mbps
1153-AP-Dev-Loc (1153-ap-dev-loc.)	ethersphere-psk	802.11an	802.11n (5 GHz)	12/28/2012 3:33 PM	9 mins	-	30 Mbps
1153-AP-Dev-Loc (1153-ap-dev-loc.)	ethersphere-psk	802.11an	802.11n (5 GHz)	12/28/2012 3:03 PM	28 mins	34	21 Mbps
1153-AP-Dev-Loc (1153-ap-dev-loc.)	ethersphere-psk	802.11an	802.11n (5 GHz)	12/28/2012 2:33 PM	28 mins	28	42 Mbps
1153-AP-Dev-Loc (1153-ap-dev-loc.)	ethersphere-psk	802.11an	802.11n (5 GHz)	12/28/2012 2:03 PM	29 mins	45	36 Mbps
1153-AP-Dev-Loc (1153-ap-dev-loc.)	ethersphere-psk	802.11an	802.11n (5 GHz)	12/28/2012 1:33 PM	29 mins	38	42 Mbps
1153-AP-Dev-Loc (1153-ap-dev-loc.)	ethersphere-psk	802.11an	802.11n (5 GHz)	12/28/2012 1:03 PM	29 mins	30	43 Mbps
1153-AP-Dev-Loc (1153-ap-dev-loc.)	ethersphere-psk	802.11an	802.11n (5 GHz)	12/28/2012 12:43 PM	19 mins	39	47 Mbps
1153-AP-Dev-Loc (1153-ap-dev-loc.)	ethersphere-psk	802.11an	802.11n (5 GHz)	12/28/2012 12:13 PM	21 mins	39	40 Mbps

Figure 19-15 Low average SNR—further analysis cont.

In this scenario, some user has complained that their performance has suddenly degraded (Figure 19-15). Notice the client changed from AP 1153 to AP 1154. Also, the signal quality dropped off significantly at this point, as well as the average speed. There are several possible causes for this.

Low average SNR—resolution

One possibility for poor SNR values is that the noise floor is high. You can explore this possibility with spectrum analysis. If co-channel interference is causing issues, you might consider adjusting AP power levels. (Or adjust ARM or AirMatch settings to encourage lower power settings).

Perhaps APs are too far apart from each other. A symptom of this is that ARM/AirMatch will increase AP power to maximum allowable values. Even so, there are coverage gaps and clients with low signal strength. You can use VisualRF to assess AP placement and RF coverage.

It could be that the client device simply does not roam very well. This could be inherent to the client hardware. It is well known that some smart phones and tablets were not designed for roaming. It could simply be related to outdated client drivers.

The pages that follow explore these possibilities.

Client diagnostic—AppRF

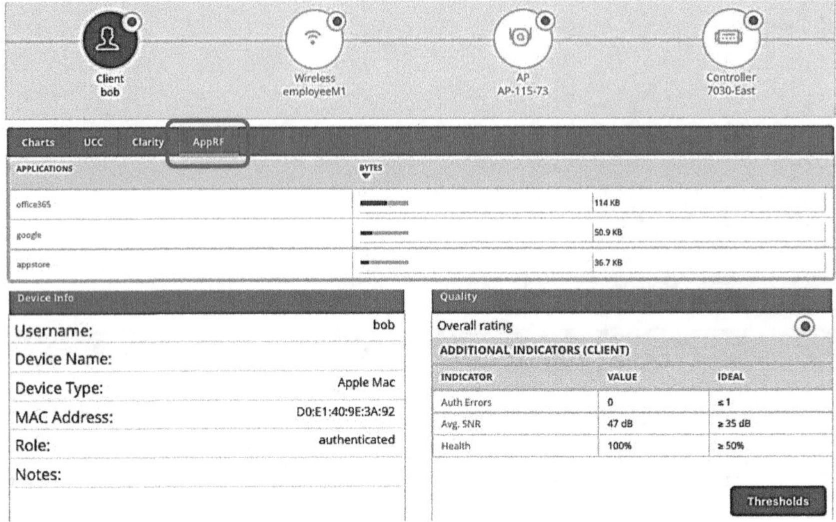

Figure 19-16 Client diagnostic—AppRF

From the diagnostic page, click on AppRF. You will see charts related to application usage for the target client. Figure 19-16 shows that Bob is using Office365, Google, and the App Store.

Client diagnostic—Clarity

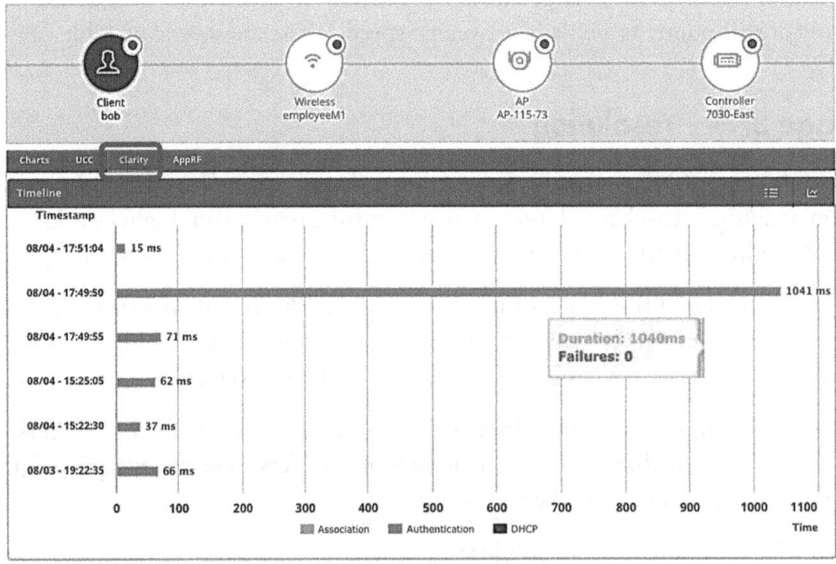

Figure 19-17 Client diagnostic—Clarity

The diagnostic page also includes a tab for Clarity. Choose this to see a timeline for the client's associating, authenticating, and DHCP times (Figure 19-17).

Note the authentication time seems quite long.

Diagnostic—radio utilization

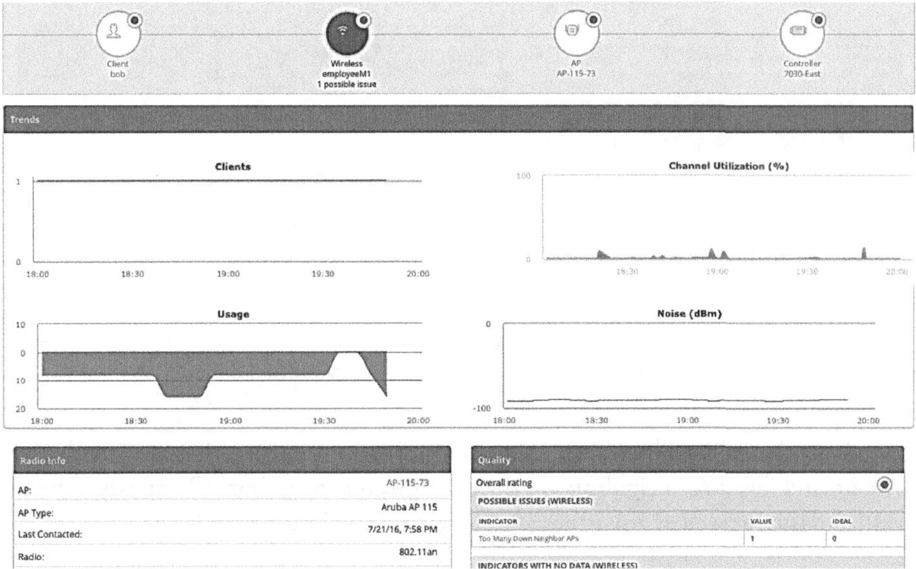

Figure 19-18 Diagnostic—radio utilization

Check the user's connected AP radio for current usage levels (Figure 19-18). Perhaps there is high user density in the area, and the radio is oversubscribed. This is another sign that APs may be too far apart from each other, or that AP load balancing should be enabled or tuned. It could also be that this APs neighbor has failed, forcing higher utilization on remaining APs.

Diagnostic—wireless quality

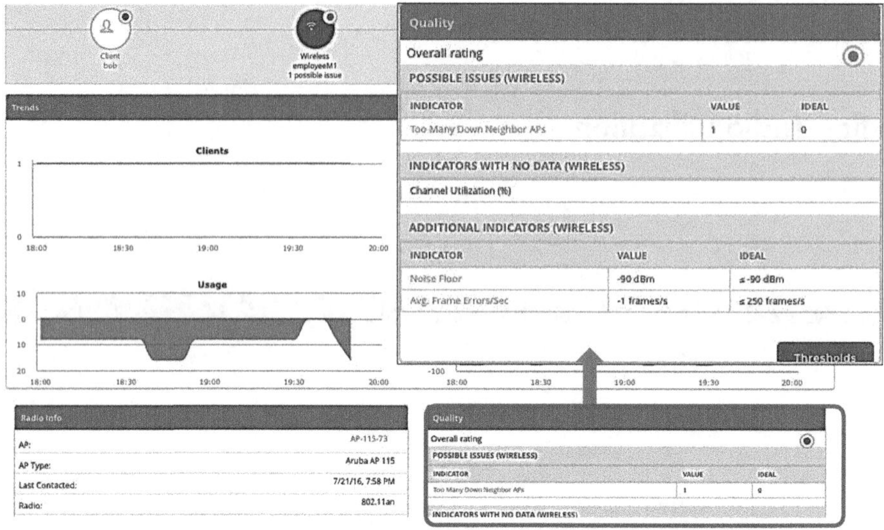

Figure 19-19 Diagnostic—wireless quality

You can also check the APs quality rating and details. This can indicate issues with channel utilization, noise floor, and failed AP neighbors. In the example, one neighbor AP appears to be down. You should investigate this, as well as any other anomalies you might discover here.

Wireless quality

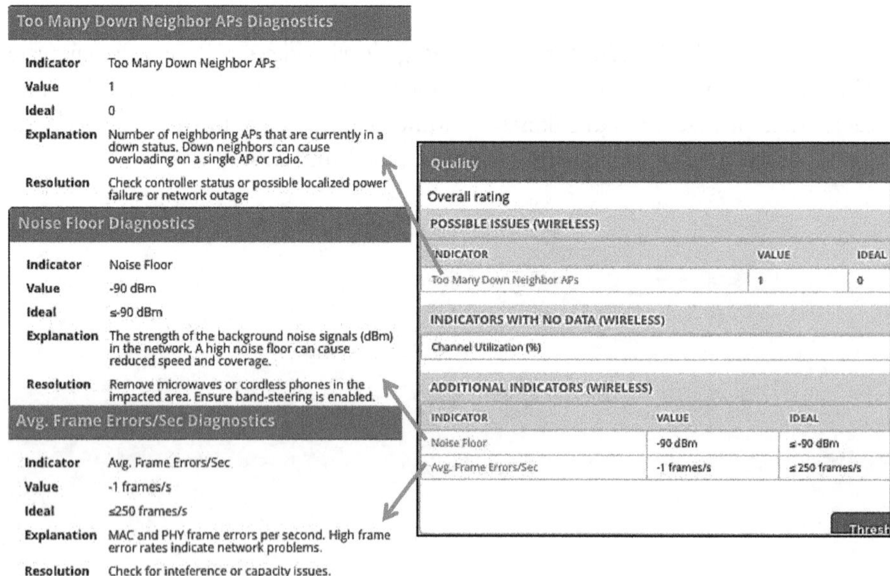

Figure 19-20 Wireless quality

Figure 19-20 shows the detail you can see from three wireless quality metrics, as described below.

- Too many downed neighbor APs would force more clients on the remaining APs. There is one neighbor down in this example.
- If the noise floor is too high, then all devices will have problems communicating with the APs. A noise floor of –90 dBm is OK, although it is right on the line of acceptability, since the ideal value is less than or equal to –90 dBm.
- A high number of frame errors can indicate overcrowding or RF health issues. In the example, there does not seem to be an issue with frame errors.

Wireless health issues

Channel utilization measures how busy a channel is. Controllers gather channel utilization statistics from APs. AirWave retrieves this information from the controller. Both Wi-Fi and non-Wi-Fi interference can cause Adjacent Channel Interference (ACI), and so both are included in this metric. Channel utilization of 0% means that the channel is completely clear and unused. Hundred percent utilization indicates the channel is busy 100% of the time.

802.11 wireless devices use a CSMA/CA scheme to sense if the medium is busy, using a Clear Channel Assessment (CCA) process. If the medium is busy, devices do not transmit. High channel utilization reduces channel availability, and client performance suffers. Clients may experience application timeouts or dropped voice calls.

You might check the AirWave diagnostics page for several clients. All clients on the same AP channel will display the same channel utilization. For example, if two 2.4 GHz clients are connected to AP1, both will display the same channel utilization.

However, clients on the same channel on different APs might display different channel utilization values, especially if the APs are not providing coverage in the same area. This is because channel utilization is measured by each individual AP. It is based on that AP's perception of its environment. APs covering the same area might display similar channel utilization stats. Of course, it is not optimal to have APs in the same area set to the same (or even adjacent) channels.

Several underlying factors can cause abnormally high Frame Errors:

- **Non-Wi-Fi interference**—Devices like microwaves and cordless phones can interfere with 802.11 transmissions. This can result in frame decode errors.
- **AP/Channel over capacity**—Overloaded AP radios increase collisions and retries.
- **Surrounding materials**—Fibrous materials can absorb radio energy, thus reducing signal strength to unacceptable levels, and perhaps cause "hidden node" issues. Metallic objects reflect radio energy, potentially causing standing waves and other issues.
- **Broken antennas**

Spectrum analysis

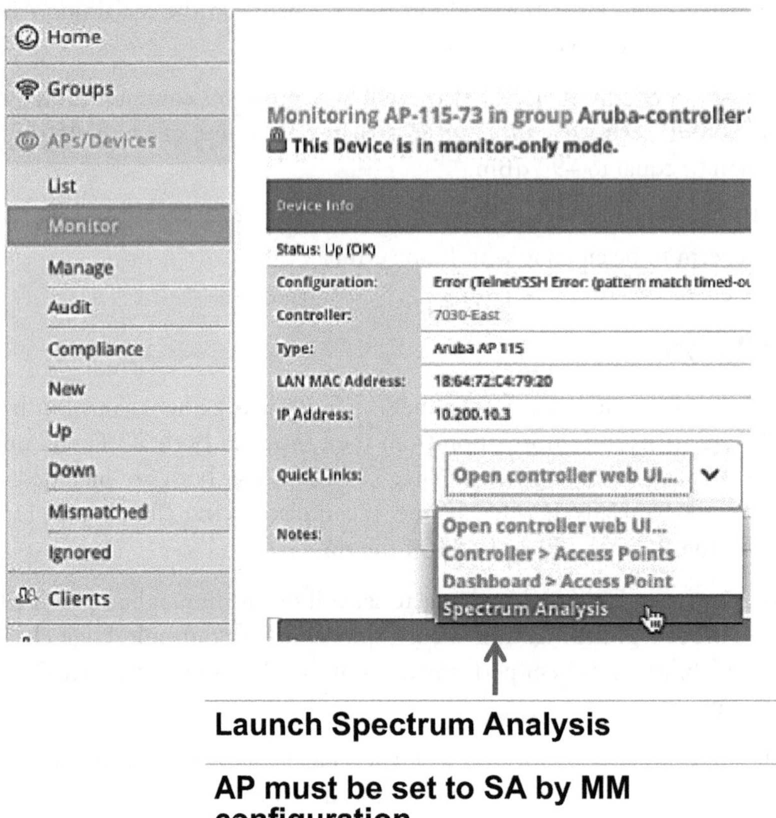

Figure 19-21 Spectrum analysis

You can access a controller's spectrum analysis feature directly from AirWave. Just use the Quick links, as shown in Figure 19-21.

AirWave opens a window to the controller, where you log in with valid credentials. AirWave does not configure APs to be Spectrum Analyzers (SA). You must do this from the controller CLI or GUI.

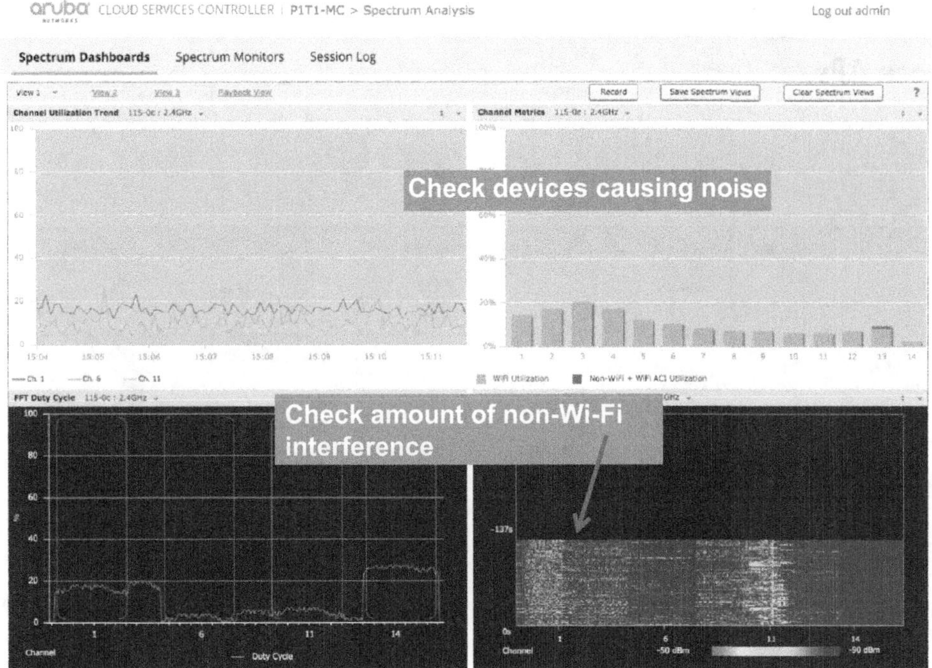

Figure 19-22 Spectrum analysis

Figure 19-22 shows the typical charts for spectrum analysis, including channel utilization trends, channel metrics, Fast Fourier Transform (FFT) duty cycle, and swept spectrogram. This can help you to identify noise from specific sources, interfering on specific channels.

Note

APs in override SA mode do not support client connectivity.

Learning check

3. You find a client but you fall into the Client Detail page and not the Diagnostic page. Why?
    a. Client is not associated to an AP.
    b. Client has not initiated 802.1X.
    c. Client is getting a Captive Portal page.
    d. Client is in an open SSID.

Diagnose and monitor

Diagnose APs

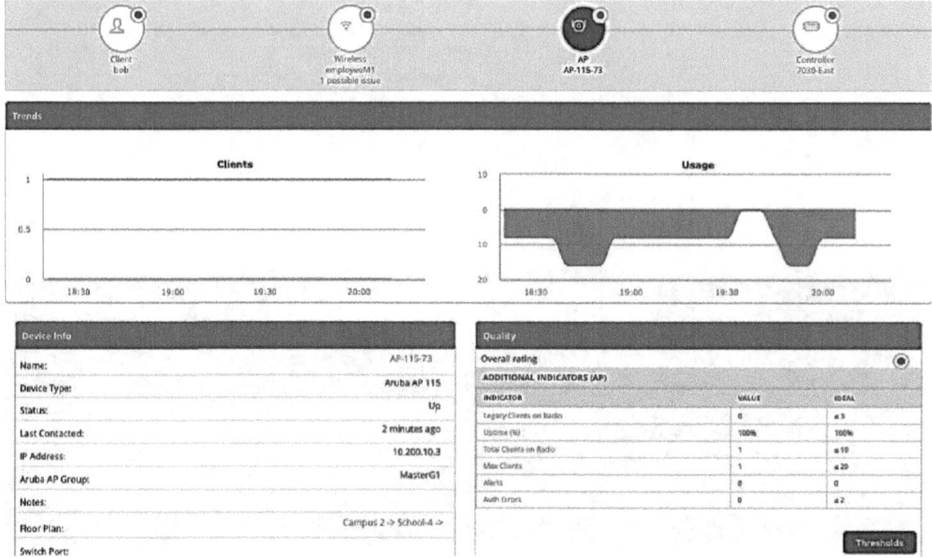

Figure 19-23 Diagnose APs

Check the AP usage graph to see if too many users are consuming radio capacity (Figure 19-23). Click in the usage graph to open the graph popup. If usage is very high (especially on an 802.11b/g/n radio), then this might affect perceived WLAN performance, since all user share the same bandwidth.

Perhaps no other users are connected to the AP. This could indicate an issue with the AP itself. Click on the clients graph to open the graph popup. Select a time range above the graph to view historical information and determine whether it is unusual for no other users to be connected now. If no other users are connected at a time when usage is normally high, it is more likely that there is an AP or radio problem that should be escalated to a Network Engineering team.

Diagnose APs—(cont.)

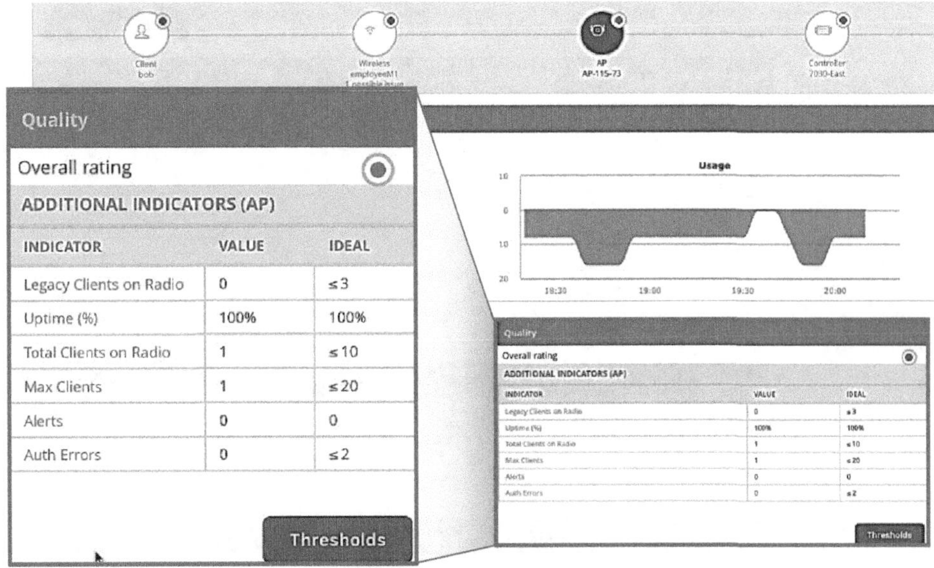

Figure 19-24 Diagnose APs—(cont.)

The Quality popup provides the following information:

- Number of non-802.11n clients connected to this radio. Legacy clients reduce overall throughput for 11n clients.
- The percentage of uptime over the last hour. Low uptime for infrastructure devices negatively impacts downstream clients.
- The total number of wireless clients currently associated to this radio. Too many clients can reduce capacity for each wireless client.
- The total number of AMP alerts associated with this object in the last 30 minutes
- The total number of authentication errors associated with this object in the last 30 minutes. This can indicate invalid credentials, security attacks, or upstream server problems.

In Figure 19-24, the trigger for Max Clients is set to 20 or fewer. This is probably too low in many areas, given the frequent warnings you are experiencing. This value should be increased in accordance with your AP type, and based on what you consider to be "normal" user density.

Monitor APs

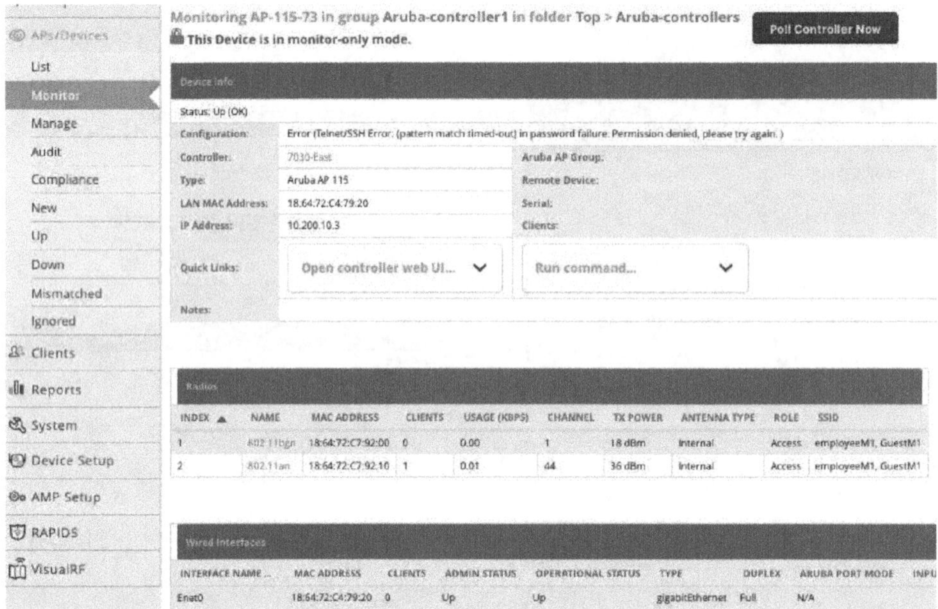

Figure 19-25 Monitor APs

The **APs/Devices > Monitor** page for controllers and APs includes a graph for users and bandwidth (Figure 19-25).

Monitor APs (cont.)

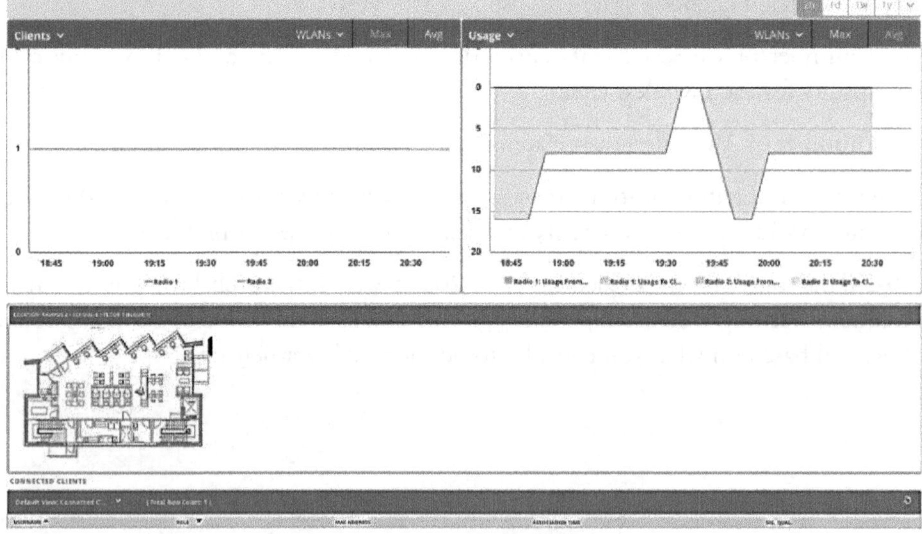

Figure 19-26 Monitor APs (cont.)

You can note the users that are associated to this AP and get a list of all RF neighbors (Figure 19-26). Both clients and RF neighbors can be the source of an AP's RF problems.

AP issues

Table 19-1 reviews of potential sources of AP issues.

Table 19-1 Reviews of potential sources of AP issues

Legacy clients	Non-802.11n clients are considered legacy
	802.11a/b/g clients take longer to transmit packets
	Impacts all clients on channel
Total clients on radio	Design best practice—plan users per radio in accordance with AP type
Low uptime	WLAN link issues
	Power outages
	Network congestion
	Upstream device failure

Modern 802.11n and 802.11ac-based client devices transmit data quickly. Legacy 802.11a/b/g devices require more time to transmit each frame. This is because their maximum data rate is only 54 mbps (11 mbps for 802.11b). Also, only modern devices support channel bonding. This results in 40 MHz channels, which increases throughput.

Arguably, the most important factor is good WLAN design and deployment. Precise AP number and placement can be done scientifically, based on RF site surveys, or based on haphazard guess work. The former will tend to result in strong, reliable coverage. ARM/AirMatch algorithms are setup for success, and will tend to tune power closer to around 50% of maximum power. Haphazard design/deployment practices can result in APs that are too close together (causing co-channel interference) or too far apart (causing coverage gaps, too many users per AP, and low client data rates).

Even if you have designed and deployed a high-quality solution, WLAN systems transmit management, broadcast, and multicast frames at the lowest (or one of the lowest) available connection speeds. On high-quality WLAN deployments, you can disable the slower speeds, such that all frames are sent at say, 6, 9, or even 12 mbps.

Note

You should be very careful about disabling slow data rates on unfamiliar networks, without proper training. You could end up making a bad situation worse. Experiment with this technique after hours, or on a test WLAN, before rolling this out on a production network.

Of course, network reliability is vital. WLAN link issues, power outages, network congestion, and uplink failures should be mitigated.

Controller/switch issues

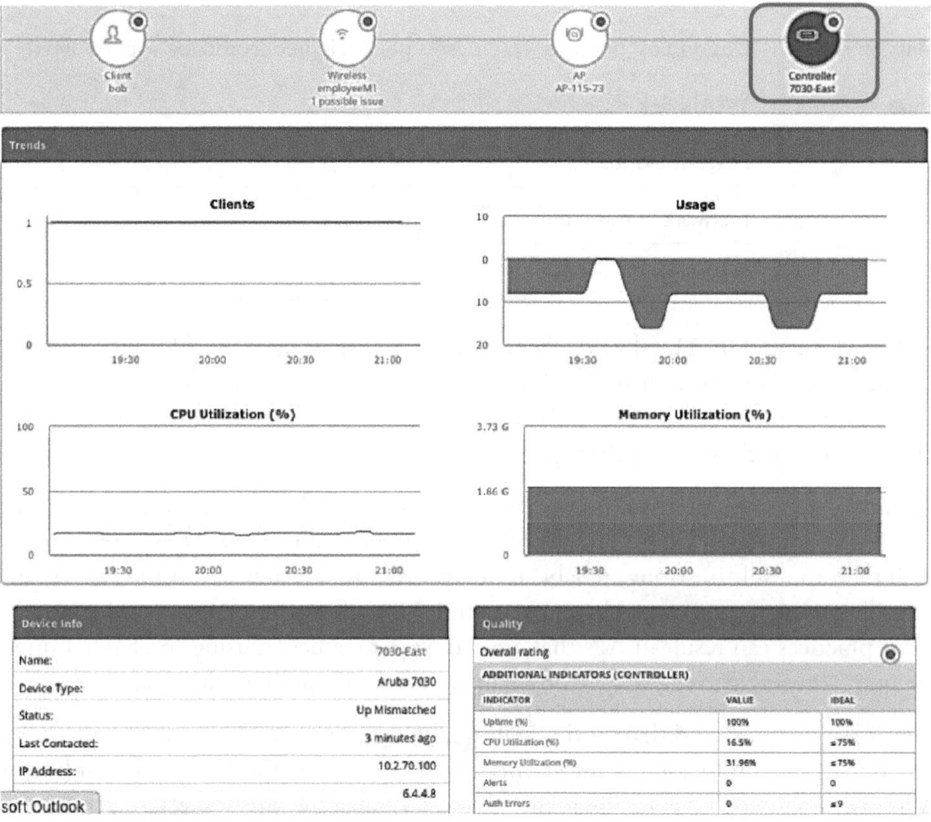

Figure 19-27 Controller/switch issues

Any wired switch issues would typically show up as multiple problems in the wireless network. If a switch fails it could take down the link to several APs, or the uplink to the controller. Controllers and switches should be assessed for overall health. This includes the following:

- Uptime
- CPU/memory utilization
- Port errors
- Authentication errors

Figure 19-27 shows the controller pages in AirWave, which can be used to assess these metrics.

Controller/switch

The following are some common issues related to controllers and switches:

- Low uptime will cause network-wide disruptions. Low uptime can be caused by:
  - WLAN link issues
  - Power outages
  - Network congestion
  - Upstream device failure
- Overutilization of a controller can reduce overall WLAN performance. Control processor applications, such as Web Server, RADIUS, SNMP, and so on, not the data path. Ideally, you want the utilization to be well below 75%.
- Port Errors on an uplink can cause network-wide disruptions. Port errors can include:
  - Link negotiation issues
  - Speed mismatch
  - Switch hardware issues
  - Cable issues
  - Check the switchport status
- Authentication errors show up in many different areas such as clients failing authentication multiple times and controllers having RADIUS access issues.

Only IAPs would show any authentication issues because regular campus APs send all their traffic to the controller.

Also, remember to set AirWave triggers properly so that you receive alerts about current or impending issues. This includes AP alerts and switch/controller alerts.

Cluster monitoring

Cluster monitor

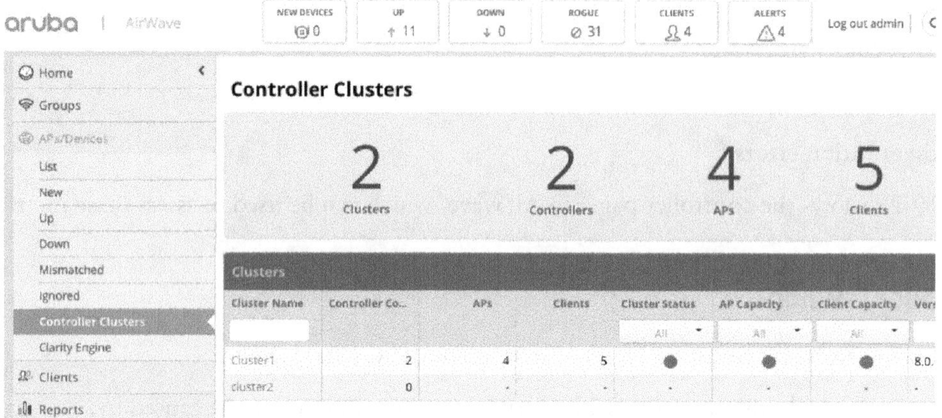

Figure 19-28 Cluster monitor

To monitor clusters, navigate to **APs/Devices > Controller Clusters** (Figure 19-28). Here you can see all the clusters and get a status summation on each cluster.

This example shows two clusters—Cluster1 and Cluster2. Cluster1 is made up of two controllers with four APs. Five clients are currently connected. Cluster2 is a newly defined cluster. No controllers are associated with this cluster.

Click on the cluster name to see details.

Monitoring Cluster1

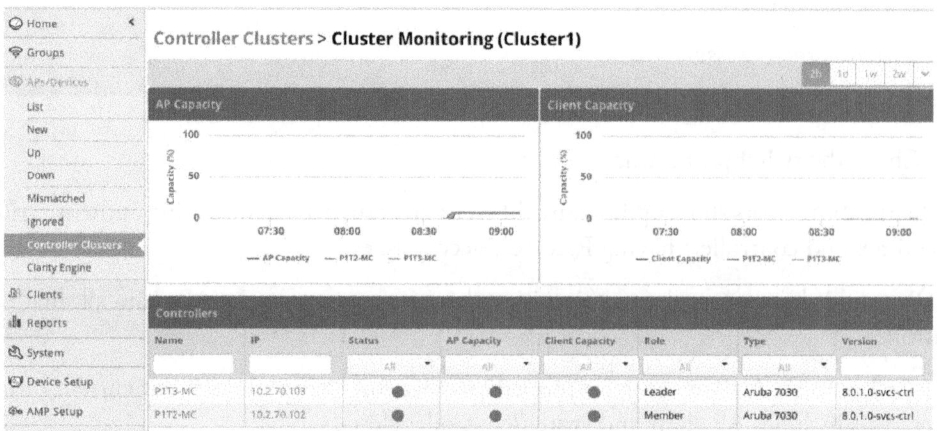

Figure 19-29 Monitoring Cluster1

In this example, you have clicked on Cluster1. You see that P1T3-MC is the leader of the cluster and all other MCs are members. You can also monitor AP capacity, client capacity, and the status of the MCs in this cluster. You can scroll down to see an events page, which is not shown in Figure 19-29.

Troubleshooting steps

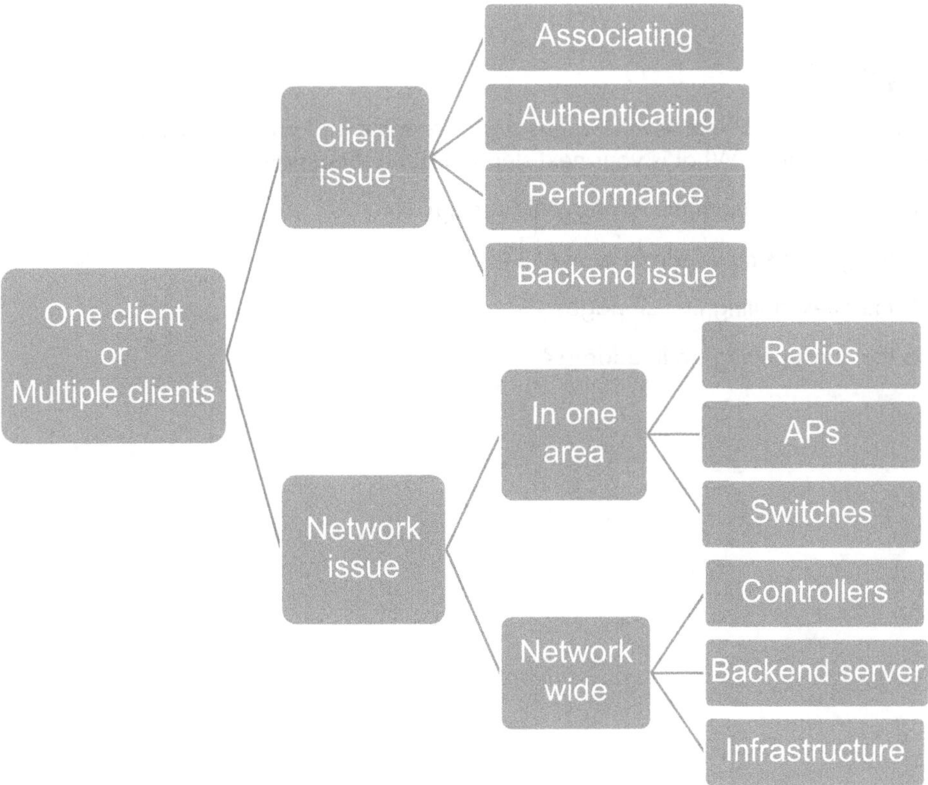

Figure 19-30 Troubleshooting steps

Many end users are quick to blame the wireless network. It has often been said that a wireless network is "guilty until proven innocent"! However, many issues can arise that can cause problems in various areas.

Figure 19-30 shows a general flow chart for diagnosing WLAN issues. Notice that the first question you might ask is "Is this problem affecting one client, or multiple clients?" Issues that affect a single client are probably caused by the client device itself, as shown in Figure 19-30.

However, if an issue affects many clients, you may have a network issue. If it only affects users in a specific area, you would of course troubleshoot in that area. You could have issues with radios, APs, or local switches. If the problems are network-wide, then the focus should be on controller, servers, and infrastructure.

For a more thorough treatment of WLAN troubleshooting, consider attending HPE's course titled "HPE WLAN troubleshooting", or HPE Aruba's Advanced Troubleshooting course.

Learning check

4. You investigate calls from several areas and determine that only guests have issues. Employees are fine. What is your next step in troubleshooting?
    a. Does the guest have the wrong WIFI setting?
    b. Is the guest using windows or MACs?
    c. Is the guest getting the CP page?
    d. Is the guest getting an IP address?

20 AirWave VisualRF, Reports, Alerts

LEARNING OBJECTIVES

✓ This chapter teaches you to use VisualRF for heat maps and to help identify the location of clients and Rogue APs. You will explore VisualRF display options, heat maps, and location information. You will then learn about the Visual AppRF and Locate features.

✓ The chapter ends with a discussion about alerts, triggers, and reports.

Understand VisualRF display options

QuickView navigation

QuickView navigation offers intuitive pull-down menus. There is a section for display and editing tools, and another for record and playback functions.

Visual RF has four views:

- User
- Access Point
- Floor plan and network
- Campus and building

For better navigation, you should migrate VisualRF to HTML5 (you may switch back to flash if desired).

Views

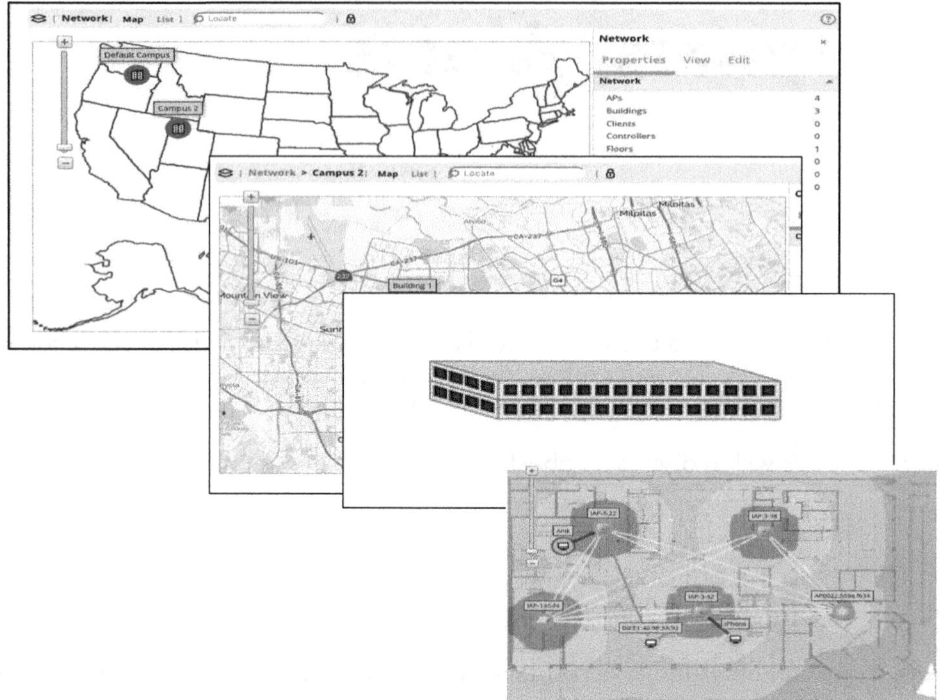

Figure 20-1 Views

You can view floors from a geographical perspective from the **VisualRF > Floor Plans** page.

Click **Show Network View**. This will launch the 3-D QuickView navigation system. This gives you access to the four views, as depicted in Figure 20-1.

- Network View—Contains all campuses within your WLAN.
- Campus View—All buildings within a campus.
- Building View—All floors within a building.
- Floor Plan View—All devices' access points, clients, and rogues within the floor.

Understand heat maps and location information

VisualRF floor view

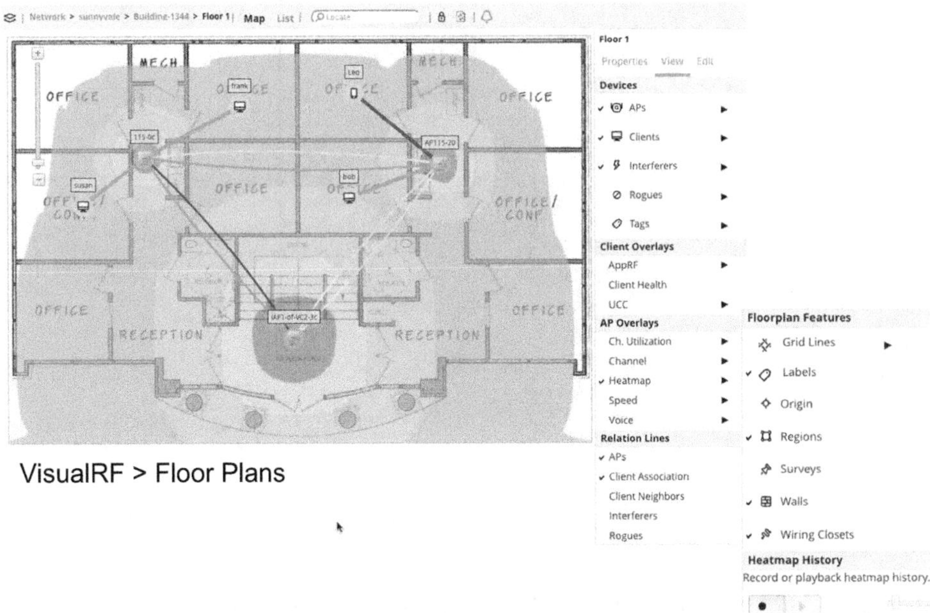

Figure 20-2 VisualRF floor view

From within AirWave, an icon representing each AP is placed on a floor plan (Figure 20-2). Of course, you must place these icons to match actual physical AP locations. Once the APs have been placed in their proper location, you can view the heat map.

Note

This output was generated by APs in a lab environment, which were close to one another.

You view a specific floor with AP overlay on all the selections. You select the 2.4 GHz or 5 GHz band and view heap maps for that band.

Under the edit view, you can select devices to display on the selected floor. The client overlay allows you to see the ten top applications used by the clients. Under AP overlays, you display heat maps and channels, specifying the frequencies you wish to see. Relation lines will indicate client-to-AP connections.

VRF AP properties

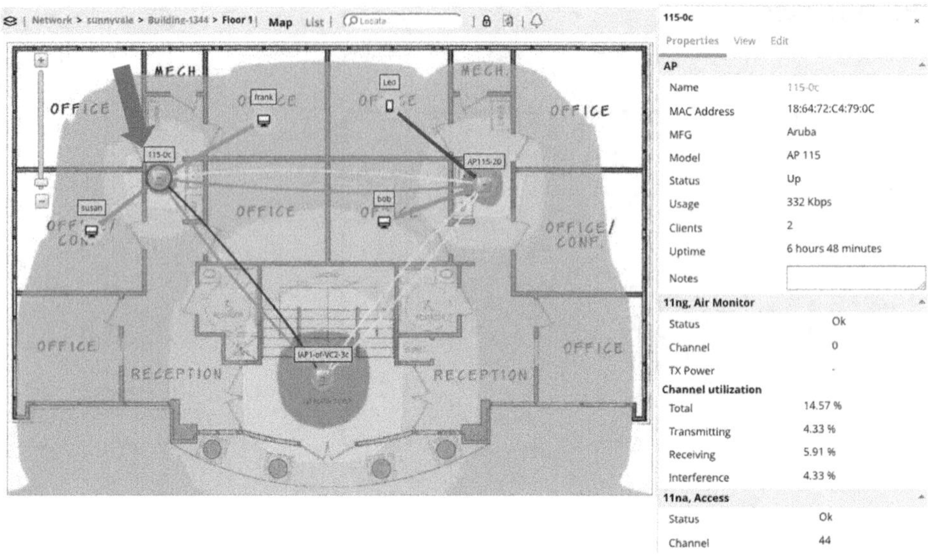

Figure 20-3 VRF AP properties

You can click on an AP in the VRF window to see its properties, listed on the right-hand side (Figure 20-3). This includes basic information about the AP as well as Air monitor statistics.

VRF client properties

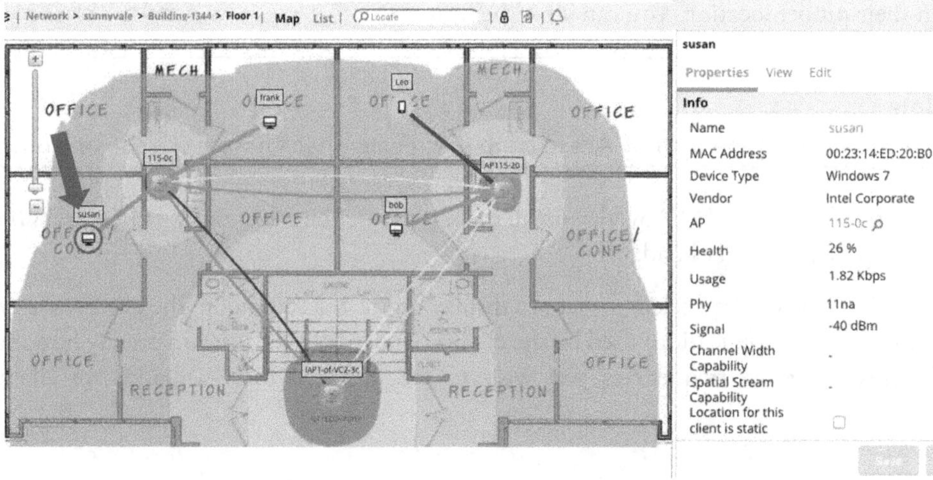

Figure 20-4 VRF client properties

Click on a client icon in the VFR window to see client properties, as shown in Figure 20-4. You see basic information and statistics for the client.

Learning check

1. How do you get a street map introduced in the building view?
   a. Automatically from Google maps
   b. Download a file from MapQuest
   c. Draw it in
   d. Screen shot of a map

Visual AppRF

VisualRF—view apps

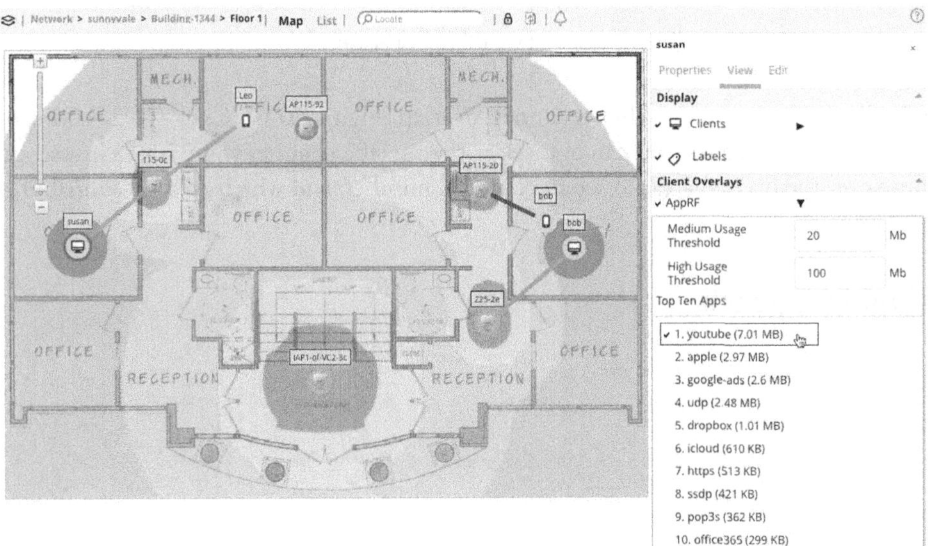

Figure 20-5 VisualRF—view apps

The AppRF overlay for clients identifies clients using the selected application.

High, medium, and low thresholds are shown in red, orange, and green, respectively. Figure 20-5 shows that Bob and Susan are using YouTube. It is shown in green, so this is not a concern.

Channel overlays

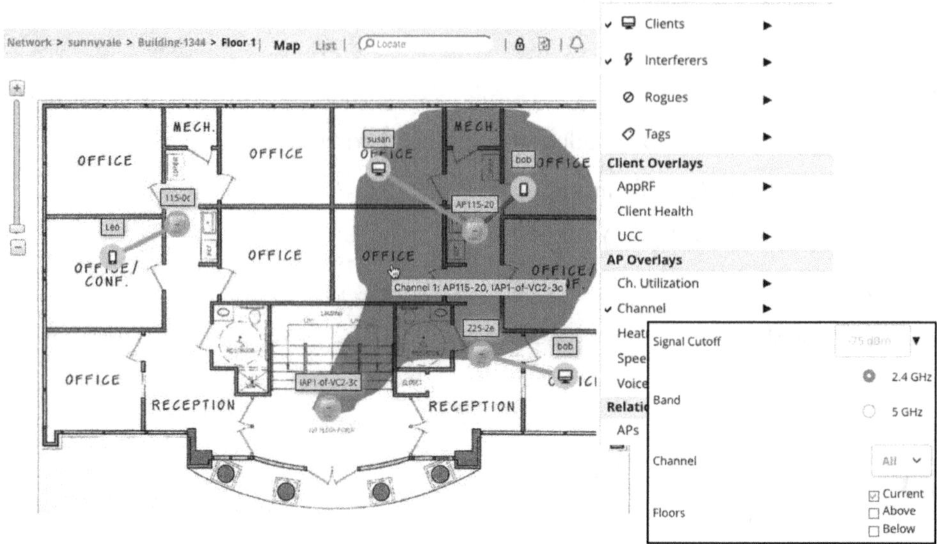

Figure 20-6 Channel overlays

Choose the channel overlay to see how channels overlap (Figure 20-6). Click the 2.4 GHz or 5 GHz radio button to select a band. You can also select the specific channel you wish to investigate. Move your mouse over the overlap areas to see the channel number, and which APs are contributing to the overlapped area.

Record and playback

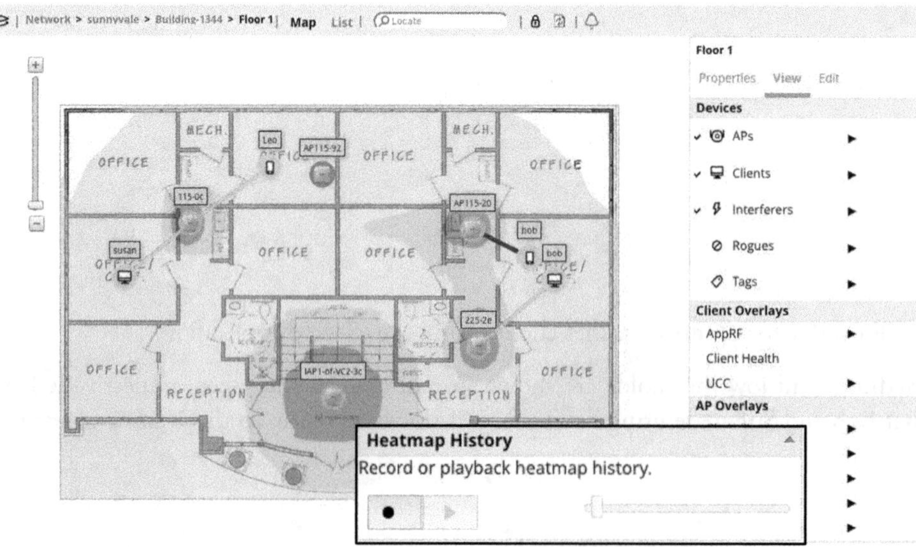

Figure 20-7 Record and playback

You can also record heat map history (Figure 20-7). It can be enlightening to see how coverage changes over time, perhaps due to interfering devices, new walls or other obstacles being erected or torn down, or large groups of people migrating in different areas.

VRF—AP/device monitor page

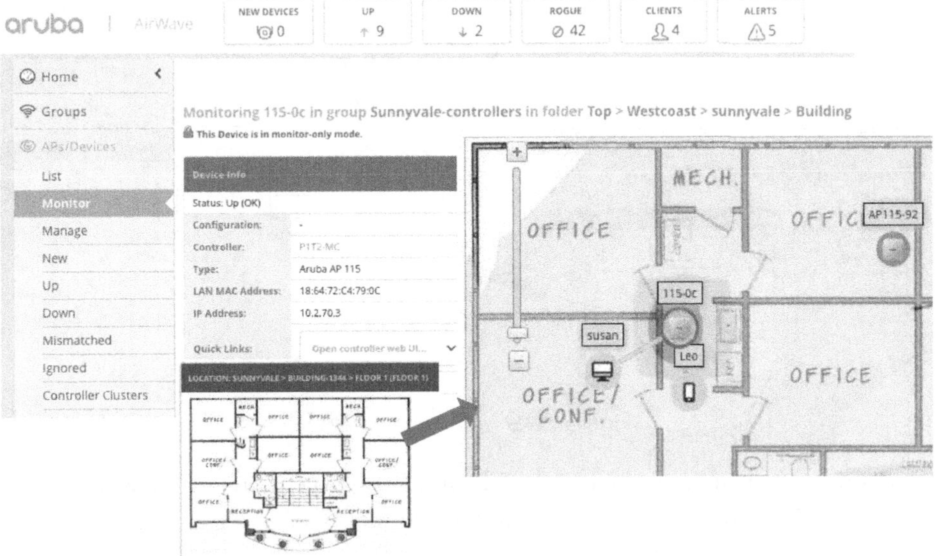

Figure 20-8 VRF—AP/device monitor page

When monitoring an AP in the APs/Devices Monitor page, you can click on the VF icon (Figure 20-8). This takes you directly to the VF floor page with a focus on the AP you are monitoring.

VRF—client detail

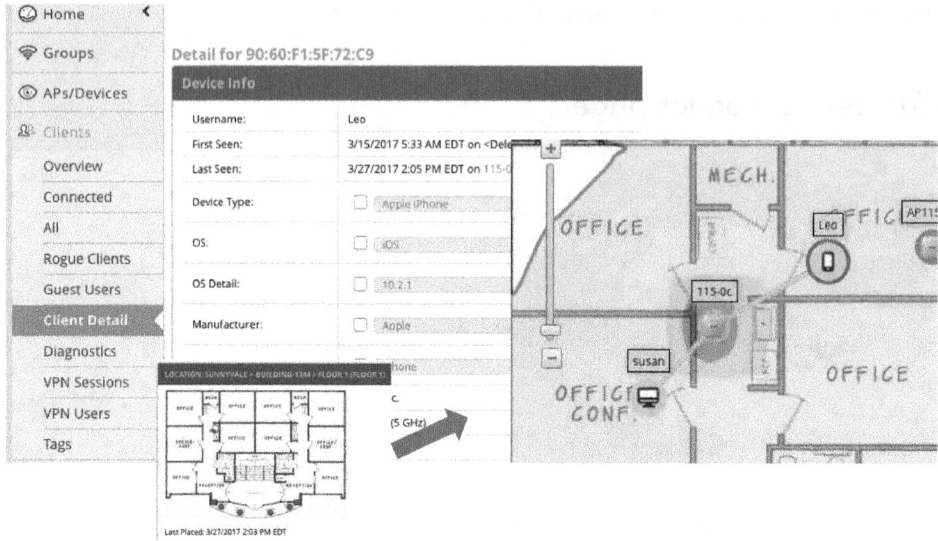

Figure 20-9 VRF—client detail

When monitoring a client in the Clients—Client Detail page, you can click on the VF icon (Figure 20-9). This icon will take you directly to the VF floor page.

Visual locate

Locate VisualRF

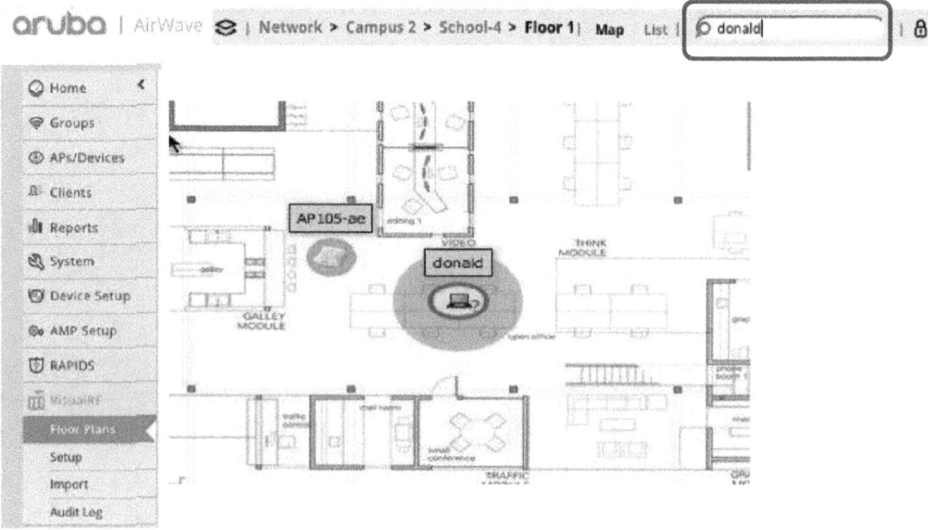

Figure 20-10 Locate VisualRF

When the visual RF map has several clients, it can look daunting, and finding a specific client can be difficult. The Locate service helps you quickly locate devices (Figure 20-10). When used, the map moves and the client device icon pulsates, to ease identification.

The accuracy of client location depends on properly deployed APs. Deploying APs for client location accuracy can be different than deploying access points for capacity. Follow these guidelines for best results:

- Insure that at least three radios can hear each client device at –85 dBm or better.
- Deploy an AP approximately every 3500 square feet.
- For square or rectangular floor plans, access points are deployed on the exterior walls of each floor and in the middle of the floor plan.

You can search for a wireless device by MAC address or username. If a device was misplaced or stolen, you can find it if it is on premise and its radio is enabled and transmitting. If so, VisualRF can triangulate its location.

AMP user roaming view allows you to track device movement, over the past 24 hours. You can better understand where the device has been, perhaps correlating failures to specific coverage areas.

If the lost device is off premise and cannot be located, you can still use historical records to track its last known location. You can review security camera videos to locate and retrieve the device. You can use the AMP device search function and User Session Reports to detect the device, should it reappear in any of your facilities. If so, the AMP location capabilities can quickly pinpoint the device's location.

Learning check

2. What is the significance of channel overlay in floor view?
    a. The color of the floor map
    b. From other floors above or below
    c. Overlay a map in VRF
    d. Overlapping channels
3. How do APs determine their position?
    a. They do not
    b. With GPS
    c. Based on distance to wall
    d. Based on Bluetooth signals

Triggers and alerts

Triggers and alerts

You were introduced to triggers and alerts in the previous section. Commonly deployed triggers include:

- **Device Down**—Checks if the APs/Controllers/Switches have gone down and are unreachable. Further options allow us to choose if we don't want to trigger an alert if the AP's upstream device is down. Also, we can exclude reboots from the count.
- **Client count per BSSID**—Every AP assigns a Basic Service Set Identifier (BSSID) for each radio SSID that it supports. This is a unique MAC address, used for L2 wireless 802.11 communications. For example, AP105 might support the Employee and Guest SSIDs on both its 2.4 GHz and 5 GHz radios. There is a four separate BSSID MAC addresses—one per SSID per radio. Therefore, client count per BSSID only checks the total client count PER RADIO for that SSID.
- **Noise floor**—Please refer to the chapter 19, the troubleshooting chapter, for more information on noise floor stats.
- **IPv4 Link-Local addresses**—This checks for 169.254 type IP addresses. This may become useful when troubleshooting DHCP issues. For example, you could check if clients are timing out before receiving DHCP IP addresses.

Creating a new trigger

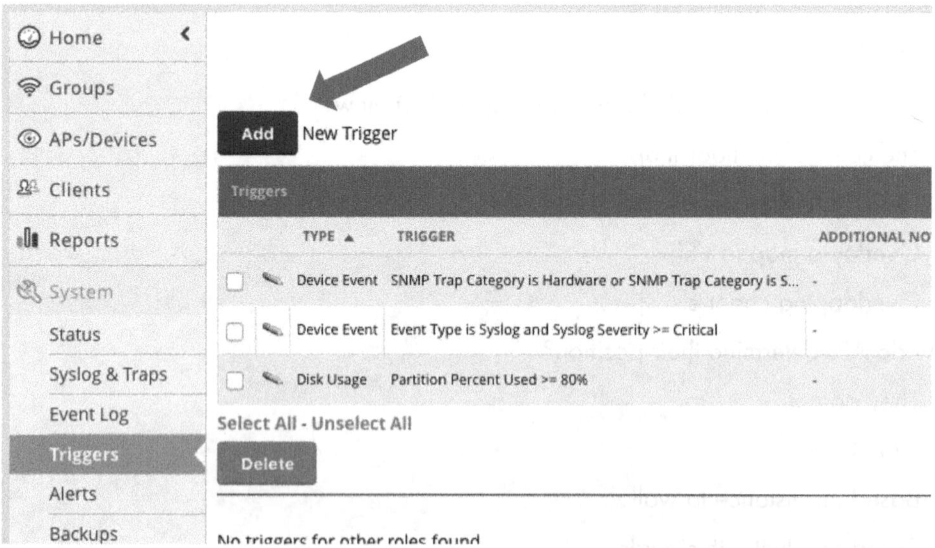

Figure 20-11 Creating a new trigger

The Add Trigger page changes, depending on the trigger type that you select (Figure 20-11). In many cases, you must configure at least one condition setting. Conditions, settings, and default values vary according to trigger type. You can configure triggers with conditions. This means the trigger will only fire when certain criteria are met.

Configuring a new trigger

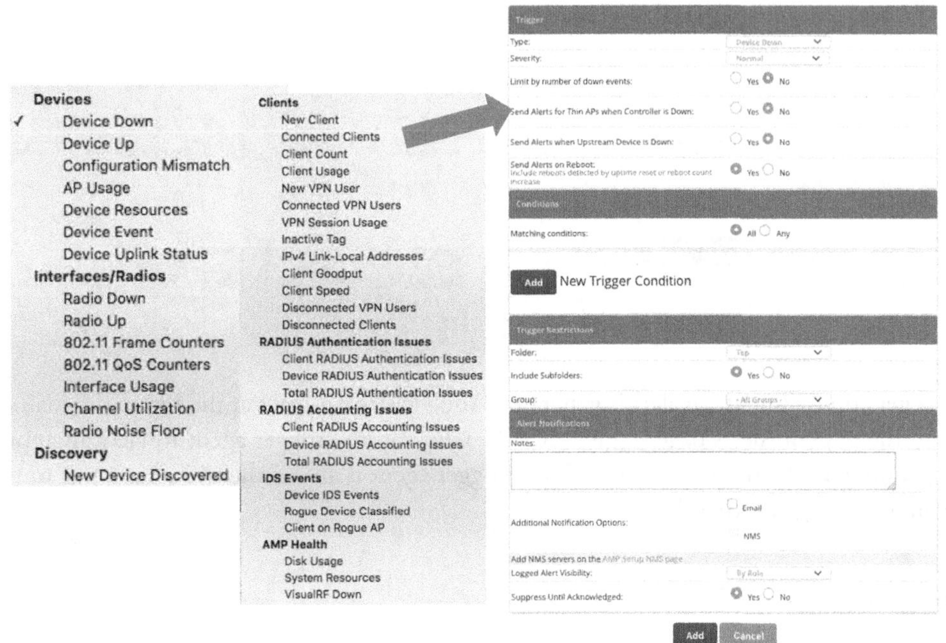

Figure 20-12 Configuring a new trigger

Figure 20-12 shows many different trigger types. Each type can be configured with its own set of conditions. You can also restrict triggers to devices in a specific folder or group.

Use the Alert Notifications section to enter a note. This note will appear with the alert on the **System > Alerts** page. You can also specify whether the alert is distributed via email to a Network Management System (NMS) or to both.

If you select email, you are prompted to set the sender and recipient email addresses.

If you select NMS, you are prompted to choose one or more predefined trap destinations. You configure these on the **AMP Setup >NMS** page.

Note

This option is only available if an NMS server has been previously added to AMP.

Alerts

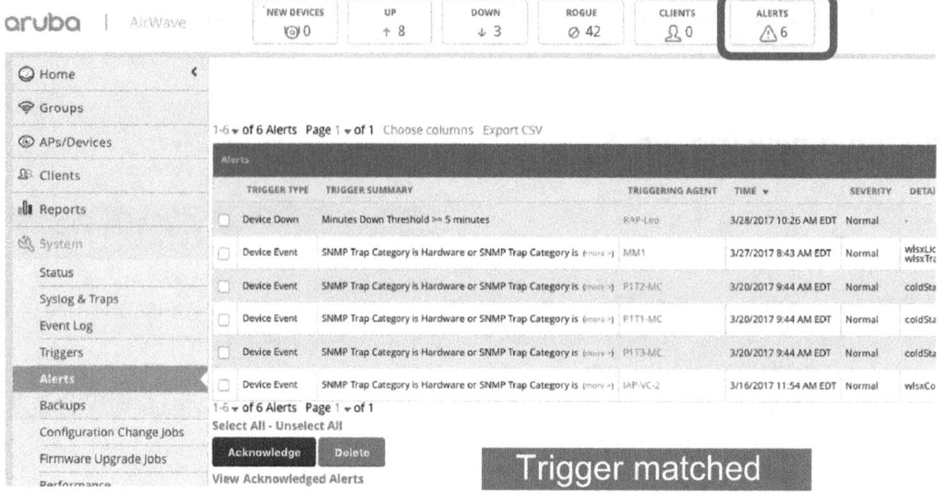

Figure 20-13 Alerts

When trigger criteria is met, an alert is generated. You view these alerts at the top of the main display bar and in the System Alerts page (Figure 20-13). Click on the trigger agent to view an appropriate page, depending on the triggering agent. If the trigger agent is an AP, then you are taken to the APs/Devices monitor page for that device.

Accessing alerts

Alert Summary

TYPE ▲	LAST 2 HOURS	LAST DAY	TOTAL	LAST EVENT
AMP Alerts	4	4	6	7/21/2016 3:50 PM EDT
IDS Events	14	86	132	7/21/2016 3:56 PM EDT
RADIUS Issues	0	142	252	7/21/2016 11:53 AM EDT

Figure 20-14 Accessing alerts

Alerts can be viewed from many different locations. The main alert in the status bar shows all alerts (Figure 20-14). However, alert summaries will depend on its category.

- **APs/Devices > List**—Choose specific Controller/AP to view Alert Summary table
- **Groups > Monitor**—All alerts related to a particular group
- **Home > Overview**—Total of all alerts AMP sees
- **Clients > Connected**—Alerts for a particular client
- **Clients > Client Detail**—Alerts for a particular client

Alert NMS integration

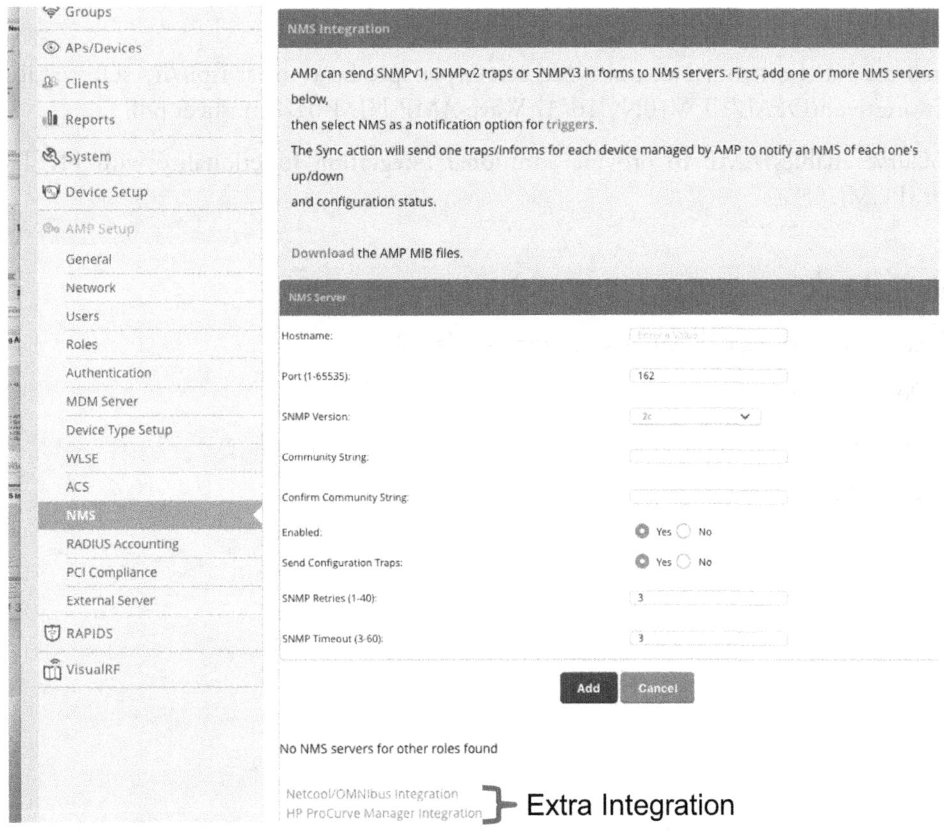

Figure 20-15 Alert NMS integration

NMS Integration allows AMP to send SNMPv1/v2 traps, or SNMPv3 informs to NMS servers (Figure 20-15). To enable this integration:

1. First add one or more NMS servers.
2. Then select NMS as a notification option for triggers.
3. The sync action sends one trap/inform for each AMP-managed device to notify an NMS of each device's up/down and configuration status.
4. Download Netcool/OMNIbus Integration Module (NIM) for AMP from the OPAL site.

AMP provides additional integration functionality with IBM's Netcool NMS. To enable this integration:

1. Download and compile the AirWave MIB listed above.
2. Download the NIM for AMP from the OPAL site.
3. Install the NIM on your Netcool NMS server per specifications at ftp://ftp.software.ibm.com/software/tivoli/OPAL/1TW10NC16/AirWave-AMP-NIM-01-Datasheet.pdf

HP ProCurve enables AMP to provide additional integration functionality with HP ProCurve Manager (PCM).

Learning check

4. Which of the options below are valid trigger alerts?
   a. Device down
   b. Device up
   c. Client count
   d. Client goodput

Reports

Generated reports

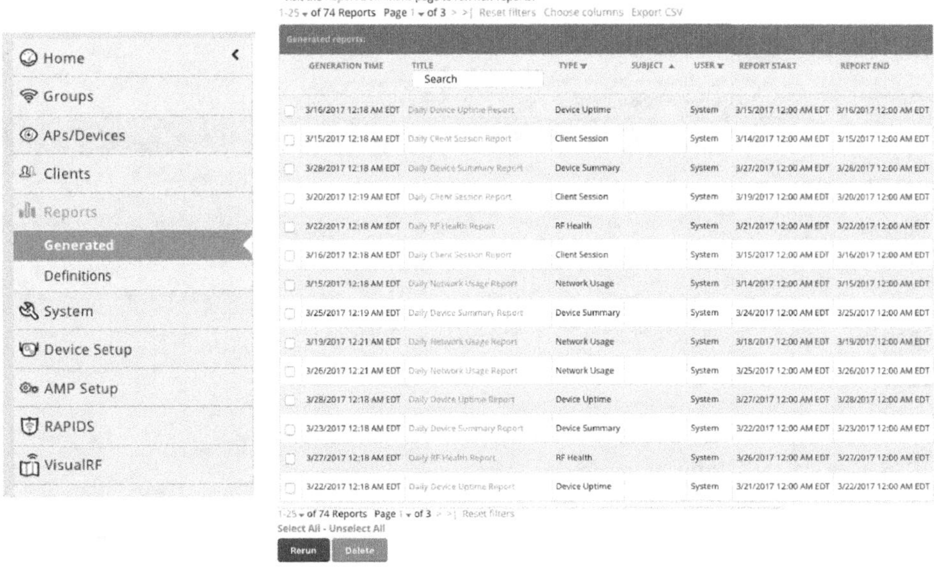

Figure 20-16 Generated reports

Reports are powerful tools in network analysis, user configuration, device optimization, and network monitoring. Among their many benefits, reports provide an interface for multiple configurations.

The **Reports > Generated** page displays reports that have been run, as well as the most recent daily version of any report (Figure 20-16). An admin user can see and edit all report definitions in AMP. Users with the Monitor Only role can see reports and definitions if they have access to all devices in the reports.

Defined reports

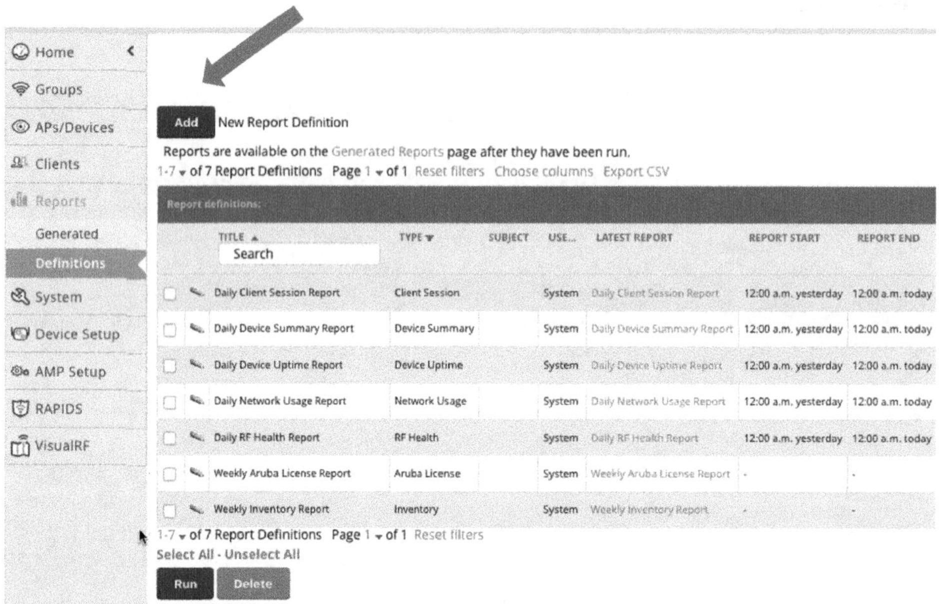

Figure 20-17 Defined reports

To create your report, with all your conditions, navigate to **Reports > Definitions** and click on the ADD button (Figure 20-17).

Defining report types

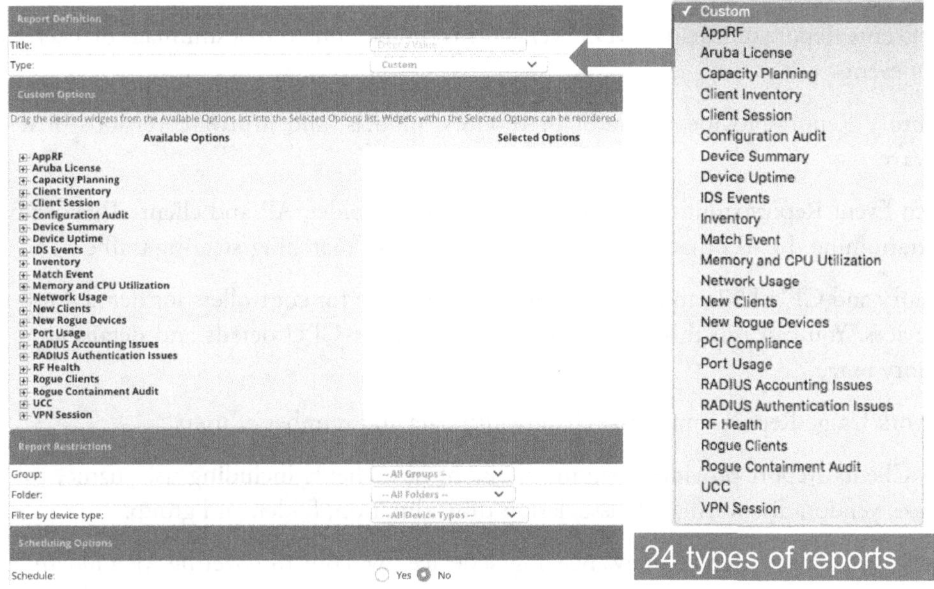

Figure 20-18 Defining report types

There are 24 types of reports to choose from (Figure 20-18). A custom report can also be selected if you need more report granularity, for example. The report types are described below.

- AppRF Report list the Top Applications Summary, Top Destinations Summary, Top 10 Applications By Device Types, Top 10 Applications By User Roles, Top 10 Applications By SSIDs, Top 3 Applications For Top 10 Users, and User Detail.
- Aruba License Report tracks the No/Yes licenses on Aruba devices in your network. This report includes information on the type, quantity, percent used, installation date, expiration date, and the license keys.
- Capacity Planning Report tracks bandwidth capacity and consumption according to thresholds for data throughput. This is a device-oriented report.
- Client Inventory Report provides information about clients that have connected to you network.
- Client Session Report summarizes user data by radio mode, SSID, and VLAN as well as lists all sessions.
- Configuration Audit Report provides a snapshot of the configuration of all specified access points in AirWave.

- Device Summary Report summarizes user and bandwidth statistics and lists devices in AirWave.
- Device Uptime Report summarizes device uptime within defined groups or folders.
- IDS Events Report summarizes IDS events. This can be limited to a summary of a certain number of events.
- Inventory Report provides an audit of vendors, models, and firmware versions of devices in AirWave.
- Match Event Report summarizes matching events per folder, AP, and client. This can be useful in determining the APs that have the highest number of matching/steering traffic.
- Memory and CPU Utilization Report summarizes usage for controllers for defined top number of devices. You can run this report with or without per-CPU details and details about device memory usage.
- Network Usage Report summarizes bandwidth data and number of users.
- New Clients Report provides a summary list of new clients including user name, role, MAC address, vendor, discovering AP, association time, duration, folder, and group.
- New Rogue Devices Report shows new rogue devices by score, discovering AP and MAC address vendor.
- PCI Compliance Report provides a summary of network compliance with PCI requirements, according to the PCI requirements enabled in AirWave using the AMP **Setup > PCI Compliance** page.
- Port Usage Report summarizes switch and port information across the network. Generates information on the unused ports. Provides a detailed list of all available switches and ports in the network.
- RADIUS Authentication Issues Report summarizes RADIUS authentication issues by controller and by user, as well as a list of all issues.
- RADIUS Accounting Issues summarizes RADIUS accounting issues by controller and by user, as well as a list of all issues.
- RF Health Report tracks problematic radios, changes, errors, and interfering devices.
- Rogue Clients Report summarizes the number of valid users that are connected to rogues. This report can be filtered by rogue classification. Ad hoc devices can be included and specific details that should be included about the clients can be selected.
- Rogue Containment Audit Report identifies discrepancies between the AP containment status specified in AirWave compared to containment status identified by the controller at report run time.

- UCC Report shows UCC data by call quality, connectivity type, call type, application type, and device type. Also, poor call quality by folders, AP and clients.
- VPN Session Report summarizes connected VPN sessions over a specified period of time. This report can be based on clients/users or devices and can be filtered by folder and device type.

Defining custom reports

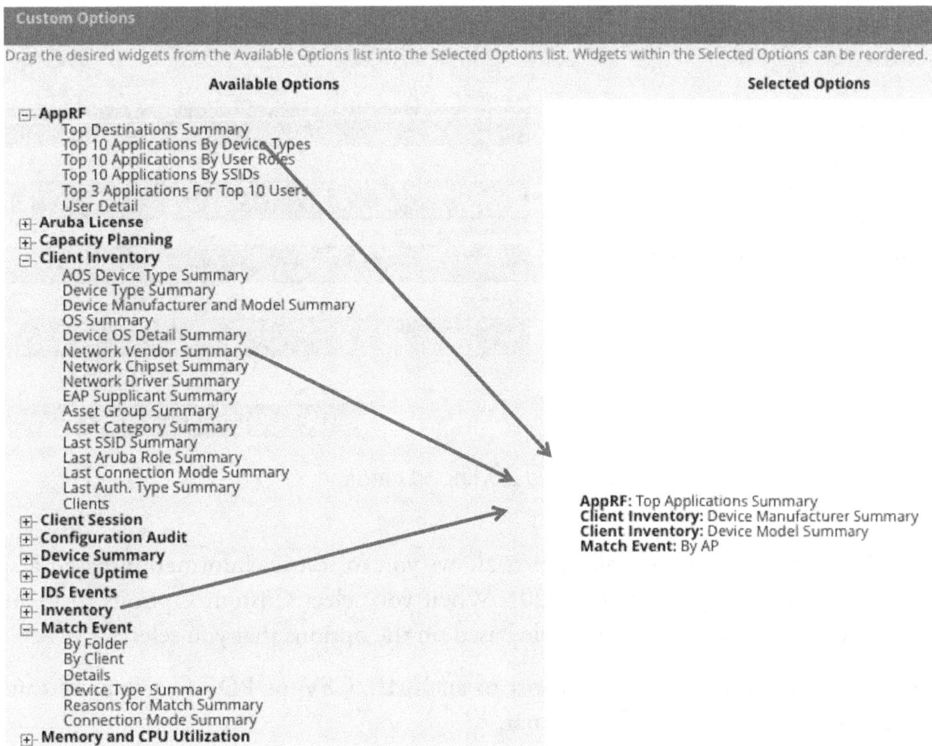

Figure 20-19 Defining custom reports

The left pane of the Custom Options section lists all available data that can be included in the report (Figure 20-19). Drag the desired data from the Available Options list on the left to the Selected Options pane on the right. The order of the data in the Selected Options section is the order that it will appear in the report. The data can be reordered by dragging an item up or down the list.

Report creation

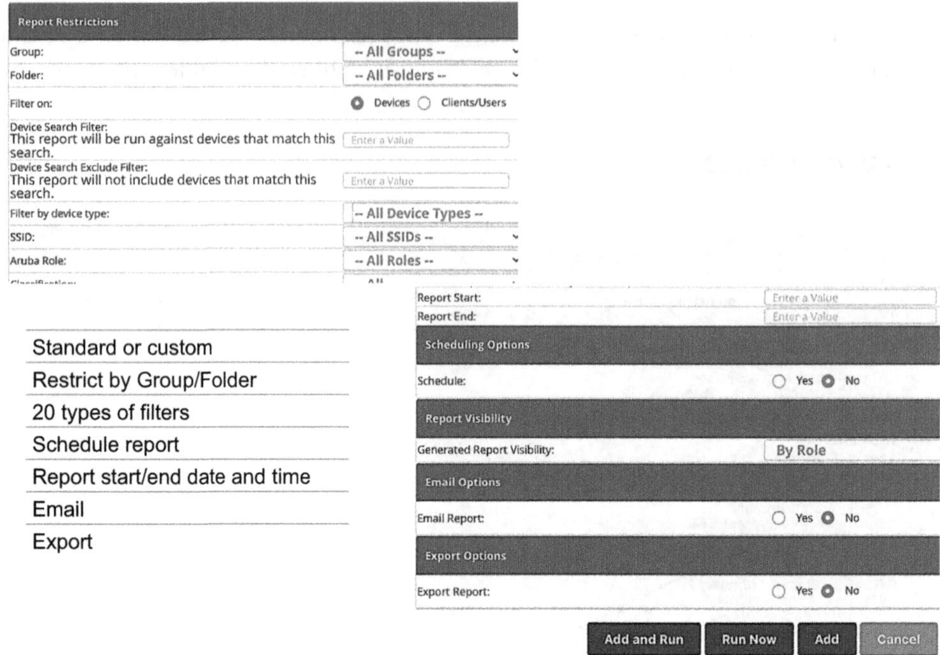

Figure 20-20 Report creation

The Report Restrictions Section for all reports allows you to restrict information based a specified group, folder, and device type (Figure 20-20). When you select Custom Options to include in a report, additional restrictions will be available based on the options that you select.

All reports contain a link to export the report to an XML, CSV, or PDF file. Reports can also be emailed in either HTML, PDF, or CSV format.

You can select Email This Report to email the report to specified email addresses, separated by commas. The reports are sent along with the sender address. You can also specify whether the report should be sent in HTML or PDF format.

Client session report example

Figure 20-21 Client session report example

This is an example of the client session report. You can see that the report starts with pie charts. The charts list client connection mode, time spent in this mode, and MB used.

There are many sections of this report that are not displayed. These are listed on the right-hand side of Figure 20-21.

Also note that this report can be exported as an XML, CSV, or PDF file. You can also email this file or simply print it.

Learning check

5. How many reports are there?
    a. 22
    b. 24
    c. 23
    d. 30
6. Which of the options below are valid ways to export reports?
    a. E-mail
    b. CSV
    c. PDF
    d. Print
    e. By osmosis

21 Answers to learning checks

Chapter 1: Introduction and Aruba Architecture

1. When planning a hierarchy what should be taken into consideration?
   a. The number of MMs
   b. The naming convention
   c. The configuration needs
   d. The monitoring needs
   e. The number of MC and Aps

2. What features does clustering give you?
   a. Redundancy
   b. Client load balancing
   c. AP balancing
   d. Mobility
   e. IAP load balancing

Chapter 2: Mobility Master Redundancy

1. What are some of the MM functions?
   a. Centralized licensing
   b. Centralized visibility, monitoring, and configuration
   c. WIDS
   d. AirMatch
   e. SDN functions
   f. UCC function
   g. WebCC proxy

h. AP Whitelist DB

i. Rule-Based Client Match (RBCM)

j. AirGroup classification

2. The Master Redundancy DB synchronization function can be enabled on mm/mynode level.

   a. True

   b. False

Chapter 3: Mobility Master and Mobility Controller Operations

1. Which of the following deployment methods require Aruba activate?

   a. Provisioning/adding local (MD/MC) to the MM manually

   b. Provisioning/adding local (MD/MC) to the MM over ZTP

   c. Deleting a local (MD/MC) from the MM

   d. Renaming a local (MD/MC) in the hierarchy

2. Which one of the following License types is device (MC) specific?

   a. AP

   b. PEF

   c. PEFV

   d. RFP

3. Which one of the following license types are consumed per AP?

   a. AP

   b. PEF

   c. PEFV

   d. RFP

Chapter 4: MultiZone

1. A DZ can have a different AOS image with a PZ.

   a. True

   b. False

2. For the DZ, you must add the MultiZone AP whitelist manually, even though auto-certprovision has been enabled on the DZ.
   a. True
   b. False

3. Why is the MultiZone guest access solution in AOS 8.1 more secure than 6.X?
   a. MultiZone guest access solution utilizes more secure encryption.
   b. MultiZone guest access solution utilizes more secure authentication.
   c. MultiZone AP establishes GRE data tunnel with DZ directly.
   d. MultiZone AP establishes IPSEC data tunnel with DZ directly.

Chapter 5: Clustering Introduction

1. In which of the following scenarios will the cluster size be limited to four?
   a. When the cluster terminates RAP
   b. When the cluster uses VMC
   c. When the cluster uses 70XX
   d. When the cluster uses 72XX
   e. When the cluster uses 72XX and 70XX in one cluster
   f. When the cluster uses 70XX and VMC in one cluster

2. Which two conditions must be setup to support stateful failover?
   a. L2 connection between cluster members.
   b. L3 connection between cluster members.
   c. The redundancy option is enabled in a clustering profile.
   d. The AP load balance option is enabled in the clustering profile.

3. What sessions can be synced to S-UAC?
   a. All traffic
   b. FTP session
   c. DPI qualified sessions
   d. Ping traffic

4. From the options below, which are the correct clustering configuration steps?
   a. Create a cluster profile in MM level.
   b. Create a cluster profile in Managed-Devices level.
   c. Attach the created profile to the cluster group membership in MM level.
   d. Attach the created profile to the cluster group membership in MC level.

Chapter 6: Advanced Clustering

1. In one cluster, the client numbers and platform models are as shown. Is LB triggered?
   - 7240 (Capacity 32,000): 4000 clients
   - 7220 (Capacity 24,000): 700 clients

   a. Yes
   b. No

2. By default, what is the status of the AP LB and client LB feature, respectively?
   a. Enabled/disabled
   b. Enabled/enabled
   c. Disabled/disabled
   d. Disabled/enabled

3. The cluster node-list has the highest priority for AP termination.
   a. True
   b. False

4. The RADIUS client IP should be VRRP IP address in VRRP configuration.
   a. True
   b. False

5. If the cluster member status is "INCOMPATIBLE", which two statements could be true?
   a. Cluster limit reached
   b. MCs run different ArubaOS versions
   c. MCs can hear heartbeat packet from peers
   d. Just a short period temporary status

Chapter 7: Mobility

1. Which entity decides when a roaming event should occur?
   a. AP
   b. MM or Master
   c. MC or Local Controller
   d. The client device

2. Which statement is correct about the comparison between clustering mobility and legacy mobility?
   a. With L3 IP mobility, client traffic is tunneled to the same controller, regardless of connected AP
   b. VLAN mobility can keep user data terminated on same controller
   c. Clustering does not support L3 roaming
   d. Clustering mobility is seamless

3. 802.11r is also useful for a WPA2-personal SSID.
   a. True
   b. False

Chapter 8: Advanced Security

1. When multiple servers are mapped to a server group, will all servers be used for validating the user credentials?
   a. Yes, all servers will be used from top to bottom.
   b. No, only first server will be used.
   c. Subsequent server will be used only when first server is down.
   d. If "Fail through" is enabled.

2. When multiple servers are mapped to a server group, can you distribute the authentication load among the servers?
   a. Yes, we can distribute based on the rules.
   b. No, only first server will be used.
   c. Subsequent server will be used only when first server is down.
   d. It depends whether "Load-balancing" is enabled.

3. With machine authentication set, when will the AAA authentication default role be assigned to the user?
   a. When machine authentication succeeds.
   b. When user authentication succeeds.
   c. When machine and user authentication both succeed.
   d. When machine authentication failed and user authentication succeeds.

4. Which of the following authentications can be configured on a controller port?
   a. 802.1X authentication
   b. Captive Portal
   c. SIP authentication
   d. MAC authentication

5. It is best practice to replace the default certificates with custom certificates?
   a. True
   b. False

6. What is the default certificate expiration alert period?
   a. One week
   b. 15 Days
   c. 30 Days
   d. 60 Days

Chapter 9: Role Derivation

1. What role derivation trumps all other role assignments?
   a. Initial role
   b. Server-derived role
   c. Authentication method default role
   d. Controller default role

2. What is NOT a valid rule type for a User Rule?
    a. BSSID
    b. ESSID
    c. Location
    d. AP type
    e. MAC Address
    f. Encryption type
    g. DHCP Options
    h. DHCP Option 77

3. A user authenticates, and ClearPass sends the VSA "Aruba-User-Role" with a value of Sales. There is no Sales Role in the MC. What happens?
    a. The user is given a Captive portal page.
    b. A Sales Role is automatically created in the MC.
    c. The user is placed in the authentication default role.
    d. The user is de-authenticated from the network.
    e. The user is blacklisted.

4. What methods can be used to assign user roles?
    a. Initial role
    b. Locally derived
    c. Authentication default role
    d. Server derived role
    e. AP derived role

Chapter 10: Remote Access

1. What are the two VPN deployment methods for RAPs?
    a. IKE/PSK
    b. RAP over VIA

c. **Certificate based**
d. Controller Activate
e. MC in DMZ

2. In split-tunnel mode, the device will receive an IP address from which of the following?
   a. From the RAP DHCP
   b. From the local network DHCP server
   c. **Corporate DHCP**
   d. Will get a public IP address
   e. Laptop own DHCP server

3. Name three ways a RAP can be directed to the MC/VPN.
   a. **Activate**
   b. **IAP Local configuration**
   c. Central server
   d. **Staged from a CAP to a RAP**
   e. RAP Local configuration

4. Name two ways to provide redundancy for RAP.
   a. **LMS Backup**
   b. Activate can redirect
   c. AirWave can redirect
   d. **USB 3G/4G/LTE**
   e. Local redirect

5. What is the web authentication profile used for?
   a. **To authenticate and download the installers**
   b. To authenticate VIA via HTTPS
   c. To authenticate VIA certificate
   d. For authentication of RAPs
   e. Has the whitelist of authenticated VIAs

6. What are the available options for remote access?
   - **a. VIA**
   - **b. RAP**
   - **c. Site-to-Site**
   - **d. IAPs**
   - e. CAPs

Chapter 11: Voice Optimization

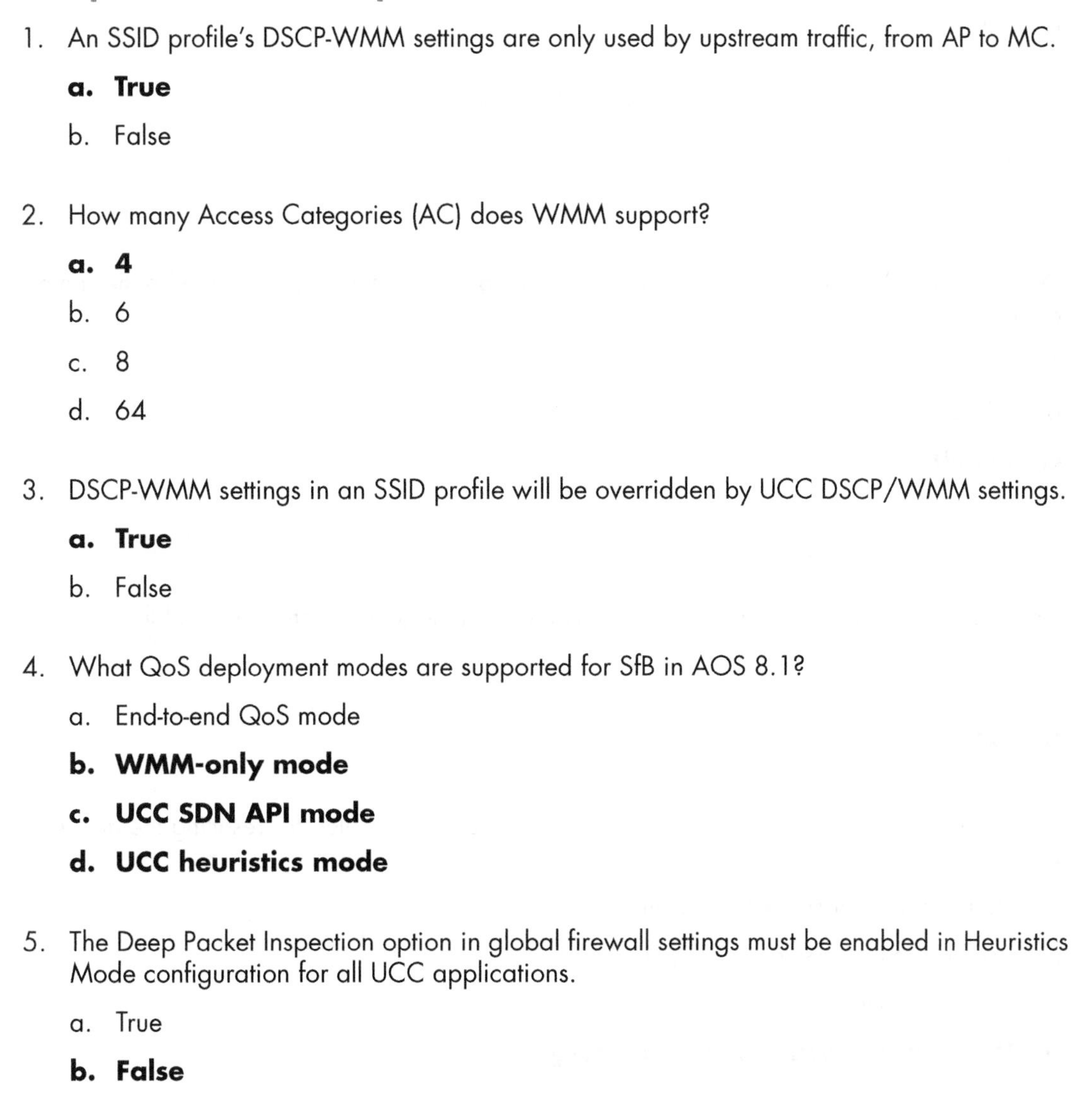

1. An SSID profile's DSCP-WMM settings are only used by upstream traffic, from AP to MC.
   - **a. True**
   - b. False

2. How many Access Categories (AC) does WMM support?
   - **a. 4**
   - b. 6
   - c. 8
   - d. 64

3. DSCP-WMM settings in an SSID profile will be overridden by UCC DSCP/WMM settings.
   - **a. True**
   - b. False

4. What QoS deployment modes are supported for SfB in AOS 8.1?
   - a. End-to-end QoS mode
   - **b. WMM-only mode**
   - **c. UCC SDN API mode**
   - **d. UCC heuristics mode**

5. The Deep Packet Inspection option in global firewall settings must be enabled in Heuristics Mode configuration for all UCC applications.
   - a. True
   - **b. False**

Chapter 12: Mesh

1. Which of the following radios is used for backhaul (mesh link) communication?
   a. Only a radio
   b. Only g radio
   c. a or g radio

2. Traffic through mesh link (backhaul) can also be encrypted.
   a. True
   b. False

3. A single cluster can have more than one Mesh-portal.
   a. True
   b. False

4. Which of the following SSIDs is used by the mesh-point to discover the neighbor in the same cluster?
   a. ESSID
   b. BSSID
   c. MSSID

Chapter 13: Administration

1. An admin user with guest-provisioning role can also manage the configuration of the controller.
   a. True
   b. False

2. Which of the following credentials are used to access the controller, for resetting the admin password?
   a. User = admin, Password = allowme!
   b. User = admin, Password = forgetme!
   c. User = password, Password = allowme!
   d. User = password, Password = forgetme!

3. You can disable/enable console access to a Managed Device.
    a. True
    b. False

Chapter 14: Operations

1. Which of the following folder names is used to keep the image file in a USB drive?
    a. Aruba/arubaimage
    b. /Arubaimage
    c. Aruba/image
    d. /image

2. Which of the following methods/protocols can be used for uploading images?
    a. FTP, TFTP, and SCP
    b. Only FTP and TFTP
    c. FTP, TFTP, and Local File
    d. FTP, TFTP, SCP, and Local file

3. Which statement is true about the AP image preload feature?
    a. AP gets image and reboots along with the controller.
    b. AP gets image after the controller is upgraded and rebooted.
    c. AP gets image after the controller is upgraded and reboots along with the controller.
    d. AP gets image along with the controller but reboots after the controller.

4. What is the primary use for disaster mode?
    a. To recover the controller when it is crashed.
    b. To recover the controller when it loses its configuration.
    c. To configure the MC when it loses connection with the MM.
    d. To configure the MC when it loses its configuration.

Chapter 16: Tunneled Node

1. The HPE Aruba switch runs OS 16.04. User-based tunneled node is supported in which of the following cases?
   - **a. MM—MC architecture**
   - **b. Cluster**
   - **c. Standalone MC**
   - d. VMC

2. When connecting to a switch in user-based mode, how are devices authenticated?
   - a. A GRE tunnel is built to the controller, then the controller sends all authentication frames to ClearPass.
   - b. Before the GRE tunnel is built to the controller, the controller sends all authentication frames to ClearPass.
   - **c. Before the GRE tunnel is built to the controller, the switch sends all authentication frames to ClearPass.**
   - d. A GRE tunnel is built to the controller, then the switch sends all authentication frames to ClearPass.

3. What MC configuration is needed for user-tunneled mode?
   - **a. Firewall roles**
   - b. AAA profile
   - **c. VLANs**
   - d. Install tunneled node license

Chapter 17: Introduction to AirWave

1. What is the top folder?
   - a. Above
   - **b. Top**
   - c. Summit
   - d. AP group

2. When adding a device what information do you need?
    a. IP address of device
    b. SNMP community
    c. MAC address
    d. User id/Password

3. What is the best way to add all devices in an Aruba network?
    a. Add MM then wait
    b. Add MM and MC and APs
    c. ZTP
    d. Discovery

Chapter 18: AirWave Network Health

1. Where can an administrator go to see a graphical view of the types of traffic?
    a. Network deviation
    b. AppRF
    c. Clarity Live
    d. Folders and Groups

2. What are the two types of Clarity?
    a. Live
    b. Answers
    c. Synthetic
    d. Abstract

Chapter 19: Airwave Troubleshooting Clients and Wireless Networks

1. A user cannot associate what could be the cause?
    a. Wi-Fi is off on the device
    b. Wrong Wi-Fi settings
    c. Bad user ID and Password
    d. AP has reached the user limits

2. During the 802.11 association process, what comes after the authentication frames?
    a. Deauthentication frame
    b. Association frames
    c. 802.11 complete frame
    d. 802.1X authentication frames

3. You find a client but you fall into the Client Detail page and not the Diagnostic page. Why?
    a. Client is not associated to an AP.
    b. Client has not initiated 802.1X.
    c. Client is getting a Captive Portal page.
    d. Client is in an open SSID.

4. You investigate calls from several areas and determine that only guests have issues. Employees are fine. What is your next step in troubleshooting?
    a. Does the guest have the wrong WIFI setting?
    b. Is the guest using windows or MACs?
    c. Is the guest getting the CP page?
    d. Is the guest getting an IP address?

Chapter 20: AirWave VisualRF, Reports, Alerts

1. How do you get a street map introduced in the building view?
    a. Automatically from Google maps
    b. Download a file from MapQuest
    c. Draw it in
    d. Screen shot of a map

2. What is the significance of channel overlay in floor view?
    a. The color of the floor map
    b. From other floors above or below
    c. Overlay a map in VRF
    d. Overlapping channels

3. How do APs determine their position?
    a. They do not
    b. With GPS
    c. Based on distance to wall
    d. Based on Bluetooth signals

4. Which of the options below are valid trigger alerts?
    a. Device down
    b. Device up
    c. Client count
    d. Client goodput

5. How many reports are there?
    a. 22
    b. 24
    c. 23
    d. 30

6. Which of the options below are valid ways to export reports?
    a. E-mail
    b. CSV
    c. PDF
    d. Print
    e. By osmosis

22 Practice Test

1. Which of the following statements accurately describes HPE Aruba best-practice recommendations, as relates to deploying an Aruba Mobility Controller (MC)?
   a. Deploy the MC to act as the Default Gateway (DG) for client VLANs, and configure BGP between the MC and an upstream router.
   b. Deploy the MC to act as a layer 2 switch, and configure static routing between it and an upstream router.
   c. Deploy the MC to act as the Default Gateway (DG) for client VLANs, and configure static routes or BGP between the MC and an upstream router
   d. Deploy the MC to act as a layer 2 switch, such that the upstream router acts as the Default Gateway (DG) for client VLANs.

2. Suppose you enable Mobility Master (MM) redundancy database synchronization. What is the result of setting an unsynchronized standby MM to a higher VRRP priority than the active MM?
   a. The active MM will detect the unsynchronized state of the standby unit and update it appropriately.
   b. The standby becomes the new active MM, overwrites the existing configuration and databases, and your entire system becomes non-functional
   c. The active MM sends a message to this improperly configured standby unit, telling it to move to a "dormant" state.
   d. You cannot set the VRRP priority on the standby MM.

3. Which statement below most accurately describes how adding Mobility Controllers (MC) to an MM-MC architecture relates to creating a group hierarchy?
   a. You are strongly encouraged to create a planned group hierarchy before adding MC. It is difficult to move an MC from one group to another.
   b. It is best to add MCs, then add groups and sub-groups, and then drag-and-drop MCs to the desired group as desired.
   c. You are automatically prompted to create the appropriate group hierarchy during MC additions.
   d. You cannot create group hierarchy until after you have added MCs.

4. As relates to the MultiZone feature, which statements below are true?
    a. It enables you to manage separate WLANs on the same APs from different controllers.
    b. The feature relies on one primary zone and one or more data zones.
    c. The feature is supported by ArubaOS 6.x and 8.x
    d. Various zones need not be on the same layer 2 subnet.
    e. The feature can improve security and help to ensure that client traffic takes a more efficient path.

5. Choose all options below that accurately describe the benefits of the clustering feature?
    a. It enables you to manage separate WLANs on the same APs from different controllers
    b. Seamless roaming
    c. Client and AP load balancing
    d. Stateful failover
    e. Seamless cluster upgrades

6. Which statements below accurately describe how the Mobility Master (MM) relates to a cluster deployment?
    a. The cluster feature requires an MM-based deployment.
    b. MMs cannot be cluster members, and this slightly reduces the systems overall usefulness.
    c. MMs cannot be cluster members, but practically speaking, this has no detrimental effect on the solution
    d. Only MC cluster members can terminate both Campus APs (CAP) and Remote APs (RAP).
    e. Only MM cluster members can terminate Mesh APs

7. Which of the following choices describes the thresholds that must be met to trigger cluster load balancing?
    a. Active Client Rebalance Threshold or the Standby Client Rebalance Threshold, and the unbalance threshold.
    b. Active Client Rebalance Threshold and the Standby Client Rebalance Threshold, and the unbalance threshold.
    c. Active Client Rebalance Threshold or the Standby Client Rebalance Threshold, or the unbalance threshold.
    d. Active Client Rebalance Threshold and the Standby Client Rebalance Threshold, or the unbalance threshold.

8. Which two statements are true about deploying legacy inter-controller mobility?
   a. If controllers have layer 2 connectivity, then enable L2 mobility, but if controllers have layer 3 connectivity, then enable L3 mobility.
   b. Legacy inter-controller mobility is only supported if controllers have layer 2 connectivity.
   c. Legacy inter-controller mobility not supported if controllers have layer 4 connectivity.
   d. You should never enable both L2 and L3 mobility on the same SSID.
   e. AOS 8.x removes support for legacy inter-controller mobility.

9. Inter-domain roaming is not seamless.
   a. True
   b. False

10. Which statements below accurately describe the use of multiple RADIUS servers to authenticate clients?
    a. With server fall-through, if the first server denies access, the next server in the list will be queried.
    b. With server fail-through, if the first server denies access, the next server in the list will be queried.
    c. Server fail-through is not supported for 802.1X authentication with a group of external RADIUS servers.
    d. MCs can dynamically select an authentication server, based on the authenticating client's domain and user name.
    e. When you configure multiple RADIUS servers, they are automatically used in a round-robin fashion, for load balancing.

11. Network location and IP address are irrelevant to role assignment.
    a. True
    b. False

12. Role derivation can occur in which of the following ways.
    a. WLAN initial role
    b. Locally derived role
    c. 802.1X default role
    d. Server derived role
    e. AP derived role

13. Which statements below accurately describe the advantages of using Remote Access Points (RAP)?
    a. Simplified, consistent user experience
    b. Eliminate need for VPN clients
    c. IT staff can use a single set of policies, regardless of whether the connection is via a RAP or via a CAP.
    d. Reduce the danger of attacks based on rogue APs
    e. No special hardware required, since all CAPs can be converted into RAPs

14. Choose the true statements from the list below, as relates to Remote Access Point (RAP) deployment.
    a. It is OK to terminate a few RAPs directly to the main corporate controller, via some third party firewall.
    b. For larger deployments, it is best to place a separate controller in your De-Militarized Zone (DMZ), behind some third party firewall.
    c. Some APs can use the cloud-based Activate service to automatically convert to RAPs
    d. For some APs, you can connect your laptop to their Ethernet port, and locally configure them to be a RAP.
    e. The cloud-based Activate service can direct RAPs to the appropriate controller.

15. The Virtual Intranet Access (VIA) client is most useful under which of the following circumstances?
    a. For traveling employees that need to work securely from a hotel
    b. For employees that must use a Remote AP (RAP) from home
    c. For temporary contractors who need access inside your corporate headquarters
    d. Guest users require elevated access from within your corporate headquarters.
    e. Traveling employees are briefly at the main office, and must work in a conference room

16. Which statement below are true, as relates to Quality of Service (QoS) features in an 802.11-based WLAN?
    a. The WMM standard provides a QoS mechanism for Wi-Fi networks.
    b. Voice-over-IP (VoIP) traffic is quite sensitive to delay and jitter.

c. Higher priority traffic is assigned more Transmission Opportunity (TXOP).

d. The Aruba solution has default configuration that maps WMM priorities to DSCP values.

e. Voice traffic can be assigned a Mean Opinion Score (MOS), which indicates the overall quality of the interaction.

17. Which of the options below are valid UCC deployment modes?

a. WMM Only Mode

b. Heuristics Mode

c. Web Mode

d. Software Defined Networking (SDN) API mode

e. Random Early Detection (RED) mode

18. When deploying a mesh network, what is the result of using the 5GHz band for both client connectivity and for a mesh link?

a. You cannot use the 5GHz radio for client connectivity with a mesh deployment.

b. You can do this, but it reduces the maximum distance between APs.

c. You can do this, but it reduces overall performance.

d. This is recommended when you need to reserve the 2.4GHz radio for mission-critical or sensitive applications, like Voice-over-IP (VoIP).

e. You should only do this if you deploy multiple Mesh Portals.

19. Which of the following are valid mesh deployment models?

a. Blanket an outdoor parking lot with Wi-Fi coverage

b. Connect a single building to another office, across the street

c. Connect two office buildings to another office, across the street

d. Connect an office in Canada to an office in Chile.

e. Extend cell phone coverage inside an office building

20. The HPE Aruba WLAN solution supports the use of both RADIUS and TACACS servers to authenticate administrative accounts?

a. True

b. False

21. What is the purpose of the Guest-provisioning user account role?
    a. Allows sub-administrators to configure WLANs that support guest access.
    b. Allows a non-technical person to create guest accounts from the Web-based user interface
    c. Allows technical personnel to create guest users from the Command Line Interface (CLI)
    d. Enables guest users to self-register
    e. Provides for guest users to be re-provisioned with elevated privileges, based on their group membership.

22. Which statements below accurately describe the AirGroup feature?
    a. It supports Bonjour services like Apple AirPrint and AirPlay
    b. It supports Digital Living Network Alliance (DLNA) for Windows and Android devices
    c. Enhances performance by reducing the overhead caused by multicast traffic
    d. Ensures cross-VLAN visibility of devices and services
    e. Matches user devices to their closest Wi-Fi based services.

23. What is the purpose of a centralized image upgrade?
    a. It provides for all APs to be upgraded via the same Mobility Master (MM).
    b. It enables one MM to upgrade several other MMs, for large, world-wide deployments.
    c. It allows the MM to upgrade itself and its associated MCs, by connecting to an image server.
    d. It allows the MM to upgrade its associated MCs and APs.
    e. It enables the upgrade of MMs, MCs, and APs from an third party image server.

24. Some controllers are equipped with an LCD panel, which you can use to facilitate the loading of a new image on the controller.
    a. True
    b. False

25. Which statements below accurately describe the Tunneled node feature?
    a. Offers both port-based and role-based configuration modes
    b. Enables more secure tunneling of wireless traffic
    c. Enables secure tunneling of wired Ethernet traffic
    d. Reduces the number of tunnels traversed by guest traffic
    e. Only newer switches like the 2930 support this feature

26. Which service can the tunneled node feature use to decide which traffic is tunneled?
    a. TACACS
    b. ClearPass
    c. AirWave Management Platform (AMP)
    d. Protected Extensible Authentication Protocol (PEAP)

27. Which statements below are true about AirWave?
    a. A single AirWave server can manage up to 5,000 devices
    b. Multiple AirWave servers can be integrated into a single management interface with Aruba Glass.
    c. AirWave can only manage HPE Aruba-based products
    d. AirWave integrates with HPE IMC, Netcool, and OMNIbus.
    e. AirWave can leverage SNMP, SSH, AMON, FTP protocols

28. Which of the options below are valid features when using AirWave to monitor network health.
    a. You can use AirWave as a packet capture and decode device, like Wireshark
    b. You can send CLI commands from AirWave to a controller, and receive the output.
    c. You can use AirWave to modify controller AirMatch settings.
    d. You can use it to create customer-facing web portals.

29. You can use AirWave to help troubleshoot client connectivity issues?
    a. True
    b. False

30. Which of the following are Visual RF display options?
    a. User view
    b. Access Point view
    c. Floor plan and network view
    d. Campus and building view
    e. Switch view
    f. Capture view

Answers to Practice Test

1. Which of the following statements accurately describes HPE Aruba best-practice recommendations, as relates to deploying an Aruba Mobility Controller (MC)?

    a. Deploy the MC to act as the Default Gateway (DG) for client VLANs, and configure BGP between the MC and an upstream router.

    b. Deploy the MC to act as a layer 2 switch, and configure static routing between it and an upstream router.

    c. Deploy the MC to act as the Default Gateway (DG) for client VLANs, and configure static routes or BGP between the MC and an upstream router

    d. **Deploy the MC to act as a layer 2 switch, such that the upstream router acts as the Default Gateway (DG) for client VLANs**.

2. Suppose you enable Mobility Master (MM) redundancy database synchronization. What is the result of setting an unsynchronized standby MM to a higher VRRP priority than the active MM?

    a. The active MM will detect the unsynchronized state of the standby unit and update it appropriately.

    b. The standby becomes the new active MM, overwrites the existing configuration and databases, and your entire system becomes non-functional

    c. The active MM sends a message to this improperly configured standby unit, telling it to move to a "dormant" state.

    d. You cannot set the VRRP priority on the standby MM.

3. Which statement below most accurately describes how adding Mobility Controllers (MC) to an MM-MC architecture relates to creating a group hierarchy?

    a. **You are strongly encouraged to create a planned group hierarchy before adding MC. It is difficult to move an MC from one group to another.**

    b. It is best to add MCs, then add groups and sub-groups, and then drag-and-drop MCs to the desired group as desired.

    c. You are automatically prompted to create the appropriate group hierarchy during MC additions.

    d. You cannot create group hierarchy until after you have added MCs.

4. As relates to the MultiZone feature, which statements below are true?

    a. **It enables you to manage separate WLANs on the same APs from different controllers.**

    b. **The feature relies on one primary zone and one or more data zones.**

c. The feature is supported by ArubaOS 6.x and 8.x

d. **Various zones need not be on the same layer 2 subnet.**

e. **The feature can improve security and help to ensure that client traffic takes a more efficient path.**

5. Choose all options below that accurately describe the benefits of the clustering feature?

   a. It enables you to manage separate WLANs on the same APs from different controllers

   b. **Seamless roaming**

   c. **Client and AP load balancing**

   d. **Stateful failover**

   e. **Seamless cluster upgrades**

6. Which statements below accurately describe how the Mobility Master (MM) relates to a cluster deployment?

   a. **The cluster feature requires an MM-based deployment**.

   b. MMs cannot be cluster members, and this slightly reduces the systems overall usefulness.

   c. **MMs cannot be cluster members, but practically speaking, this has no detrimental effect on the solution**

   d. **Only MC cluster members can terminate both Campus APs (CAP) and Remote APs (RAP)**.

   e. Only MM cluster members can terminate Mesh APs

7. Which of the following choices describes the thresholds that must be met to trigger cluster load balancing?

   a. **Active Client Rebalance Threshold or the Standby Client Rebalance Threshold, and the unbalance threshold**.

   b. Active Client Rebalance Threshold and the Standby Client Rebalance Threshold, and the unbalance threshold.

   c. Active Client Rebalance Threshold or the Standby Client Rebalance Threshold, or the unbalance threshold.

   d. Active Client Rebalance Threshold and the Standby Client Rebalance Threshold, or the unbalance threshold.

8. Which two statements are true about deploying legacy inter-controller mobility?

    a. **If controllers have layer 2 connectivity, then enable L2 mobility, but if controllers have layer 3 connectivity, then enable L3 mobility**.

    b. Legacy inter-controller mobility is only supported if controllers have layer 2 connectivity.

    c. Legacy inter-controller mobility not supported if controllers have layer 4 connectivity.

    d. **You should never enable both L2 and L3 mobility on the same SSID.**

    e. AOS 8.x removes support for legacy inter-controller mobility.

9. Inter-domain roaming is not seamless.

    a. **True**

    b. False

10. Which statements below accurately describe the use of multiple RADIUS servers to authenticate clients?

    a. With server fall-through, if the first server denies access, the next server in the list will be queried.

    b. **With server fail-through, if the first server denies access, the next server in the list will be queried**.

    c. **Server fail-through is not supported for 802.1X authentication with a group of external RADIUS servers**.

    d. **MCs can dynamically select an authentication server, based on the authenticating client's domain and user name**.

    e. When you configure multiple RADIUS servers, they are automatically used in a round-robin fashion, for load balancing.

11. Network location and IP address are irrelevant to role assignment.

    a. **True**

    b. False

12. Role derivation can occur in which of the following ways.

    a. **WLAN initial role**

    b. **Locally derived role**

    c. **802.1X default role**

    d. **Server derived role**

    e. AP derived role

13. Which statements below accurately describe the advantages of using Remote Access Points (RAP)?

    a. **Simplified, consistent user experience**

    b. **Eliminate need for VPN clients**

    c. **IT staff can use a single set of policies, regardless of whether the connection is via a RAP or via a CAP.**

    d. Reduce the danger of attacks based on rogue APs

    e. **No special hardware required, since all CAPs can be converted into RAPs**

14. Choose the true statements from the list below, as relates to Remote Access Point (RAP) deployment.

    a. **It is OK to terminate a few RAPs directly to the main corporate controller, via some third party firewall.**

    b. **For larger deployments, it is best to place a separate controller in your De-Militarized Zone (DMZ), behind some third party firewall.**

    c. **Some APs can use the cloud-based Activate service to automatically convert to RAPs**

    d. **For some APs, you can connect your laptop to their Ethernet port, and locally configure them to be a RAP.**

    e. **The cloud-based Activate service can direct RAPs to the appropriate controller.**

15. The Virtual Intranet Access (VIA) client is most useful under which of the following circumstances?

    a. **For traveling employees that need to work securely from a hotel**

    b. For employees that must use a Remote AP (RAP) from home

    c. For temporary contractors who need access inside your corporate headquarters

    d. Guest users require elevated access from within your corporate headquarters.

    e. Traveling employees are briefly at the main office, and must work in a conference room

16. Which statement below are true, as relates to Quality of Service (QoS) features in an 802.11-based WLAN?

    a. **The WMM standard provides a QoS mechanism for Wi-Fi networks.**

    b. **Voice-over-IP (VoIP) traffic is quite sensitive to delay and jitter.**

    c. **Higher priority traffic is assigned more Transmission Opportunity (TXOP).**

d. **The Aruba solution has default configuration that maps WMM priorities to DSCP values.**

e. **Voice traffic can be assigned a Mean Opinion Score (MOS), which indicates the overall quality of the interaction**.

17. Which of the options below are valid UCC deployment modes?

 a. **WMM Only Mode**

 b. **Heuristics Mode**

 c. Web Mode

 d. **Software Defined Networking (SDN) API mode**

 e. Random Early Detection (RED) mode

18. When deploying a mesh network, what is the result of using the 5GHz band for both client connectivity and for a mesh link?

 a. You cannot use the 5GHz radio for client connectivity with a mesh deployment.

 b. You can do this, but it reduces the maximum distance between APs.

 c. **You can do this, but it reduces overall performance**.

 d. This is recommended when you need to reserve the 2.4GHz radio for mission-critical or sensitive applications, like Voice-over-IP (VoIP).

 e. You should only do this if you deploy multiple Mesh Portals.

19. Which of the following are valid mesh deployment models?

 a. **Blanket an outdoor parking lot with Wi-Fi coverage**

 b. **Connect a single building to another office, across the street**

 c. **Connect two office buildings to another office, across the street**

 d. Connect an office in Canada to an office in Chile.

 e. Extend cell phone coverage inside an office building

20. The HPE Aruba WLAN solution supports the use of both RADIUS and TACACS servers to authenticate administrative accounts?

 a. **True**

 b. False

21. What is the purpose of the Guest-provisioning user account role?
    a. Allows sub-administrators to configure WLANs that support guest access.
    b. **Allows a non-technical person to create guest accounts from the Web-based user interface**
    c. Allows technical personnel to create guest users from the Command Line Interface (CLI)
    d. Enables guest users to self-register
    e. Provides for guest users to be re-provisioned with elevated privileges, based on their group membership.

22. Which statements below accurately describe the AirGroup feature?
    a. **It supports Bonjour services like Apple AirPrint and AirPlay**
    b. **It supports Digital Living Network Alliance (DLNA) for Windows and Android devices**
    c. **Enhances performance by reducing the overhead caused by multicast traffic**
    d. **Ensures cross-VLAN visibility of devices and services**
    e. **Matches user devices to their closest Wi-Fi based services**.

23. What is the purpose of a centralized image upgrade?
    a. It provides for all APs to be upgraded via the same Mobility Master (MM).
    b. It enables one MM to upgrade several other MMs, for large, world-wide deployments.
    c. **It allows the MM to upgrade itself and its associated MCs, by connecting to an image server**.
    d. It allows the MM to upgrade its associated MCs and APs.
    e. It enables the upgrade of MMs, MCs, and APs from an third party image server.

24. Some controllers are equipped with an LCD panel, which you can use to facilitate the loading of a new image on the controller.
    a. **True**
    b. False

25. Which statements below accurately describe the Tunneled node feature?
    a. **Offers both port-based and role-based configuration modes**
    b. Enables more secure tunneling of wireless traffic

c. **Enables secure tunneling of wired Ethernet traffic**

d. Reduces the number of tunnels traversed by guest traffic

e. **Only newer switches like the 2930 support this feature**

26. Which service can the tunneled node feature use to decide which traffic is tunneled?

a. TACACS

b. **ClearPass**

c. AirWave Management Platform (AMP)

d. Protected Extensible Authentication Protocol (PEAP)

27. Which statements below are true about AirWave?

a. **A single AirWave server can manage up to 5,000 devices**

b. **Multiple AirWave servers can be integrated into a single management interface with Aruba Glass.**

c. AirWave can only manage HPE Aruba-based products

d. **AirWave integrates with HPE IMC, Netcool, and OMNIbus.**

e. **AirWave can leverage SNMP, SSH, AMON, FTP protocols**

28. Which of the options below are valid features when using AirWave to monitor network health.

a. You can use AirWave as a packet capture and decode device, like Wireshark

b. **You can send CLI commands from AirWave to a controller, and receive the output.**

c. **You can use AirWave to modify controller AirMatch settings.**

d. You can use it to create customer-facing web portals.

29. You can use AirWave to help troubleshoot client connectivity issues?

a. **True**

b. False

30. Which of the following are Visual RF display options?
    a. **User view**
    b. **Access Point view**
    c. **Floor plan and network view**
    d. **Campus and building view**
    e. Switch view
    f. Capture view

Index

A

D

I

K

L

M

N

O

P

S

V